Algebra II

A Reference Guide
and Problem Sets

Book Staff and Contributors

Paul Thomas   *Senior Content Specialist*
Harold Lawrance   *Content Specialist*
Suzanne Montazer   *Senior Art Director*
Sasha Blanton   *Senior Print Designer, Cover Designer*
Stephanie Shaw   *Print Designer*
Lee Horton   *Media Editor*
Tom Glass   *Text Editor*
Susan Raley   *Quality Control Specialist*
Sandi Conklin   *Project Manager*

Bror Saxberg   *Chief Learning Officer*
John Holdren   *Senior Vice President for Content and Curriculum*
Maria Szalay   *Senior Vice President for Product Development*
David Pelizzari   *Senior Director, Content and Curriculum*
Ralf Provant   *Instructional Design Manager, 6–12*
Kim Barcas   *Creative Director*
Jeff Burridge   *Managing Editor*
Sally Russell   *Senior Manager, Media*
Chris Frescholtz   *Senior Project Manager, High School*
Corey Maender   *Program Manager, High School*

Lisa Dimaio Iekel   *Production Manager*
John G. Agnone   *Director of Publications*

About K12 Inc.

K12 Inc., a technology-based education company, is the nation's leading provider of proprietary curriculum and online education programs to students in grades K–12. K12 provides its curriculum and academic services to online schools, traditional classrooms, blended school programs, and directly to families. K12 Inc. also operates the K12 International Academy, an accredited, diploma-granting online private school serving students worldwide. K12's mission is to provide any child the curriculum and tools to maximize success in life, regardless of geographic, financial, or demographic circumstances. K12 Inc. is accredited by CITA. More information can be found at www.K12.com.

978-1-60153-022-6

Printed by RR Donnelley & Sons, Roanoke, VA, USA, May 2014

Algebra II

A Reference Guide
and Problem Sets

Contents

How to Use This Book

Welcome to *Algebra II: A Reference Guide and Problem Sets*

This reference guide was developed to accompany the online portion of K12 Inc.'s High School Algebra II program and also serves as a reference for any student of algebra. Each section of the book presents an overview of a topic area. You can use this book to familiarize yourself with aspects of algebra, or to review materials you are studying in other books or online sources.

How This Book Is Organized

Units of Study

The following units of study are included in this reference guide.

- Numbers, Expressions, and Equations
- Linear Equations and Systems
- Functions
- Inequalities
- Polynomials and Power Functions

- Rational Equations
- Radicals and Complex Numbers
- Quadratic Functions
- Solving and Graphing Polynomials
- Exponentials and Logarithms

- Sequences and Series
- Counting and Probability
- Statistics
- Vectors and Matrices
- Conic Sections

Pronunciation Guide

See page 644 for a key to the pronunciations in the Glossary.

Glossary

See page 645 for a Glossary with brief definitions of some key terms.

Symbols

See page 651 for a list of mathematical symbols.

Formulary

See page 653 for a list of formulas with illustrations.

Selected Answers

See page 660 for answers to selected problem-set questions.

Navigating a Topic

Topic Each section explores a topic in algebra.

Definitions Words introduced with this topic will be **boldface** when they are explained in the text.

Examples Study the examples and their solutions that illustrate the topics and concepts covered in each unit of this reference guide.

Fractional Exponents and Higher Roots

An expression that contains a radical sign, $\sqrt{}$, is a **radical expression**.

Examples of radical expressions are $\sqrt{3x}$, $\sqrt[4]{x^3y^3}$, and $\sqrt[5]{32}$.

THINK ABOUT IT
If a and b are real numbers and $a^2 = b$, then a is the square root of b. This also applies to roots other than square roots.

DEFINITIONS
If a and b are real numbers, n is a positive integer, and $a^n = b$, then a is an **nth root** of b.
The nth root of b is written $\sqrt[n]{b}$, where n is the **index** of the radical and b is the **radicand**. The index is always an integer greater than 1, and the radicand can be a real number or an algebraic expression.

NOTATION
$\sqrt[n]{b}$ indicates the nth root of b when n is a positive integer

Finding Real nth Roots

REAL nTH ROOTS OF b

	n is even	n is odd
$b > 0$	two real roots (one positive and one negative)	one real root
$b < 0$	no real roots	one real root
$b = 0$	one real root, $\sqrt[n]{0} = 0$	

Example 1

A Find the cube roots of -64.

Solution The cube root means that n is 3. Since n is odd and $b < 0$, there is one real root: $(-4)^3 = -64$. So the cube root of -64 is -4. ∎

B Find the fourth roots of -625.

Solution Since n is even and $b < 0$, there are no real roots. ∎

C Find the fourth roots of 81.

Solution Since n is even and $b > 0$, there are two real roots: $(-3)^4 = 81$ and $3^4 = 81$. So the fourth roots of 81 are ± 3. ∎

FRACTIONAL EXPONENTS AND HIGHER ROOTS   251

Introduction Start here. Important concepts and skills you will learn about this topic are identified at the beginning of each section.

Helpful Information Reminders about things you've learned and other helpful tips are highlighted in the page margins in this way.

Step-by-Step Instructions Procedures are called out clearly so it's easy to see how to do things.

SOLVING RADICAL EQUATIONS

Step 1 Isolate the radical on one side of the equation.
Step 2 Raise both sides of the equation to the same power to eliminate the radical.
Step 3 Solve the equivalent equation.
Step 4 Check each solution by substituting into the original equation.

Selected Answers See how you did with the problem set by checking the selected answers in the back of the book.

Problem Set The end of each topic is where you will do the math so you can learn the math.

Problem Set

Find the equation of the quadratic function that has the given x-intercepts and point.

1. x-intercepts: -1 and 3
    point: $(2, -6)$

2. x-intercepts: -2 and 4
    point: $(3, -15)$

3. x-intercepts: -3 and 1
    point: $(-1, -4)$

4. x-intercepts: -2 and 2
    point: $(1, 6)$

5. x-intercepts: -1 and 4
    point: $(3, -4)$

6. x-intercepts: 1 and 2
    point:

7. x-intercepts: 2 and 4
    point: $(1, -3)$

8. x-intercepts: -9 and -2
    point: $(-1, 3)$

9. x-intercepts: 3 and 4
    point:

Page 315

1. $y = 2x^2 - 4x - 6$ 3. $y = x^2 + 2x - 3$ 5. $y = x^2 - 3x - 4$

7. $y = -x^2 + 6x - 8$ 9. $y = \frac{1}{2}x^2 - \frac{11}{4}x + 3$

11. $y = x^2 + 2x - 1$ 13. $y = 2x^2 - 8x + 7$

15. $y = -x^2 - 4x - 5$ 17. $y = -3x^2 + 6x - 4$

Introduction

Algebra is the key to unlocking the power of math.
This reference guide will help you extend your knowledge of mathematical tools such as equations, functions, and data analysis. It will also introduce new tools such as complex numbers, matrices, and conic sections. Each new or extended tool will help you solve more problems you encounter in school, work, and life.

Math is learned at the tip of a pencil. As you work through the topics in this book, you will see several worked examples that show you how to solve some problems, but the most important part of each topic is the problem set at the end. Reading problem solutions can help you find good strategies and best practices for solving problems, but only when you solve problems yourself will you really learn math. Do the math to learn the math.

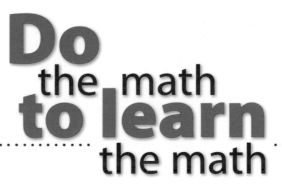

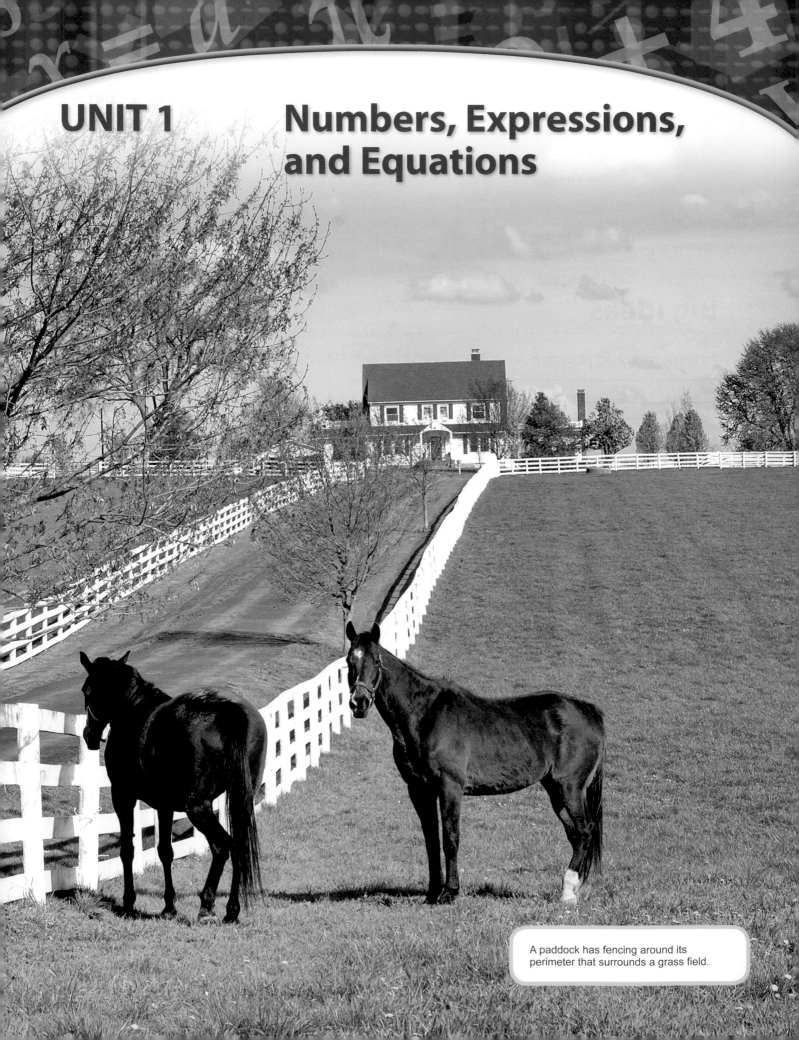

UNIT 1

Numbers, Expressions, and Equations

A paddock has fencing around its perimeter that surrounds a grass field.

Farmers and ranchers use formulas to calculate perimeter, area, and volume—for instance, the perimeter of a fence, the area of grass in a field, or the volume of grain in a storage silo.

Big Ideas

- ▶ Expressions, equations, and inequalities express relationships between different entities.
- ▶ You can use the laws of arithmetic to solve algebraic equations and inequalities.
- ▶ Solving an equation or inequality means finding values for the variable or variables that make the equation or inequality a true statement.

Unit Topics

- ▶ Foundations for Unit 1
- ▶ Sets of Numbers
- ▶ Number Lines and Absolute Value
- ▶ Number Properties
- ▶ Evaluating Expressions
- ▶ Solving Equations
- ▶ Solving Absolute Value Equations
- ▶ Applications: Formulas

Foundations for Unit 1

Before you study numbers and their properties, you should know how to do the following:

▶ Read and plot points on a number line.

▶ Add, subtract, multiply, and divide integers, decimals, and fractions.

Numbers on a Number Line

Definitions

number line   a line that has equally spaced intervals labeled with coordinates

coordinate   a number that indicates the location of a point on a number line

origin   the point with coordinate zero

Numbers to the left of the origin are negative. Numbers to the right of the origin are positive. Points can be plotted anywhere on the line, even between tick marks. The position of points on a number line helps you compare numbers.

Example 1

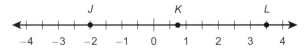

The coordinate of point J is -2.

The coordinate of point K is 0.75.

The coordinate of point L can be stated as $\frac{7}{2}$, $3\frac{1}{2}$, or 3.5.

> **REMEMBER**
>
> A number can be written in infinite ways. The expressions $\frac{7}{2}$, $3\frac{1}{2}$, and 3.5 are *equivalent* representations of the same number.

Problem Set A

Determine the coordinate of each point.

1.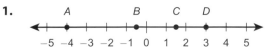

2.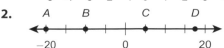

3. A number line from -3 to 3 with points A, B, C, D.

4.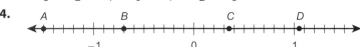

Draw each number line.

5. Draw a number line from -2 to 2 scaled by fourths. Plot and label $A = -\dfrac{3}{4}$ and $B = 1\dfrac{1}{4}$.

6. Draw a number line from -3 to 1 scaled by fifths. Plot and label $A = -2\dfrac{1}{5}$ and $B = 0.8$.

Adding and Subtracting

A number line is one way to visualize addition and subtraction. For addition, start at the origin and move right for positive addends; move left for negative addends. For subtraction, start at the origin and move right for positive minuends; move left for negative minuends. Move left for positive subtrahends and right for negative subtrahends.

$2 + (-5) = -3$

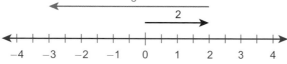

$5 - 2 = 3$

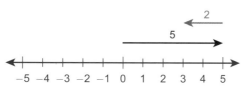

REMEMBER

In a subtraction problem $a - b$, a is the *minuend* and b is the *subtrahend*.

Subtraction with signed numbers requires the following definition.

Definition

opposite   the number that when added to a given number gives a sum of zero

Subtraction Property

Subtracting a number is equivalent to adding the number's opposite.

$$a - b \text{ is the same as } a + (-b)$$

Example 2

A $\begin{aligned}4 - (-10) &= 4 + (-(-10)) \\ &= \underbrace{4 + 10}_{\text{add the opposite}} \\ &= 14\end{aligned}$

B $\begin{aligned}\dfrac{3}{8} - \dfrac{7}{2} &= \dfrac{3}{8} - \dfrac{7}{2} \cdot \dfrac{4}{4} \\ &= \dfrac{3}{8} - \dfrac{28}{8} = \dfrac{-25}{8}\end{aligned}$

C $0.4 + 0.28$

$$\begin{aligned}&0.4 \\ &\underline{+\ 0.28} \\ &0.68\end{aligned}$$

Problem Set B

Perform the operations without a calculator.

7. $-8 + (-5)$

8. $-6 + 9$

9. $-12 - 6$

10. $-\dfrac{2}{3} + \dfrac{5}{9}$

11. $-\dfrac{2}{3} + \left(-4\dfrac{1}{2}\right)$

12. $\dfrac{3}{5} - \dfrac{1}{4}$

13. $1.25 + 3.92$

14. $-6.5 + 8.3$

15. $3.04 - 1.9$

Multiplying and Dividing

When you multiply or divide two numbers with opposite signs, the result is negative. When you multiply or divide two numbers with the same sign (both positive or both negative), the result is positive. You use *reciprocals* to divide by a fraction.

Definition

reciprocal   the number that when multiplied by a given number gives a product of 1; for a number written in fractional form, you can find the reciprocal by interchanging the numerator and denominator

Division Property

Dividing by a number is equivalent to multiplying by the number's reciprocal.

$$a \div b \text{ is the same as } a \cdot \dfrac{1}{b}$$

Example 3

A $4 \cdot 0 = 0$

B $\dfrac{7}{10} \div 5\dfrac{1}{2} = \dfrac{7}{10} \div \dfrac{11}{2}$
$$= \dfrac{7}{10} \cdot \dfrac{2}{11} = \dfrac{7}{55}$$

C $-1.5 \cdot 0.32$

$$
\begin{array}{r}
-1.5 \\
\times\ 0.32 \\
\hline
30 \\
450 \\
\hline
-0.480
\end{array}
$$

Problem Set C

Perform the operations without a calculator.

16. $-4 \cdot 5$

17. $\dfrac{24}{-6}$

18. $\dfrac{7}{12}\left(-\dfrac{8}{21}\right)$

19. $-2\dfrac{1}{3} \cdot 4\dfrac{1}{5}$

20. $-\dfrac{10}{33} \div \left(-\dfrac{42}{55}\right)$

21. $5\dfrac{1}{3} \div \dfrac{4}{9}$

22. $-0.25 \cdot 4.7$

23. $-3.8 \cdot (-1.33)$

24. $2.65 \div 0.4$

Sets of Numbers

A **set** is a collection of objects. Sets can be indicated in different ways.

DEFINITIONS

An **element** is a member of a set.
A **finite set** has a number of elements that can be described with a whole number.
An **infinite set** is not finite; the number of elements is boundless.

Special Sets of Numbers

The diagram below shows the relationship between common sets of numbers.

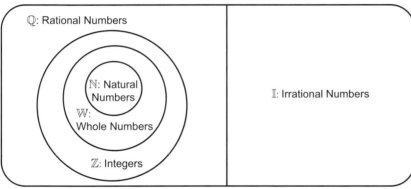

DEFINITIONS

The **natural numbers** are the set of numbers $\mathbb{N} = \{1, 2, 3, \ldots\}$. Natural numbers are also called **counting numbers** or **positive integers**.
The **whole numbers** are the set of numbers $\mathbb{W} = \{0, 1, 2, 3, \ldots\}$.
The **integers** are all the natural numbers, their opposites, and zero. The integers are denoted $\mathbb{Z} = \{\ldots, -2, -1, 0, 1, 2, \ldots\}$.
The set of **rational numbers** contains every number that can be written as a quotient $\frac{a}{b}$, where a and b are integers and $b \neq 0$. The rational numbers are denoted $\mathbb{Q}$.
The set of **irrational numbers** contains any number that can be written as a decimal, but not as the quotient of two integers. The letter $\mathbb{I}$ denotes the irrational numbers.
The **real numbers** are the set of numbers that can be written as decimals. When you combine the rational and irrational numbers, you get the real numbers. The letter $\mathbb{R}$ denotes the set of real numbers.

TIP

In decimal form, rational numbers are either terminating or repeating decimals. Irrational numbers are nonterminating decimals in which no single digit or block of digits repeats.

Example 1 For each number in the table, name the set or sets of which it is an element.

Solution

Number	Sets to Which the Number Belongs
1.24	**rational numbers, real numbers** 1.24 terminates and is equivalent to the quotient $\frac{124}{100}$.
-6	**integers, rational numbers, real numbers** To identify -6 as rational, think of $\frac{-6}{1}$.
π	**irrational numbers, real numbers** As a decimal, π is nonterminating and nonrepeating: $\pi = 3.1415926...$
$\sqrt{5}$	**irrational numbers, real numbers** $\sqrt{5} \approx 2.2360679$. Any decimal representation of an irrational number is only an approximation.
$\sqrt{9}$	**natural numbers, whole numbers, integers, rational numbers, real numbers** $\sqrt{9} = 3$
$\sqrt{\frac{16}{9}}$	**rational numbers, real numbers** $\sqrt{\frac{16}{9}} = \frac{4}{3} = 1.333...$
$1.\overline{45}$	**rational numbers, real numbers** $1.\overline{45}$ represents the repeating decimal $1.454545... = \frac{144}{99}$ ∎

Using Notation for Sets

Some of the ways to describe a set are by verbal description, roster notation (listing its elements), and set-builder notation.

Example 2 For each given description, describe the set in two other ways.

Ⓐ Verbal description: A is the set of odd positive integers less than 10.

Solution

Roster notation: $A = \{1, 3, 5, 7, 9\}$

Set-builder notation:
$A = \{x \mid x \text{ is an odd positive integer less than } 10\}$
or
$A = \{x \mid x = 2n + 1, n \in \mathbb{W}, n \leq 4\}$ ∎

Ⓑ Set-builder notation: $P = \{x \mid x < 10\}$

Solution

Verbal description: P is the set of all real numbers less than 10.

Roster notation is not possible because the set is infinite. It is not possible to list all the elements. ∎

> **TIP**
> Read the | symbol as "such that."

> **THINK ABOUT IT**
> There are infinitely many real numbers less than any given number. Two numbers less than 10 are $8\frac{1}{53}$ and -1261.

Identifying Set Relationships

Venn diagrams use simple closed curves to show all possible relations between sets. Overlapping regions represent intersections of the sets.

Example 3   For each pair of sets, draw a Venn diagram, identify the intersection and union, and determine whether one set is a subset of the other set.

A $A = \{1, 2, 3, 4, 6, 12\}$ and $B = \{1, 2, 4, 5, 10, 20\}$

Solution

The intersection is $A \cap B = \{1, 2, 4\}$.

The union is $A \cup B = \{1, 2, 3, 4, 5, 6, 10, 12, 20\}$.

Neither is a subset of the other. ∎

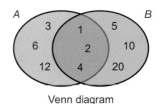

Venn diagram

B $X = \{3, 6, 9, 12, 15, 18\}$ and $Y = \{6, 12, 18\}$

Solution

The intersection is $X \cap Y = \{6, 12, 18\} = Y$.

The union is $X \cup Y = \{3, 6, 9, 12, 15, 18\} = X$.

Y is a subset of X: $Y \subseteq X$.

Furthermore, Y is a proper subset of X: $Y \subset X$. ∎

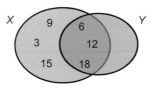

Venn diagram

C $\mathbb{Q}$ (set of rational numbers) and $\mathbb{R}$ (set of real numbers)

Solution

The intersection is $\mathbb{Q} \cap \mathbb{R} = \mathbb{Q}$.

The union is $\mathbb{Q} \cup \mathbb{R} = \mathbb{R}$.

$\mathbb{Q}$ is a proper subset of $\mathbb{R}$: $\mathbb{Q} \subset \mathbb{R}$. ∎

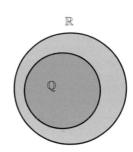

Application: Volunteer Staff

Sets do not need to be composed of numbers. They can be useful in organizing and understanding groups of people or objects.

Example 4   The table shows the volunteer sign-up for a charity telethon.

Volunteer Sign-up		
Morning (8 a.m.–12 p.m.)	Afternoon (12 p.m.–4 p.m.)	Evening (4 p.m.–8 p.m.)
Beth Campbell Nikhil	Beth Nikhil Patterson Sonya Umberto	Beth Campbell Sonya Troy

A What is the union of morning, afternoon, and evening volunteers? What does this union tell you?

B What is the intersection of morning, afternoon, and evening volunteers? What does this intersection tell you?

C The director of the telethon would like two volunteers working each shift. Is this possible? If so, suggest a volunteer schedule.

Solution   A Venn diagram shows the relationships between the three sets.

A The union of morning, afternoon, and evening volunteers is the set {Beth, Campbell, Nikhil, Patterson, Sonya, Troy, Umberto}. The union indicates the total collection of people who have signed up. There are seven elements in the union, so seven people signed up to volunteer.

B The intersection of morning, afternoon, and evening volunteers is the set {Beth}. The intersection indicates the set of people who signed up for all three sessions. Beth is the only volunteer who is available all day.

C Yes, the director can have two volunteers working each shift. One possible schedule is Campbell and Nikhil in the morning, Patterson and Umberto in the afternoon, and Troy and Sonya in the evening. Beth could serve as a backup for any shift in case someone cancels. ∎

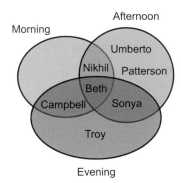

Problem Set

For each number, name the set(s) of which it is an element. Choose from the following sets: *natural numbers, whole numbers, integers, rational numbers, irrational numbers,* and *real numbers.*

1. 25,000

2. -5.2

3. $\dfrac{3}{8}$

4. $-\sqrt{49}$

5. $\sqrt{50}$

6. $0.\overline{3}$

7. -2π

8. $\sqrt{\dfrac{25}{100}}$

9. $1.23233233323333233333\ldots$

10. $\sqrt{0.01}$

For each given description, describe the set in two other ways. Choose from the following types of descriptions: *verbal description, roster notation,* and *set-builder notation.*

11. A is the set of multiples of 3 between -10 and 10.

12. $X = \{0, 1, 2, 3, 4, 5\}$

13. $M = \{x \mid x \in \mathbb{N} \text{ and } x > -5\}$

14. P is the set of prime numbers less than 2.

For each pair of sets, do the following:

A. Draw a Venn diagram showing the relationship between the sets.
B. Find the intersection.
C. Find the union.
D. Determine whether one set is a subset of the other set.

15. $A = \{-5, -3, -1, 1, 3, 5\}$ and $B = \{-4, -2, 0, 2, 4\}$

16. C is the set of whole-number factors of 30 and D is the set of whole-number factors of 9.

17. $\mathbb{W}$ (set of whole numbers) and $\mathbb{N}$ (set of natural numbers)

18. $K = \{x \mid x \in \mathbb{Z} \text{ and } x > -5\}$ and $L = \{x \mid x \in \mathbb{Z} \text{ and } x \le 5\}$

For the given sets, identify the union(s) and intersection(s).

19. $A = \{-10, -5, 0, 5, 10\}$, $B = \{5, 10, 15, 20, 25\}$, $C = \{-10, 0, 10\}$

   A. $A \cap B$

   B. $B \cap C$

   C. $A \cap B \cap C$

   D. $B \cup C$

   E. $A \cup B$

   F. $A \cup B \cup C$

20. $\mathbb{Z}$ (set of integers), $\mathbb{Q}$ (set of rational numbers), $\mathbb{I}$ (set of irrational numbers)

   A. $\mathbb{Q} \cap \mathbb{Z}$

   B. $\mathbb{Z} \cap \mathbb{I}$

   C. $\mathbb{Z} \cap \mathbb{Q} \cap \mathbb{I}$

   D. $\mathbb{Q} \cup \mathbb{Z}$

   E. $\mathbb{Q} \cup \mathbb{I}$

   F. $\mathbb{Z} \cup \mathbb{Q} \cup \mathbb{I}$

Give an example of a number that fits each description.

21. an element of $\mathbb{Z}$ but not an element of $\mathbb{W}$

22. an element of $\mathbb{W}$ but not an element of $\mathbb{N}$

23. an element of $\mathbb{N}$ but not an element of $\mathbb{Q}$

24. an element of the set of prime numbers but not an element of the set of odd natural numbers

For each Venn diagram, describe each set in roster notation.

25.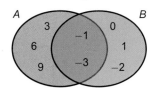

   A. A

   B. B

   C. $A \cap B$

26.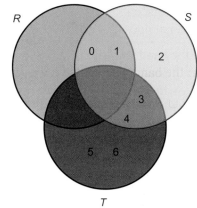

   A. S

   B. $S \cup T$

   C. $R \cap T$

Solve.

27. Sanja's cruise offers the following activities each day.

Morning	Afternoon	Evening
Swimming	Swimming	Dancing
Sunbathing	Sunbathing	Cooking Class
Yoga	Video Game Arcade	Video Game Arcade
Shuffleboard	Pilates	Movie Theater
	Shuffleboard	Sauna

   A. What is the union of morning, afternoon, and evening activities? What does this union represent?

   B. What is the intersection of morning, afternoon, and evening activities? What does this intersection represent?

   C. Sanja plans to do three activities in the morning, three in the afternoon, and three in the evening. Is it possible for her to do every activity in a single day? If so, suggest an activity schedule.

28. The table shows the members of a rock band through the decades.

1970s	1980s	1990s
David	Sammy	Gary
Eddie	Eddie	Eddie
Alex	Alex	Alex
Mark	Michael	Michael

A. What is the union of the 1970s, 1980s, and 1990s band members? What does this union represent?

B. What is the intersection of the 1970s, 1980s, and 1990s band members? What does this intersection represent?

C. If a fan of the band wants one autograph by everyone who has been a member of the band, what is the fewest number of autographs needed?

29. **Challenge** If $A \cup B = \varnothing$, what can you say about A and B?

30. **Challenge** If $A \cap B = \varnothing$, what can you say about the number of elements in $A \cup B$?

31. **Challenge** For any two sets A and B, the *relative complement* of A, written $B - A$, is the set of elements in B but not in A. Given $A = \{1, 2, 3\}$ and $B = \{2, 3, 4\}$, find the following.

A. $B - A$

B. $A - B$

C. $(A \cup B) - (A \cap B)$

Number Lines and Absolute Value

You can use a number line to find the absolute value of a number.

Opposites

You know how to use opposites to subtract signed numbers. The idea of opposites can also be extended to expressions with variables. If a is any number, its opposite is $-a$. The opposite of 0 is 0. The opposite of $-a$ is $-(-a) = a$.

NOTATION

$-a$ the opposite of a

PROPERTIES OF OPPOSITES

Let a be any real number.

Property	Literal Translation
If $a > 0$, then $-a < 0$.	The opposite of a positive number is negative.
If $a = 0$, then $-a = 0$.	The opposite of zero is zero.
If $a < 0$, then $-a > 0$.	The opposite of a negative number is positive.

Opposites are an equal distance from 0 on the number line, but in opposite directions. For example, 3 and -3 are opposites, and they are both three units from zero.

THINK ABOUT IT

Distance is always at least zero. If you calculate a distance and get a negative number, the sign usually indicates a direction for the distance.

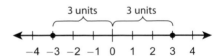

Example 1   Evaluate each expression.

A $-x$ when $x = 5$

Solution

$-x = -5$ ∎

B $-k$ when $k = -7.5$

Solution

$-k = -(-7.5) = 7.5$ ∎

The fact that $-(-a) = a$ is sometimes called the *double negative property*. A similar property exists in the English language, where two negatives make a positive. For example, "I don't want nothing" logically means, "I want something."

Absolute Value

For any pair of opposite nonzero real numbers, the positive number is the absolute value of each number. The absolute value of 0 is 0.

PROPERTIES OF ABSOLUTE VALUE

Let a be any real number.

Property	Literal Translation
If $a > 0$, then $|a| = a$.	The absolute value of a positive number is itself.
If $a = 0$, then $|a| = 0$.	The absolute value of zero is zero.
If $a < 0$, then $|a| = -a$.	The absolute value of a negative number is its opposite.

On the number line, -3 is three units from the origin, so $|-3| = 3$.

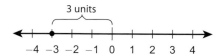

Absolute value indicates distance without direction. It is similar to saying, "We drove 3 miles," without saying whether you drove north, east, south, or west.

Example 2   Evaluate each expression.

A $|6|$

Solution   Because $6 > 0$, $|6| = 6$. ∎

B $|n|$ when $n = -4.8$

Solution   Because $-4.8 < 0$, $|n| = -n = -(-4.8) = 4.8$.

Or simply $|-4.8| = 4.8$. ∎

C $|-4 + 9|$

Solution

$|-4 + 9| = |5|$ Simplify within the absolute value.

$\qquad\quad = 5$ Use the definition of absolute value. ∎

D $2 - |x - 10|$ when $x = 1$

Solution $2 - |x - 10| = 2 - |1 - 10|$ Substitute 1 for x.

$\qquad\qquad\qquad = 2 - |-9|$ Simplify within the absolute value.

$\qquad\qquad\qquad = 2 - 9$ Use the definition of absolute value.

$\qquad\qquad\qquad = -7$ Subtract. ∎

Distance on the Number Line

One application of absolute value is to measure *undirected* distance. Given the coordinates of two points on the number line, A and B, the undirected distance between those points is calculated as $|A - B|$ or $|B - A|$. For example, the distance between $A = -2$ and $B = 3$ is shown below.

$$|A - B| = |-2 - 3| = |-5| = 5$$
$$\text{or}$$
$$|B - A| = |3 - (-2)| = |5| = 5$$

The distance between A and B is 5 units.

Example 3 Find the distance between each pair of numbers on the number line.

Ⓐ $P = 4$ and $Q = 18$

Ⓑ $X = -8$ and $Y = 25$

Solution

$|P - Q| = |4 - 18| = |-14| = 14$

The distance is 14 units. ∎

Solution

$|Y - X| = |25 - (-8)| = |33| = 33$

The distance is 33 units. ∎

Example 4 The distance between points R and S is 8 units. If $R = 5$, find the possible coordinates of S.

Solution Sketch a number line. Locate $R = 5$ and count 8 units right and left.

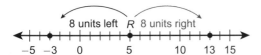

8 units left R 8 units right

Check

$|R - S| = |5 - (-3)| = |8| = 8 \checkmark$ or $|R - S| = |5 - 13| = |-8| = 8 \checkmark$

The coordinate of S is either $S = -3$ or $S = 13$. ∎

You will learn how to use algebra to solve this type of problem in a future topic.

Density of Rational Numbers

Mathematicians say that rational numbers are *dense* on the number line. This means that for any two rational numbers, there are infinitely many rational numbers between them. This concept is formally stated as follows:

DENSITY PROPERTY FOR RATIONAL NUMBERS

Given $a \in \mathbb{Q}$ and $b \in \mathbb{Q}$, with $a < b$, there exists $r \in \mathbb{Q}$ such that $a < r < b$.

This property means you can calculate a portion of the entire distance between any two rational numbers.

Example 5 Find a rational number one-fourth of the way between 2.85 and 3.02.

Solution First, find the entire distance between 2.85 and 3.02.

$|3.02 - 2.85| = |0.17| = 0.17$

Next, find one-fourth, or 0.25, of this distance.

$0.25 \cdot 0.17 = 0.0425$

Last, add this portion of the distance to the lesser of the original values.

$2.85 + 0.0425 = 2.8925$

The rational number 2.8925 is one-fourth of the way between 2.85 and 3.02. ∎

THINK ABOUT IT

The solution 2.8925 is specifically one-fourth of the way from 2.85. An alternate solution is one-fourth of the way from 3.02.

$3.02 - 0.0425 = 2.9775$

Problem Set

Evaluate each expression for each of the given values.

1. $-a$
   A. $a = 12$
   B. $a = -\dfrac{1}{2}$
   C. $a = \sqrt{5}$

2. $-(-b)$
   A. $b = -6.8$
   B. $b = -\sqrt{9}$
   C. $b = \dfrac{2}{7}$

Evaluate each expression.

3. $|-15 + 7|$

4. $|25.7 - 4.3|$

5. $\left|-\dfrac{3}{5} - \dfrac{7}{8}\right|$

6. $|-8 \cdot 3|$

7. $4 + |5 - 8|$

8. $-10 - |-6 + 12|$

9. $|x|$ when $x = 9$

10. $|k|$ when $k = -\dfrac{2}{3}$

11. $|n - 8|$ when $n = -5$

12. $|n| - 8$ when $n = -5$

13. $|-3 + x| - 10$ when $x = 3$

14. $z + |-z + 1.25|$ when $z = 7.5$

15. $a \cdot b \cdot c$ when $a = 2$, $b = |-5|$, and $c = 1.5$

16. $s + |-4 \cdot t|$ when $s = -2$ and $t = -\dfrac{1}{2}$

Use $>$, $<$, or $=$ to compare each pair of expressions.

17. $-(-|-3.2|)$ ▮ $-(-(-3.2))$

18. $|8 - 5| - 3$ ▮ $8 - |5 - 3|$

19. $|t - 20|$ ▮ $|20 - t|$ when $t = -2$

20. $-a$ ▮ $|a|$ when $a < 0$

Find the distance between each pair of numbers on the number line.

21. $P = -3$ and $Q = 7$

22. $A = 5$ and $B = -12$

23. $X = 2.3$ and $Y = 8.1$

24. $C = 8.1$ and $D = -4.1$

Find each rational number with the given characteristics.

25. a rational number one-half of the way between 3 and 8.5

26. a rational number one-third of the way between -3.4 and 3.2

27. a rational number one-half of the way between -2.5 and 1.5

28. a rational number two-thirds of the way between -1.2 and 0.4

29. a rational number three-fourths of the way between 4.96 and 5.11

30. a rational number two-fifths of the way between -3.012 and -3.011

Solve.

*31. **Challenge** Michele owns stock in a computer company and tracks the value of the stock each day. According to the table, during which day did the stock price experience the greatest overall change?

Start of Day Monday	Stock Price at End of Day ($)				
	Monday	Tuesday	Wednesday	Thursday	Friday
26.69	26.48	26.29	26.32	24.91	23.40

Number Properties

Certain properties apply to operations with expressions.

You can use number properties to rewrite mathematical expressions.

PROPERTIES OF REAL NUMBERS

The following properties apply for all real numbers a, b, and c.

Property	Addition	Multiplication
Identity Property	$a + 0 = a$ and $0 + a = a$	$a \cdot 1 = a$ and $1 \cdot a = a$
Inverse Property	$a + (-a) = 0$ and $(-a) + a = 0$	If $a \neq 0$, then $a \cdot \frac{1}{a} = 1$ and $\frac{1}{a} \cdot a = 1$
Commutative Property	$a + b = b + a$	$ab = ba$
Associative Property	$(a + b) + c = a + (b + c)$	$(ab)c = a(bc)$
Distributive Property	$a(b + c) = ab + ac$	

Identifying Properties of Real Numbers

Example 1 Identify the property shown by each statement in the table.

Solution

Statement	Property
$(2 \cdot 3) \cdot 8 = 2 \cdot (3 \cdot 8)$	Associative Property of Multiplication
$10 \cdot 15 = 15 \cdot 10$	Commutative Property of Multiplication
$4 + (-4) = 0$	Additive Inverse Property
$4(7 + a) = 4 \cdot 7 + 4 \cdot a$	Distributive Property
$2.5 + a = a + 2.5$	Commutative Property of Addition
$1 \cdot \frac{3}{8} = \frac{3}{8}$	Multiplicative Identity Property
$(8 + 12) + 7 = 8 + (12 + 7)$	Associative Property of Addition
$-2(5 + 9) = -2 \cdot 5 + (-2) \cdot 9$	Distributive Property
$0.25 \cdot 4 = 1$	Multiplicative Inverse Property
$2x + 4 = 2(x + 2)$	Distributive Property

> **TIP**
>
> Using the distributive property to remove a common factor, as in $2x + 4 = 2(x + 2)$, is one form of *factoring*.

Using Properties of Real Numbers to Simplify

Operations, definitions, and properties allow you to simplify expressions.

Example 2 Simplify each expression. Justify the steps.

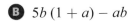 $21a + (15 - 7a)$

Solution

$$
\begin{aligned}
21a + (15 - 7a) &= 21a + [15 + (-7a)] && \text{Definition of Subtraction} \\
&= 21a + [(-7a) + 15] && \text{Commutative Property} \\
& && \text{of Addition} \\
&= [21a + (-7a)] + 15 && \text{Associative Property} \\
& && \text{of Addition} \\
&= a[21 + (-7)] + 15 && \text{Distributive Property} \\
&= a \cdot 14 + 15 && \text{Addition} \\
&= 14a + 15 && \text{Commutative Property} \\
& && \text{of Multiplication} \ \blacksquare
\end{aligned}
$$

B $5b(1 + a) - ab$

Solution

$$
\begin{aligned}
5b(1 + a) - ab &= (5b \cdot 1 + 5b \cdot a) - ab && \text{Distributive Property} \\
&= (5b + 5ba) - ab && \text{Multiplication} \\
&= (5b + 5ab) - ab && \text{Commutative Property} \\
& && \text{of Multiplication} \\
&= (5b + 5ab) + (-ab) && \text{Definition of Subtraction} \\
&= 5b + [5ab + (-ab)] && \text{Associative Property} \\
& && \text{of Addition} \\
&= 5b + ab[5 + (-1)] && \text{Distributive Property} \\
&= 5b + ab \cdot 4 && \text{Addition} \\
&= 5b + 4ab && \text{Commutative Property} \\
& && \text{of Multiplication} \ \blacksquare
\end{aligned}
$$

Closure

A set is **closed** under an operation if the result of the operation on any two elements of the set is also an element of the set. The set of real numbers is closed under addition, subtraction, multiplication, and division.

THINK ABOUT IT

Division by zero is *undefined*, so it does not affect closure. That is, the statement $\frac{a}{b} \in \mathbb{R}$ automatically excludes situations where $b = 0$.

CLOSURE PROPERTIES FOR THE SET OF REAL NUMBERS

Let $a \in \mathbb{R}$ and $b \in \mathbb{R}$; then $a + b \in \mathbb{R}$, $a - b \in \mathbb{R}$, $ab \in \mathbb{R}$, and $\frac{a}{b} \in \mathbb{R}$.

The following example shows that not all subsets of the real numbers are closed under all operations.

Example 3   Determine whether each set is closed under the given operation.

Ⓐ the set of integers under addition

Solution   Yes, the set of integers is closed under addition. The sum of any two integers is another integer. You could state this concept formally as follows: If $a \in \mathbb{Z}$ and $b \in \mathbb{Z}$; then $a + b \in \mathbb{Z}$. ∎

Ⓑ the set of integers under division

Solution   No, the set of integers is not closed under division. Use a counterexample to show this. If $a = 5$ and $b = 2$, then $\frac{a}{b} = \frac{5}{2} = 2.5$, which is not an integer. ∎

Ⓒ the set of natural numbers under subtraction

Solution   No, the set of natural numbers is not closed under subtraction. Use a counterexample to show this. If $a = 5$ and $b = 7$, then $a - b = -2$, which is not a natural number. ∎

> **TIP**
>
> A *counterexample* is an example that shows that a statement is false.
>
> You need only a single counterexample to show that a statement is false.

Powers and Exponents

> **DEFINITIONS**
>
> A **power** is an expression that contains a *base* and an *exponent*, or the value of such an expression. When the exponent is a natural number, a power represents repeated multiplication.
> The **base** is a number, variable, or expression that is raised to a power. When the exponent is a natural number, the base is the factor in repeated multiplication.
> A natural number **exponent** in a power indicates how many times the base is used as a factor.
> **Example**
> $5^3 = 5 \times 5 \times 5 = 125$
> 5 is the base; it is the repeated factor.
> 3 is the exponent.
> 125 is the third power of 5.
> 5^3 is read "5 to the third power"
>   or "5 to the third."

Example 4   Identify the base and exponent. Then evaluate the expression.

Ⓐ 3^4

Solution   The base is 3 and the exponent is 4. To evaluate, use 3 as a factor four times.

$3^4 = 3 \cdot 3 \cdot 3 \cdot 3 = 81$

> **TIP**
>
> Two powers have special names. When you raise a number to the second power, you are *squaring* the number. When you raise a number to the third power, you are *cubing* the number.

B $(-2)^6$

Solution The base is -2 and the exponent is 6.

$$(-2)^6 = (-2) \cdot (-2) \cdot (-2) \cdot (-2) \cdot (-2) \cdot (-2) = 64 \quad \blacksquare$$

C -2^6

Solution Because this expression does not have parentheses around -2, the base is actually 2. You could rewrite it as $-1 \cdot 2^6$.

$$-2^6 = -1 \cdot 2^6 = -1 \cdot 2 \cdot 2 \cdot 2 \cdot 2 \cdot 2 \cdot 2 = -64 \quad \blacksquare$$

Like Terms

> **DEFINITIONS**
>
> **Terms** are the parts of an expression that are added together. Terms can be products or quotients of numerals or variables.
> A **constant** is a term that has no variable factors.
> A **coefficient** is the numerical factor of a term. Constants are their own coefficients.
> **Like terms** are terms that contain the same variables raised to the same powers. Constants are like terms with each other.

The properties of real numbers allow you to combine like terms.

Example 5 Identify the like terms and then simplify.

$4x^3 + 3 - x^3 + 2$

Solution Use the definition of subtraction to write the expression as terms that are added.

$4x^3 + 3 + (-1x^3) + 2$

There are two pairs of like terms: the third-power terms $4x^3$ and $-1x^3$, and the constants 3 and 2. Rearrange then simplify.

$$\begin{aligned}
4x^3 + 3 + (-1x^3) + 2 &= 4x^3 + \left[3 + (-1x^3)\right] + 2 && \text{Associative Property of Addition} \\
&= 4x^3 + \left[(-1x^3) + 3\right] + 2 && \text{Commutative Property of Addition} \\
&= \left[4x^3 + (-1x^3)\right] + [3 + 2] && \text{Associative Property of Addition} \\
&= x^3\left[4 + (-1)\right] + [3 + 2] && \text{Distributive Property} \\
&= x^3 \cdot 3 + 5 && \text{Addition} \\
&= 3x^3 + 5 && \text{Commutative Property of Multiplication} \quad \blacksquare
\end{aligned}$$

In Example 5, combining the like terms $4x^3$ and $-1x^3$ resulted in $3x^3$. Notice that the sum of the coefficients, $4 + (-1)$, is the coefficient of the simplified term, 3. Another strategy for quickly combining like terms is to add their coefficients, keeping the same variable factors.

Example 6   Simplify by combining like terms.

A $21a + 15 - 7a$

Solution $21a + 15 - 7a = 21a + 15 + (-7a)$ The like terms are $21a$ and $-7a$.

$\qquad\qquad\qquad\qquad\quad = 14a + 15$ Add the coefficients: $21 + (-7) = 14.$ ∎

B $8 - 4xy^2 + 15x + 3xy^2 - 7x + 6 + 3x$

Solution   Because this expression has several terms, grouping like terms before adding coefficients is a helpful strategy.

$8 - 4xy^2 + 15x + 3xy^2 - 7x + 6 + 3x$

$\quad = 8 + (-4xy^2) + 15x + 3xy^2 + (-7x) + 6 + 3x$

$\quad = [8 + 6] + [-4xy^2 + 3xy^2] + [15x + (-7x) + 3x]$

$\quad = 14 - 1xy^2 + 11x$ ∎

Problem Set

Identify the property shown by each statement.

1. $-8 \cdot 15 = 15 \cdot (-8)$

2. $3(x + 7) = 3 \cdot x + 3 \cdot 7$

3. $2.5 + 0 = 2.5$

4. $5\frac{1}{3} \cdot 1 = 5\frac{1}{3}$

5. $6.8 + 3.2 = 3.2 + 6.8$

6. $(-6 \cdot 2) \cdot 5 = -6 \cdot (2 \cdot 5)$

7. $\frac{2}{9} + \left(-\frac{2}{9}\right) = 0$

8. $10x^3 + 15xy = 5x\,(2x^2 + 3y)$

9. $(1 + 2) + 3 = (2 + 1) + 3$

10. $\frac{4}{5} \cdot \frac{5}{4} = 1$

*11. **Challenge** $-1xy^2 = -xy^2$

Fill in the missing reason(s) and step(s) for each proof.

12. Prove that $4 - 2(x - 2) = -2x + 8$.

Statement	Reason
$4 - 2(x - 2) = 4 + (-2)\,[x + (-2)]$	Definition of Subtraction
$= 4 + [(-2) \cdot x + (-2) \cdot (-2)]$	**A.** ▧
$= 4 + [(-2x) + 4]$	Multiplication
$= [4 + (-2x)] + 4$	**B.** ▧
$= [-2x + 4] + 4$	**C.** ▧
$= -2x + [4 + 4]$	Associative Property of Addition
$= -2x + 8$	Addition

13. Prove that $2x \cdot 3x = 6x^2$.

Statement	Reason
$2x \cdot 3x = (2 \cdot x) \cdot (3 \cdot x)$	Multiplication (Factoring)
$= 2 \cdot (x \cdot 3) \cdot x$	**A.** ▨
$= 2 \cdot (3 \cdot x) \cdot x$	**B.** ▨
$= (2 \cdot 3) \cdot (x \cdot x)$	**C.** ▨
$= (2 \cdot 3) \cdot (x^2)$	Definition of Exponent
$= 6 \cdot x^2$	Multiplication
$= 6x^2$	Multiplication

14. Prove that $7a + 3b + 9a + 8b = 16a + 11b$.

Statement	Reason
$7a + 3b + 9a + 8b = 7a + (3b + 9a) + 8b$	Associative Property of Addition
$= 7a + (9a + 3b) + 8b$	**A.** ▨
$= (7a + 9a) + (3b + 8b)$	Associative Property of Addition
$= $ **B.** ▨	Distributive Property
$= a \cdot 16 + b \cdot 11$	Addition
$= 16a + 11b$	**C.** ▨

15. Prove that $\frac{1}{3}(x + 3) - 1 = \frac{1}{3}x$.

Statement	Reason
$\frac{1}{3}(x + 3) - 1 = \frac{1}{3}(x + 3) + (-1)$	Definition of Subtraction
$= \frac{1}{3} \cdot x + \frac{1}{3} \cdot 3 + (-1)$	Distributive Property
$= $ **A.** ▨	Inverse Property of Multiplication
$= \frac{1}{3}x + [1 + (-1)]$	Associative Property of Addition
$= $ **B.** ▨	Inverse Property of Addition
$= \frac{1}{3}x$	**C.** ▨

Combine like terms to simplify each expression.

16. $5x + 12 + 2x - 3$

17. $-4x^2 + 3x + 8x^2 - 10 - 20x$

18. $9mn + 2mn^2 - 3mn + 4m - 7n + 8mn^2 + 4n$

19. $2.5k - 1.8k^2 + 15.2 - 10k + 12.3k^2$

Simplify each expression.

20. 2^5

21. -5^3

22. $(-5)^3$

23. $(-3)^4$

24. -3^4

25. $6(p - 4)$

26. $3(a - b) - 5(a + 2) + 10b$

27. $(4xy \cdot 3x^2) + [2x^3 \cdot (-5y)]$

28. $2[4x + 3(x + 2)]$

29. $2(x - 3) - 4(x + 1) + 5\left(\frac{1}{10}x + 2\right)$

Determine whether each set is closed under the given operation. If it is not closed under that operation, give a counterexample.

30. the set of rational numbers under

    A. addition   **B.** multiplication

31. the set of integers under

    A. subtraction   **B.** division

32. the set $\{-1, 0, 1\}$ under

    A. addition   **B.** subtraction   **C.** multiplication   **D.** division

Solve.

*33. **Challenge** The set of even integers can be defined as $\{x \mid x = 2n$ where $n \in \mathbb{Z}\}$. The set of odd integers can be defined as $\{y \mid y = 2n + 1$ where $n \in \mathbb{Z}\}$. That is, -8 is even because $-8 = 2(-4)$ and $-4 \in \mathbb{Z}$; and 13 is odd because $13 = 2 \cdot 6 + 1$ and $6 \in \mathbb{Z}$. Complete this proof that the sum of two odd integers is an even integer.

Prove that the sum of two odd integers is an even integer.

Let $2a + 1$ and $2b + 1$, where $a \in \mathbb{Z}$ and $b \in \mathbb{Z}$, represent any two odd integers.

Their sum is $(2a + 1) + (2b + 1)$.

Statement	Reason
$(2a + 1) + (2b + 1) = 2a + (1 + 2b) + 1$	**A.** ▨
$= 2a + (2b + 1) + 1$	**B.** ▨
$= (2a + 2b) + (1 + 1)$	Associative Property of Addition
$= 2(a + b) + (1 + 1)$	Distributive Property
$= 2(a + b) + 2$	Addition
$= 2(a + b) + 2 \cdot 1$	Identity Property of Multiplication
$= 2[(a + b) + 1]$	**C.** ▨

The set of integers is closed under addition. So, because $a \in \mathbb{Z}$, $b \in \mathbb{Z}$, and $1 \in \mathbb{Z}$, it follows that **D.** ▨ .

The sum $2[(a + b) + 1]$ is in the form $2n$, where $n = [(a + b) + 1]$, so $2[(a + b) + 1]$ is a(n) **E.** ▨ .

Therefore, the sum of any two odd integers is an even integer.

Evaluating Expressions

An **expression** is a meaningful group of math symbols.

A **numerical expression** consists of numbers, operations, and sometimes grouping symbols. Commonly used grouping symbols are parentheses ( ), brackets [ ], and braces { }. Fraction bars also act as grouping symbols. To find the value of an expression, or to *evaluate* the expression, you use the **order of operations**.

TIP

You can use **PEMDAS** to remember the order of operations.

P: Parentheses
E: Exponents
M/D: Multiply and Divide
A/S: Add and Subtract

ORDER OF OPERATIONS

Step 1 Perform operations within grouping symbols. For nested grouping symbols, simplify in the innermost group first.
Step 2 Evaluate powers.
Step 3 Multiply and divide from left to right.
Step 4 Add and subtract from left to right.

Evaluating Numerical Expressions

Example 1 Evaluate.

A $2 - 5^3 + 10$

Solution

$$
\begin{aligned}
2 - 5^3 + 10 &= 2 - 125 + 10 && \text{Evaluate the power.} \\
&= -123 + 10 && \text{Subtract.} \\
&= -113 && \text{Add.} \ \blacksquare
\end{aligned}
$$

B $20 - (4 + 26) \div 3 \cdot 2$

Solution

$$
\begin{aligned}
20 - (4 + 26) \div 3 \cdot 2 &= 20 - (30) \div 3 \cdot 2 && \text{Add within the parentheses.} \\
&= 20 - 10 \cdot 2 && \text{Divide.} \\
&= 20 - 20 && \text{Multiply.} \\
&= 0 && \text{Subtract.} \ \blacksquare
\end{aligned}
$$

C $\dfrac{2(8 - 18)^3}{4}$

Solution

$$
\begin{aligned}
\frac{2(8 - 18)^3}{4} &= \frac{2(-10)^3}{4} && \text{Subtract within the parentheses.} \\
&= \frac{2(-1000)}{4} && \text{Evaluate the power.} \\
&= \frac{-2000}{4} && \text{The fraction bar is a grouping symbol.} \\
& && \text{Evaluate the numerator.} \\
&= -500 && \text{Divide.} \ \blacksquare
\end{aligned}
$$

Evaluating Algebraic Expressions

An **algebraic expression**, also called a **variable expression**, is a combination of variables, numbers, and operations. To evaluate an algebraic expression, substitute values for the variables and then evaluate the resulting numerical expression.

Example 2 Evaluate.

Ⓐ $x^3 + 13x$ when $x = 2$

Solution

$$
\begin{aligned}
x^3 + 13x &= (2)^3 + 13 \cdot 2 && \text{Subtitute 2 for } x. \\
&= 8 + 13 \cdot 2 && \text{Evaluate the power.} \\
&= 8 + 26 && \text{Multiply.} \\
&= 34 && \text{Add.} \ \blacksquare
\end{aligned}
$$

Ⓑ $-a + 3b^2$ when $a = 5$ and $b = -4$

Solution

$$
\begin{aligned}
-a^2 + 3b^2 &= -(5)^2 + 3\,(-4)^2 && \text{Substitute 5 for } a \text{ and } -4 \text{ for } b. \\
&= -25 + 3 \cdot 16 && \text{Evaluate the powers.} \\
&= -25 + 48 && \text{Multiply.} \\
&= 23 && \text{Add.} \ \blacksquare
\end{aligned}
$$

> **TIP**
>
> When you substitute for a variable, it can be helpful to enclose the substitution in parentheses, especially when exponents or negatives are involved.

Ⓒ $8\,[1 + 2(4 - x)]$ when $x = -1.4$

Solution

$$
\begin{aligned}
8[1 + 2(4 - x)] &= 8[1 + 2(4 - (-1.4))] && \text{Substitute } -1.4 \text{ for } x. \\
&= 8[1 + 2(4 + 1.4)] && \text{Apply the definition of} \\
& && \text{subtraction.} \\
&= 8[1 + 2 \cdot 5.4] && \text{Perform the operations inside} \\
&= 8[1 + 10.8] && \text{the grouping symbols,} \\
&= 8[11.8] && \text{working from the innermost.} \\
&= 94.4 && \text{Multiply.} \ \blacksquare
\end{aligned}
$$

Ⓓ $(c - d)^2 (c + d)$ when $c = \frac{1}{2}$ and $d = 3$

Solution

$$
\begin{aligned}
(c - d)^2 (c + d) &= \left(\tfrac{1}{2} - 3\right)^2 \left(\tfrac{1}{2} + 3\right) && \text{Subtitute } \tfrac{1}{2} \text{ for } c \text{ and 3 for } d. \\
&= \left(\tfrac{1}{2} - \tfrac{6}{2}\right)^2 \left(\tfrac{1}{2} + \tfrac{6}{2}\right) && \text{Use common denominators to} \\
& && \text{add or subtract fractions.} \\
&= \left(-\tfrac{5}{2}\right)^2 \left(\tfrac{7}{2}\right) && \text{Perform the operations inside the} \\
& && \text{parentheses.} \\
&= \tfrac{25}{4} \cdot \tfrac{7}{2} && \text{Evaluate the power.} \\
&= \tfrac{175}{8} = 21\tfrac{7}{8} && \text{Multiply.} \ \blacksquare
\end{aligned}
$$

Comparing Expressions

You can use the symbols $=, >, <, \geq,$ and $\leq$ to compare expressions.

Example 3 Compare.

Ⓐ $|2x + 3|$ and $2x + 3$ when $x = -7$

Solution When $x = -7$,

$|2x + 3| = |2(-7) + 3| = |-14 + 3| = |-11| = 11$, and

$2x + 3 = 2(-7) + 3 = -14 + 3 = -11$.

So, $|2x + 3| > 2x + 3$ when $x = -7$.

(It is also true that $|2x + 3| \geq 2x + 3$ when $x = -7$.) ∎

Ⓑ $\dfrac{a + 2}{a - 3}$ and $\dfrac{a^2 + 4a + 4}{a^2 - a - 6}$ when $a = 5$

Solution When $a = 5$,

$\dfrac{a + 2}{a - 3} = \dfrac{5 + 2}{5 - 3} = \dfrac{7}{2}$, and

$\dfrac{a^2 + 4a + 4}{a^2 - a - 6} = \dfrac{(5)^2 + 4 \cdot 5 + 4}{(5)^2 - 5 - 6} = \dfrac{25 + 20 + 4}{25 - 5 - 6} = \dfrac{49}{14} = \dfrac{7}{2}$.

So, $\dfrac{a + 2}{a - 3} = \dfrac{a^2 + 4a + 4}{a^2 - a - 6}$ when $a = 5$. ∎

> **NOTATION**
>
> | | |
> |---|---|
> | $=$ | **is equal to** |
> | $>$ | **is greater than** |
> | $\geq$ | **is greater than or equal to** |
> | $<$ | **is less than** |
> | $\leq$ | **is less than or equal to** |

Application: Total Cost

You can write expressions to solve many types of problems, including those involving price and cost.

Example 4 At a baseball game, hot dogs cost $4.50 each, and bottles of water cost $1.75 each. Omar is at the concession stand to order some food for his friends.

Ⓐ Write an expression to represent the total Omar would pay for x hot dogs and y bottles of water.

Solution Write an expression.

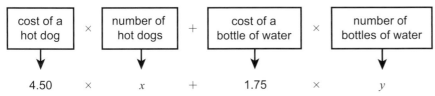

The total cost of x hot dogs and y bottles of water, in dollars, is represented by the expression $4.50x + 1.75y$. ∎

Ⓑ Evaluate the expression to find the total that Omar will pay for 5 hot dogs and 7 bottles of water.

Solution Substitute 5 for x and 7 for y. Then use the order of operations.

$$4.50x + 1.75y = 4.50 \cdot 5 + 1.75 \cdot 7$$
$$= 22.50 + 12.25$$
$$= 34.75$$

Omar will pay $34.75 for 5 hot dogs and 7 bottles of water. ∎

Problem Set

Evaluate.

1. $2.3 + 5.1 \cdot 4$

2. $\frac{1}{4} \div \frac{1}{2} - 2 + 6 \div 4$

3. $\frac{1}{2}(3^2 - 2 \cdot 5) + \frac{3}{4}$

4. $4 + [3 - (14 \cdot 8) \div 2] \cdot 5$

5. $5 \cdot |5.7 - (2.8 - 3.5)^2| - 10.4$

6. $-2^3 + |(-2)^4 + (-1)^5| - 1^6$

7. $\sqrt{(9-5)^2 + 3^2}$

8. $\dfrac{5 + (2-4)^3 \div 2}{4 \cdot (3^2 - 1)}$

9. $\dfrac{8 - |-24| \div |3|}{2|4-5| + 9}$

10. $\dfrac{(7-2)^2}{30 - 3 \cdot (2+4)} + \dfrac{12 - (27 \div 3)}{|60 - 4^3|}$

11. $\frac{2}{3}x^2 - 5x$ when $x = 6$

12. $3m + 4n^3 - 2$ when $m = -0.7$ and $n = 3$

13. $8a - 2a \cdot (a-5)^2$ when $a = 4$

14. $\dfrac{10 \cdot x + y - 8}{10(x+y) - 8}$ when $x = 2$ and $y = 5$

15. $\dfrac{a^3 + 3a^2b + 3ab^2 + b^3}{a+b}$ when $a = -1$ and $b = 3$

16. $5(x^2 - x)$ when $x = \frac{1}{2}$

17. $|-8 + 2 \cdot k| + 3 \cdot k$ when $k = 3.5$

18. $6z - \left[(z+2)^3 - \left(\frac{1}{3}\right)^2\right]^2$ when $z = -1$

19. $(|p| - |q|) \cdot |p - q|$ when $p = -2$ and $q = \frac{3}{5}$

20. $\dfrac{-b + \sqrt{b^2 - 4ac}}{2a}$ when $a = 2$, $b = 3$, and $c = -1$

Compare.

21. $18 - 6 \div 3 + 5$ and $(18 - 6) \div 3 + 5$

22. $(2 \cdot 8) + \left(\frac{1}{2}\right)^3$ and $2 \cdot \left[8 + \left(\frac{1}{2}\right)^3\right]$

23. $2^3 + 3^3$ and $(2 + 3)^3$

24. $\sqrt{4} \cdot \sqrt{9}$ and $\sqrt{4 \cdot 9}$

25. $\dfrac{8 \cdot 3 \div 4 + 2}{5 + 2 \cdot (3-6)}$ and $\dfrac{8 \cdot 3 \div 4}{5} + \dfrac{2}{2(3-6)}$

26. $a + 2 \cdot b - 3$ and $(a+2) \cdot (b-3)$ when $a = -4.2$ and $b = 0.75$

27. $\dfrac{x^2 + 3x - 5}{x^2 - 5x}$ and $3x$ when $x = 10$

28. $(2 \cdot P)(1 + r)^t$ and $P\left[1 + (2 \cdot r)\right]^t$ when $P = 1000$, $r = 0.3$, and $t = 2$

29. $(a+b)^2$ and $a^2 + 2ab + b^2$ when $a = 5$ and $b = -2$

*30. Challenge $|x - y|$ and $(x - y)$ when $x < y$

Write and evaluate an expression for each problem.

31. At a concert, T-shirts cost \$30 each and programs cost \$10 each. The Estrada family is picking out items at the souvenir stand.

   A. Write an expression to represent the total price the Estrada family will pay for x T-shirts and y programs.

   B. Evaluate the expression to find the total price the Estrada family will pay for 4 T-shirts and 2 programs.

32. A cell phone plan has unlimited minutes but charges \$0.25 per text message and \$1.50 for each ringtone download. Alisa considers joining the plan.

   A. Write an expression to represent the total Alisa will pay for t text messages and r ringtones.

   B. Evaluate the expression to find the total Alisa will pay for 15 text messages and 3 ringtones.

33. Chocolate pretzels are $10.99 per pound. Yogurt raisins are $3.49 per pound. Ethan wants to buy some of each.

A. Write an expression to represent the total Ethan will pay for p pounds of chocolate pretzels and r pounds of yogurt raisins.

B. Evaluate the expression to find the total Ethan will pay for $\frac{1}{4}$ pound of chocolate pretzels and $\frac{2}{3}$ pound of yogurt raisins. Round your answer to the nearest cent.

34. Mr. Burns calculates each student's test score by finding the product of the number of items correct and the number of points per item. He then adds the number of homework assignments completed as bonus points.

A. Write an expression to represent a student's test score when c items are correct, each is worth p points, and h homework assignments were completed.

B. Justin got 18 items correct, each item was worth 4 points, and he completed 12 homework assignments. Evaluate the expression to find Justin's test score.

35. A banquet facility adds a $2 service gratuity to the net cost of each meal served. The total cost of a banquet is the product of the number of guests and the sum of the net cost of each meal and the service gratuity. Rebecca wants to use the facility for an event.

A. Write an expression to represent the total Rebecca will pay if g guests attend her event and the net cost of each meal is m dollars.

B. Evaluate the expression to find the total Rebecca will pay if 150 guests attend her event and the net cost of each meal is $12.50.

36. Benjamin plans to buy his neighbor's car for $4500. He wants to pay an initial down payment and then make monthly interest-free payments. The amount of each monthly payment is the difference between the price and the down payment, divided by the number of months.

A. Write an expression to represent the amount of Benjamin's monthly payment if his down payment is d dollars and he makes m monthly payments.

B. Evaluate the expression to find the amount of Benjamin's monthly payment if his down payment is $1800 and he makes 6 monthly payments.

*C. Challenge Find a way that Benjamin could make his monthly payment be $250. You can try changing the down payment, the number of payments, or both.

*37. Challenge For each set of numbers, use each number exactly once to write an expression that evaluates to 30. You may use any of the four basic operations: $+$, $-$, $\times$, and $\div$. You may also use parentheses as grouping symbols. Multiple answers are possible.

Example:
Given: 2, 3, 6, 6
Possible solution: $(6 \cdot 3) + (6 \cdot 2)$
Alternate solution: $(6 \cdot 6) - (2 \cdot 3)$

A. 1, 2, 4, 8

B. 3, 5, 8, 7

C. 1, 2, 4, 4

Solving Equations

An **equation** is a number sentence that indicates two expressions are equal. A **solution** is a value of the variable that makes the equation true.

To **solve** an equation means to find all of the solutions for the equation. The following properties of equality are useful for solving equations.

PROPERTIES OF EQUALITY

The following properties apply for all real numbers a, b, and c.

Property	Statement
Addition Property	If $a = b$, then $a + c = b + c$.
Subtraction Property	If $a = b$, then $a - c = b - c$.
Multiplication Property	If $a = b$, then $a \cdot c = b \cdot c$.
Division Property	If $a = b$ and $c \neq 0$, then $a \div c = b \div c$.
Reflexive Property	$a = a$
Symmetric Property	If $a = b$, then $b = a$.
Transitive Property	If $a = b$ and $b = c$, then $a = c$.

Solving an Equation with the Variable on One Side

When an equation has the variable on one side, use the properties of equality and the properties of real numbers to *isolate* the variable. You should always check your solution by substituting back into the original equation.

Example 1   Solve $2x + 7 = 1$.

Solution

$$2x + 7 = 1$$
$2x + 7 - 7 = 1 - 7$ Use the subtraction property to isolate the variable term.
$$2x = -6$$ Simplify.
$$\frac{2x}{2} = \frac{-6}{2}$$ Use the division property to isolate the variable.
$$x = -3$$ Simplify.

The solution is -3. The solution set is $\{-3\}$.

Check

$$2x + 7 = 1$$

$$2(-3) + 7 \stackrel{?}{=} 1$$

$$-6 + 7 \stackrel{?}{=} 1$$

$$1 = 1 \checkmark \blacksquare$$

Solving an Equation with Variables on Both Sides

When the variable appears on both sides of an equation, collect the variable terms on one side and the constants on the other side.

Example 2 Solve $\frac{1}{2}(n - 4) = -3(2n + 1)$.

Solution

$$\frac{1}{2}(n - 4) = -3(2n + 1)$$

$\frac{1}{2}n - 2 = -6n - 3$	Distributive Property
$\frac{1}{2}n + 6n - 2 = -6n + 6n - 3$	Addition Property
$\frac{1}{2}n + 6n - 2 = -3$	Simplify. The variable terms are only on the left now.
$\frac{13}{2}n - 2 = -3$	Simplify. $\frac{1}{2}n + 6n = \frac{1}{2}n + \frac{12}{2}n = \frac{13}{2}n$
$\frac{13}{2}n - 2 + 2 = -3 + 2$	Addition Property
$\frac{13}{2}n = -1$	Simplify. The constant is only on the right.
$\frac{2}{13} \cdot \frac{13}{2}n = \frac{2}{13} \cdot (-1)$	Multiplication Property
$n = -\frac{2}{13}$	

The solution is $-\frac{2}{13}$. The solution set is $\left\{-\frac{2}{13}\right\}$.

Check

$$\frac{1}{2}(n - 4) = -3(2n + 1)$$

$$\frac{1}{2}\left(-\frac{2}{13} - 4\right) \stackrel{?}{=} -3\left(2\left(-\frac{2}{13}\right) + 1\right)$$

$$\frac{1}{2}\left(-\frac{2}{13} - \frac{52}{13}\right) \stackrel{?}{=} -3\left(-\frac{4}{13} + \frac{13}{13}\right)$$

$$\frac{1}{2}\left(-\frac{54}{13}\right) \stackrel{?}{=} -3\left(\frac{9}{13}\right)$$

$$-\frac{27}{13} = -\frac{27}{13} \checkmark \blacksquare$$

> **THINK ABOUT IT**
>
> When you use transformations to solve an equation, the equation in each step is *equivalent* to the equation in the previous step. Equivalent equations have the same solution(s). So the final equation and the original equation have the same solution(s).

Types of Equations

You can categorize an equation according to its number of solutions.

> **DEFINITIONS**
>
> A **conditional equation** is true for some values of the variable but not for others.
> An **identity** is an equation that is true for any value of the variable.
> A **contradiction** is an equation that is never true for any value of the variable.

Example 3 Solve $-4w + 8 + 5w = w + 2$.

Solution

$$
\begin{aligned}
-4w + 8 + 5w &= w + 2 \\
w + 8 &= w + 2 & \text{Combine like terms.} \\
w - w + 8 &= w - w + 2 & \text{Subtraction Property} \\
8 &\neq 2 & \text{Simplify.}
\end{aligned}
$$

Since $8 \neq 2$, the original equation is a contradiction. There is no solution. The solution set is $\{\ \}$. ■

> **REMEMBER**
>
> $-4w + 5w = 1w$
>
> By the identity property of multiplication, $1w = w$.

Example 4 Solve $\dfrac{x}{3} + \dfrac{x}{6} = \dfrac{x}{2}$.

Solution

$$
\begin{aligned}
\frac{x}{3} + \frac{x}{6} &= \frac{x}{2} \\
\frac{2}{2} \cdot \frac{x}{3} + \frac{x}{6} &= \frac{3}{3} \cdot \frac{x}{2} & \text{Simplify with common denominators.} \\
\frac{2x}{6} + \frac{x}{6} &= \frac{3x}{6} \\
\frac{3x}{6} &= \frac{3x}{6} & \text{Both sides of the equation are identical.}
\end{aligned}
$$

If the solution process results in identical expressions on both sides, then the original equation is an identity.

The solution set is all real numbers. In other words, $x \in \mathbb{R}$. ■

> **THINK ABOUT IT**
>
> Division is the same as multiplying by a reciprocal and subtraction is the same as adding an opposite, so you don't really need the division and subtraction properties of equality. They aren't really necessary, but they can be convenient.

Restricted Domain

The **domain** of a variable is the set of allowable values. When solving an equation, we generally assume the domain to be all real numbers, $\mathbb{R}$. However, in some cases, the domain may be restricted to a specific subset of the real numbers.

Example 5   Solve $2x + 5 = 4x - 8$ for the domain $\{x \mid x \in \mathbb{Z}\}$.

Solution

$$2x + 5 = 4x - 8$$
$$2x - 2x + 5 = 4x - 2x - 8 \qquad \text{Subtraction Property}$$
$$5 = 2x - 8$$
$$5 + 8 = 2x - 8 + 8 \qquad \text{Addition Property}$$
$$13 = 2x$$
$$13 \div 2 = 2x \div 2 \qquad \text{Division Property}$$
$$6.5 = x$$
$$x = 6.5 \qquad \text{Symmetric Property}$$

Because 6.5 is not an integer, there is no solution within the domain. ■

> **REMEMBER**
>
> $\mathbb{Z}$ is the set of integers.

Application: Spending

Example 6   Kimber arrives at the amusement park with $50. Admission is $20, and she plays several midway games that cost $2.50 each. At the end of the day, she has spent all of her money. How many games did she play?

Solution   Define g as the unknown number of games. Kimber cannot play a fraction of a game, so the domain is restricted: $\{g \mid g \in \mathbb{W}\}$.

Write and solve an equation.

$$\underbrace{\text{admission in dollars}}_{20} + \underbrace{\text{price of games in dollars}}_{2.50g} = \underbrace{\text{total spent in dollars}}_{50}$$

$$20 - 20 + 2.50g = 50 - 20$$
$$2.50g = 30$$
$$2.50g \div 2.50 = 30 \div 2.50$$
$$g = 12$$

The solution is a whole number, so Kimber played 12 games.

> **REMEMBER**
>
> $\mathbb{W}$ is the set of whole numbers.

Check

$$20 + 2.50g = 50$$
$$20 + 2.50 \cdot 12 \overset{?}{=} 50$$
$$20 + 30 \overset{?}{=} 50$$
$$50 = 50 \checkmark \ ■$$

Problem Set

Solve each equation. State the solution set and check your answer when appropriate.

1. $x + 7 = 10$

2. $2 = n - 4$

3. $\frac{1}{3}z = 6$

4. $5k = 8$

5. $15 = 0.25p$

6. $4x + 5 = -3$

7. $15 - 10c = 13$

8. $2y - 7 = -1$

9. $2 = \frac{11}{4} + \frac{1}{8}x$

10. $-0.6x + 6 = -9$

11. $-4(2 - c) = 12$

12. $2(6x + 5) - 4(3x - 1) = 2$

13. $\frac{0.12(a + 2)}{3} = 0.114$

14. $6w + 8 = 3w - 5$

15. $\frac{1}{4}x = \frac{1}{4} - \frac{3}{8}x$

16. $5(3a + 2) + a = -2(2a - 7) - 9$

17. $\frac{3}{16}(x - 2) = \frac{1}{2}(x + 3)$

18. $2(2 - 3n) = -[5n - (4 - n)]$

19. $-2[3(2q + 1) - 5] + 7 = 3(5 - 4q) + 2$

*20. **Challenge** $0.75b + 6 - 1.50b = 7 - 0.5b - 1$

Solve each equation for the given domain.

A. $\mathbb{R}$ B. $\mathbb{Z}$ C. $\mathbb{N}$

21. $11x + 23 = 2x - 1$

22. $\frac{4 - 5n}{9} = 2$

23. $4(3x + 2) = 2(x + 2) + 4$

24. $3(2z + 1) - 5z = z + 3$

For each problem:

A. **Define a variable for the unknown and state the domain.**
B. **Write an equation to model the problem.**
C. **Solve the equation.**
D. **Give your answer in a complete sentence.**

25. A carousel rotates at a speed of 6.5 revolutions per minute. During his ride, Benito counts that he made 39 revolutions. How long was Benito's carousel ride?

26. Ms. Jenkins decides to join a shopping club to buy supplies for her convenience store. On her first visit, she buys the $55 membership and several cases of soda for $7.50 each. The total for her first visit is exactly $100. (There is no tax on the soda.) How many cases of soda did she buy?

27. Casey's parents allow her to work 15 hours after school during the week. She has two part-time jobs, one that pays $7 per hour and another that pays $8 per hour. She wants to earn $115 in one week to buy a music player. How should she divide her time between jobs? (*Hint*: If Casey works x hours at one job, she can work $15 - x$ at the other.)

28. Supta bought two types of nuts to make a 5-lb bag of trail mix. Almonds cost $6.49 per pound and cashews cost $5.99 per pound. If Supta spent $31.45, how many pounds of almonds and how many pounds of cashews did he buy? (*Hint*: If Supta bought p pounds of one type of nut, he bought $5 - p$ of the other.)

29. Shar plans to go to a movie theater or a smoothie place each night this week. Each visit to the movie theater costs $10 and each visit to the smoothie place costs $3. Shar wants to spend exactly $35. How many times will she attend a movie and how many times will she go to the smoothie place? (*Hint*: If Shar goes to the movies m nights, she can go to the smoothie place $7 - m$ nights.)

Solving Absolute Value Equations

You solve absolute value equations by setting up two separate equations that do not contain absolute value.

If you know the result of an absolute value is the positive number a, then the value of the expression within the absolute value could have been a or $-a$.

PROPERTY OF ABSOLUTE VALUE

If $|x| = a$ and $a \geq 0$, then $x = a$ or $x = -a$.

Solving Simple Absolute Value Equations

You can use the property of absolute value to solve absolute value equations.

Example 1 Solve $|x| = 8$.

Solution

$$|x| = 8$$
$$x = 8 \quad \text{or} \quad x = -8 \qquad \text{Property of Absolute Value}$$

Check Check both solutions.
$$|x| = 8$$
$$|8| = 8 \checkmark \quad \text{or} \quad |-8| = 8 \checkmark$$

The solutions are 8 and -8. The solution set is $\{-8, 8\}$. ■

Example 2 Solve $|n + 3| = 12$.

Solution

$$|n + 3| = 12$$
$$n + 3 = 12 \quad \text{or} \quad n + 3 = -12 \qquad \text{Property of Absolute Value}$$
$$n + 3 - 3 = 12 - 3 \quad n + 3 - 3 = -12 - 3 \quad \text{Subtract 3 from both sides.}$$
$$n = 9 \qquad\qquad n = -15$$

Check $\qquad |n + 3| = 12$

$$|n + 3| = 12 \qquad \text{or} \qquad |n + 3| = 12$$
$$|9 + 3| \overset{?}{=} 12 \qquad\qquad |-15 + 3| \overset{?}{=} 12$$
$$|12| \overset{?}{=} 12 \qquad\qquad |-12| \overset{?}{=} 12$$
$$12 = 12 \checkmark \qquad\qquad 12 = 12 \checkmark$$

The solutions are 9 and -15. The solution set is $\{-15, 9\}$. ■

Solving an Absolute Value Equation Equal to Zero

By definition, zero is the only number whose absolute value is zero. Therefore, if the result of an absolute value expression is zero, then the expression inside the absolute value also equals zero.

Example 3   Solve $|3x - 21| = 0$.

Solution   ► **Check**

$$|3x - 21| = 0$$ $$|3x - 21| = 0$$

$$3x - 21 = 0$$ $$|3 \cdot 7 - 21| \overset{?}{=} 0$$

$$3x - 21 + 21 = 0 + 21$$ $$|21 - 21| \overset{?}{=} 0$$

$$3x = 21$$ $$|0| \overset{?}{=} 0$$

$$\frac{3x}{3} = \frac{21}{3}$$ $$0 = 0 \checkmark$$

$$x = 7$$

The solution is 7. The solution set is $\{7\}$. ∎

Determining When an Equation Has No Solution

Example 4   Solve $|2x + 4| + 12 = 2$.

Solution

$$|2x + 4| + 12 = 2$$

$$|2x + 4| = -10 \qquad \text{Isolate the absolute value.}$$

An absolute value cannot be negative. This equation is a contradiction.

The original equation has no solution. The solution set is $\{\ \}$. ∎

Solving Equations with Extraneous Solutions

You should always check your solutions. When solving absolute value equations, you may find that not all of your answers check out. That doesn't necessarily mean you made a mistake.

You *must* exclude extraneous solutions from a solution set.

DEFINITION

An **extraneous solution** is a solution that results from the process of solving an equation, but does not make the original equation true.

Example 5 Solve $|x - 8| = 4x + 7$.

Solution

$x - 8 = 4x + 7$	or	$x - 8 = -(4x + 7)$
$-3x - 8 = 7$		$x - 8 = -4x - 7$
$-3x = 15$		$5x - 8 = -7$
$x = -5$		$5x = 1$
		$x = \dfrac{1}{5}$

Use the property of absolute value to form two equations. Then solve each equation separately.

Check

$$|x - 8| = 4x + 7 \qquad \text{or} \qquad |x - 8| = 4x + 7$$

$$|-5 - 8| \stackrel{?}{=} 4 \cdot (-5) + 7 \qquad \left|\frac{1}{5} - 8\right| \stackrel{?}{=} 4 \cdot \frac{1}{5} + 7$$

$$|-13| \stackrel{?}{=} -20 + 7 \qquad \left|-7\frac{4}{5}\right| \stackrel{?}{=} \frac{4}{5} + 7$$

$$13 \neq -13 \qquad 7\frac{4}{5} = 7\frac{4}{5} \checkmark$$

-5 is an extraneous solution.

The only solution is $\frac{1}{5}$. That is, the solution set is $\left\{\frac{1}{5}\right\}$. ∎

Problem Set

Solve each equation. Be sure to check for extraneous solutions.

1. $|x| = 12$

2. $|n| = \dfrac{4}{5}$

3. $|w| = 0$

4. $|t| = -3$

5. $y = |-5|$

6. $|m| - 3 = 10$

7. $2 \cdot |k| + 5 = 13$

8. $8 - |c| = 2$

9. $-5|x| + 3 = 6$

10. $|w + 2| = 5$

11. $|p - 12| = 3$

12. $|5 - 2x| = 0$

13. $|3s + 4| = -1$

14. $|2x - 0.5| = 7.5$

15. $3|8 + y| = 12$

16. $\left|\dfrac{1}{2}n - 6\right| - 10 = -7$

17. $\dfrac{1}{2}|n - 6| - 10 = -7$

18. $15 - |8x + 5| = 6$

19. $2x - 3 = |4 - 15|$

20. $|6x - 4| = x + 4$

21. $|x + 1| = 7 - 2x$

22. $|2t - 5| = t - 3$

23. $|6x + 2| + 3x + 2 = 7 - x$

24. $|3a + 6| - 4 = 3a - 4$

25. $4x + |0.5x + 1| = 2.5x + 2$

26. $5 - |4m - 3| = 2m + 1$

*27. **Challenge** $|x + 3| = |2x - 1|$

*28. **Challenge** $|x + 2| = x + 2$

Solve.

29. One interpretation of an equation of the form $|x - n| = d$ is the numbers whose graphs are a distance of d units from n on the number line.

Example:

$|x - 5| = 2$ represents the numbers that are 2 units in either direction from 5 on the number line.

The solution set is $\{3, 7\}$.

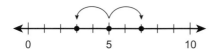

A. Solve $|x - 5| = 2$ algebraically to verify the graphical solution above.

B. Use the graphical interpretation to solve $|x - 3| = 8$.

C. Use the graphical interpretation to solve $|x + 4| = 3$. (*Hint*: Use the definition of subtraction to first rewrite the equation in the form $|x - n| = d$.)

Applications: Formulas

Formulas can be very helpful when solving many real-world problems.

> **DEFINITIONS**
>
> A **literal equation** is an equation with two or more variables.
> A **formula** is an equation that defines the relationship between two or more quantities.

Solving Literal Equations and Formulas

Example 1 The formula for the perimeter of a rectangle is $P = 2l + 2w$. Find the perimeter of a rectangle with length $l = 6$ in. and width $w = 3$ in.

Solution

$$P = 2l + 2w$$
$$= 2 \cdot 6 + 2 \cdot 3 \qquad \text{Substitute 6 for } l \text{ and 3 for } w.$$
$$= 12 + 6 \qquad\qquad \text{Multiply.}$$
$$= 18 \qquad\qquad\quad \text{Add.}$$

The perimeter of the rectangle is 18 in. ∎

Example 2 Find the width of a rectangle with $P = 20$ m and the given length.

A $l = 4$ m

B $l = 6$ m

C $l = 9$ m

Solution

$$P = 2l + 2w$$
$$20 = 2 \cdot 4 + 2w$$
$$20 = 8 + 2w$$
$$12 = 2w$$
$$6 = w$$

The width is 6 m. ∎

Solution

$$P = 2l + 2w$$
$$20 = 2 \cdot 6 + 2w$$
$$20 = 12 + 2w$$
$$8 = 2w$$
$$4 = w$$

The width is 4 m. ∎

Solution

$$P = 2l + 2w$$
$$20 = 2 \cdot 9 + 2w$$
$$20 = 18 + 2w$$
$$2 = 2w$$
$$1 = w$$

The width is 1 m. ∎

In Example 2, you substituted values into the formula $P = 2l + 2w$ three times to find the value of w. When you solve for w, you perform the exact same transformations every time. To save time and reduce error, you can first solve $P = 2l + 2w$ for w and then substitute any given values and simplify.

You can solve a literal equation or formula for one of its variables with the same methods and properties that you use for one-variable equations.

Example 3   Find the widths of rectangles with $P = 30.5$ cm and $l_1 = 4.2$ cm, $l_2 = 2.1$ cm, and $l_3 = 3.1$ cm.

Solution

Step 1   Solve the formula $P = 2l + 2w$ for w.

$$P = 2l + 2w$$

$$P - 2l = 2w \qquad \text{Subtract } 2l \text{ from both sides.}$$

$$\frac{P - 2l}{2} = w \qquad \text{Divide both sides by 2.}$$

Step 2   Find the width of each rectangle.

$$\frac{P - 2l_1}{2} = w \qquad \frac{P - 2l_2}{2} = w \qquad \frac{P - 2l_3}{2} = w$$

$$\frac{30.5 - 2 \cdot 4.2}{2} = w \qquad \frac{30.5 - 2 \cdot 2.1}{2} = w \qquad \frac{30.5 - 2 \cdot 3.1}{2} = w$$

$$\frac{30.5 - 8.4}{2} = w \qquad \frac{30.5 - 4.2}{2} = w \qquad \frac{30.5 - 6.2}{2} = w$$

$$\frac{22.1}{2} = w \qquad \frac{26.3}{2} = w \qquad \frac{24.3}{2} = w$$

$$11.05 = w \qquad 13.15 = w \qquad 12.15 = w$$

The widths are 11.05 cm, 13.15 cm, and 12.15 cm, respectively. ∎

Geometric Applications

GEOMETRIC FORMULAS

	Perimeter *P* or Circumference *C*	Area *A*
Triangle	$P = a + b + c$	$A = \frac{1}{2}bh$
Square	$P = 4s$	$A = s^2$
Rectangle	$P = 2l + 2w$	$A = lw$
Regular *n*-gon Example: Regular Hexagon	$P = ns$ $P = 6s$	$A = \frac{1}{2}aP$ $A = \frac{1}{2}a \cdot 6s$
Circle	$C = 2\pi r$	$A = \pi r^2$

Example 4

A Solve the formula for the perimeter of a regular octagon for side length s.

Solution

$P = ns$ Write the formula for perimeter of a regular n-gon.

$P = 8s$ An octagon has 8 sides. Substitute 8 for n.

$\dfrac{P}{8} = s$ Divide both sides by 8. ∎

B Find the side lengths of three regular octagons with perimeters $P_1 = 24$ ft, $P_2 = 22$ ft, and $P_3 = 20$ ft.

Solution   Substitute the perimeter values and simplify.

$$\frac{P_1}{8} = s_1 \qquad\qquad \frac{P_2}{8} = s_2 \qquad\qquad \frac{P_3}{8} = s_3$$

$$\frac{24}{8} = s_1 \qquad\qquad \frac{22}{8} = s_2 \qquad\qquad \frac{20}{8} = s_3$$

$$3 = s_1 \qquad\qquad 2.75 = s_2 \qquad\qquad 2.5 = s_3$$

The side lengths are 3 ft, 2.75 ft, and 2.5 ft, respectively. ∎

Example 5   A farmer wants to build a new road from point Q to Route 32 and form a triangular field. He wants the area of the field to be 4840 square yards, which is one acre. To locate the correct point of intersection on Route 32, he needs to know the height of the triangle. What is the required height of the triangle?

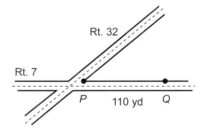

Solution   Let R be the required point on Route 32. Draw triangle PQR.

$A = \dfrac{1}{2} bh$ Write the formula for area of a triangle.

$2A = bh$ Multiply both sides by 2.

$\dfrac{2A}{b} = h$ Divide both sides by b to solve for h.

$\dfrac{2 \cdot 4840}{110} = h$ Substitute 4840 for the area A and 110 for the base b.

$88 = h$ Simplify.

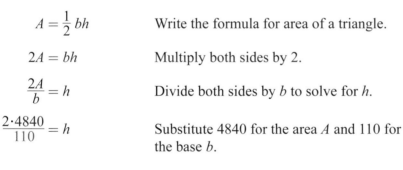

The required height of the triangle is 88 yards. ∎

Example 6 Ray wants to create a circular garden. What is the area of the circle he can form with 100 meters of border?

Solution The border will form the circumference. First find the radius.

$$C = 2\pi r$$ Write the formula for circumference.

$$\frac{C}{2\pi} = r$$ Divide both sides by 2π to solve for r.

$$\frac{100}{2\pi} = r$$ Substitute 100 for C.

$$\frac{50}{\pi} = r$$ Simplify.

Next, find the area.

$$A = \pi r^2$$ Write the formula for area.

$$A = \pi \left(\frac{50}{\pi}\right)^2$$ Substitute $\left(\frac{50}{\pi}\right)$ for r.

$$A = \pi \left(\frac{2500}{\pi^2}\right)$$ Square $\left(\frac{50}{\pi}\right)$.

$$A = \frac{2500}{\pi} \approx 796$$ Simplify and then approximate.

Ray can form a circle with an area of approximately 796 square meters. ■

> **TIP**
> The exact value of r is $\frac{50}{\pi}$. An approximate value of r is 15.9. It is better to use exact values in your calculations, and then find an approximate value for the final answer.

Other Applications

OTHER FORMULAS

Distance	$d = rt$	d is distance, r is rate, and t is time.
Simple Interest	$I = Prt$	I is simple interest, P is the principal (amount borrowed, deposited, or invested), r is the annual interest rate, and t is the time in years.
Temperature Conversion	$F = \frac{9}{5}C + 32$	F is degrees Fahrenheit and C is degrees Celsius.

Example 7 If you deposit $6000 in a bank account that pays an annual simple interest rate of 4.5%, how long will it take to earn $500 in interest?

Solution To find "how long," solve for time t.

$$I = Prt$$ Write the formula for simple interest.

$$\frac{I}{Pr} = t$$ Divide both sides by Pr to solve for t.

$$\frac{500}{6000 \cdot 0.045} = t$$ Substitute 500 for I, 6000 for P, and 0.045 for r.

$$1.85 \approx t$$

It will take approximately 1.85 years. ■

> **TIP**
> To compute $\dfrac{500}{6000 \cdot 0.045}$ on a calculator, enter
> 500 ÷ 6000 ÷ 0.045 or
> 500 ÷ (6000 × 0.045).

Problem Set

Use the formula to complete the table of values. When necessary, round final answers to the nearest tenth.

1. $P = 4s$

Perimeter P	Side length s
A.	3 in.
B.	18.25 cm
20 km	**C.**
75 ft	**D.**

3. $A = \frac{1}{2}aP$

Area A	Apothem length a	Perimeter P
A.	5.2 yd	36 yd
B.	12.1 in.	40 in.
314.4 m²	**C.**	66 m
4.8 mi²	**D.**	8 mi

2. $C = 2\pi r$

Circumference C	Radius r
A.	$\frac{1}{2}$ mi
B.	5 mm
10 ft	**C.**
95.3 in.	**D.**

4. $d = rt$

Distance d	Rate r	Time t
A.	46 m/s	2 s
B.	65 mi/h	2.5 h
18.3 m	**C.**	3 s
26 mi	**D.**	$2\frac{1}{3}$ h
115 km	95.8 km/h	**E.**
2 ft	7 ft/s	**F.**

Solve each formula for the desired variable.

5. $A = lw$ for l

6. $P = a + b + c$ for c

7. $I = Prt$ for r

8. $A = \frac{1}{2}bh$ for h

9. $F = \frac{9}{5}C + 32$ for C

*10. Challenge $A = \pi r^2$ for r

*11. Challenge $z = \frac{x - \mu}{\sigma}$ for σ

Solve.

12. Nikhil has a model airplane that flies on the end of a string. He wants to calculate its speed by timing how long it can fly in a circle with a circumference of 25 feet.

   A. How long should Nikhil make the string for a 25-foot circle?

   B. In order to prevent his plane from a "crash," how much free area does Nikhil need in the back yard?

   C. Nikhil uses a stopwatch and finds that his plane travels one full circle in 4 seconds. Use the distance formula to calculate the plane's speed in feet per second.

13. Consider the formula for the perimeter of a regular pentagon.

   A. Solve the formula for side length s.

   B. Find the side lengths of three regular pentagons with perimeters $P_1 = 30$ cm, $P_2 = 26$ cm, and $P_3 = 22$ cm.

14. Nevena goes camping and makes a simple triangular tent by draping a plastic sheet over a 4.5-foot tall center support. She wants the of opening to have a cross-sectional area 18 square feet. To locate where to stake the plastic sheet, she needs to know the base of the triangle. What is the required base?

15. Mr. Burnside buys 70 meters of fence to make a rectangular dog run. He wants the dog run to be 30 meters long. What is the area of the dog run if Mr. Burnside uses all of the fence he bought?

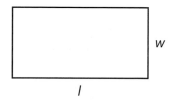

16. Mrs. Sandoval deposits $1500 in a bank account that pays an annual simple interest rate of 2.8%. How long will it take for Mrs. Sandoval to earn $300 in interest?

17. Hong's bank account pays an annual simple interest rate of 4.5%. How much does he need to deposit now so that he will earn $1000 in interest by the end of 5 years?

18. Deshawn types essays at the library's computer lab.

    A. The word-count feature says the first essay is 1050 words. A timer says he has been typing for 25 minutes. What is his typing rate in words per minute?

    B. Deshawn's second essay is 2500 words. If he types at the same rate, how long will it take to type the second essay?

19. A Japanese bullet train travels 192 km between Hiroshima and Kokura at an average speed of 262 km/h.

    A. Using the distance formula, how long is the train trip in hours?

    B. The formula $m = 60t$ relates time t in hours and time m in minutes. How long is the train trip to the nearest minute?

20. A circle is inscribed in a regular hexagon with side length 10 cm and approximate area 260 cm². What is the radius of the circle?

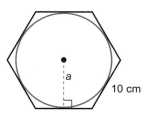

*21. **Challenge** Rectangular prisms have three pairs of congruent rectangular faces. The formula for the surface area of a rectangular prism is $S = 2lw + 2hl + 2hw$.

    A. Solve the surface area formula for w.

    B. A particular rectangular prism has length 8 in., height 2 in., and surface area 94 in². What is its width?

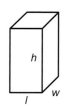

*22. **Challenge** The formula for the volume of a cylinder is $V = \pi r^2 h$. A sealed can of soup has lost its label. Powell uses a tape measure to find that the can's circumference is 30 cm and its height is 12 cm. What is the volume of the can in cubic centimeters? (One cubic centimeter is equivalent to one milliliter. Volume is measured in either unit.)

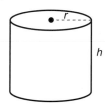

UNIT 2

Linear Equations and Systems

You can use a linear equation to describe a car's speed or the distance it travels.

Anything involving a constant rate can be described with a linear equation. You can find constant rates when driving a car, calculating a cost, or getting paid an hourly wage.

Big Ideas

▸ A family of functions has the same general form.

▸ The values of the parameters in the equation create transformed versions of other family members.

Unit Topics

▸ Foundations for Unit 2

▸ Graphs of Lines

▸ Forms of Linear Equations

▸ Writing Equations of Lines

▸ Applications: Linear Equations

▸ Systems of Linear Equations

▸ Applications: Linear Systems

Foundations for Unit 2

Before you study linear equations and systems, you should know how to do the following:

▶ Plot a point in a coordinate plane.

▶ Find the coordinates of a point.

▶ Identify the quadrants of a coordinate plane.

___

Ordered Pairs in a Coordinate Plane

Definition

coordinate plane   a plane in which the **coordinates** of any point are the point's distances from two intersecting perpendicular lines called **axes**

TIP

Unless otherwise noted, *coordinate plane* means *rectangular coordinate plane*, and the axes are horizontal and vertical.

In a coordinate plane, the perpendicular axes are number lines. The horizontal axis is the **x-axis** and the vertical axis is the **y-axis**. The intersection of the axes is the **origin**.

An ordered pair shows the coordinates of a point in the coordinate plane. In an ordered pair, the **x-coordinate** is the first number and the **y-coordinate** is the second number. For example, in the ordered pair $(7, -2)$, 7 is the x-coordinate and -2 is the y-coordinate.

TIP

In an ordered pair, the x-coordinate comes before the y-coordinate; in the alphabet, X comes before Y.

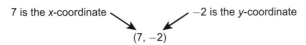

7 is the x-coordinate -2 is the y-coordinate

$(7, -2)$

A point is the graph of an ordered pair, and an ordered pair contains the coordinates of a point.

Example 1   Locate each point in the same coordinate plane:

$A(3, 6), B(-4, -1), C(0, -5)$

Solution   To locate x-coordinates, move from the origin to the right for positive values and to the left for negative values. To locate y-coordinates, move up for positive values and down for negative values.

$A(3, 6)$: Start at the origin. Move 3 units to the right, and then move 6 units up.

$B(-4, -1)$: Start at the origin. Move 4 units to the left, and then move 1 unit down.

$C(0, -5)$: Start at the origin. Move 0 units to the right or left (stay at the origin), and then move 5 units down.

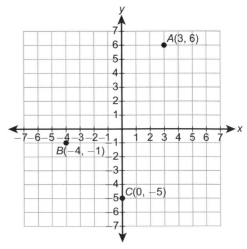

Problem Set A

Plot each ordered pair.

1. $A(-3, -2)$

2. $B(0, 5)$

3. $C(3, 5)$

4. $D(4, 0)$

5. $E(-1, 3)$

6. $F(2, -4)$

7. $R(-4.2, 0)$

8. $S\left(4, 6\frac{2}{3}\right)$

9. $T(-4.9, -3.3)$

10. $U\left(2\frac{1}{2}, -6\right)$

11. $V(0, -3.7)$

12. $W\left(2\frac{3}{4}, 1.5\right)$

Finding the Coordinates of a Point

Find the coordinates of a point by starting at the origin and counting left or right and up or down.

Example 2   Identify the coordinates of each point shown in the coordinate plane.

Solution

Point E: From the origin, point E is 2 units right and 5 units down. The coordinates are $(2, -5)$.

Point F: From the origin, point F is 3 units right and 0 units up or down. The coordinates are $(3, 0)$.

Point G: From the origin, point G is 2 units left and 3 units down. The coordinates are $(-2, -3)$.

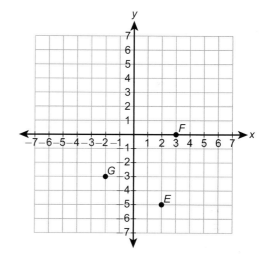

Problem Set B

Identify the coordinates of each point.

13. A

14. B

15. C

16. D

17. E

18. F

19. R

20. S

21. T

22. U

23. V

24. W

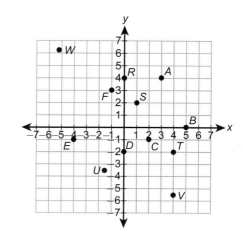

Identifying Quadrants

The *x*- and *y*-axes divide the coordinate plane into four regions called *quadrants*. They are numbered I, II, III, and IV, starting at the top right and moving counterclockwise.

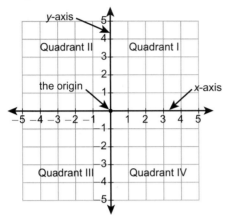

Except for the origin, every point in the coordinate plane is located either in one of the quadrants or on one of the axes. The origin is located on both axes.

Problem Set C

For each point, name the axis it is on or the quadrant it lies in.

25. $A(-3, -2)$

26. $B(0, 5)$

27. $C(3, 5)$

28. $D(4, 0)$

29. $E(-1, 3)$

30. $F(2, -4)$

31. $R(-4.2, 0)$

32. $S\left(4, 6\frac{2}{3}\right)$

33. $T(-4.9, -3.3)$

34. $U\left(2\frac{1}{2}, -6\right)$

35. $V(0, -3.7)$

36. $W\left(2\frac{3}{4}, 1.5\right)$

Answer each question.

37. In which quadrant(s) is the *x*-coordinate negative?

38. In which quadrant(s) is the *x*-coordinate positive?

39. In which quadrant(s) is the *y*-coordinate negative?

40. In which quadrant(s) is the *y*-coordinate positive?

Graphs of Lines

You can graph a line in the coordinate plane.

Graphing a Linear Equation

A **linear equation** is an equation whose graph in a coordinate plane is a line. You can graph a linear equation by plotting two ordered pairs that make the equation true, and then drawing a line through those points. But, to guard against errors, it is best to plot three or more ordered pairs.

Example 1 Graph the linear equation $y = -x + 6$.

Solution Use a table to find three ordered pairs that are solutions of the equation. Pick any three x-values and calculate the corresponding y-values.

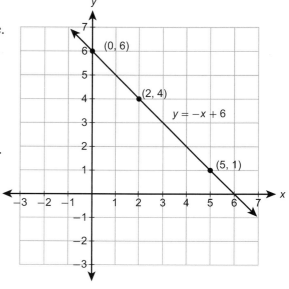

x	y
0	6
2	4
5	1

How to calculate the y-value:

$y = -0 + 6 = 6$

$y = -2 + 6 = 4$

$y = -5 + 6 = 1$

Plot the points and draw a line through them. If all three points are not on the same line, double-check your calculations. ■

Determining Whether a Point Lies on a Line

The coordinates of any point on a line make the equation of that line true. The coordinates of any point *not* on a line make the equation of that line false.

Example 2 Determine whether each point is on the line $y = -x + 6$.

A $(3, -1)$

B $(-8.25, 14.25)$

Solution Substitute the x- and y-coordinates into the equation.

$y = -x + 6$
$-1 \overset{?}{=} -3 + 6$
$-1 \overset{?}{=} -3 + 6$
$-1 \neq 3$

$y = -x + 6$
$14.25 \overset{?}{=} -(-8.25) + 6$
$14.25 \overset{?}{=} 8.25 + 6$
$14.25 = 14.25$

The point $(3, -1)$ is *not* on the line $y = -x + 6$. (See the graph in Example 1.) ■

The point $(-8.25, 14.25)$ *is* on the line $y = -x + 6$. ■

> **TIP**
>
> Strictly speaking, $y = -x + 6$ is an equation, not a line. However, its graph is a line, and mathematicians often use phrases such as "the line $y = -x + 6$."

Using Intercepts to Graph a Linear Equation

Finding the points where a graph crosses the axes is often useful. When a graph is a diagonal line, it intersects each axis at no more than one point.

> ### DEFINITIONS
>
> An **x-intercept** is the x-coordinate of a point where a graph intersects the x-axis.
>
> A **y-intercept** is the y-coordinate of a point where a graph intersects the y-axis.

Example 3   Find the x- and y-intercepts of the equation $2x - 5y = 20$. Then graph the equation.

Solution   The point that contains the x-intercept has a y-coordinate of zero, and the point that contains the y-intercept has an x-coordinate of zero.

To find the x-intercept, substitute 0 for y in the equation and solve for x.

$$2x - 5y = 20$$
$$2x - 5 \cdot 0 = 20$$
$$2x = 20$$
$$x = 10$$

The x-intercept is 10, so the point (10, 0) is on the line.

To find the y-intercept, substitute 0 for x in the equation and solve for y.

$$2x - 5y = 20$$
$$2 \cdot 0 - 5y = 20$$
$$-5y = 20$$
$$y = -4$$

The y-intercept is −4, so the point (0, −4) is on the line.

> **REMEMBER**
>
> Every point on the x-axis has y-coordinate zero.
>
> Every point on the y-axis has x-coordinate zero.

Plot the points (10, 0) and (0, −4), and then draw the line through them.

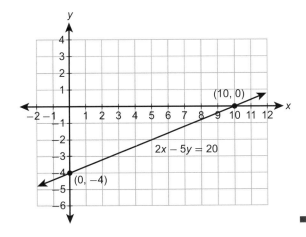

> **TIP**
>
> To check your work, find a third ordered pair solution to the equation and make sure the graph of that ordered pair is a point on the line.

Simplifying and Graphing Linear Equations in One Variable

Some linear equations have just one variable. These special linear equations have graphs that are *vertical* or *horizontal* lines.

Example 4

Ⓐ Simplify and graph $2x = 10$.

Solution Divide both sides by 2 to get $x = 5$. To graph the equation, plot some points that have an x-coordinate of 5, such as $(5, 1)$, $(5, 3)$, and $(5, -2)$. The graph is shown below.

Ⓑ Simplify and graph $y + 5 = 2$.

Solution Subtract 5 from both sides to get $y = -3$. To graph the equation, plot some points that have a y-coordinate of -3, such as $(-4, -3)$, $(0, -3)$, and $(2, -3)$. The graph is shown below.

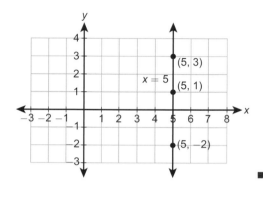

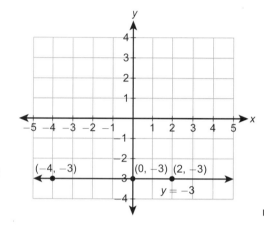

Any equation that can be written in the form $x = k$, where k is a constant, has a graph that is a **vertical line.**

Any equation that can be written in the form $y = k$, where k is a constant, has a graph that is a **horizontal line.**

Calculating Slope from a Graph

Another useful skill is knowing how to describe the slant of a line: which direction it runs and how steep it is. You can determine this information by finding a line's *slope*.

DEFINITION

The **slope** of a line is the ratio of its vertical change to its horizontal change.

TIP

Slope is sometimes described as "rise over run."

Example 5   What is the slope of the line graphed at the right?

Solution   Pick any two points on the line, for example $(8, -1)$ and $(-1, 2)$. Move from one point to the other by moving only vertically and horizontally. To move from $(8, -1)$ to $(-1, 2)$, you can move up 3 units and then left 9 units. Therefore, the vertical change is $+3$, and the horizontal change is -9. The slope of the line is $\frac{+3}{-9}$, which simplifies to $-\frac{1}{3}$. ∎

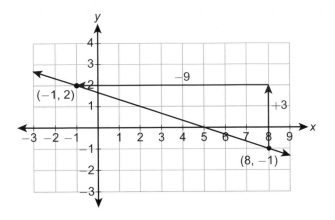

Calculating Slope from a Linear Equation

The vertical change between any two points is the difference in the y-coordinates, and the horizontal change is the difference in the x-coordinates. So if you know the coordinates of two points on a line, you can calculate the slope without a graph.

DEFINITION

The **slope formula** gives the slope of the line through two distinct points, (x_1, y_1) and (x_2, y_2).

$$\text{slope} = \frac{\text{rise}}{\text{run}} = \frac{\text{vertical change}}{\text{horizontal change}} = \frac{y_2 - y_1}{x_2 - x_1}$$

Example 6   Calculate the slope of the line with equation $-3x + 4y = 24$.

Solution   Find any two points on the line. In this case, it is easy to find the two points that contain the intercepts.

Substitute 0 for x:
$-3 \cdot 0 + 4y = 24 \Rightarrow y = 6$.
So the point $(0, 6)$ is on the line.

Substitute 0 for y:
$-3x + 4 \cdot 0 = 24 \Rightarrow x = -8$.
So the point $(-8, 0)$ is on the line.

Then substitute the coordinates of the two points into the slope formula.

Let $(x_1, y_1) = (0, 6)$ and $(x_2, y_2) = (-8, 0)$.

$$\text{slope} = \frac{y_2 - y_1}{x_2 - x_1} = \frac{0 - 6}{(-8) - 0} = \frac{-6}{-8} = \frac{3}{4}$$

The slope of the line with equation $-3x + 4y = 24$ is $\frac{3}{4}$. ∎

THINK ABOUT IT

It doesn't matter which point you use as (x_1, y_1) or (x_2, y_2). If you reverse the substitution of $(0, 6)$ and $(-8, 0)$, the signs change in the numerator and denominator, but you still get the same slope.

$$\frac{6 - 0}{0 - (-8)} = \frac{6}{8} = \frac{3}{4}$$

Classification of Lines by Slope

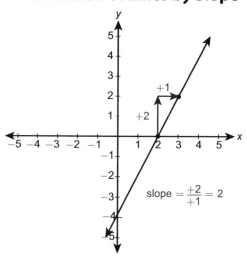

A line with **positive** slope
rises left to right.

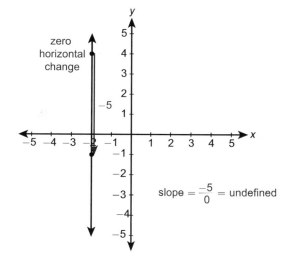

A line with **negative** slope
falls left to right.

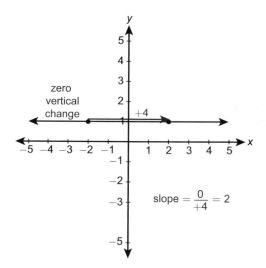

A line with **zero slope** is
horizontal.

A line with **undefined slope** is
vertical.

Problem Set

Find the *x*- and *y*-intercepts.

1. $x + y = -4$

2. $3x - y = 9$

3. $x + 5y = -15$

4. $3y - 2x = 18$

5. $6y + 4x = 22$

6. $\dfrac{5y}{3} - 4x = 15$

Determine whether each point lies on the graph of $y = -1 - 2x$.

7. $(5, -11)$

8. $(-2, 7)$

9. $(4, -9)$

Determine the slope of the line.

10. $y = 2x + 4$

12. $y = 6x - 8$

14. $y = 0.5x + 7$

11. $y = -3x - 7$

13. $y = -5x$

15. $y = -\dfrac{1}{8}x + 12$

16.

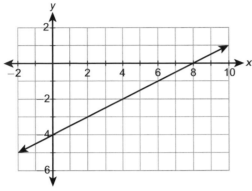

17.

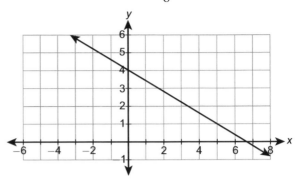

Graph the equation.

18. $x + 9 = 0$

21. $x + 2 = -5$

24. $x - y = 6$

19. $y = 6x + 3$

22. $y = 0.75x$

25. $y - 2x = 2$

20. $y - 1 = 4$

23. $y = -\dfrac{1}{4}x + 7$

26. $3y + x = 4$

Determine whether the slope of the line is positive, negative, zero, or undefined.

27. $4y = 20$

29. $10x + 5y = -40$

28. $9x - 2y = 18$

30. $\dfrac{1}{5}x = 10$

Solve.

***31.** **Challenge** Find a so the slope of the line through $(-2, -2)$ and $\left(4, \dfrac{a}{2}\right)$ is -1.

***32.** **Challenge** Find b so the slope of the line through $(0.5b, 5)$ and $(6, 3)$ is -4.

***33.** **Challenge** The slope of the line that passes through $(-3, c)$ and $(-4, -2)$ is equal to the slope of the line that passes through $(-5, -11)$ and $(0, 4)$. What is the value of c?

Forms of Linear Equations

You can write linear equations in different forms.

All linear equations have the following characteristics in common:

- There is no variable with an exponent other than 1 or zero.
- The variables are not multiplied together.
- It is possible to write the equation without any variable in the denominator of a fraction.
- The graph of the equation in a coordinate plane is a line.

Converting Between Forms of Linear Equations

Three forms of linear equations are most common.

> **DEFINITIONS**
>
> The **standard form** of a linear equation is $Ax + By = C$,
> where A, B, and C are integers, and A and B are not both zero.
> The **slope-intercept form** of a linear equation is $y = mx + b$,
> where m is the slope and b is the y-intercept of the corresponding line.
> The **point-slope form** of a linear equation is $y - y_1 = m(x - x_1)$,
> where m is the slope and (x_1, y_1) is a point on the corresponding line.

Example 1

A Write the equation $4x + 3y = 15$ in slope-intercept form.

Solution To convert to slope-intercept form, solve the equation for y.

$4x + 3y = 15$	Original equation
$3y = -4x + 15$	Subtract $4x$ from both sides.
$y = -\dfrac{4}{3}x + 5$	Divide both sides by 3. ∎

> **TIP**
>
> To divide $-4x + 15$ by 3, divide each term by 3:
> $$\frac{-4x + 15}{3} = -\frac{4x}{3} + \frac{15}{3}$$
> $$= -\frac{4x}{3} + 5$$

B Write the equation $y - 4 = \dfrac{1}{5}(x + 7)$ in standard form.

Solution To convert to standard form, isolate the variables from the constants.

$y - 4 = \dfrac{1}{5}(x + 7)$	Original equation
$5y - 20 = x + 7$	Multiply both sides by 5 to clear the fraction.
$-x + 5y - 20 = 7$	Subtract x from both sides.
$-x + 5y = 27$	Add 20 to both sides. ∎

> **THINK ABOUT IT**
>
> The final equation in Part B, $-x + 5y = 27$, is in standard form. An equivalent equation, also in standard form, is $x - 5y = -27$.

C Write the equation $y + 2 = 3(x - 4)$ in slope-intercept form.

Solution To convert to slope-intercept form, isolate the variable y.

$y + 2 = 3(x - 4)$	Original equation
$y + 2 = 3x - 12$	Distribute 3.
$y = 3x - 14$	Subtract 2 from both sides. ∎

Graphing a Linear Equation in Slope-Intercept Form

Example 2   Graph $y = \frac{1}{2}x - 3$.

Solution   This equation is in the form $y = mx + b$.

$$y = \frac{1}{2}x + (-3)$$

The slope is $\frac{1}{2}$.

The y-intercept is -3, so the point $(0, -3)$ is on the line.

Plot the y-intercept at $(0, -3)$. From that point, count the vertical and horizontal change in the slope ratio to plot another point on the line. As a good graphing habit, do this several times, plotting several more points. Then draw a line through the points.

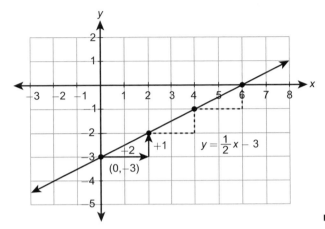

∎

Graphing a Linear Equation in Standard Form

Example 3   Graph $5x + 4y = 6$ using two different methods.

Solution

Method A Convert the equation to slope-intercept form. Then use the graphing method shown in Example 2 above.

$$5x + 4y = 6$$

$4y = -5x + 6$	Subtract $5x$ from both sides.
$y = -\frac{5}{4}x + \frac{3}{2}$	Divide through by 4.

Plot the y-intercept at $\left(0, \frac{3}{2}\right)$. Then count, using the slope $-\frac{5}{4}$, to plot another point.

Method B Find both intercepts and use them to draw the line.

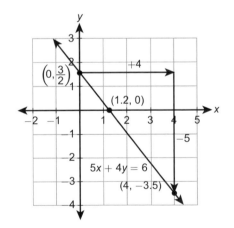

Find the x-intercept:

$$5x + 4y = 6$$
$$5x + 4 \cdot 0 = 6$$
$$5x = 6$$
$$x = \frac{6}{5}$$

Find the y-intercept:

$$5x + 4y = 6$$
$$5 \cdot 0 + 4y = 6$$
$$4y = 6$$
$$y = \frac{3}{2}$$

Plot the point $\left(\frac{6}{5}, 0\right)$.

Plot the point $\left(0, \frac{3}{2}\right)$.

Draw the line through these points. The line is the same as in Method A. ∎

Graphing a Linear Equation in Point-Slope Form

Example 4   Graph $y - 2 = 4(x + 3)$.

Solution   The slope is 4 and $(-3, 2)$ is a point on the corresponding line. Plot $(-3, 2)$. Then count, using the slope $\frac{4}{1}$, to plot another point. Another point on the line is $(-2, 6)$. Draw the line through the two points.

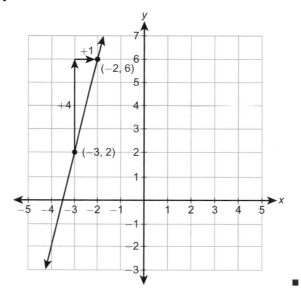

■

Linear Graph Family: $y = mx + b$

Any changes to the parameters m and b in equations of the form $f(x) = mx + b$ will change the graphs of the lines.

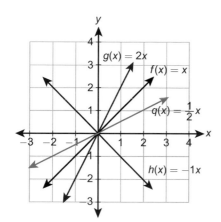

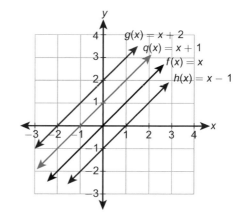

If you change only the parameter m, you get lines through the origin, but with different slopes.

If you change only the parameter b, you get lines with the same slope but different y-intercepts.

Problem Set

. . . .

Write each equation in the indicated form.

1. $2x + 5y = 20$ in slope-intercept form

2. $y - 1 = \frac{1}{2}(x + 3)$ in standard form

3. $10x + 4y = 16$ in slope-intercept form

4. $y + 3 = \frac{1}{4}x$ in standard form

5. $y - 5 = \frac{1}{3}(x - 4)$ in standard form

6. $4x - 5y = 12$ in slope-intercept form

7. $y = \frac{1}{9}(x + 7) - 12$ in standard form

Graph.

8. $y = \frac{1}{4}x + 2$

9. $x + y = 8$

10. $y = -\frac{1}{3}x + 4$

11. $y - 4.1 = 2.5(x + 1)$

12. $y + 1 = 3(x + 6)$

13. $3x - 2y = 10$

14. $y = -\frac{1}{7}x$

15. $7x + 2y = 14$

16. $y = -\frac{1}{2}(x - 5)$

17. $4x + 3y = 14$

18. $y = -6x - 2.3$

19. $y + 3.8 = -\frac{1}{7}x$

20. $10x + \frac{1}{2}y = 4$

21. $y = 0.75x + 5$

22. $y - 3 = \frac{1}{6}(x + 5)$

23. $y - 6 = -\frac{3}{4}(x - 2)$

24. $x - 7y = 12$

25. $y = 0$

26. $y + 4 = -\frac{2}{3}\left(x + \frac{1}{3}\right)$

27. $x + \frac{1}{3}y = \frac{3}{2}$

28. $x = 0$

Solve.

29. Yosef is fencing his triangular backyard. The equations of the three sides of fencing are $3x - 5y = 15$, $y = -\frac{1}{2}x + 7$, and $x = 0$. Graph the three equations that enclose Yosef's backyard.

*30. **Challenge** Camilla is painting diagonal stripes on a lot to mark off parking spaces. She begins with two lines whose equations are $y = 3x - 2$ and $y = 3x + 1$. What are the equations of five other lines that mark the spaces? The lines must be parallel and equally spaced.

Answer each question.

31. What effect does increasing a have on the graph of equation $y = ax$?

32. What effect does decreasing b have on the graph of equation $y = x + b$?

Writing Equations of Lines

You can use given information to write the equation of a line.

Finding a Linear Equation, Given the Slope and the y-intercept

You can write an equation of a line if you know the slope and the y-intercept.

Example 1 Find an equation of the line with slope $-\frac{2}{5}$ and y-intercept 6.

Solution The slope-intercept form of a linear equation is $y = mx + b$, where m is the slope and b is the y-intercept. So, in this case, $m = -\frac{2}{5}$ and $b = 6$. An equation of the line is $y = -\frac{2}{5}x + 6$. ∎

TIP

You can convert an equation in slope-intercept form to standard form:

$$y = -\frac{2}{5}x + 6$$

$$2x + 5y = 30$$

Finding a Linear Equation, Given the Slope and a Point on the Line

Given the slope and a point on the line, you can use the point-slope form of a linear equation to write an equation of the line.

Example 2 Find an equation of the line that has slope 3 and passes through the point $(1, -2)$. Write the equation in slope-intercept form.

Solution The point-slope form of a linear equation is $y - y_1 = m(x - x_1)$, where m is the slope and (x_1, y_1) is a point on the corresponding line.

$y - y_1 = m(x - x_1)$	Point-slope form
$y - (-2) = 3(x - 1)$	Substitute 3 for m, 1 for x_1, and -2 for y_1.
$y + 2 = 3(x - 1)$	Simplify the left side of the equation.
$y + 2 = 3x - 3$	Distribute 3 on the right side.
$y = 3x - 5$	Subtract 2 from both sides.

The equation of the line in slope-intercept form is $y = 3x - 5$. ∎

Finding a Linear Equation, Given Two Points

You do not need to see a graph in order to find an equation of a line. If you know the coordinates of two points, or if you know the coordinates of one point and the slope, you have enough information to determine an equation.

Example 3   Find an equation of the line that passes through the points (1, 2) and (2, 1). Write the equation in standard form.

Solution   Use the known points on the line, $(x_1, y_1) = (1, 2)$ and $(x_2, y_2) = (2, 1)$, to calculate the slope m between them.

$$m = \frac{y_2 - y_1}{x_2 - x_1} = \frac{1 - 2}{2 - 1} = \frac{-1}{1} = -1$$

(Count on the grid from one point to the other to verify the slope.)

Substitute the coordinates of one point and the slope into the point-slope form, and then convert the equation to standard form.

$y - y_1 = m(x - x_1)$	Point-slope form
$y - 2 = -1(x - 1)$	Substitute for x_1, y_1, and m.
$y - 2 = -1x + 1$	Distribute.
$x + y = 3$	Isolate the variables from the constants.

An equation of the line in standard form is $x + y = 3$. ■

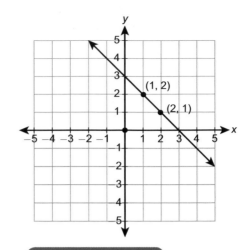

THINK ABOUT IT

In Example 3, the point (1, 2) is substituted in the point-slope form for (x_1, y_1). But you can substitute any point that you know is on the line.

Determining Whether Two Lines Are Parallel, Perpendicular, or Neither

PROPERTIES OF PARALLEL AND PERPENDICULAR LINES

Two nonvertical lines are **parallel** if and only if they have **equal slopes**.

Two nonvertical lines are **perpendicular** if and only if they have **opposite reciprocal slopes**.

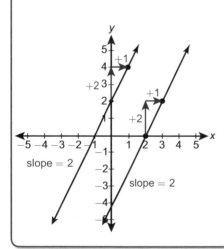

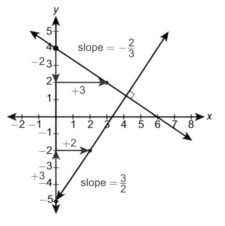

THINK ABOUT IT

Here is an alternate way to state the property of perpendicular lines:

Two nonvertical lines are perpendicular if and only if the product of their slopes is -1.

Note that $\left(-\frac{2}{3}\right)\left(\frac{3}{2}\right) = -1$.

Example 4   Determine whether each pair of lines is parallel, perpendicular, or neither.

A $x + y = 3$
$\quad y = 3x - 4$

Solution   Write the equation $x + y = 3$ in slope-intercept form, $y = -x + 3$. The slope is -1. The slope of $y = 3x - 4$ is 3. The slopes are not equal and are not opposite reciprocals. The lines are neither parallel nor perpendicular. ∎

B $y = -3x + 5$
$\quad 2y = 6 - 6x$

Solution   Write the equation $2y = 6 - 6x$ in slope-intercept form, $y = -3x + 3$. The slopes of the lines are equal. The lines are parallel. ∎

C $4x + 3y = 7$
$\quad 3x - 4y = 5$

Solution   Write each equation in slope-intercept form.
$$y = -\frac{4}{3}x + \frac{7}{3}$$
$$y = \frac{3}{4}x - \frac{5}{4}$$
The slopes are opposite reciprocals. The lines are perpendicular. ∎

Using Properties of Parallel or Perpendicular Lines to Find a Linear Equation

Example 5

A Find an equation of the line that is parallel to $y = 5x - 6$ and passes through the point $(2, -3)$. Write the equation in slope-intercept form.

Solution   The slope of the line $y = 5x - 6$ is 5. Because parallel lines have equal slopes, the desired line also has a slope of 5.

Substitute the slope and the coordinates of the known point into the slope-intercept form, and solve to find the desired y-intercept.

$$y = mx + b$$
$$-3 = 5 \cdot 2 + b$$
$$-3 = 10 + b$$
$$-13 = b$$

Use m and b to write the equation: $y = 5x - 13$. ∎

B Find an equation of the line that is perpendicular to $3x + y = 10$ and passes through the point $(-6, 2)$. Write the equation in slope-intercept form.

Solution   Write the given equation in slope-intercept form: $y = -3x + 10$. The slope is -3. Perpendicular lines have opposite reciprocal slopes, so the desired line has a slope of $\frac{1}{3}$. Substitute the coordinates of the slope and the known point into the point-slope form, and then convert it to slope-intercept form.

$$y - y_1 = m(x - x_1)$$
$$y - 2 = \tfrac{1}{3}[x - (-6)]$$
$$y - 2 = \tfrac{1}{3}x + 2$$
$$y = \tfrac{1}{3}x + 4$$

The equation is $y = \tfrac{1}{3}x + 4$. ■

Problem Set

Write an equation for each line.

1. $m = -\tfrac{1}{2}$, y-intercept 3

2. $m = 2$, passes through the point $(1, 3)$

3. $m = 3$, y-intercept 10

4. $m = \tfrac{7}{12}$, passes through the point $\left(\tfrac{1}{2}, -1\right)$

5. $m = -4$, passes through the point $(7, 6)$

6. $m = \tfrac{1}{5}$, passes through the point $(0, 9)$

7. $m = 0$, y-intercept $\tfrac{1}{3}$

8. $m = -\tfrac{2}{3}$, passes through the point $(4, -7)$

9. $m = \tfrac{4}{5}$, y-intercept $-\tfrac{3}{7}$

Write an equation for each line.

10. parallel to $y = 2x - 10$ and passes through the point $(-2, 11)$

11. perpendicular to $y = 3x - 9$ and passes through the point $(3, 1)$

12. perpendicular to $2x + 4y = 5$ and passes through the point $(-8, 2)$

13. undefined slope and passes through the point $(-5, 6)$

14. perpendicular to $5x - 4y = 10$ and passes through the point $(-1, -6)$

15. undefined slope and x-intercept 7

16. parallel to $y = x + 2$ and passes through the point $(1, -4)$

For each pair of points, do the following:

A. Write an equation of the line in point-slope form.
B. Write the equation in standard form.
C. Write the equation in slope-intercept form.

17. $(2, 0)$ and $(3, 4)$

18. $(1, 4)$ and $(0, 1)$

19. $(3, 8)$ and $(6, 5)$

20. $(-3, -3)$ and $(4, 5)$

21. $(8.3, -1)$ and $(-1, 7.6)$

22. $\left(-2, \tfrac{1}{2}\right)$ and $(1, 8)$

Determine whether the lines are parallel, perpendicular, or neither.

23. $x + 2y = 5$ and $y = -\tfrac{1}{2}x + 12$

24. $y = -5x + 10$ and $5y = x + 15$

25. $2x + 7y = 14$ and $7x - 2y = 10$

26. $y = 3x + 4$ and $3y = x + 33$

27. $x = 2$ and $y = 4$

28. $8x - 2y = 7$ and $2y - 8x = 1$

Solve.

*29. **Challenge** Sam wants to build a pool in an enclosed area behind his house. He wants one end of the pool to be perpendicular to the back wall of his house. If the line running along the house has equation $2x - 3y = 10$, and the point $(3, -5)$ will rest on the end of the pool, find the equation of the line that is perpendicular to the back wall of Sam's house and passes through $(3, -5)$.

*30. **Challenge** A decorator is painting a wall with stripes. The equation of the first gray stripe is $3x - y = 7$. Find the equation of the third stripe if it is parallel to the first and passes through the point $(2, 4)$.

Applications: Linear Equations

Many real-world situations involve slope and linear equations.

Using a Linear Model to Estimate

Example 1 Dan and Ben begin a road trip. They set the trip meter to 0. Dan drives first, and then Ben begins driving at noon. Ben drives at a fairly constant speed. At 2 p.m., the trip meter reading is 180 miles. At 3:30 p.m., the reading is 267 miles.

A Write a linear equation in slope-intercept form that approximates the relationship between the trip meter reading and the amount of time Ben drives. Graph the equation.

B Describe what the slope represents.

C Estimate the number of miles Dan drove.

THINK ABOUT IT

If Ben drives at a *constant speed*, then the equation developed below is an *exact* model of the situation. But because Ben drives at a *fairly* constant speed, the equation is only an *approximate* model. The only exact data values that are known are those stated in the problem.

Solution

A Slope-intercept form is $y = mx + b$. Let x represent the number of hours Ben drives, and let y represent the trip meter reading, in miles. At 2 p.m., Ben has been driving for 2 hours, and at 3:30 p.m., he has been driving for 3.5 hours, so you know the following two data points: $(x_1, y_1) = (2, 180)$ and $(x_2, y_2) = (3.5, 267)$. Plot these two points. Find the slope:

$$\text{slope} = m = \frac{y_2 - y_1}{x_2 - x_1} = \frac{267 \text{ mi} - 180 \text{ mi}}{3.5 \text{ h} - 2 \text{ h}} = \frac{87 \text{ mi}}{1.5 \text{ h}} = \frac{58 \text{ mi}}{1 \text{ h}} = 58 \text{ mph}$$

To solve for the y-intercept b, substitute 58 for m and $(2, 180)$ for (x, y) in the slope-intercept form:

$$y = mx + b$$
$$180 = 58 \cdot 2 + b$$
$$180 = 116 + b$$
$$64 = b$$

The equation is $y = 58x + 64$. The graph of the equation is the line through the points $(2, 180)$ and $(3.5, 267)$.

B Use units to figure this out. Since the numerator is miles and the denominator is hours, the ratio is miles per hour. In this situation, it is Ben's average speed, $\dfrac{58 \text{ miles}}{\text{hour}}$.

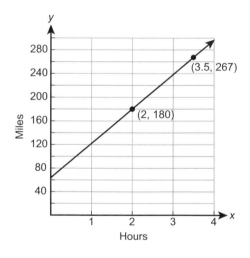

C When Ben begins driving, $x = 0$. If $x = 0$ in the equation $y = 58x + 64$, then $y = 64$. So, based on the facts presented in the problem, 64 miles is the best estimate of the number of miles Dan drove. Verify that 64 is reasonable for the y-intercept of the graph. ■

Using a Linear Model to Solve a Problem

Example 2   Leslie earns a base pay of $12.50 per hour. She also earns "time-and-a-half" for overtime (any hours over 40 hours in a week).

A Write and graph a linear equation that models Leslie's earnings for a week in which she works at least 40 hours.

B What does the slope of the equation represent?

C Leslie reports her hours in quarter-hour increments. How many hours does Leslie need to work to earn $750 in one week?

Solution

A Let t represent the number of hours of overtime Leslie works in a week. Let e represent her earnings for that week, in dollars.

| 40 hours at | Multiply $12.50 by | t is the number of |
| $12.50 per hour | 1.5 for time-and-a-half | overtime hours |

$$e = 40 \cdot 12.5 + 1.5 \cdot 12.5 \cdot t$$
$$e = 500 + 18.75t$$
$$e = 18.75t + 500$$

The equation $e = 18.75t + 500$ models Leslie's earnings for a week in which she works at least 40 hours. To graph the equation, start with some ordered pairs and then draw a line through the points.

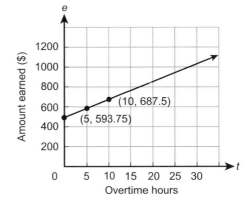

t	0	5	10
e	500	593.75	687.50

Leslie works at least 40 hours, so only points with values $t \geq 0$ apply in this case.

B The slope, which is 18.75, represents the number of dollars per hour that Leslie earns at the overtime rate.

C To find the number of hours Leslie needs to work to earn $750 in one week, substitute 750 for e and solve for t.

$$e = 18.75t + 500$$
$$750 = 18.75t + 500$$
$$250 = 18.75t$$
$$13.33 = t$$

If Leslie needs to works 13.33 overtime hours, she needs to work a total of $40 + 13.33 = 53.33$ hours.

Leslie reports her hours in quarter-hour increments, and $53.\overline{3}$ is between 53.25 and 53.5. So Leslie needs to work 53.5 hours to earn $750 in one week. ■

Using a Linear Model to Interpret Solutions

Example 3 Ed is a lumber dealer. He sells two types of decking, earning 20% profit on synthetic decking and 16% profit on wood decking. Ed has a goal of earning a $2000 profit during the next month.

A Write an equation that represents the sales, in dollars, of each type of decking Ed can sell to earn a $2000 profit.

B Graph the equation.

C Identify three solutions to the equation and interpret their meaning.

Solution

A Let s represent sales, in dollars, of synthetic decking.
Let w represent sales, in dollars, of wood decking.
Write an equation:

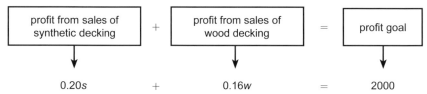

THINK ABOUT IT

In this situation, either variable can be the independent variable.

You could label the horizontal axis w and the vertical axis s, obtaining a different graph.

B Find the intercepts and use them to graph the equation. Label the horizontal axis s and the vertical axis w; points on the graph will have the form (s, w).

Find the s-intercept:

$$0.20s + 0.16w = 2000$$
$$0.20s + 0.16 \cdot 0 = 2000$$
$$0.20s = 2000$$
$$s = 10,000$$

Plot the point $(10,000, 0)$.

Find the w-intercept:

$$0.20s + 0.16w = 2000$$
$$0.20 \cdot 0 + 0.16w = 2000$$
$$0.16w = 2000$$
$$w = 12,500$$

Plot the point $(0, 12,500)$.

Connect the points with a line segment. The graph of the equation is a line, but in this application, only positive values make sense. So just use Quadrant I.

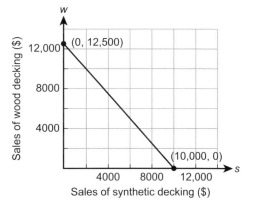

C Two solutions to the equation were found in Part B: $(10,000, 0)$ and $(0, 12,500)$. To find another solution, substitute a convenient value for one variable in the equation and solve for the other variable. Substitute 6000 for s and solve to find that $w = 5000$.

$$0.20s + 0.16w = 2000$$
$$0.20 \cdot 6000 + 0.16w = 2000$$
$$1200 + 0.16w = 2000$$
$$0.16w = 800$$
$$w = 5000$$

So a third solution is $(6000, 5000)$. Each solution is a combination of sales that result in a total profit of $2000.

Solution	What It Represents
$(10,000, 0)$	$10,000 sales of synthetic, $0 sales of wood
$(0, 12,500)$	$0 sales of synthetic, $12,500 sales of wood
$(6000, 5000)$	$6000 sales of synthetic, $5000 sales of wood

Using a Linear Model to Make a Prediction

Example 4   The table at the right gives the median weekly earnings of full-time workers in the United States for the years 1980–2004. Find a model for the data. Then use your model to predict the median weekly earnings in 2010.

Solution   Let x represent the year and let y represent the median weekly earnings in dollars. Graph the ordered pairs. (The graph is called a *scatter plot.*) The data points form a linear pattern, so a linear function is a good model for the data. Draw a line that approximates the pattern.

Year	Median Weekly Earnings ($)
1980	262
1982	302
1984	326
1986	359
1988	385
1990	412
1992	440
1994	467
1996	490
1998	523
2000	576
2002	608
2004	638

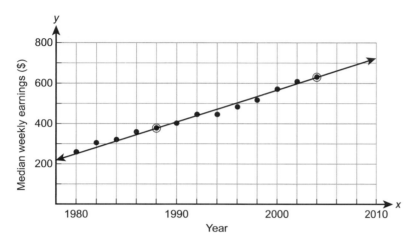

Finding the line of best fit is a strategy that makes it easy to find an equation to model the data. This line of fit passes through (1988, 385) and (2004, 638). Find an equation of the line. Use the point-slope form of a linear equation.

$$\text{slope} = \frac{638 - 385}{2004 - 1988} \approx 15.8$$

$$y - y_1 = m(x - x_1)$$
$$y - 385 = 15.8(x - 1988)$$
$$y - 385 = 15.8x - 31{,}410.4$$
$$y = 15.8x - 31{,}025.4$$

So a good linear model for the data is $f(x) = 15.8x - 31{,}025.4$.
To predict the median weekly earnings in 2010, substitute 2010 for x.

$$y = 15.8x - 31{,}025.4$$

$$y = 15.8 \cdot 2010 - 31{,}025.4$$

$$y = 732.6$$

According to this linear model, the predicted 2010 median weekly earnings for a full-time worker is about $733. ∎

Problem Set

For each problem, do the following:

A. Define variables for the unknowns.
B. Write an equation to model the problem.
C. Graph the equation.
D. Answer the question.

1. A child completes tasks to earn rewards. Yesterday, the child completed 4 tasks and earned 2 rewards. Today, the child earned 4 rewards by completing 6 tasks. How many tasks must the child complete to earn 10 rewards?

2. There is a linear relationship between a car's weight and its gas mileage. An average car that weighs 2100 pounds gets 35 miles to the gallon, while a 3000-pound car gets 27 miles per gallon. If a car gets 25 miles per gallon, how much should it weigh?

3. A class has collected $40 to spend on a holiday party. Each paper decoration costs $2, and each party favor costs $4.50. If the class buys 8 decorations, how many party favors can the class afford?

For each problem, do the following:

A. Write an equation to model the problem.
B. Explain what the slope represents.
C. Answer the question.

4. A store sells cards by the box. Engraved cards sell for $20 per box, and all-occasion cards sell for $10 per box. All purchases must total $150. If a person bought 3 boxes of engraved cards, how many all-occasion cards must he or she buy?

5. Gabrielle ran a marathon. From the start to the first checkpoint, Gabrielle ran at a constant rate of 10 miles in 130 minutes. At the second checkpoint, her total distance was 20 miles and her total time was 260 minutes. If the finish line is at 26.2 miles, what would be her time if she continued at the same rate?

6. A pot of water is heating on a stove at a constant rate. At 8 a.m., the temperature of the water is 82°F. At 8:04 a.m., the temperature has risen to 100°F. Find the temperature of the water at 8:08 a.m.

7. A carpenter, working at a constant rate, made 6 tables in 2 days last week. This week, he made 9 tables in 3 days. Find the number of tables the carpenter can make in 10 days.

8. A doctor measured a baby's length at 21 inches when the baby was one month old. At the baby's six-month doctor's appointment, the baby's length was 26 inches. Find the baby's length when the baby is one year old if his length increases at a constant rate.

9. On September 15, the value of a stock was $121 per share. Five days later, the stock's value was $100 per share. What is the value of the stock on October 1 if the value changes at a constant rate?

10. Jamal weighed 200 pounds on the first of the month. Two weeks later, he weighed 196 pounds. What will Jamal weigh four weeks after his initial weigh-in if his weight decreases at a constant rate?

11. Tyrone earns a base pay of $10.75 per hour. He also earns "time-and-a-half" for overtime (any hours over 40 hours in a week). How many hours does Tyrone need to work to earn $500 in one week?

12. The average winning speed of a car race increased at a constant rate each year the race was held. In 2000, the winning speed was 101 miles per hour, then in 2008 the winning speed was 110 miles per hour. Estimate the winning speed for 2011.

13. A phone company charges a flat fee of $100 for one phone installation plus $40 for each additional phone jack. How many phones could be installed for $420?

14. A restaurant suggests that all patrons tip the help staff. A waitress earned a $3.75 tip for a $25.20 meal and $4.95 for a meal that cost $32.50. Estimate the cost of a meal that will yield a $6 tip.

For each problem, do the following:

A. **Define variables for the unknowns.**
B. **Write an equation to model the data.**
C. **Use your model to make the indicated prediction.**

15. The table shows the average hours per day a person in the United States spent engaged in his or her children's education for the years 2003–2007. Predict the average hours per day a person will spend on his or her children's education in 2010.

Year	Average Hours
2003	1.02
2004	1.01
2005	1.00
2006	0.98
2007	0.93

16. The table gives the employment population percentages of 15-year-olds to 17-year-olds for the years 1983 to 1989. Predict the percentage of 15-year-olds to 17-year-olds employed in 1992.

Year	Percentage
1983	24
1984	25
1985	26
1986	27
1987	27.5
1988	28.5
1989	29

17. The table gives the average percentage of Americans who go to work each day. The data were collected for the years 2003–2007. Predict the percentage of Americans who will go to work each day in 2010.

Year	Percentage
2003	46.0
2004	45.7
2005	46.1
2006	46.5
2007	47.8

18. The table gives the primary energy consumption (trillion Btu) in the United States residential sector, beginning with the year 1999. Predict the primary residential energy consumption in 2006.

Year	Btu
1999	6784
2001	6879
2002	6938
2004	7019

19. The table gives the percentage of all individual tax returns filed in the United States for the years 1999–2006 for taxpayers with adjusted gross income between $100,000 and $200,000. Predict the year the percentage of filed income tax returns reaches 9 percent.

Year	%
1999	5.6
2000	6.2
2001	6.5
2002	6.5
2003	6.8
2004	7.4
2005	8.0
2006	8.7

Systems of Linear Equations

When equations with the same variables are grouped together, a *system of equations* is formed.

Determining Whether a Given Ordered Pair Is a Solution to a System

> **DEFINITION**
>
> A **system of equations** is two or more equations that contain the same variables.

A given ordered pair is a solution to a system if it satisfies all of the equations.

Example 1 Determine whether each point is a solution to the system:

$$\begin{cases} 2x - 4y = 8 \\ y = 3x - 7 \end{cases}$$

A $(2, -1)$ **B** $(8, 2)$

Solution Substitute the coordinates of each point into each equation.

A

$2x - 4y = 8$	$y = 3x - 7$
$2 \cdot 2 - 4 \cdot (-1) \overset{?}{=} 8$	$-1 \overset{?}{=} 3 \cdot 2 - 7$
$4 + 4 \overset{?}{=} 8$	$-1 \overset{?}{=} 6 - 7$
$8 = 8 \checkmark$	$-1 = -1 \checkmark$

The point $(2, -1)$ is a solution to the system because it makes both equations true. ∎

B

$2x - 4y = 8$	$y = 3x - 7$
$2 \cdot 8 - 4 \cdot 2 \overset{?}{=} 8$	$2 \overset{?}{=} 3 \cdot 8 - 7$
$16 - 8 \overset{?}{=} 8$	$2 \overset{?}{=} 24 - 7$
$8 = 8 \checkmark$	$2 \neq 17$

The point $(8, 2)$ is *not* a solution to the system because it does not make both equations true. ∎

Solving Systems by Graphing

One way to solve a system of equations is to graph each equation to determine where they intersect. The point of intersection represents the solution to the system.

Example 2 Solve each system by graphing.

A $\begin{cases} y = 3x - 2 \\ y = -\dfrac{1}{2}x + 5 \end{cases}$

Solution Graph the two lines. The lines appear to intersect at $(2, 4)$.

You can check that $(2, 4)$ is a solution to both equations.

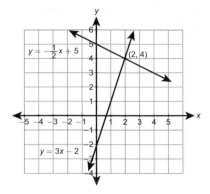

$$y = 3x - 2 \qquad\qquad y = -\frac{1}{2}x + 5$$
$$4 \stackrel{?}{=} 3 \cdot 2 - 2 \qquad\qquad 4 \stackrel{?}{=} -\frac{1}{2} \cdot 2 + 5$$
$$4 \stackrel{?}{=} 6 - 2 \qquad\qquad 4 \stackrel{?}{=} -1 + 5$$
$$4 = 4 \checkmark \qquad\qquad 4 = 4 \checkmark \quad \blacksquare$$

B $\begin{cases} 10x - 4y = 24 \\ y = \dfrac{5}{2}x - 3 \end{cases}$

Solution Find the x- and y-intercepts of the first equation:

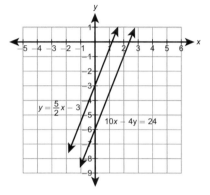

$$10x - 4y = 24 \qquad\qquad 10x - 4y = 24$$
$$10 \cdot 0 - 4y = 24 \qquad\qquad 10x - 4 \cdot 0 = 24$$
$$-4y = 24 \qquad\qquad 10x = 24$$
$$y = -6 \qquad\qquad x = 2.4$$

Then graph each line. Because the lines are parallel, they never intersect. This system has no solution. $\blacksquare$

Classifying Systems of Linear Equations

A system of two linear equations can have one solution, no solution, or infinitely many solutions. The table below shows how linear systems are classified according to the number of solutions.

Classifying Systems of Linear Equations

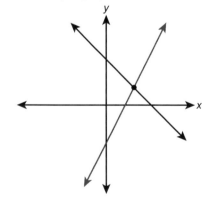

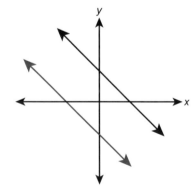

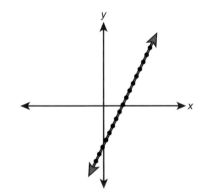

A linear system is **consistent and independent** if its graphs intersect at one point (one solution).

A linear system is **inconsistent** if the lines are parallel (no solution).

A linear system is **consistent and dependent** if the lines coincide (infinitely many solutions).

Solving Linear Systems by the Substitution Method

Algebraic methods, such as the substitution method, can be used to solve linear systems and often yield more accurate results than graphing.

HOW TO SOLVE A SYSTEM BY THE SUBSTITUTION METHOD

Step 1 Solve one equation for one of the variables.
Step 2 Substitute the expression obtained from Step 1 in place of the corresponding variable in the other equation, and solve the resulting equation.
Step 3 Substitute the value of the variable from Step 2 into either of the original equations. Solve this equation to find the value of the other variable.

TIP

You can always check your work by making sure that your solution satisfies both equations in the system.

Example 3   Solve the system by substitution.

$$-x + 4y = 6$$
$$3x - 12y = -18$$

Solution

Step 1   Both equations are in standard form, so solve one of the equations for x or y. It is easiest to solve the first equation for x.

$$-x + 4y = 6$$
$$-x = -4y + 6$$
$$x = 4y - 6$$

TIP

When a system solved algebraically results in an equation that is true for all real numbers, the system has infinitely many solutions. When it results in an equation that is not true for any real number, the system has no solution.

Step 2   Substitute the expression $4y - 6$ for x in the second equation. The equation $-18 = -18$ is true for all real numbers. This means that there are infinitely many solutions.

$$3x - 12y = -18$$
$$3(4y - 6) - 12y = -18$$
$$12y - 18 - 12y = -18$$
$$-18 = -18$$

Step 3   Because there is no single value of y that is a solution, you don't have to complete Step 3.

So the system is consistent and dependent, and there are infinitely many solutions. ■

Solving Linear Systems by the Linear Combination Method

Another algebraic method to solve a system is the linear combination method.

HOW TO SOLVE A SYSTEM BY THE LINEAR COMBINATION METHOD

Step 1 Convert both equations to standard form.
Step 2 Multiply one or both of the equations by a real number so that the coefficient of one variable in one equation is the additive inverse of the coefficient of the same variable in the other equation.
Step 3 Add the equations, and then solve the resulting equation.
Step 4 Substitute the value of the variable from Step 3 into either of the original equations. Solve this equation for the second variable.

REMEMBER

The sum of a number and its additive inverse is 0.

Example 4 Solve the system by linear combination.

$$\begin{cases} 2x + 5y = 1 \\ y = \dfrac{3}{4}x - \dfrac{13}{4} \end{cases}$$

Solution

Step 1 Convert the second equation to standard form by mutiplying through by 4 and subtracting $3x$ from both sides.

$$\begin{cases} 2x + 5y = 1 \\ -3x + 4y = -13 \end{cases}$$

THINK ABOUT IT

The solution to a linear system of equations does not change when you multiply one or both of the equations by a nonzero real number.

Step 2 Multiply the first equation by 3 and the second equation by 2 so that the coefficients of x are additive inverses.

Step 3 Add the equations to eliminate x.
Solve the result for y.

$$\begin{aligned} 6x + 15y &= 3 \\ -6x + 8y &= -26 \\ \hline 23y &= -23 \Rightarrow y = -1 \end{aligned}$$

Step 4 Substitute -1 for y in either of the original equations to find x.

$$2x + 5 \cdot (-1) = 1 \Rightarrow 2x - 5 = 1 \Rightarrow 2x = 6 \Rightarrow x = 3$$

So the solution to the system is $(3, -1)$. ∎

Solving a System of Three Equations with Three Variables

It is also possible to solve a system of three equations containing three variables. The solution of a system of three equations in three variables can have one solution, infinitely many solutions, or no solution. A system of three equations is solved by finding **ordered triples** that satisfy all of the equations.

HOW TO SOLVE A SYSTEM OF THREE EQUATIONS WITH THREE VARIABLES

Step 1 Convert each equation to standard form.

Step 2 Eliminate one variable from two of the equations.

Step 3 Using these two equations and substitution or linear combination, solve for one of the remaining variables.

Step 4 Substitute the value of the variable from Step 3 into either of the equations in Step 2. Solve this equation for the second variable.

Step 5 Substitute the value of the variables from Step 3 and Step 4 into any of the original equations.

Example 5 Solve the system.

$$\begin{cases} 2x + 5y - z = -8 \\ -x + y + z = -3 \\ -3x - y + 2z = -1 \end{cases}$$

Solution

Step 1 The system has three equations in standard form. Eliminate the z variable from the first two equations by combining them.

$$\begin{array}{r} 2x + 5y - z = -8 \\ -x + y + z = -3 \\ \hline x + 6y \phantom{{}+ z} = -11 \end{array}$$

Step 2 Multiply the second equation by -2. Then combine the second equation with the third equation to eliminate the z variable.

$$\begin{array}{r} 2x - 2y - 2z = 6 \\ -3x - y + 2z = -1 \\ \hline -x - 3y \phantom{{}+ 2z} = 5 \end{array}$$

Step 3 Now you have a system of two linear equations with two variables. Combine the equations to solve the system.

$$\begin{array}{r} x + 6y = -11 \\ -x - 3y = 5 \\ \hline 3y = -6 \\ y = -2 \end{array}$$

Step 4 Use the value of y to solve for x in any of the two equations. Then substitute the value of x and y into one of the original equations to solve for z.

$$x + 6 \cdot (-2) = -11 \Rightarrow x - 12 = -11 \Rightarrow x = 1$$

$$2 \cdot 1 + 5 \cdot (-2) - z = -8 \Rightarrow 2 - 10 - z = -8$$

$$\Rightarrow -8 - z = -8 \Rightarrow z = 0$$

The solution to the system is $(1, -2, 0)$. ■

Problem Set

Determine whether the given ordered pair or triple is a solution to the system.

1. $(3, 1)$, $\begin{cases} x - 2y = 1 \\ y = 4x - 11 \end{cases}$

2. $(-2, 0)$, $\begin{cases} 3x - y = -6 \\ y = 7x + 5 \end{cases}$

3. $(5, 7)$, $\begin{cases} 4x - 2y = 6 \\ 3x + 2y = 29 \end{cases}$

4. $(-4, -2)$, $\begin{cases} x - 6y = 7 \\ 4x - y = -14 \end{cases}$

5. $(-1, -1)$, $\begin{cases} 5x - 6y = 1 \\ 6x - 5y = -1 \end{cases}$

6. $(1, 0, -2)$, $\begin{cases} x + 2y - z = 3 \\ 2x + 3y + 4z = -6 \\ x + y + z = -1 \end{cases}$

7. $(3, 1, -3)$, $\begin{cases} x + 3y + 2z = 0 \\ x + 5y + z = 5 \\ -2x + 4y + z = -5 \end{cases}$

8. $(3, 3, 1)$, $\begin{cases} x + 7y - 2z = 22 \\ x + y - z = 4 \\ x - y - z = -1 \end{cases}$

9. $(0, -1, 2)$, $\begin{cases} x + 2z = 4 \\ 5y + z = -3 \\ x + 3y = -3 \end{cases}$

10. $(0, 12, 5)$, $\begin{cases} x + 3y + z = 41 \\ 2x + z = 5 \\ -x + 4y + z = 53 \end{cases}$

Solve each system by graphing.

11. $\begin{cases} y = -2x + 6 \\ y = 3x - 4 \end{cases}$

12. $\begin{cases} y = -\dfrac{1}{2}x + 4 \\ y = -\dfrac{2}{3}x + 3 \end{cases}$

13. $\begin{cases} 6x + 2y = 10 \\ 5x - 10y = 20 \end{cases}$

14. $\begin{cases} -3x + 4y = 6 \\ 9x + 6y = -9 \end{cases}$

Solve each system by substitution.

15. $\begin{cases} 2x + 8y = 18 \\ y = -x + 6 \end{cases}$

16. $\begin{cases} 3x - 4y = -5 \\ -x + 2y = 3 \end{cases}$

17. $\begin{cases} \dfrac{1}{2}x - y = 3 \\ -6x + \dfrac{2}{3}y = -9 \end{cases}$

18. $\begin{cases} -x + 4y = -1 \\ 2x - y = 5.5 \end{cases}$

Solve each system by linear combination.

19. $\begin{cases} 5x - 2y = 27 \\ -3x + 2y = -17 \end{cases}$

20. $\begin{cases} 3x - 4y = 9 \\ -3x + 2y = -9 \end{cases}$

21. $\begin{cases} 6x + y = 14 \\ -2x - y = -4 \end{cases}$

22. $\begin{cases} 5x - 2y = 6 \\ -3x + y = 2 \end{cases}$

23. $\begin{cases} 3.2x - 4.8y = -9.6 \\ 2.5x + 5y = -13.9 \end{cases}$

24. $\begin{cases} 4x + 2y = 3 \\ y = -2x + \dfrac{3}{2} \end{cases}$

25. $\begin{cases} x + 2y - z = -1 \\ x - 4y - z = -4 \\ 2x - 2y + 3z = 15 \end{cases}$

26. $\begin{cases} x - 3y + 2z = 1 \\ -x + 4y - 4z = 1 \\ 5x - y + 6z = 9 \end{cases}$

27. $\begin{cases} -0.4x + 0.5y = 9 \\ y = \dfrac{8}{10}x - 20 \end{cases}$

28. $\begin{cases} 3x - 2y + 4z = -3 \\ 4y - 8z = 0 \\ -x + 2y = 2 \end{cases}$

Applications: Linear Systems

Many real-world problems can be solved with a system of linear equations.

Solving an Investment Problem

Example 1 Linda invested $4000, separating it into two mutual funds. The percent return on Star Spangled Corporation at the end of a year was 5%, and the percent return on Joe Dow's Industries was 7%. The combined return on both funds was $256. How much did Linda invest in each fund?

Solution

Step 1 Let x represent the dollar amount invested in Star Spangled Corporation. Let y represent the dollar amount invested in Joe Dow's Industries. Write two equations to represent the situation.

> **TIP**
>
> Percent means hundredths. To write a percent in decimal form, use the meaning of percent:
>
> $$5\% = \frac{5}{100} = 0.05$$
>
> Or just remove the % symbol and move the decimal point two places to the left:
>
> $$5\% = 5.\% = 0.05$$

Equation 1:

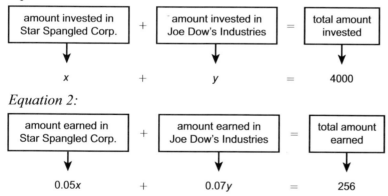

amount invested in Star Spangled Corp.	+	amount invested in Joe Dow's Industries	=	total amount invested
x	+	y	=	4000

Equation 2:

amount earned in Star Spangled Corp.	+	amount earned in Joe Dow's Industries	=	total amount earned
$0.05x$	+	$0.07y$	=	256

Step 2 Solve the system.

$\begin{cases} x + y = 4000 \\ 0.05x + 0.07y = 256 \end{cases}$ Use Equations 1 and 2 to write a system.

$\underline{\begin{aligned} -0.05x - 0.05y &= -200 \\ 0.05x + 0.07y &= 256 \end{aligned}}$ Multiply both sides of Equation 1 by -0.05 to get opposite x-coefficients.

$0.02y = 56$ Add to eliminate x.

$y = 2800$ Solve for y.

$x + 2800 = 4000$ Substitute 2800 for y in Equation 1.

$x = 1200$ Solve for x.

Linda invested $1200 in Star Spangled Corporation and $2800 in Joe Dow's Industries. ∎

Solving a Mixture Problem

Example 2 A certain brand of orange juice has 16.7% of the recommended daily allowance (RDA) of vitamin C per ounce. The same brand of pineapple juice has 5.5% of the RDA of vitamin C per ounce. An 8-ounce mixture of these juices contains 120% of the RDA of vitamin C. How much orange juice and how much pineapple juice are in the mixture?

TIP

Percent is a ratio that compares a number to 100. Mixture problems can use ratios in other forms, such as unit prices or servings per container.

Solution

Step 1 Let x represent the number of ounces of orange juice. Let y represent the number of ounces of pineapple juice. Write two equations.

Equation 1:

The first equation represents the sum of the two amounts of juice, which must equal the total amount of the mixture, in ounces.

$$x + y = 8$$

Equation 2:

The second equation represents portions of the RDA of vitamin C.

One ounce of orange juice contains 0.167 of the RDA of vitamin C, so x ounces contain $0.167x$ of the RDA of vitamin C.

One ounce of pineapple juice contains 0.055 of the RDA of vitamin C, so y ounces contain $0.055y$ of the RDA of vitamin C.

The mixture contains 1.20 times the RDA of vitamin C.

$$0.167x + 0.055y = 1.20$$

THINK ABOUT IT

You could write Equation 2, using percents instead of their decimal equivalents, as follows:

$$16.7x + 5.5y = 120$$

The system would have the same solution.

Step 2 Solve the system.

$$\begin{cases} x + y = 8 \\ 0.167x + 0.055y = 1.20 \end{cases}$$

$$\begin{cases} x + y = 8 \\ 167x + 55y = 1200 \end{cases}$$ Multiply the second equation by 1000 to eliminate the decimals.

$$\begin{aligned} -55x - 55y &= -440 \\ 167x + 55y &= 1200 \end{aligned}$$ Multiply both sides of Equation 1 by -55 to get opposite y-coefficients.

$$112x = 760$$ Add to eliminate y.

$$x \approx 6.8$$ Divide by 112 to solve for x.

$$6.8 + y \approx 8$$ Substitute 6.8 for x in Equation 1.

$$y \approx 1.2$$ Solve for y.

There are about 6.8 ounces of orange juice and about 1.2 ounces of pineapple juice in the mixture. ■

Solving a Sports Problem

Example 3 In the 2007–2008 National Basketball Association season, Cleveland's LeBron James scored 2250 points, making a total of 1343 shots, including one-point free throws, two-point field goals, and three-point field goals. He made 19 more two-point field goals than three-point field goals and one-point free throws combined. Find the number of each type of shot he made.

Solution

Step 1 Let x represent the number of three-point field goals made, let y represent the number of two-point field goals made, and let z represent the number of one-point free throws made. Write three equations.

Equation 1: Number of shots made: $x + y + z = 1343$

Equation 2: Number of points scored: $3x + 2y + z = 2250$

Equation 3: Relationship between types of shots:
$$y = x + z + 19 \Rightarrow -x + y - z = 19$$

Step 2 Solve the system.

$$\begin{cases} x + y + z = 1343 \\ 3x + 2y + z = 2250 \\ -x + y - z = 19 \end{cases}$$

$$\begin{aligned} x + y + z &= 1343 \\ \underline{-x + y - z} &= \underline{19} \\ 2y &= 1362 \\ y &= 681 \end{aligned}$$

Eliminate x and z from the first equation and the third equation by adding them.

$$\begin{cases} x + 681 + z = 1343 \\ 3x + 2 \cdot 681 + z = 2250 \end{cases}$$

Substitute 681 for y in Equation 1 and Equation 2.

$$\begin{cases} x + z = 662 \\ 3x + 1362 + z = 2250 \end{cases}$$

Simplify.

$$\begin{aligned} x + z &= 662 \\ \underline{3x + z} &= \underline{888} \\ -2x &= -226 \\ x &= 113 \end{aligned}$$

Solve the resulting system.

$$\begin{aligned} 113 + 681 + z &= 1343 \\ 794 + z &= 1343 \\ z &= 549 \end{aligned}$$

Substitute 681 for y and 113 for x in Equation 1 and solve for z.

LeBron James made 113 three-point field goals, 681 two-point field goals, and 549 one-point free throws. ∎

Problem Set

For each problem, do the following:

A. **Define variables for the unknowns.**
B. **Write a system of equations to model the problem.**
C. **Solve the system.**
D. **Give your answer in a complete sentence.**

1. Tyler invested $4500 in certificates of deposit. One certificate of deposit pays 4% in interest, and the other pays 6.5% in interest. He earned $220 combined from the certificates of deposit. How much did Tyler invest in each certificate of deposit?

2. A grocery store sells pears for $1.99 per pound and apples for $1.49 per pound. A customer purchases 9 pounds of pears and apples for $15.41. How many pounds of each did the customer purchase?

3. At a movie theater, an adult ticket costs $10 and a child ticket costs $6. There were 350 people at a movie showing. The revenue for that showing was $3292. How many adults were at the showing? How many children were at the showing?

4. A football team scored on 7 plays in a game for a total of 33 points. How many touchdowns did the team score? How many field goals did the team make? (Count touchdowns as 7 points and field goals as 3 points.)

5. Kianna invested $6000, separating it into two mutual funds. The percent return on Tidewater Corporation at the end of a year was 3%, and the percent return on Lincoln, Inc., was 4%. The combined return on both funds was $225. How much did Kianna invest in each fund?

6. A chemistry experiment requires a mixture of a 20% hydrogen solution and a 30% hydrogen solution. How many liters of each solution are required for 4 liters of 24% hydrogen solution?

7. Chang and his brother, Min, use different cell phone plans from the Global Connection phone company. In one month, the two brothers use a total of 500 minutes. Chang pays $0.20 per minute used and Min pays $0.25 per minute used. If their total bill adds up to $111, how many minutes did each brother use for the month?

8. Darion spent $175 on a coat and three shirts. Each shirt cost the same amount. The coat cost four times the amount of one shirt. What was the price of the coat? What was the price of each shirt?

9. The Perfect Electronics store buys computers from two different companies. Company A produces 3 defective computers for every 200 computers sold, and Company B produces 5 defective computers for every 250 computers sold. In one year, the store purchases a total of 1000 computers. If the total number of defective computers for that year was 18, how many computers did the store purchase from each company?

10. Mario invested $7400 in two mutual fund accounts. One account pays 7.5% in interest, and the other pays 9% in interest. He earned $636 combined from the accounts. How much did Mario invest in each account?

11. A farmer harvests corn and wheat. He earns $3 per bushel of corn and $4.50 per bushel of wheat. Last year, he harvested a total of 1000 bushels and earned $3781.50. How many bushels of corn and wheat did the farmer harvest?

12. Sam's Chicken buys sets of small aprons and large aprons. A set of 5 small aprons costs $30, and a set of 3 large aprons costs $20. The restaurant spends $180 on 7 sets of aprons. How many individual small aprons and individual large aprons did they purchase altogether?

13. At a coffee shop, a bagel costs $1.29 and a muffin costs $1.50. On Monday, sales for muffins and bagels totaled $316.50. There were 25 fewer bagels sold than muffins. How many bagels were sold? How many muffins were sold?

14. The residents of a city voted on a proposal. There were 40,000 people who cast a vote. There were four times the number of people for the proposal than people against the proposal. How many people voted for the proposal? How many people voted against the proposal?

15. A total of $13.50 worth of quarters and dimes was in a parking meter. If the total number of coins was 72, how many of each coin were in the meter?

16. A basketball player made two-point field goals and three-point field goals for a total of 34 points. She made 16 shots. How many two-point field goals did she make? How many three-point field goals did she make?

17. People bought 528 tickets for the county fair. There were three times as many children at the fair as adults. How many adults were at the fair? How many children were at the fair?

18. Clarissa purchases three kinds of beads to make 5 necklaces for her friends. Multi-colored beads cost $0.20 each, sparkling beads costs $0.25 each, and regular beads costs $0.15 each. Clarissa buys a total of 50 beads. She buys the same number of multicolored beads as regular beads. How many of each kind of bead did Clarissa buy?

19. Casey invests $4000 in three mutual funds at 5%, 7.5%, and 6.25% interest. He invested $300 more at 5% than at 7.5%. How much did he invest at each rate if the total interest he earned was $246.25?

20. A quarterback gained 480 yards in a football game. He gained four times the number of yards by passing than he did by running. How many yards did he gain by passing the ball? How many yards did he gain by running the ball?

21. A collection of 120 coins consists of quarters, dimes, and nickels. There are five times more quarters than dimes. The value of the coins is $16.50. How many of each coin are there?

22. West Friendship School sold 500 tickets for a play. Tickets for adults cost $12 each, for senior citizens $8 each, and for children $4 each. The school sold 10 more senior citizen tickets than child tickets. The sales from the tickets totaled $4880. How many of each type of ticket did the school sell?

23. The local deli sold a total of 26 pounds of cheese, turkey, and salami at a time when cheese cost $1.99 per pound, turkey cost $2.49 per pound, and salami cost $1.89 per pound. The sales from cheese, turkey, and salami totaled $57.14. The deli sold twice as much turkey as salami. How many pounds of each were sold?

24. In a playoff game, a basketball player scored 25 points. He made a total of 14 three-point field goals, two-point field goals, and one-point free throws. He made the same number of two-point field goals as three-point field goals and one-point free throws combined. How many of each type did he make?

UNIT 3   Functions

Like an oven, a function turns inputs into outputs.

An oven is a machine that takes in uncooked food and turns it into cooked food. Similarly, a function is a mathematical machine that takes a number as its input and outputs another number. You could even use a function to describe the number of loaves of bread an oven makes over time.

Big Ideas

▶ In a function, every input has only one output, but different inputs may have the same output.

▶ In a family of functions, once you know the graph of the parent function, you can use transformations to graph related functions.

Unit Topics

▶ Foundations for Unit 3

▶ Function Basics

▶ Function Equations

▶ Absolute Value Functions

▶ Piecewise Functions

▶ Step Functions

▶ Function Operations

▶ Function Inverses

Foundations for Unit 3

Before you study functions, you should
know how to do the following:

▶ Represent a relation in a mapping diagram, a table, and a graph.

▶ Determine the domain and range from a given set of ordered
pairs, table, or mapping diagram.

▶ Determine the domain and range from a graph.

Relations, Domain, and Range

Definition

relation   **a mapping from one set, called the domain, to another set,
called the range** ·

The mapping described above results in a set of ordered pairs, so a relation
can also be defined as a set of ordered pairs. The *domain* is the set of all
input values, and the *range* is the set of all **output** values. Some ways of
representing a relation are through a list of the ordered pairs in the set, a
mapping diagram, a table, and a graph.

> **THINK ABOUT IT**
>
> A relation is a set whose
> elements are ordered pairs.
> The domain and range are sets
> whose elements are single
> values.

Example 1   Represent the relation $\{(-2, 3), (0, 3), (1, -1), (3, 3), (3, 3.5)\}$
in a mapping diagram, a table, and a graph. Identify the domain and range.

Mapping Diagram

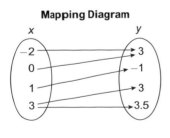

Table

x	y
−2	3
0	3
1	−1
3	3
3	3.5

Graph

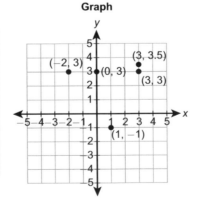

> **TIP**
>
> When you list the elements of
> a domain or range, write each
> different element only once.

The domain is $\{-2, 0, 1, 3\}$. The range is $\{-1, 3, 3.5\}$.

Problem Set A

Represent each set of ordered pairs in a mapping diagram, a table, and a graph.

1. $\{(-3, 1), (-1, 1), (0, 1), (1, 1)\}$

2. $\{(2, -1), (2, 0), (2, 3), (2, 4)\}$

3. $\{(5, 6), (6, 7), (7, 8), (8, 9), (9, 10)\}$

4. $\{(-2, -8), (0, 0), (1, 1), (2, 8)\}$

Determining the Domain and Range

The relation in Example 1 has a finite number of ordered pairs, and you can easily determine the domain and range. For some relations, though, listing all the ordered pairs is impractical or impossible. A relation can have a finite number of ordered pairs, yet have so many that listing all of them would be impractical. A relation can also have an infinite number of ordered pairs. For some relations, you can just look at an equation to determine its domain or range.

Example 2 Find the domain and range of each relation.

Ⓐ A relation with a finite number of ordered pairs:

$\{(x, y) \mid x \text{ is a positive integer less than } 1000 \text{ and } y = 2x\}$

This relation has 999 ordered pairs: (1, 2), (2, 4), (3, 6), …, (998, 1996), (999, 1998). The domain is $\{x \mid x \text{ is an integer and } 1 \leq x \leq 999\}$ and the range is $\{y \mid y \text{ is an even integer and } 2 \leq y \leq 1998\}$.

Ⓑ A relation with an infinite number of ordered pairs:

$\left\{(x, y) \mid y = \dfrac{1}{x}\right\}$

The domain is $\{x \mid x \neq 0\}$ because you cannot divide by zero. The value of y can be any number except 0, so the range is $\{y \mid y \neq 0\}$.

> **REMEMBER**
>
> The set-builder notation, $\{x \mid \ldots \ldots\}$, means "the set of all real numbers x such that …."
>
> So $\{x \mid x \geq -2\}$ is "the set of all real numbers x such that $x \geq -2$," or simply "the set of all real numbers greater than or equal to -2."

Problem Set B

Find the domain and range of each relation.

5. $\{(5, 6), (6, 5), (7, 4), (8, 3)\}$

6. $\{(-2, 2), (0, 2), (1, 2), (2, 2)\}$

7. $\left\{(x, y) \mid y = \dfrac{1}{x - 3}\right\}$

8. $\{(x, y) \mid y = \sqrt{x}\}$

9. $\{(x, y) \mid y = x\}$

Determining the Domain and Range Graphically

You may want to use graphs or equations to represent some relations with an infinite number of ordered pairs.

Example 3 Identify the domain and range of each relation.

The domain is the set of all x-values, and the range is the set of all y-values.

A

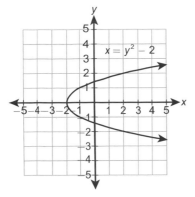

The left-most point on the graph is $(-2, 0)$, so the least x-value is -2. The arrowheads show that the graph extends without end to the right, so there is no greatest x-value. **Domain:** $\{x \mid x \geq -2\}$

The arrowheads show that the graph extends without end up and down, so there is neither a least y-value nor a greatest y-value. **Range:** {all real numbers}

B

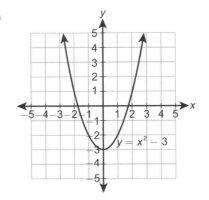

The arrowheads show that the graph extends without end both left and right, so there is neither a least x-value nor a greatest x-value. **Domain:** {all real numbers}

The lowest point on the graph is $(0, -3)$, so the least y value is -3. The arrowheads show that the graph extends up without end, so there is no greatest y-value. **Range:** $\{y \mid y \geq -3\}$

Problem Set C

Find the domain and range of each relation.

10.

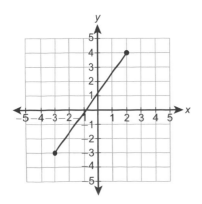

11.

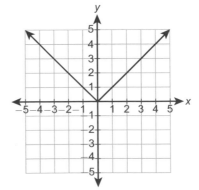

Function Basics

A mapping that pairs a member of one set to exactly one member of another set is a *function*.

Identifying Functions

> **DEFINITION**
>
> A **function** is a relation in which each member of the domain is assigned to exactly one member of the range.

When a relation is a function, the first coordinate is never used more than once. That is, each input can have only one output. However, the second coordinate may be used more than once. As a result, different inputs can have the same output.

THINK ABOUT IT

All functions are relations, but not all relations are functions.

Example 1 Determine whether the relation is a function. Explain your answer.

A {(6, 3), (1, −2), (0, 5), (5, −2), (4, 7)}

Solution Each *x*-value is assigned to only one *y*-value. The relation is a function. ∎

B {(1, 4), (3, −6), (1, 0)}

Solution The *x*-value 1 is assigned to both 4 and 0. The relation is not a function. ∎

C

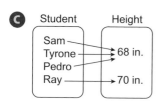

Solution Each student is assigned to only one height. The relation is a function. ∎

D

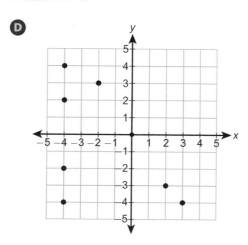

Solution The *x*-value −4 is assigned to four different *y*-values. The relation is not a function. ∎

Finding the Domain and Range of a Function

The domain of a function is the set of allowable inputs. The range is the set of possible outputs. When you look at ordered pairs, the domain is the set of first coordinates and the range is the set of second coordinates.

Example 2   Determine the domain and range of each function.

A $\{(1, -1), (2, -2), (3, -3), (4, -4)\}$ **B** $\{(7, 0), (2, 0), (-4, 0), (0, 0)\}$

Solution
D: $\{1, 2, 3, 4\}$, R: $\{-4, -3, -2, -1\}$ ■

Solution
D: $\{-4, 0, 2, 7\}$, R: $\{0\}$ ■

C

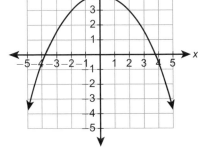

Solution   The graph exists for all x-values and for y-values less than or equal to 4. D: all real numbers, R: $\{y \mid y \leq 4\}$ ■

D

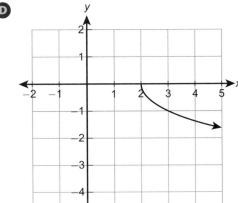

Solution   The graph exists for all x-values greater than or equal to 2 and for y-values less than or equal to 0. D: $\{x \mid x \geq 2\}$, R: $\{y \mid y \leq 0\}$ ■

Using the Vertical Line Test

When an x-value is paired with more than one y-value, the graph of the points lies on a single vertical line. The figure to the right demonstrates this. The x-coordinate 4 is paired with both -1 and 3.

DEFINITION

The **vertical line test** is a test used to determine whether a graphed relation is a function. If the graph is a function, then there is no vertical line that passes through the graph more than once.

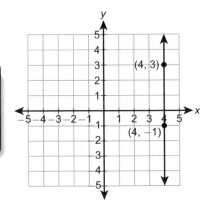

Example 3   Determine whether each relation is a function.

 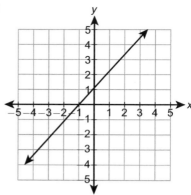

 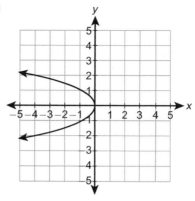

Solution   Any vertical line will intersect the graph only once. The relation is a function. ■

Solution   There are an infinite number of vertical lines that intersect the graph at more than one point. For instance, the lines $x = -1$ and $x = -3$ both intersect the graph at two points. The relation is not a function. ■

Graphing for Problem Situations

You can sketch a function graph that models a given problem situation.

Example 4   A bus travels a total distance of 10 miles from the first bus stop to the last stop. It takes the bus 4 minutes to travel 2 miles between each stop. The bus waits 2 minutes at each stop. There are five stops altogether.

Draw a graph that models the bus's distance over time, beginning when the bus starts to wait at the first stop.

Solution

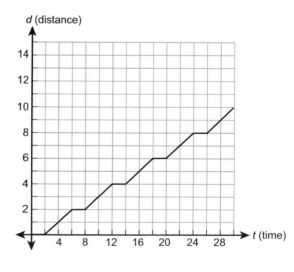

The flat parts of the graph correspond to the times the bus does not move. The slanted parts of the graph model a constant rate when the bus is moving between stops.

■

Problem Set

· ·

Determine whether the relation is a function. Explain your answer.

1. $\{(2, 5), (1, 4), (0, 7), (-3, 6), (-4, 10)\}$

2. $\{(1, -2), (2, -2), (3, -7), (4, 5), (2, -3)\}$

3.

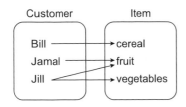

6.

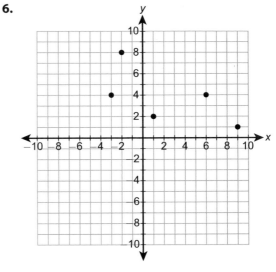

4.

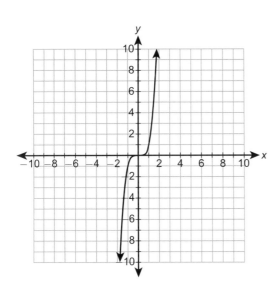

5.

7.

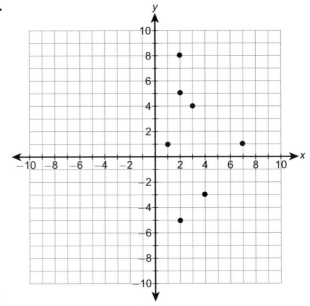

Determine the domain and range of the function.

8. $\{(0, 0), (1, 6), (8, 3), (-2, 4)\}$

12. $\{(-3, 0), (-5, 2), (-4, 7), (2, 0)\}$

9.

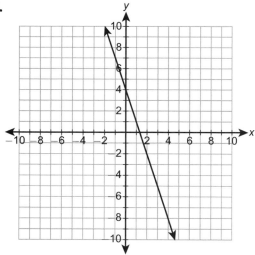

13.

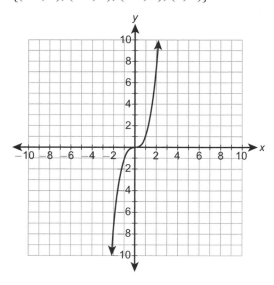

10.

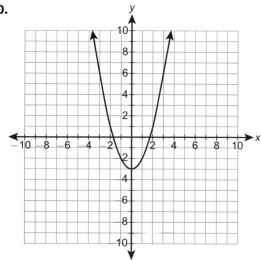

14.

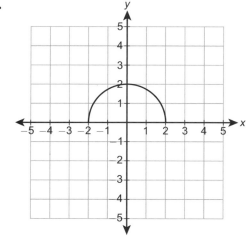

*15.   Challenge

11.

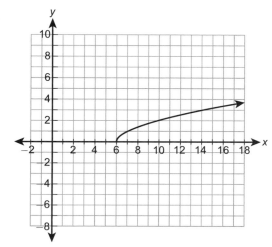

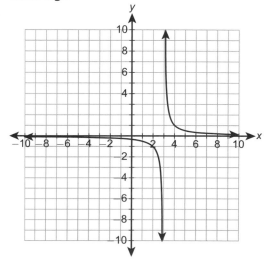

Determine whether the relation is a function.

16.

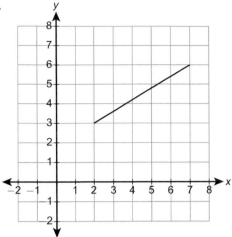

17.

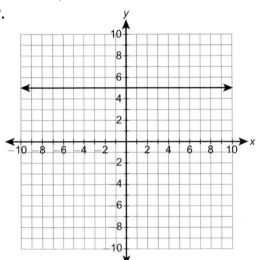

18.

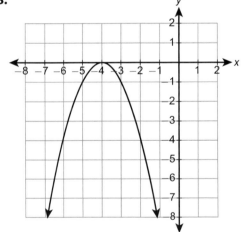

19.

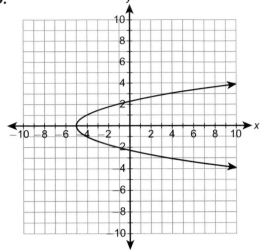

20.

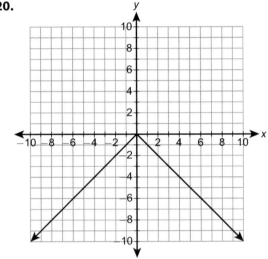

21.

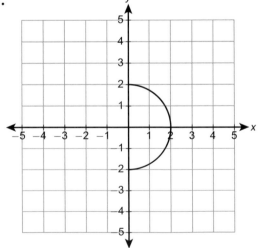

22.

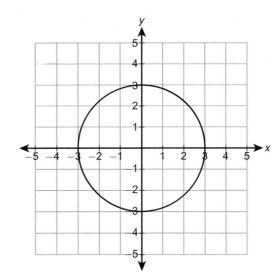

23.

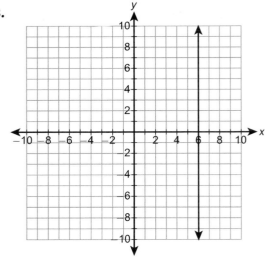

Draw a graph that represents each situation.

24. Amitesh is driving on the highway. From a traffic stop, it takes him 2 minutes to increase his speed to 50 mph. Amitesh then drives at a constant speed for 10 more minutes. Draw a graph that models the car's mph over time.

25. It takes Delilah 10 minutes to drag her sled up a 200-foot, snow-covered hill. She rests 1 minute at the top and then climbs onto her sled. Delilah slides down the hill in 20 seconds. Draw a graph that models Delilah's vertical distance from the bottom of the hill over time.

26. Ching Lan is driving a bumper car at a carnival. She accelerates to 10 mph in 2 seconds before crashing into a wall and losing power. Draw a graph that models Ching Lan's speed over time.

27. Dominick is walking from home to the mall, which is 2 miles away. Twenty minutes later and halfway to the mall, he realizes that he forgot to bring money, so he turns around, returns home, and then walks to the mall. Draw a graph that models Dominick's distance from home over time. Assume that he is walking at the same speed the entire trip.

28. Annika is swinging on a swing. When she climbs on the swing, the seat is 2 feet from the ground. Five seconds later, Annika is at her highest point when the seat is 15 feet from the ground. Draw a graph that models Annika's distance from the ground over time.

29. Seamus works at an assembly plant. For five days, his crew increases its productivity 10% per day. For days 6 and 7, his crew's productivity remains constant. For day 8 through day 10, it drops 5% per day. Draw a graph that models the crew's percent increase in productivity over time.

*30. **Challenge** Elsa plays piano in an orchestra. At the completion of an outstanding performance, the audience's applause gradually increases for 4 minutes. At 1 minute, 100 people are standing and applauding. At 4 minutes, 200 people are standing and applauding. Draw a graph that models the number of people applauding over time, from 0 minutes to 4 minutes. Use a parabolic model.

Function Equations

You can write a function described by an equation, such as $y = x^2$, in function notation.

There are two common ways to write $y = x^2$ as a function. One way is in the form $f: D \rightarrow R$, where D is the domain or input x, and R is the range or output x^2. The other way is to replace y with $f(x)$, which is read "f of x."

Function notations for $y = x^2$:

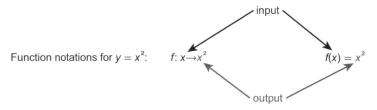

In the function notation above, f is the name of the function.

Using Function Notation

Example 1

A For $f(x) = 2x + 5$, find $f(1)$ and $f(3)$.

Solution Substitute 1 and 3 for x:

$$f(1) = 2 \cdot 1 + 5 = 7$$
$$f(3) = 2 \cdot 3 + 5 = 11 \blacksquare$$

B For $g: t \rightarrow -t$, find $g(5)$ and $g(-5)$.

Solution Substitute 5 and -5 for t:

$$g(5) = -5$$
$$g(-5) = -(-5) = 5 \blacksquare$$

Representing Functions as Graphs

Because functions are sets of ordered pairs, they can be represented by graphs.

Example 2   Graph the function $f(x) = 3x - 4$.

Solution

Step 1   Make a table of values.

x	3x − 4	f(x)
−1	3 · (−1) − 4	−7
0	3 · 0 − 4	−4
1	3 · 1 − 4	−1
2	3 · 2 − 4	2

Step 2   Plot the ordered pairs $(x, f(x))$.

Step 3   Connect the points.

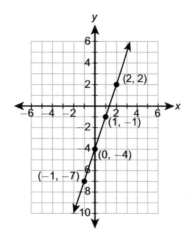

> **TIP**
>
> Only connect the points in the graph of a function if you know the general shape of the graph. In this case, you know the function is linear, so you connect the points with a line. If the function is not linear, you may need to find additional points and sketch a curve.

Finding the Domain and Range when Given a Function Equation

For some functions, you can look at an equation to determine its domain or range.

Example 3   For each function, determine the domain and range.

Ⓐ $f(x) = x - 4$

Solution   There are no restrictions on x-values because you can subtract 4 from any number. So the domain is the set of all real numbers. There are no restrictions on the $f(x)$ values, so the range is the set of all real numbers. ∎

Ⓑ $g(a) = a^2 - 3$

Solution   There are no restrictions on a-values because any number can be squared. So the domain is the set of all real numbers. But the square of any number is at least 0, so the least possible value of $g(a)$ is $0^2 - 3$, or -3. So the range is the set of all real numbers greater than or equal to -3. ∎

Ⓒ $h(t) = |t| + 1$

Solution   There are no restrictions on t-values because you can find the absolute value of any number. Therefore, the domain is the set of all real numbers. But the absolute value of any number is at least 0, so the least possible value of $h(t)$ is $|0| + 1$, or $+1$. So the range is the set of all real numbers greater than or equal to 1. ∎

Identifying Independent and Dependent Variables in Real-World Situations

In a function, the input is the **independent variable** and the output is the **dependent variable**. In $f(x) = 3x - 4$, the value of $f(x)$ depends on which value is chosen for x. In other words, the output depends on the input.

You can use functions to describe real-life situations. For example, the cost of tiling a room is a function of the size of the room. The independent variable is the size of the room. The dependent variable is the cost of tiling the room. It is dependent because the cost depends on the size.

Example 4 For each situation, determine which variable is the independent variable and which variable is the dependent variable.

A Mr. Gonzalez waters his lawn less often in the rainy season and more often in the dry season. The variables are frequency of watering and the season.

Solution The frequency with which Mr. Gonzalez waters his lawn depends on the season.
Independent variable: season
Dependent variable: frequency of watering ■

B Bananas cost $0.38 per pound. The variables are weight of bananas and cost.

Solution The cost depends on the weight of the bananas.
Independent variable: weight of bananas
Dependent variable: cost ■

C The plants that receive more sunlight are taller than those that receive less sunlight. The variables are height and amount of sunlight.

Solution The height of the plants depends on the amount of sunlight they receive.
Independent variable: amount of sunlight
Dependent variable: height ■

> **TIP**
> It is easy to remember that the input is the independent variable because both begin with *in-*.

> **THINK ABOUT IT**
> Many events in the physical world can be modeled by functions.

Problem Set

Evaluate each function for the given values.

1. If $f(x) = 7 - x$, find $f(6)$ and $f(8)$.

2. If $f: a \rightarrow a^2 - 3$, find $f(5)$ and $f(-5)$.

3. If $g: x \rightarrow \dfrac{4 - x}{x - 2}$, find $g(0)$ and $g(1)$.

4. If $g(t) = t^2 - t - 2$, find $g(2)$ and $g(-1)$.

5. If $h: x \rightarrow \dfrac{7 - x}{x + 3}$, find $h(7)$ and $h(2)$.

*6. **Challenge** If $f(x) = x^2 - 2x + 1$, find $f(a^2)$.

Draw the graph of each function.

7. $f(x) = 2x$

8. $f(x) = -3x - 3$

9. $f(x) = 0.5x + 1$

10. $f(x) = x^2 - 2x$

Determine the domain and range of each function.

11. $f(x) = 3x$

12. $f(m) = m^2$

13. $f(x) = x^2 - 4$

14. $a(x) = x^2 + 4$

15. $b(n) = n^3$

16. $p(x) = |x|$

17. $q(a) = |a - 5|$

18. $f(x) = |x| - 5$

19. $t(y) = \sqrt{y}$

*20. **Challenge** $f(x) = \dfrac{7}{x}$

For each situation, determine which variable is the independent variable and which variable is the dependent variable.

21. A tomato plant that gets the right amount of fertilizer yields more tomatoes than a plant that gets too much or too little fertilizer. The variables are number of tomatoes and amount of fertilizer.

22. People with master's degrees earn more money than people with bachelor's degrees, and people with bachelor's degrees earn more than people who did not graduate from college. The variables are educational level and income.

23. Valley High School's football team, which won 12 games, finished the season higher in the standings than Lakewood High School's team, which won 10 games. The variables are number of games won and place in the standings.

24. Britta studied for two hours for her mathematics test, but only one hour for her biology test. She received a 90 on her math test and an 88 on her biology test. The variables are amount of time spent studying and grade on the test.

25. A compact car gets more miles per gallon of gasoline than an SUV. The variables are number of miles per gallon and size of vehicle.

26. Critics write movie reviews before the release of a movie. More people see a movie that gets good reviews than a movie that gets mediocre or bad reviews. The variables are the quality of reviews and number of people who see a movie.

27. In science class, Monique observed that more sugar dissolved in a beaker of water when she heated the water. The variables are amount of sugar dissolved and temperature of the water.

28. A two-carat diamond costs more than a one-carat diamond. The variables are number of carats and cost of diamond.

29. A telephone call to someone who lives in another city costs more than a telephone call to someone who lives nearby. The variables are cost of a phone call and distance from the person being called.

30. A large horse has a longer stride than a small horse. The variables are size of the horse and length of the stride.

Absolute Value Functions

A **family** of functions is a group of functions with the same fundamental characteristics.

> **DEFINITION**
>
> An **absolute value function** is a function whose rule contains an absolute value expression.

The basic function in a family of functions is called the **parent function**. The parent function of the absolute value family of functions is $f(x) = |x|$. A table of ordered pairs and the graph of the function are shown below.

x	|x|	f(x)
−3	|−3|	3
−2	|−2|	2
−1	|−1|	1
0	|0|	0
1	|1|	1
2	|2|	2
3	|3|	3

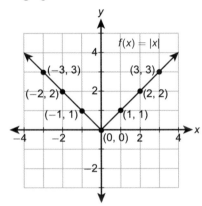

> **REMEMBER**
>
> The absolute value of a number is its distance from zero on the number line.

The graph is made up of two pieces—two rays that extend from a common vertex—forming a V-shape. All absolute value functions are V-shaped. Their vertex position, orientation, and width, however, can vary.

Graphing Absolute Value Functions by Plotting Points

Example 1   Graph $f(x) = |x − 4| − 3$.

Solution   Make a table of values and plot the ordered pairs.

x	|x − 4| − 3	f(x)
1	|1 − 4| − 3	0
2	|2 − 4| − 3	−1
3	|3 − 4| − 3	−2
4	|4 − 4| − 3	−3
5	|5 − 4| − 3	−2
6	|6 − 4| − 3	−1
7	|7 − 4| − 3	0

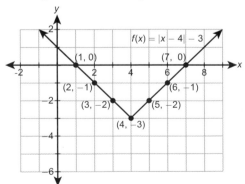

> **TIP**
>
> Choose x-values that allow you to determine the position of the vertex as well as both rays.

■

Translating Absolute Value Functions

Graphing an absolute value function by plotting points can take some guess-and-check work to determine which values in the domain you should use. In a family of functions, however, once you know the graph of the parent function, you can use **transformations** to graph related functions. Recall from geometry that a transformation is a one-to-one mapping between two sets of points. One type of transformation is a **translation**, or slide. You can translate a function horizontally, vertically, or both.

Absolute Value Function Graph Family: $f(x) = |x - h| + k$

When $f(x) = |x|$ is translated k units vertically and h units horizontally, the function becomes $g(x) = |x - h| + k$. The vertex shifts from $(0, 0)$ to (h, k).

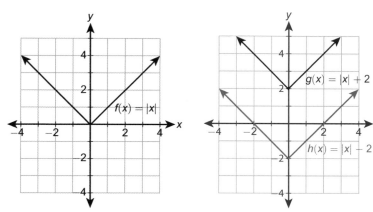

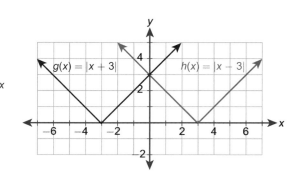

If k is positive, then the vertex is shifted up. If k is negative, then the vertex is shifted down.

If h is positive, then the vertex is shifted right. If h is negative, then the vertex is shifted left.

It may seem odd that a negative sign before h indicates a translation to the right and a positive sign indicates a translation to the left. The key is the minus sign in $g(x) = |x - h| + k$. For a translation 3 units to the left, $h = -3$ and $k = 0$ in the general form $g(x) = |x - h| + k$. In that case, the function is written $g(x) = |x - (-3)| = |x + 3|$.

Example 2   Sketch the graph of each function.

Ⓐ $g(x) = |x - 2|$

Solution   The graph is a horizontal translation of the parent function, 2 units to the right. You can write the function as $g(x) = |x - 2| + 0$; the vertex (h, k) is located at $(2, 0)$.

Ⓑ $h(x) = |x + 1| - 2$

Solution   The graph is a vertical and horizontal translation of the parent function. It is translated 1 unit left and 2 units down. You can write the function as $h(x) = |x - (-1)| + (-2)$; the vertex is located at $(-1, -2)$.

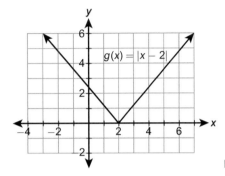

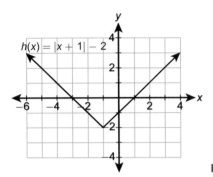

Describing Graphs of Absolute Value Functions

When the absolute value expression in the parent function $f(x) = |x|$ is multiplied by -1, the graph is reflected across the x-axis, making an upside-down V-shape. You can write this function as $g(x) = -1|x|$ or $g(x) = -|x|$.

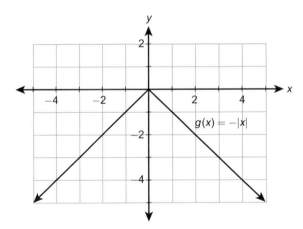

If the absolute value expression is multiplied by any factor other than 1 or -1, the graph becomes narrower or wider. For $g(x) = a|x|$, the graph becomes wider (or vertically compressed) if $0 < |a| < 1$ and narrower (or vertically stretched) if $|a| > 1$.

Compare the graphs of $g(x) = \frac{1}{4}|x|$ and $h(x) = 4|x|$ to $f(x) = |x|$.

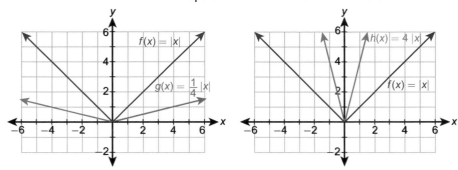

Example 3 Describe how the graph of each function differs from the graph of $f(x) = |x|$. Then determine the domain and range.

A $g(x) = 0.8|x|$

Solution Because $|a|$ is between 0 and 1, the graph will be wider than the graph of the parent function. The vertex remains at $(0, 0)$.

Domain: $\{x \mid x \in \mathbb{R}\}$ Range: $\{y \mid y \geq 0\}$ ∎

B $g(x) = 3|x - 8|$

Solution The graph is translated 8 units to the right. Because $|a| > 1$, the graph will be narrower than the graph of the parent function.

Domain: $\{x \mid x \in \mathbb{R}\}$ Range: $\{y \mid y \geq 0\}$ ∎

C $g(x) = -2|x| + 5$

Solution The graph is translated 5 units up. Because $|a| > 1$, the graph will be narrower than the graph of the parent function. Because a is negative, the shape of the graph is an upside-down V.

Domain: $\{x \mid x \in \mathbb{R}\}$ Range: $\{y \mid y \leq 5\}$ ∎

Finding the Equation of an Absolute Value Function

Example 4 Write the equation of the function graphed at right.

Solution The vertex is located at $(3, -2)$. Using the parent function $f(x) = |x|$ as a reference, the horizontal and vertical translations indicate that $h = 3$ and $k = -2$.

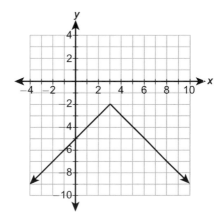

The graph, which moves up or down 1 unit for every horizontal move of 1 unit, is neither narrower nor wider than that of the parent function, so $|a| = 1$. Because the graph is upside-down, $a = -1$. This makes the equation $f(x) = -|x - 3| - 2$. ∎

Problem Set

Sketch the graph of each function.

1. $f(x) = |x + 1|$

2. $f(x) = |x + 3| - 1$

3. $f(x) = |x - 2| - 3$

4. $f(x) = |x + 4| + 2$

5. $h(x) = |x| + 5$

6. $h(x) = -|x - 1| + 2$

Describe how the graph of each function differs from the graph of $f(x) = |x|$.

7. $g(x) = 5|x|$

8. $g(x) = 2|x + 7|$

9. $g(x) = -0.2|x| - 1$

Identify the vertex of each function.

10. $f(x) = |x| - 2$

11. $f(x) = |x - 1|$

12. $f(x) = |x - 4| + 7$

13. $f(x) = 3|x + 5| - 1$

Write the equation of each function.

14.

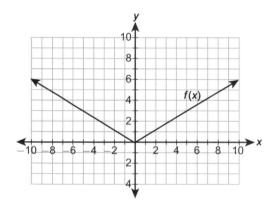

16.

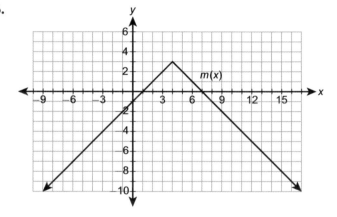

15.

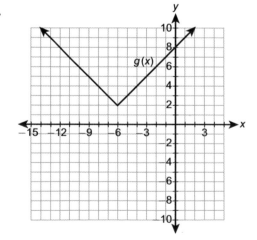

17.

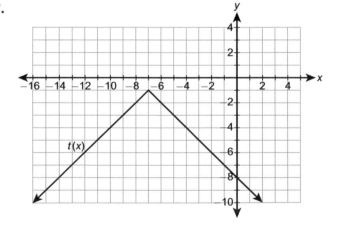

Write the function that results when translating $f(x) = |x|$.

18. 3 units left and 4 units down

19. 8 units right

20. 2 units right and 10 units up

21. 12 units left and flipped upside-down

Find the domain and range of each function.

22. $f(x) = 7|x|$

23. $f(x) = |x + 3| - 3$

24. $f(x) = -|x| + 5$

25. $f(x) = |x - 8|$

Solve.

*26. Challenge It takes you 3 seconds to climb down a 3-foot ladder that you are using to do a job. You immediately climb back up the ladder to finish the job. Let x represent time and y represent height. Write the equation of an absolute value function that models this problem.

*27. Challenge After resting for 1 minute, you walk up a 200-foot hill. You reach the top in 4 minutes. Without resting, you walk down the hill at the same rate. Let x represent time and y represent distance. Write the equation of an absolute value function that models this problem.

Piecewise Functions

Some functions, such as absolute value functions, can be defined in pieces.

The functions in the following examples are piecewise functions.

> **DEFINITION**
>
> A **piecewise function** is a function defined using different rules for different intervals of the domain.

Graphing a Special Piecewise Function

Example 1   Graph the piecewise function $f(x) = \begin{cases} -x \text{ if } x \leq 0 \\ x \text{ if } x > 0. \end{cases}$

Solution

Create a table of ordered pairs for the first piece in the function.

x	f(x)
−3	3
−2	2
−1	1
0	0

The domain of the first piece includes 0 because it is defined for $x \leq 0$.

Create a table of ordered pairs for the second piece in the function.

x	f(x)
1	1
2	2
3	3
4	4

The domain of the second piece includes all numbers greater than 0.

Plot the points from both tables. Since both pieces of the function are linear, connect the points of each piece with a ray, starting at (0, 0).

Together, the pieces of the graph form the graph of the absolute value function, $f(x) = |x|$.

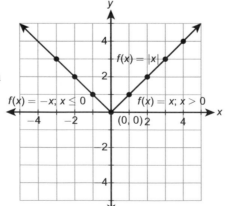

Writing an Absolute Value Function as a Piecewise Function

Example 2   Write the absolute value function $f(x) = |x + 4|$ as a piecewise function.

Solution   There are two pieces.

The piece on the left is a ray with a boundary point at $(-4, 0)$. Study the table of ordered pairs for points of that piece and determine a rule.

Each range value is 4 subtracted from the opposite of the domain value: $f(x) = -x - 4$.

The piece on the right is also a ray with a boundary point at $(-4, 0)$. Study the table of ordered pairs for points of that piece and determine a rule.

Each range value is 4 added to the domain value: $f(x) = x + 4$.

Put both rules together. Include the boundary point in only one of the pieces.

$$f(x) = \begin{cases} -x - 4 & \text{if } x \leq -4 \\ x + 4 & \text{if } x > -4 \end{cases} \; \blacksquare$$

x	f(x)
−7	3
−6	2
−5	1
−4	0

x	f(x)
−4	0
−3	1
−2	2
−1	3

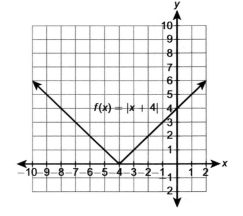

Graphing a Piecewise Function

Example 3   Graph the function $g(x) = \begin{cases} 2x & \text{if } x < 1 \\ 1 & \text{if } x = 1 \\ x + 3 & \text{if } x > 1. \end{cases}$

Solution   The domain is divided into three intervals.

For the interval $x < 1$, make a table of values. Although 1 is not included in this interval, use 1 as a value in the table. The point that has 1 as its x-coordinate will be a boundary for this section of the graph. Use an open circle when graphing the boundary point.

For the value $x = 1$, $g(x) = 1$, so graph the point $(1, 1)$.

For the interval $x > 1$, make a table of values. Again, 1 is not included in this interval, but use 1 as a value in the table and use an open circle when graphing the boundary point.

Graph the function.

x	g(x) = 2x
−2	2(−2) = −4
−1	2(−1) = −2
0	2(0) = 0
1	2(1) = 2

x	g(x) = x + 3
1	1 + 3 = 4
2	2 + 3 = 5
3	3 + 3 = 6
4	4 + 3 = 7

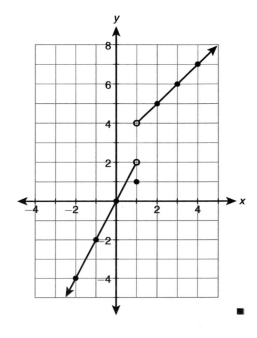

$\blacksquare$

Writing a Rule for a Piecewise Function

Example 4

Ⓐ Write a rule for the piecewise function at right.

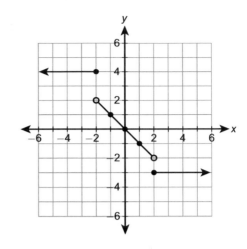

Solution The left piece is a horizontal ray that extends to the left without end from the point $(-2, 4)$. So it has a constant function value of 4, and the interval of domain values is given by the inequality $x \le -2$. The rule for this piece is $f(x) = 4$.

The center piece is a line segment that slants down from the point $(-2, 2)$ to the point $(2, -2)$. However, the open circles at $(-2, 2)$ and $(2, -2)$ indicate that these two points are not included in this piece of the graph. Therefore, the interval of domain values is given by the compound inequality $-2 < x < 2$. To find a rule for this piece, create a chart and look for a pattern.

x	−1	0	1
y	1	0	−1

REMEMBER

Use open circles for $<$ and $>$.
Use closed circles for $\le$ and $\ge$.

Because y is the opposite of x, the rule is $y = -x$, or $f(x) = -x$.

The right piece is a horizontal ray that extends to the right without end from the point $(2, -3)$. So it has a constant function value of -3, and the interval of domain values is given by the inequality $x \ge 2$. The rule for this piece is $f(x) = -3$.

Altogether, the rule for the function is $f(x) = \begin{cases} 4 \text{ if } x \le -2 \\ -x \text{ if } -2 < x < 2 \\ -3 \text{ if } x \ge 2 \end{cases}$. ∎

Ⓑ Write a rule for the piecewise function at right.

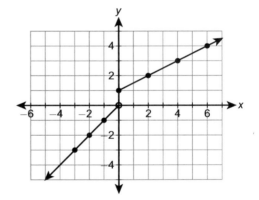

Solution The left piece is a ray that slants down to the left without end from the point $(0, 0)$, but it does not include $(0, 0)$. To find a rule for this piece, create a chart and look for a pattern.

x	−1	−2	−3
y	−1	−2	−3

The rule is $y = x$, or $f(x) = x$.

The right piece is a ray that slants up to the right without end from the point $(0, 1)$ and includes $(0, 1)$. Find a rule for this piece.

x	0	2	4	6
y	1	2	3	4

The rule is $y = \frac{1}{2}x + 1$, or $f(x) = \frac{1}{2}x + 1$.

The rule for the function is $f(x) = \begin{cases} x \text{ if } x < 0 \\ \frac{1}{2}x + 1 \text{ if } x \ge 0. \end{cases}$ ∎

Finding Function Values of a Piecewise Function

Example 5 Find $g(-5)$, $g(-3)$, $g(1)$, and $g(4)$ for the function g defined below.

$$g(x) = \begin{cases} x - 1 \text{ if } x < -3 \\ x^2 - 1 \text{ if } -3 \leq x \leq 3 \\ 2x + 1 \text{ if } x > 3 \end{cases}$$

Solution Because -5 is in the interval $x < -3$, $g(-5) = -5 - 1 = -6$; -3 is in the interval $-3 \leq x \leq 3$, so $g(-3) = (-3)^2 - 1 = 9 - 1 = 8$; 1 is in the interval $-3 \leq x \leq 3$, so $g(1) = (1)^2 - 1 = 1 - 1 = 0$; and 4 is in the interval $x > 3$, so $g(4) = 2 \cdot 4 + 1 = 8 + 1 = 9$. ∎

Problem Set

Write each absolute value function as a piecewise function.

1. $f(x) = |3x|$

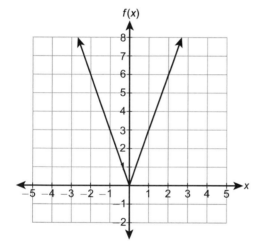

3. $f(x) = -2|x|$

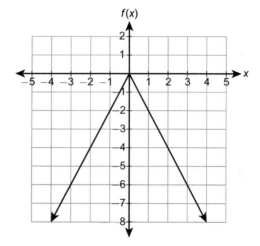

2. $a(x) = \left| \dfrac{x}{2} \right|$

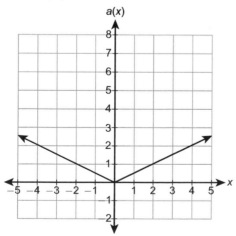

4. $x(t) = |t + 5|$

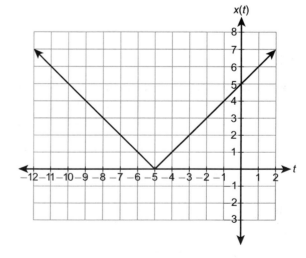

5. $r(x) = |x - 3|$

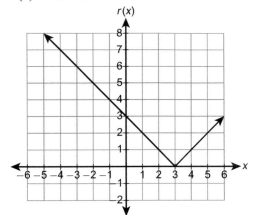

*6. Challenge $f(x) = -5|x + 1|$

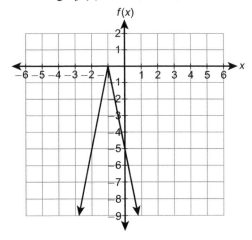

Write a rule for each piecewise function whose graph is shown.

7.

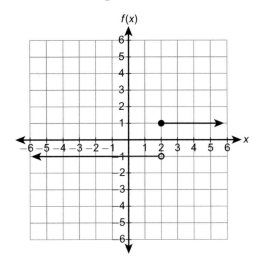

9.

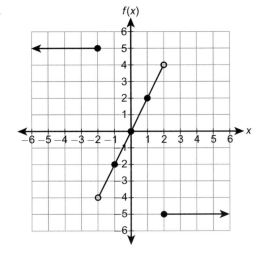

8.

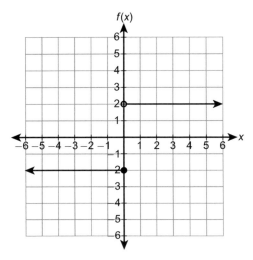

10.

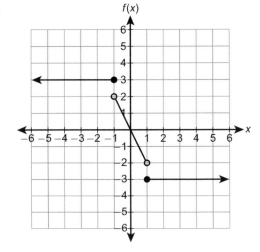

11.

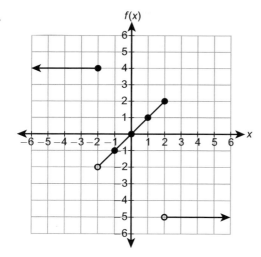

14.

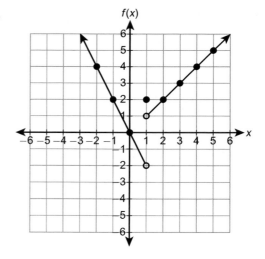

12.

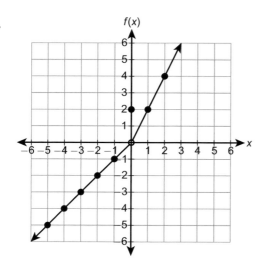

15.

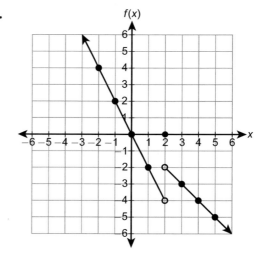

13.

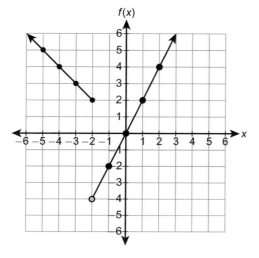

16.

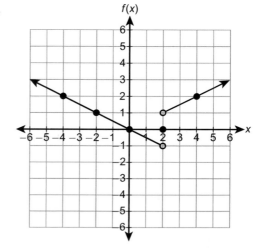

17.

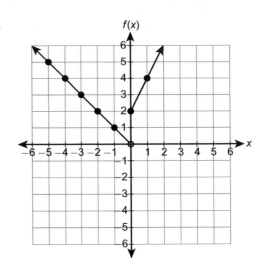

*18. Challenge

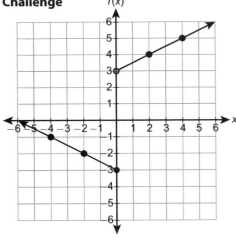

Graph each piecewise function.

19. $k(x) = \begin{cases} -2 \text{ if } x < 3 \\ 4 \text{ if } x \geq 3 \end{cases}$

20. $f(x) = \begin{cases} 3 \text{ if } x \leq -1 \\ x \text{ if } -1 < x \leq 1 \\ -4 \text{ if } x > 1 \end{cases}$

21. $f(x) = \begin{cases} -2x \text{ if } x \leq -1 \\ x \text{ if } x > -1 \end{cases}$

22. $p(x) = \begin{cases} -x \text{ if } x < 3 \\ 1 \text{ if } x = 3 \\ x \text{ if } x > 3 \end{cases}$

23. $f(x) = \begin{cases} x + 2 \text{ if } x < 0 \\ x \text{ if } x \geq 0 \end{cases}$

24. $C(x) = \begin{cases} \frac{1}{2}x - 1 \text{ if } x \leq 0 \\ -\frac{1}{2}x + 2 \text{ if } x > 0 \end{cases}$

Evaluate each piecewise function for the given values.

25. Find $f(-4), f(0),$ and $f(2)$.

$$f(x) = \begin{cases} -4 \text{ if } x \leq 0 \\ 3 \text{ if } x > 0 \end{cases}$$

26. Find $g(-2), g(-1), g(1),$ and $g(2)$.

$$g(x) = \begin{cases} 2 \text{ if } x \leq -1 \\ -3x \text{ if } -1 < x \leq 1 \\ -5 \text{ if } x > 1 \end{cases}$$

27. Find $P(-1), P(0), P(1),$ and $P(4)$.

$$P(x) = \begin{cases} 7 \text{ if } x \leq -1 \\ -1.5x \text{ if } -1 < x < 1 \\ 3.25x \text{ if } x \geq 1 \end{cases}$$

28. Find $f(-6)$ and $f(12)$.

$$f(x) = \begin{cases} -\frac{2}{3}x \text{ if } x < 0 \\ 1 \text{ if } x = 0 \\ \frac{2}{3}x \text{ if } x > 0 \end{cases}$$

29. Find $f(-4), f(-3), f(-2),$ and $f(2)$.

$$f(x) = \begin{cases} -x - 6 \text{ if } x \leq -3 \\ -x + 6 \text{ if } x > -3 \end{cases}$$

30. Find $w(-4), w(3),$ and $w(6)$.

$$w(x) = \begin{cases} x + 3 \text{ if } x \leq 3 \\ -\frac{1}{3}x - 3 \text{ if } x > 3 \end{cases}$$

Step Functions

One type of piecewise function is the step function.

As the name implies, the graph of a step function looks like a set of stairs. Each step is just a line segment with an open or closed circle on each end. Where the segments are placed and how long they are, as well as whether each endpoint is open or closed, depends on the particular function.

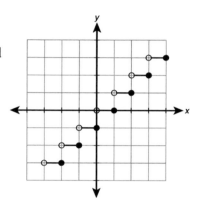

The Greatest Integer Function

The **greatest integer function**, denoted by $f(x) = \lfloor x \rfloor$, assigns the greatest integer less than or equal to each real number in an interval.

Example 1   Graph the function $f(x) = \lfloor x \rfloor$ over the interval $-3 \leq x \leq 3$.

Solution   Make a table of values to examine how the function behaves. The function will behave the same way in each unit interval.

x	$f(x) = \lfloor x \rfloor$
-2.6	-3
-2	-2
-1.3	-2
0	0
0.7	0
1	1
1.2	1
1.5	1
1.9	1
2	2

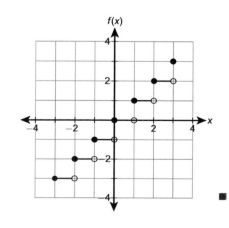

Greatest Integer Function Graph Family: $f(x) = a\lfloor x \rfloor + k$

Each change in the values of a or k results in a different transformation of the parent graph, $f(x) = \lfloor x \rfloor$.

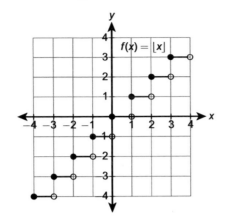

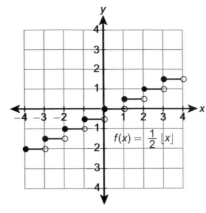

Changing only the parameter a causes the function to stretch or compress.

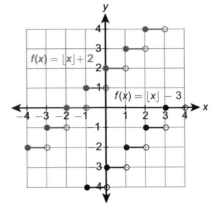

Changing only the parameter k causes the function to shift up or down the y-axis.

The Least Integer Function

The **least integer function**, denoted by $f(x) = \lceil x \rceil$, assigns the least integer greater than or equal to each real number in an interval.

Example 2 Write a rule for $f(x) = \lceil x \rceil$ over the interval $-2 \le x \le 2$.

Solution There are four segments. The left endpoint of each segment is graphed with an open circle; the right endpoint is graphed with a solid circle.

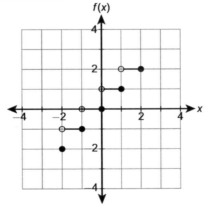

x	$f(x) = \lceil x \rceil$
-2	-2
-1.8	-1
-1	-1
-0.3	0
0	0
0.5	1
1	1
1.6	2
2	2

To every real number in the interval $(-2, -1]$, the function assigns the value -1. The rule for this piece is $f(x) = -1$. That is to say, -1 is the least integer greater than or equal to every number in the interval $(-2, -1]$.

The rule for the function is

$$f(x) = \begin{cases} -2 & \text{if } x = -2 \\ -1 & \text{if } -2 < x \le -1 \\ 0 & \text{if } -1 < x \le 0 \\ 1 & \text{if } 0 < x \le 1 \\ 2 & \text{if } 1 < x \le 2 \end{cases} \quad . \blacksquare$$

Least Integer Function Graph Family: $f(x) = a\lceil x \rceil + k$

Each change in the values of a or k results in a different transformation of the parent graph, $f(x) = \lceil x \rceil$.

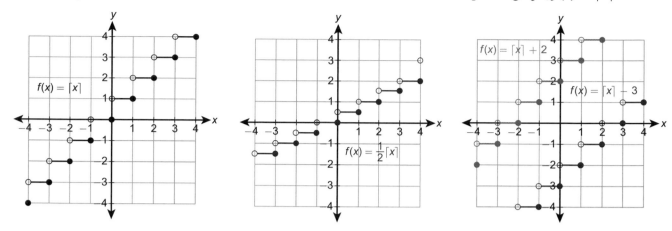

Changing only the parameter a causes the function to stretch or compress.

Changing only the parameter k causes the function to shift up or down on the x-axis.

Analyzing the Graph of the Nearest Integer Function

The **nearest integer function**, denoted by nint(x), assigns the nearest integer to each real number in an interval. To avoid confusion for numbers such as -1.5 and 3.5, the function assigns the nearest even integer to each input value. So nint(-1.5) $= -2$, while nint(3.5) $= 4$. The nearest integer for numbers in the interval $[-0.5, 0.5]$ is zero.

TIP

The nearest integer function is sometimes called the *round function*.

Example 3 Graph the function $f(x) = \text{nint}(x)$ over the interval $-2.5 \leq x \leq 2.5$. Explain the pattern of horizontal segments on the graph.

x	f(x) = nint(x)
-2.5	-2
-2.3	-2
-2.0	-2
-1.8	-2
-1.5	-2

Solution Study a table of values of the function for x in the interval $-2.5 \leq x \leq -1.5$. The value of the function for every real number in this interval, including the endpoints, is -2. The horizontal segment on the graph for this interval will include the endpoints -2.5 and -1.5.

x	f(x) = nint(x)
-1.5	-2
-1.3	-1
-1.0	-1
-0.8	-1
-0.5	0

Next study a table of values of the function for x in the interval $-1.5 \leq x \leq -0.5$. The values assigned to the endpoints of this interval are not the same as the value assigned to the other numbers in the interval. Therefore, the horizontal segment on the graph for this interval will not include the endpoints -1.5 and -0.5.

On the graph of the nearest integer function, the segments alternate between those including endpoints (solid circles) and those excluding the endpoints (open circles). This is a result of the rule to round each number to the nearest even integer.

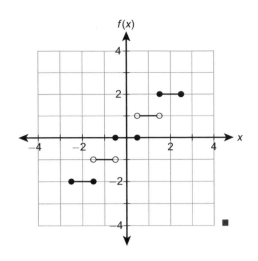

Problem Set

Evaluate each step function for the given values of *x*.

1. $x = 0, 1, 2, 2.2, 3$

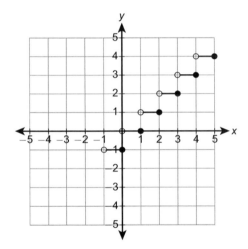

3. $x = -3.2, -3, -2, -1.5, 0$

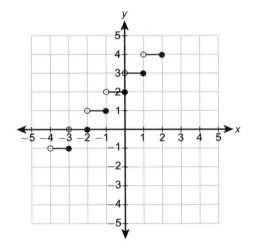

2. $x = -2, -1, -0.5, 1.3, 2$

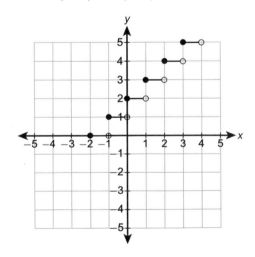

4. $x = 1, 1.4, 2, 2.5, 2.7$

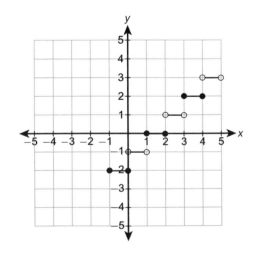

Graph the function over the given interval.

5. $f(x) = \lceil x \rceil,\ -3 \le x \le 3$

6. $f(x) = \text{nint}(x),\ -3.5 \le x \le 3.5$

7. $f(x) = \lfloor x \rfloor,\ -2 \le x \le 2$

8. $f(x) = \text{nint}(x),\ -1.5 \le x \le 1.5$

9. $f(x) = \lfloor x \rfloor,\ -4 \le x \le 4$

10. $f(x) = \lceil x \rceil,\ -4 \le x \le 4$

Write a rule for the given graph of a step function.

11.

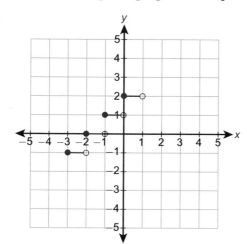

14.

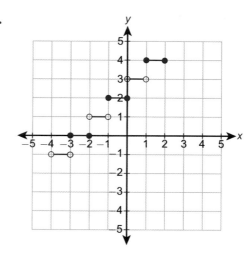

12.

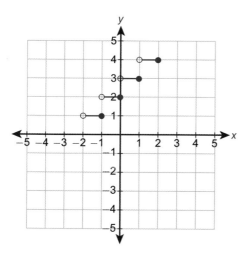

15.

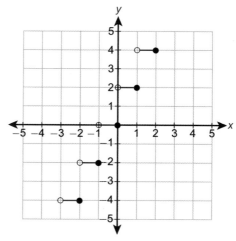

13.

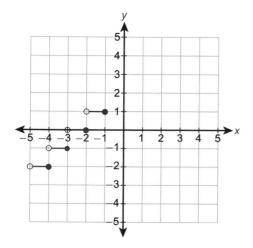

16.

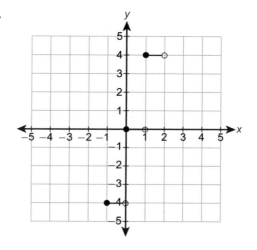

For each function, do the following:

A. Find the domain and range.
B. Describe the differences between the graph and its parent function.
C. Determine which other functions in this section have the same graph.

17. $f(x) = 2\lceil x \rceil$

18. $f(x) = \lceil x \rceil + 1$

19. $f(x) = \frac{1}{2}\lfloor x \rfloor$

20. $f(x) = \lceil x \rceil - 3$

21. $f(x) = 3\lceil x \rceil + 1$

22. $f(x) = \lfloor x \rfloor - 4$

23. $f(x) = 2\lfloor x \rfloor - 3$

24. $f(x) = \lceil x \rceil + 4$

25. $f(x) = 0.5\lfloor x \rfloor + 6$

***26.** **Challenge** $f(x) = -\lfloor x \rfloor$

***27.** **Challenge** $f(x) = \lfloor x \rfloor + 2$

Solve.

***28.** **Challenge** Determine how to make the steps of the greatest integer function longer and shorter.

***29.** **Challenge** A weight-loss program uses tokens to track calories. The table below lists calories consumed and assigned tokens. Graph and write a rule for this step function over the interval $0 < x \leq 300$.

Tokens	Calories
1	$0 < x \leq 100$
2	$100 < x \leq 200$
3	$200 < x \leq 300$

***30.** **Challenge** A teacher awards grades according to the table below. Graph and write a rule for this step function over the interval $70 \leq x < 100$.

Grade	Points
C	$70 \leq x < 80$
B	$80 \leq x < 90$
A	$90 \leq x < 100$

Function Operations

You can add, subtract, multiply, and divide functions just as you would with real numbers.

The Sum, Difference, Product, and Quotient of Functions

OPERATIONS WITH FUNCTIONS

Let f and g be two functions. The **sum, difference, product,** and **quotient of f and g** are as follows:

$(f + g)(x) = f(x) + g(x)$

$(f - g)(x) = f(x) - g(x)$

$(fg)(x) = f(x) \cdot g(x)$

$\left(\dfrac{f}{g}\right)(x) = \dfrac{f(x)}{g(x)}, g(x) \neq 0$

Example 1 Find the sum, difference, product, and quotient of $f(x) = x^2 - 4$ and $g(x) = x - 2$.

Solution

$(f + g)(x) = f(x) + g(x) = (x^2 - 4) + (x - 2) = x^2 + x - 6$

$(f - g)(x) = f(x) - g(x) = (x^2 - 4) - (x - 2) = x^2 - x - 2$

$(fg)(x) = f(x) \cdot g(x) = (x^2 - 4)(x - 2) = x^3 - 2x^2 - 4x + 8$

$\left(\dfrac{f}{g}\right)(x) = \dfrac{f(x)}{g(x)} = \dfrac{x^2 - 4}{x - 2} = \dfrac{(x + 2)(x - 2)}{(x - 2)} = x + 2, (x \neq 2)$ ∎

> **THINK ABOUT IT**
>
> The quotient of two functions is
> $\left(\dfrac{f}{g}\right)(x) = \dfrac{f(x)}{g(x)}, g(x) \neq 0.$
> If $g(x) = x - 2$, then 2 is not in the domain of the quotient.

The domain of a function that is the result of adding, subtracting, multiplying, or dividing functions is the intersection of the domains of the given functions, but with more restrictions as needed (for instance, to not allow division by zero). For the first three functions above, the domain is all real numbers. For the last function, the domain is all real numbers except 2.

Determining the Domain of a Function that Is the Result of Operations on Two or More Functions

Example 2 Determine the domain of $\left(\dfrac{f}{g}\right)(x)$ for $f(x) = \sqrt{1 - x}$ and $g(x) = \sqrt{9 - x^2}$.

Solution

$\left(\dfrac{f}{g}\right)(x) = \dfrac{\sqrt{1 - x}}{\sqrt{9 - x^2}}$

The domain of f is $\{x \mid x \le 1\}$. The domain of g is $\{x \mid -3 \le x \le 3\}$.

The intersection of these domains is $\{x \mid -3 \le x \le 1\}$.

So the domain of $\left(\dfrac{f}{g}\right)(x) = \dfrac{\sqrt{1-x}}{\sqrt{9-x^2}}$ is $\{x \mid -3 \le x \le 1\}$. ∎

Evaluating the Sum, Difference, Product, or Quotient of Two Functions

Example 3   If $f(x) = 6 - 2x$ and $g(x) = (x+1)^2$, find $(f - 2g)(-3)$.

Solution

Step 1 Find $(f - 2g)(x)$.

$$(f - 2g)(x) = (6 - 2x) - 2(x + 1)^2$$
$$= 6 - 2x - 2(x^2 + 2x + 1)$$
$$= 6 - 2x - 2x^2 - 4x - 2$$
$$= -2x^2 - 6x + 4$$

Step 2 Find $(f - 2g)(-3)$.

$$(f - 2g)(-3) = -2(-3)^2 - 6(-3) + 4$$
$$= -2 \cdot 9 + 18 + 4$$
$$= -18 + 18 + 4$$
$$= 4 \quad ∎$$

Composition of Functions

Another way two functions can be combined is by function composition.

> **DEFINITION**
>
> A **function composition** is a mapping in which each element of the range of one function is the domain of another function.
> If f and g are functions of x, the composition of f with g is denoted by $f \circ g$ and is defined as $f(g(x))$.
> The domain of $f(g(x))$ is the set of the domain values of g whose range values are in the domain of f.

THINK ABOUT IT

You can compose two functions f and g in two ways:

$$f \circ g \qquad g \circ f$$

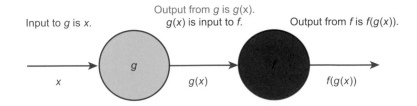

Input to g is x.

Output from g is $g(x)$.
$g(x)$ is input to f.

Output from f is $f(g(x))$.

x g $g(x)$ $f(g(x))$

Example 4   Let $f(x) = x^2 + 2$ and $g(x) = 5x$. Find each of the following:

Ⓐ $f \cdot g$

Solution

$$(f \cdot g)(x) = f(g(x))$$
$$= f(5x)$$
$$= (5x)^2 + 2$$
$$= 25x^2 + 2 \quad \blacksquare$$

Ⓑ $g \cdot f$

Solution

$$(g \cdot f)(x) = g(f(x))$$
$$= g(x^2 + 2)$$
$$= 5(x^2 + 2)$$
$$= 5x^2 + 10 \quad \blacksquare$$

Ⓒ $g \cdot f \cdot f$

Solution

$$(g \cdot f \cdot f)(x) = g(f(f(x)))$$
$$= g(f(x^2 + 2))$$
$$= g((x^2 + 2)^2 + 2)$$
$$= g(x^4 + 4x^2 + 4 + 2)$$
$$= 5 \cdot (x^4 + 4x^2 + 6)$$
$$= 5x^4 + 20x^2 + 30 \quad \blacksquare$$

Ⓓ $g \cdot g \cdot g$

Solution

$$(g \cdot g \cdot g)(x) = g(g(g(x)))$$
$$= g(g(5x))$$
$$= g(5 \cdot 5x)$$
$$= g(25x)$$
$$= 5 \cdot (25x)$$
$$= 125x \quad \blacksquare$$

> **THINK ABOUT IT**
>
> Compare $f \cdot g$ and $g \cdot f$ in Example 4:
> $$f \cdot g = 25x^2 + 2$$
> $$g \cdot f = 5x^2 + 10$$
>
> The composites $f \cdot g$ and $g \cdot f$ are *rarely* the same. So the composition of functions is *not* a commutative operation.

Evaluating a Composite Function for a Given Value

Example 5   Let $f(x) = 3x - 5$ and $g(x) = x - 7$. Find each of the following:

Ⓐ $(f \cdot g)(0)$

Solution

Step 1 Find $g(0)$.
$$g(0) = 0 - 7 = -7$$

Step 2 Find $f(-7)$.
$$f(-7) = 3 \cdot (-7) - 5 = -21 - 5 = -26 \quad \blacksquare$$

Ⓑ $(g \cdot g)(15)$

Solution

Step 1 Find $g(15)$.
$$g(15) = 15 - 7 = 8$$

Step 2 Find $g(8)$.
$$g(8) = 8 - 7 = 1 \quad \blacksquare$$

> **THINK ABOUT IT**
>
> You can also find the composite function, $f \cdot g$, and then evaluate it for $x = 0$.
> $$f \cdot g = 3x - 26$$
> $$(f \cdot g)(0) = -26$$

Finding the Domain and Range of Composite Functions

Example 6 Let $f(x) = 2^x$ and $g(x) = \frac{1}{x}$. Find the domain and range of $f \circ g$.

Solution

Step 1 Find the composition $f \circ g$.

$(f \circ g)(x) = f(g(x)) = f\left(\frac{1}{x}\right) = 2^{\frac{1}{x}}$.

Step 2 Find the domain and range of the composition function.

The domain of $f \circ g$ is all real numbers other than 0. The value 0 is not included because division by 0 is undefined. This domain is the same as the domain of the function g.

The range of $f \circ g$ is all real numbers greater than 0. This range is the same as the range of f. ■

Example 7 Let $f(x) = \frac{1}{x}$; $g(x) = \sqrt{x}$. Find the domain and range of $f \circ g$, and compare them to the domains and ranges of f and g.

Solution Find $f \circ g$: $(f \circ g)(x) = f(g(x)) = f(\sqrt{x}) = \frac{1}{\sqrt{x}}$

The domain of $f \circ g$ is all real numbers greater than 0. This is a restriction of the domain of g, which includes 0 because the function $g(x)$ is defined when $x = 0$. But the composition function is not defined for $x = 0$ because division by 0 is undefined.

The function $f \circ g$ produces only positive outputs, so its range is all positive real numbers. This is a restriction of the range of f, which includes all real numbers, both positive and negative, with the exception of 0. ■

> **REMEMBER**
>
> The number 0 is not considered to be either positive or negative. In the set of positive real numbers, 0 is not included.

Problem Set

For each problem, find the following rules and simplify:

A. $(f + g)(x)$
B. $(f - g)(x)$
C. $(fg)(x)$

D. $\left(\frac{f}{g}\right)(x)$

1. $f(x) = x^2 - 9, g(x) = x + 3$
2. $f(x) = x^2 - 1, g(x) = x - 1$
3. $f(x) = 2x^2 + x, g(x) = 2x + 1$
4. $f(x) = x^2 + 7x + 12, g(x) = x + 4$

Find the compositions, given $f(x)$ and $g(x)$:

A. $f \circ g$
B. $g \circ f$

5. $f(x) = x^2 + 1, g(x) = 4x$
6. $f(x) = 2x^2 + 5, g(x) = -3x$
7. $f(x) = -3x^2 - 4, g(x) = 2x$
8. $f(x) = 5x^2 - 6, g(x) = x^2$

Evaluate the indicated operations with $f(x)$ and $g(x)$.

9. $f(x) = 3 - 4x, g(x) = (x + 2)^2, (f - g)(-4)$

10. $f(x) = 4x - 5, g(x) = (x + 3)^2, (f + 3g)(2)$

11. $f(x) = 10 - 9x, g(x) = (x - 4)^2, (2fg)(-1)$

12. $f(x) = 3x + 1, g(x) = (x + 1)^2, \left(\dfrac{2f}{g}\right)(-3)$

Determine the domain of the function that is the result of the indicated quotient.

13. $\left(\dfrac{f}{g}\right)x, f(x) = \sqrt{1 - x}, g(x) = \sqrt{4 - x^2}$

14. $\left(\dfrac{f}{g}\right)x, f(x) = \sqrt{x - 2}, g(x) = \sqrt{x^2 - 4}$

15. $\left(\dfrac{g}{f}\right)x, f(x) = \sqrt{4 - x}, g(x) = \sqrt{16 - x^2}$

16. $\left(\dfrac{g}{f}\right)x, f(x) = \sqrt{x + 3}, g(x) = \sqrt{x^2 + x - 6}$

Evaluate each composite function.

17. $f(x) = 2x - 10, g(x) = x - 3$
   A. $(f \circ g)(0)$ **B.** $(g \circ g)(10)$

18. $f(x) = 3x + 2, g(x) = x + 10$
   A. $(f \circ g)(-1)$ **B.** $(g \circ f)(2)$

19. $f(x) = 9x + 1, g(x) = 5 - 2x$
   A. $(f \circ f)(0)$ **B.** $(g \circ g)(5)$

20. $f(x) = x^2, g(x) = 4x + 5$
   A. $(f \circ g)(-3)$ **B.** $(g \circ f)(3)$

Given $g(x)$ and $f(x)$, find a rule for $h(x) = (f \circ g)(x)$.

21. $g(x) = 2x - 4, f(x) = x - 4$

22. $g(x) = x^2 + 1, f(x) = x + 1$

23. $g(x) = \dfrac{3}{2}x - 2, f(x) = 3x - 2$

24. $g(x) = 9x^2 - 18, f(x) = 9x$

Determine the domain and range of $f \circ g$ and compare them to the domains and ranges of f and g.

25. $f(x) = 3^x, g(x) = \dfrac{4}{x}$

26. $f(x) = \dfrac{1}{3x}, g(x) = \sqrt{x}$

27. $f(x) = |x|, g(x) = \dfrac{1}{x}$

28. $f(x) = \dfrac{1}{x + 2}, g(x) = \sqrt{x + 1}$

Solve.

*29. **Challenge** Given $f(x) = 2x + 1$ and $g(x) = \dfrac{1}{2}x - \dfrac{1}{2}$, determine $(f \circ g)(x)$ and $(g \circ f)(x)$. What is the relationship between $f(x)$ and $g(x)$?

*30. **Challenge** Xavier owns a music store that sells CDs. CD sales this month were 20 more than three times sales for last month. Next month he hopes to double sales from this month.

   A. Write a function for this month's sales and a function for next month's sales.

   B. Write a composite function to represent the sales at the end of next month.

   C. To determine the money Xavier hopes to make next month, evaluate the composite if last month's sales were $2400.

Function Inverses

The additive inverse of 2 is -2. The multiplicative inverse of 2 is 0.5. What is the functional inverse of $f(x) = x^2$?

DEFINITIONS

The **inverse of a relation** interchanges the members of the ordered pairs of the original relation. The domain of the inverse relation is the range of the original relation. The range of the inverse relation is the domain of the original relation.

Two functions f and g that "undo" each other are called **inverse functions**. If you start with a value x, apply f, and then apply g, the result is the original value x. More precisely,

$$(f \circ g)(x) = x \text{ and } (g \circ f)(x) = x.$$

The inverse of a function f is denoted by f^{-1} ("f inverse"). For every pair of inverse functions, if $f^{-1} = g$, then $g^{-1} = f$.

REMEMBER

The notation f^{-1} does **not** mean "f raised to the negative 1 power." While this notation may seem confusing, it is the standard way of denoting inverse functions.

Finding the Inverse of a Function

Example 1   Find the inverse of each function. Then determine whether the inverse relation is a function. Find the domain and range of the inverse.

Ⓐ $f(x) = 5x - 3$

Solution

Step 1   Rewrite $f(x) = 5x - 3$ as $y = 5x - 3$. Exchange x and y. Then solve for y.

$$y = 5x - 3 \xrightarrow[\text{roles of } x \text{ and } y]{\text{Exchange the}} x = 5y - 3$$

$$x + 3 = 5y$$

$$\frac{x + 3}{5} = y$$

$$y = \frac{1}{5}x + \frac{3}{5}$$

Step 2 Use the vertical line test to determine whether the inverse is a function. The vertical line test shows that the inverse is a function.

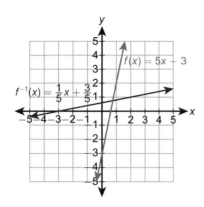

When a relation is linear and not vertical, the vertical line test is not needed. But if the relation is not linear, you will need to use the test.

Step 3 Determine the domain and range of the inverse function.

Domain: the set of all real numbers
Range: the set of all real numbers ∎

B $f(x) = x^2$

Solution

Step 1 Rewrite $f(x) = x^2$ as $y = x^2$. Exchange x and y. Then solve for y.

$$y = x^2 \xrightarrow[\text{roles of }x\text{ and }y]{\text{Exchange the}} x = y^2$$

$$y = \pm \sqrt{x}$$

Step 2 Use the vertical line test to determine whether the inverse relation is a function.

The function (in blue) and its inverse (in red) are shown on the graph.

The vertical line test shows that an x-value is paired with more than one y-value. The inverse relation is not a function.

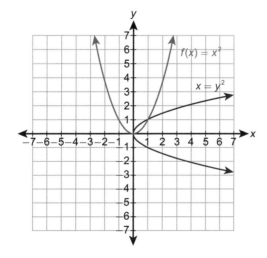

Step 3 Find the domain and range of the inverse relation.

Notice that the inverse relation is a reflection of the original function across the line $y = x$.

The domain of the inverse relation is $x \geq 0$, which is the range of f. The range of the inverse relation is the set of real numbers, which is the domain of f. ∎

Using Restricted Domains to Write the Inverses of Functions

As the previous example shows, not all functions have inverses that are functions, but you might be able to restrict the domain of the original function to create an inverse that is a function.

Example 2   If $f(x) = x^2$, $x \leq 0$, write the equation of $f^{-1}(x)$.

Solution   The domain of $f(x)$ is $x \leq 0$ and the range is $y \geq 0$. So the domain of $f^{-1}(x)$ is $x \geq 0$, the range is $y \leq 0$, and $f^{-1}(x) = -\sqrt{x}$. By the vertical line test, $f^{-1}(x)$ is a function.

> **TIP**
>
> The graphical representation of a relation and its inverse are reflections across the line $y = x$.

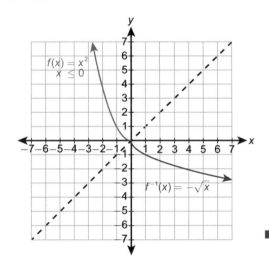

Verifying that Two Functions Are Inverses

By definition, if f and g are inverse functions, $(f \circ g)(x) = x$ and $(g \circ f)(x) = x$.

Example 3   Verify that $f(x) = 2x + 10$ and $g(x) = \frac{1}{2}x - 5$ are inverse functions.

Solution

$$
\begin{aligned}
(f \circ g)(x) &= f(g(x)) \\
&= f\left(\frac{1}{2}x - 5\right) \\
&= 2\left(\frac{1}{2}x - 5\right) + 10 \\
&= x - 10 + 10 \\
&= x
\end{aligned}
\qquad
\begin{aligned}
(g \circ f)(x) &= g(f(x)) \\
&= g(2x + 10) \\
&= \frac{1}{2}(2x + 10) - 5 \\
&= x + 5 - 5 \\
&= x
\end{aligned}
$$

Because $(f \circ g)(x) = x$ and $(g \circ f)(x) = x$, f and g are inverses of each other. ■

Evaluating Inverse Function Values

Example 4   If $g(x) = 2 + 5x$, find $g^{-1}(-3)$.

Solution   Rewrite the function as $y = 2 + 5x$. Exchange x and y. Then solve for y.

$$y = 2 + 5x \xrightarrow{\substack{\text{Exchange the} \\ \text{roles of } x \text{ and } y}} x = 2 + 5y$$

$$x - 2 = 5y$$

$$\frac{x - 2}{5} = y$$

$$y = \frac{1}{5}x - \frac{2}{5}$$

$$g^{-1}(x) = \frac{1}{5}x - \frac{2}{5}$$

$$g^{-1}(-3) = \frac{1}{5}(-3) - \frac{2}{5}$$

$$= -\frac{3}{5} - \frac{2}{5}$$

$$= -1$$

So $g^{-1}(-3) = -1$. ■

> **THINK ABOUT IT**
>
> Because $g^{-1}(-3) = -1$, $(-3, -1)$ is an ordered pair in g^{-1}. So $(-1, -3)$ must be an ordered pair in g.
>
> $$g(x) = 2 + 5x$$
> $$g(-1) = 2 + 5(-1)$$
> $$= 2 - 5$$
> $$= -3 \checkmark$$

Problem Set

Find the inverse of each function. Then find the domain and range of the inverse.

1. $f(x) = 2x + 4$

2. $f(x) = -\frac{1}{3}x + 5$

3. $f(x) = 3$

4. $f(x) = -8x + 5$

For each function:

A. Find and simplify a rule for the inverse.
B. Determine whether the inverse is a function.
C. Find the domain and range of the inverse.

5. $f(x) = 7x + 11$

6. $f(x) = 4$

7. $f(x) = x^2 - 3$

8. $f(x) = x^3$

9. $f(x) = x^2 + 1, x \geq 0$

10. $f(x) = 7 - x^2, x \leq 0$

11. $f(x) = \sqrt{16 - x^2}, 0 \leq x \leq 4, 0 \leq y \leq 4$

12. $f(x) = |x|, x \geq 0$

13. $f(x) = x^2 + 4, x \leq 0$

Verify that $f(x)$ and $g(x)$ are inverse functions.

14. $f(x) = -5x + 6, g(x) = -\frac{1}{5}x + \frac{6}{5}$

15. $f(x) = -\frac{3}{4}x + 2, g(x) = -\frac{4}{3}x + \frac{8}{3}$

16. $f(x) = -9x + 10, g(x) = -\frac{1}{9}x + \frac{10}{9}$

17. $f(x) = x^2 - 9, x \geq 0, g(x) = \sqrt{x + 9}$

18. $f(x) = x^2 + 8, x \geq 0, g(x) = \sqrt{x - 8}$

Evaluate the inverse of each function at the given value.

19. $g(x) = -2x + 7, g^{-1}(-2)$

20. $g(x) = \frac{1}{7}x - 1, g^{-1}(6)$

21. $g(x) = -10x + 4, g^{-1}\left(\frac{1}{10}\right)$

22. $g(x) = x^2 + 12, x \geq 0, g^{-1}(15)$

23. $g(x) = 2x^2 - 1, x \geq 0, g^{-1}(-2)$

Given $f(x)$, solve the inverse function equation.

24. $f(x) = \frac{1}{x + 4}, f^{-1}(x) = 3$

25. $f(x) = \frac{1}{x - 5}, f^{-1}(x) = -10$

26. $f(x) = -6x + 3, f^{-1}(x) = 2$

27. $f(x) = \frac{1}{3x - 19}, f^{-1}(x) = 5$

28. $f(x) = \frac{-2}{4x - 3}, f^{-1}(x) = -1$

Solve.

*29. **Challenge** To determine the area of a circle, given the radius, you use the formula $A = \pi r^2$. If the area of the earth is approximately 80,894,451 square kilometers, use an inverse function to find the earth's radius.

*30. **Challenge** To convert a Fahrenheit temperature to a Celsius temperature, you use the formula $C = \frac{5}{9}(F - 32)$. If the temperature is 35°C, use an inverse function to find the corresponding Fahrenheit temperature.

UNIT 4 Inequalities

A painter mixes the desired amount of each paint color.

A painter has a limited amount of white paint, dark blue paint, and light blue paint. Inequalities help us model situations that have constraints such as supply or time.

Big Ideas

· ·

▶ You can use an inequality symbol, interval notation, or a graph to represent an inequality.

▶ Just as solutions to an equation are those values that make the equation true, the solutions of an inequality are the numbers that make the inequality statement true.

Unit Topics

· ·

▶ Foundations for Unit 4

▶ Inequalities in One Variable

▶ Compound Inequalities

▶ Absolute Value Inequalities

▶ Inequalities in Two Variables

▶ Systems of Linear Inequalities

▶ Linear Programming

Foundations for Unit 4

Before you study inequalities, you should know how to do the following:

▶ Determine whether a given ordered pair makes an open sentence true.

▶ Graph an inequality on a number line.

▶ Write an inequality in one variable, given the graph.

Open Sentences

Definitions

inequality	**a statement formed by placing one of the inequality symbols $<$, $>$, $\leq$, $\geq$, or $\neq$ between two expressions**
open sentence	**an equation or inequality that contains one or more variables**

Example 1 Which of the following ordered pairs make the open sentence $2x - 3y > 6$ true?

Ⓐ $(1, 2)$

$$2x - 3y > 6$$
$$2 \cdot 1 - 3 \cdot 2 \overset{?}{>} 6$$
$$2 - 6 \overset{?}{>} 6$$
$$-4 \not> 6$$

Because -4 is not greater than 6, $(1, 2)$ does not make the open sentence true.

Ⓑ $(6, 1)$

$$2x - 3y > 6$$
$$2 \cdot 6 - 3 \cdot 1 \overset{?}{>} 6$$
$$12 - 3 \overset{?}{>} 6$$
$$9 > 6 \checkmark$$

Because 9 is greater than 6, $(6, 1)$ makes the open sentence true.

Ⓒ $(3, -4)$

$$2x - 3y > 6$$
$$2 \cdot 3 - 3 \cdot (-4) \overset{?}{>} 6$$
$$6 + 12 \overset{?}{>} 6$$
$$18 > 6 \checkmark$$

Because 18 is greater than 6, $(3, -4)$ makes the open sentence true.

Problem Set A

Determine whether the open sentence is true for the given ordered pair.

1. $3x + y < 6; (2, -2)$

2. $y \geq x + 4; (3, 8)$

3. $x - 3 > 2y; (3, 5)$

4. $-x + y \leq -\frac{1}{2}; (-1, 3)$

5. $x + y \geq 3; (2, 1)$

6. $y < 2x - 3; (4.2, 5.7)$

7. $\frac{3}{4}x < 7 - y; (3, -6)$

8. $x - 3y < 5; (1, -1)$

9. $4x - 3y \geq -2; \left(7, \frac{2}{3}\right)$

10. $y > 5 - 2.6x; (-1, -3)$

Graphing an Inequality on a Number Line

Example 2   Graph each inequality on a number line.

A $x > 3$

Use an open circle at the endpoint because 3 is not included in the set.

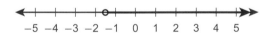

THINK ABOUT IT

An inequality that uses $<$ or $>$ can be called a *strict inequality*. An inequality that uses $\leq$ or $\geq$ can be called a *nonstrict inequality*.

B $x \leq 0$

Use a closed circle at the endpoint because 0 is included in the set.

C $x > -1.5$

Use an open circle at the endpoint because -1.5 is not included in the set.

Problem Set B

Graph each inequality on a number line.

11. $x > 1$

12. $x \geq -1.5$

13. $x \leq -2$

14. $x < 5$

15. $x \geq 0$

16. $x < -3$

17. $x \leq 0$

18. $x + 5 \leq 0$

19. $x - 4 > 0$

20. $x + 2 > 0$

Writing an Inequality in One Variable for a Given Graph

You can determine inequalities represented by graphs on a number line.

Example 3   Write an inequality represented by each graph.

Ⓐ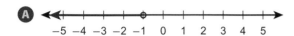

The graph is unbounded to the left. It is a ray pointing toward "negative infinity." The open circle indicates that -1 *is not* included in the set. $x < -1$

Ⓑ

The graph is unbounded to the right. It is a ray pointing toward "positive infinity." The closed circle indicates that 6 *is* included in the set. $x \geq 6$

Problem Set C

Write an inequality represented by each graph.

21.
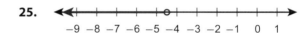

24.

22.

25.

23.

26.

Inequalities in One Variable

You can represent an inequality by using an inequality symbol, interval notation, or a graph.

> **DEFINITIONS**
>
> A **bounded interval** is the set of all real numbers between two numbers, called **endpoints**; the endpoints may or may not be included.
>
> An **unbounded interval** is the set of all real numbers on one side of a number, called an **endpoint**; the endpoint may or may not be included.

A **bounded closed interval** includes both endpoints.

This bounded closed interval is the set of all real numbers between -2 and 2, *including* both -2 and 2.

A **bounded open interval** does not include either endpoint.

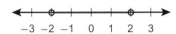

This bounded open interval is the set of all real numbers between -2 and 2, *excluding* both -2 and 2.

A **bounded half-open interval** includes one and only one endpoint.

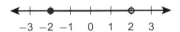

This bounded half-open interval is the set of all real numbers between -2 and 2, *including* -2 but *excluding* 2.

Interval Notation

A simple inequality using $<$, $>$, $\leq$, or $\geq$ indicates an unbounded interval.

In interval notation, a bracket means the endpoint is included, and a parenthesis means the endpoint is not included.

Interval notation for $x > 4$ is $x \in (4, \infty)$. The ∞ symbol is read "positive infinity," and it means that the interval is unbounded to the right.

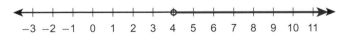

Interval notation for $x \leq 1$ is $x \in (-\infty, 1]$. The $-\infty$ symbol is read "negative infinity," and it means that the interval is unbounded to the left.

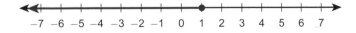

The table below shows the four cases of unbounded intervals.

Inequality Notation	Graph	Interval Notation
$x > a$		$x \in (a, \infty)$
$x \geq a$		$x \in [a, \infty)$
$x < a$		$x \in (-\infty, a)$
$x \leq a$		$x \in (-\infty, a]$

In interval notation, the set of all real numbers is $(-\infty, \infty)$.

Example 1   Write each in interval notation, and then graph.

A $x > 3$

Solution   Interval notation for $x > 3$ is $x \in (3, \infty)$. The interval is unbounded to the right, and does not include the left endpoint.

B $m \leq 0$

Solution   Interval notation for $m \leq 0$ is $m \in (-\infty, 0]$. The interval is unbounded to the left, and includes the right endpoint.

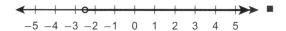

C $t > -2.5$

Solution   Interval notation for $t > -2.5$ is $t \in (-2.5, \infty)$. The interval is unbounded to the right, and does not include the left endpoint.

> **REMEMBER**
>
> The symbol $\in$ is read "is an element of."

> **TIP**
>
> In interval notation, always put the lesser number on the left.

> **TIP**
>
> In interval notation, you can never put a bracket next to an infinity symbol because infinity is not a number that can be included in an interval.

Writing Interval Notation for a Given Graph

Example 2 Write an inequality represented by each graph in interval notation.

A

Solution The graph is unbounded to the left. It is a ray pointing toward "negative infinity." The open circle indicates that -1 is not included in the set. $x \in (-\infty, -1)$. ∎

B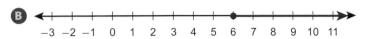

Solution The graph is unbounded to the right. It is a ray pointing toward "positive infinity." The closed circle indicates that 6 is included in the set. $x \in [6, \infty)$. ∎

> **THINK ABOUT IT**
>
> The symbols ∞ and $-\infty$ do not denote real numbers. They simply denote unbounded intervals.

Solving an Inequality in One Variable with a Restricted Domain

When you solve inequalities, the domain of the variable may be whole numbers, integers, or real numbers.

Example 3 Solve each inequality over the domain of whole numbers. Graph the solution set.

A $\frac{x}{2} - 1 \leq 1$

Solution Solve an inequality as you would solve an equation, but reverse the inequality sign when you multiply or divide by a negative number.

$\frac{x}{2} - 1 \leq 1$ Original inequality

$\frac{x}{2} \leq 2$ Add 1 to both sides.

$x \leq 4$ Multiply both sides by 2.

$x \in \{0, 1, 2, 3, 4\}$

B $-2 < 4 - a$

Solution

$-2 < 4 - a$ Original inequality

$-6 < -a$ Subtract 4 from both sides.

$\frac{-6}{-1} > \frac{-1 \cdot a}{-1}$ Divide both sides by -1, reversing the inequality sign.

$6 > a$

$a \in \{0, 1, 2, 3, 4, 5\}$

Example 4 Solve each inequality over the domain of integers. Graph the solution set.

(A) $\frac{n}{3} + 3 > 4$

Solution

$\frac{n}{3} + 3 > 4$ Original inequality

$\frac{n}{3} > 1$ Subtract 3 from both sides.

$n > 3$ Multiply both sides by 3.

$n \in \{4, 5, 6, ...\}$

The graph is the set of points with coordinates that are integers greater than 3.

(B) $-7x \geq 3 - 2x$

Solution

$-7x \geq 3 - 2x$ Original inequality

$-5x \geq 3$ Add $2x$ to both sides.

$\frac{-5x}{-5} \leq \frac{3}{-5}$ Divide both sides by -5, reversing the inequality sign.

$x \leq -\frac{3}{5}$

$x \in \{..., -3, -2, -1\}$

The graph is the set of points with coordinates that are integers less than or equal to $-\frac{3}{5}$.

Example 5 Solve each inequality over the domain of real numbers. Graph the solution set.

(A) $x + 6 \geq 3(x + 1) - 11$

Solution

$x + 6 \geq 3(x + 1) - 11$ Original inequality

$x + 6 \geq 3x + 3 - 11$ Distribute 3.

$x + 6 \geq 3x - 8$

$x + 14 \geq 3x$ Add 8 to both sides.

$14 \geq 2x$ Subtract x from both sides.

$7 \geq x$ Divide both sides by 2.

$x \in (-\infty, 7]$

> **REMEMBER**
>
> $7 \geq x$ is the same as $x \leq 7$.

B $-9 - 3x > 3 - 5x$

Solution

$-9 - 3x > 3 - 5x$	Original inequality
$-3x > 12 - 5x$	Add 9 to both sides.
$2x > 12$	Add $5x$ to both sides.
$x > 6$	Divide both sides by 2.

$x \in (6, \infty)$

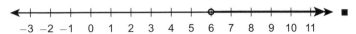

Problem Set

Write each inequality in interval notation.

1. $t \geq 2$

2. $x \leq -1$

3. $x < 5$

4. $c > -3.4$

Use interval notation to write the inequality represented by each graph.

5.

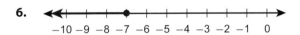

8.

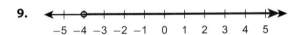

6.

9.

7.

Solve and graph the solution over each domain:

A. Reals
B. Integers
C. Whole numbers

10. $4 > x + 2$

11. $-8 < 2 - b$

12. $\frac{x}{3} + 2 \leq 5$

13. $6 \geq p - 1$

14. $9 < -x + 3$

15. $\frac{x}{4} + 1 \geq 2$

16. $-5x > 2 - 4x$

17. $\frac{t}{2} - 3 < 2$

18. $-4q \leq 5q + 5$

19. $-8x > -2x - 13$

20. $x + 4 \geq 2(x - 1) - 3$

21. $-8h - 2h > -1 - 4h$

22. $x + 10 < 4(x + 2) - 9$

23. $x - 5 \geq -2(x - 3) + 1$

24. $-10 - 5t \leq 4 - 7t$

Solve.

*25. Challenge Tien is marking off a rectangular plot of land to use as a garden. The length of the garden will be 4 meters more than three times the garden's width. The perimeter must be less than 100 meters. What is the width of Tien's garden?

*26. Challenge Santiago is 4 years younger than half of his father's age. In 18 years, Santiago will be younger than his mother is now. Santiago's mother is 2 years older than his father. How old is Santiago's father?

Compound Inequalities

When two statements are joined, they form a
compound statement.

DEFINITIONS

A **conjunction** is a compound statement that uses the word *and*.
A **disjunction** is a compound statement that uses the word *or*.
A **compound inequality** is a pair of inequalities joined by the word *and*
or the word *or*. A compound inequality is a type of compound statement.

	Examples
Conjunction	$x < 0$ and $x \geq -3$
Disjunction	$x = 0$ or $x = 5$
	$x > 0$ or $x < 23$

Conjunction and Inequalities

The solution set of a conjunction inequality is the set of all numbers that
satisfy both inequalities.

Example 1   Graph each compound inequality and then express it in
interval notation.

	Graph	Interval Notation
Ⓐ $x > 2$ and $x \leq 7$ (also written $2 < x \leq 7$)	 This is the set of all numbers between 2 and 7, not including 2 but including 7.	$x \in (2, 7]$ ∎
Ⓑ $x > 5$ and $x > 7$	 If a number is both greater than 5 and greater than 7, then it must be greater than 7.	$x \in (7, \infty)$ ∎
Ⓒ $x > 0$ and $x < -2$	 There is no number that is both greater than 0 and less than -2.	There is no interval. The solution set is $\varnothing$, the empty set. ∎

The four general cases for conjunction inequalities, such as the one in Example 1A above, are shown in the following table.

<table>
<tr><th>Inequality Notation</th><th>Graph</th><th>Interval Notation</th></tr>
<tr><td>$a < x < b$</td><td></td><td>$x \in (a, b)$</td></tr>
<tr><td>$a \leq x \leq b$</td><td></td><td>$x \in [a, b]$</td></tr>
<tr><td>$a < x \leq b$</td><td></td><td>$x \in (a, b]$</td></tr>
<tr><td>$a \leq x < b$</td><td></td><td>$x \in [a, b)$</td></tr>
</table>

> **REMEMBER**
>
> An *open interval* has neither endpoint included, a *closed interval* has both endpoints included, and a *half-open interval* (also called a *half-closed interval*) has one endpoint included.

Disjunction and Inequalities

The solution set of a disjunction inequality is the set of all numbers that satisfy either or both inequalities.

Example 2 Graph each compound inequality, and then express it in interval notation.

<table>
<tr><th></th><th>Graph</th><th>Interval Notation</th></tr>
<tr><td>**A** $x \leq -1$ or $x > 3$</td><td>

This is the set of all numbers that are either less than or equal to -1 or greater than 3.</td><td>$x \in (-\infty, -1] \cup$

$x \in (3, \infty)$ ∎</td></tr>
<tr><td>**B** $t > 4$ or $t > 9$</td><td>

The set of all numbers that are either greater than 4 or greater than 9 is just the set of all numbers that are greater than 4.</td><td>$t \in (4, \infty)$ ∎</td></tr>
<tr><td>**C** $z > -2$ or $z < 1$</td><td>

The set of all numbers that are either greater than -2 or less than 1 is the set of all real numbers.</td><td>$z \in (-\infty, \infty)$ ∎</td></tr>
</table>

Writing a Compound Inequality and Interval Notation for a Given Graph

Example 3 For each graph, write a compound inequality and interval notation.

A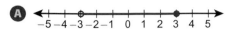

Solution This is the set of numbers between -3 and 3, excluding -3 but including 3.

Inequality: $-3 < x \le 3$
Interval Notation: $x \in (-3, 3]$ ∎

B

Solution This is the set of numbers that are either less than 1 or greater than 5.

Inequality: $x < 1$ or $x > 5$
Interval Notation:
  $x \in (-\infty, 1) \cup (5, \infty)$ ∎

Solving and Graphing a Compound Inequality in One Variable

Example 4 Solve each compound inequality. Graph the solution set.

A $5 + x < 7$ or $-2x \le -10$

Solution Solve each inequality separately.

First inequality	$5 + x < 7$ or $-2x \le -10$	Second inequality
Subtract 5 from both sides.	$x < 2$ or $x \ge 5$	Divide both sides by -2, reversing the inequality sign.

 ∎

B $3x - 1 \ge 14$ and $6x \le 48$

Solution Solve each inequality separately.

$$3x - 1 \ge 14 \text{ and } 6x \le 48$$

Add 1 to both sides.	$3x \ge 15$ and $x \le 8$	Divide both sides by 6.
Divide both sides by 3.	$x \ge 5$ and $x \le 8$	

 ∎

C $4 \le 2n + 10 \le 18$

Solution

$4 \le 2n + 10 \le 18$	Original inequality
$-6 \le 2n \le 8$	Subtract 10 from all expressions.
$-3 \le n \le 4$	Divide all expressions by 2.

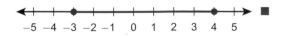 ∎

Problem Set

Graph the conjunction inequality and write it using interval notation.

1. $x > 3$ and $x \leq 6$

2. $t > 1$ and $t > 4$

3. $x > -1$ and $x < -3$

4. $0 < g < 5$

5. $x < 6$ and $x < 5$

6. $q \geq 9$ and $q < 2$

Graph the disjunction inequality and write it using interval notation.

7. $r \leq 2$ or $r \geq 5$

8. $x > 1$ or $x > 7$

9. $m \geq -3$ or $m < 2$

10. $x > 0$ or $x < -1$

11. $y > -3$ or $y > 4$

12. $d < 6$ or $d \geq 1$

Write an inequality and interval notation for each graph.

13.

14.

15.

16.

17.

18.

19.

Solve each compound inequality and graph the solution set.

20. $8 \leq 2m < 16$

21. $10 < x + 5$ or $x - 2 > 9$

22. $4 < x + 7 < 8$

23. $6 + x < 9$ or $-4x \leq -8$

24. $4t - 6 \geq 10$ and $6t \leq 36$

25. $5 \leq 3a + 12 \leq 16$

26. $x + 4 \leq 8$ or $2x + 1 \geq 9$

27. $3x + 1 \geq 8$ and $10x \leq 15$

28. $-3s + 7 \leq 8$ or $-2s + 4 \geq 12$

29. $-4 \leq -2x + 6 \leq 13$

Solve.

*30. Challenge The U.S. population in 2008 was 902,305 more than 1.08 times the U.S. population in 2000. If the population in 2008 was between 300,000,000 and 350,000,000, estimate the population in 2000.

*31. Challenge In the 2004 U.S. presidential election, the Democratic vote total in California was 6,745,485 and the Republican vote total was 5,509,826. There were independent votes as well. In that election, 254 times the number of independent votes was greater than the Democratic total; meanwhile, 20,000 more than 206 times the number of independent votes was less than the Republican total. Write a conjunction inequality in interval notation that represents the number of independent votes in California.

Absolute Value Inequalities

Absolute value inequalities can be represented by compound inequalities.

The table below shows that absolute value inequalities using $<$ or $\leq$ are conjunctions, while inequalities using $>$ or $\geq$ are disjunctions.

Inequality	Words	Compound Inequality	Graph
$|k| < a$	the set of real numbers less than a units from 0	$k > -a$ and $k < a$	
$|k| \leq a$	the set of real numbers less than or equal to a units from 0	$k \geq -a$ and $k \leq a$	
$|k| > a$	the set of real numbers greater than a units from 0	$k < -a$ or $k > a$	
$|k| \geq a$	the set of real numbers greater than or equal to a units from 0	$k \leq -a$ or $k \geq a$	

In this table, the letter k represents any algebraic expression, as shown in the examples throughout this topic.

Solving Absolute Value Inequalities (Conjunctions)

To solve an absolute value inequality, isolate the absolute value expression (if needed) and write it as a compound inequality. Then solve the compound inequality to obtain the solution set.

Example 1 Solve each absolute value inequality and graph the solution set.

Ⓐ $|5 + 6x| < 13$

Solution   The absolute value expression is already isolated.

$$5 + 6x > -13 \quad \text{and} \quad 5 + 6x < 13 \qquad \text{Write as a compound inequality.}$$
$$6x > -18 \qquad\qquad 6x < 8 \qquad\quad \text{Solve.}$$
$$x > -3 \qquad\qquad\quad x < \frac{4}{3}$$

The solution set is $x \in \left(-3, \ \frac{4}{3}\right)$.

The graph of the solution set is:

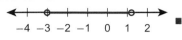

B $5|2t - 8| \leq -20$

Solution

$$5|2t - 8| \leq -20$$
$$|2t - 8| \leq -4 \qquad \text{Isolate the absolute value expression.}$$

$$2t - 8 \geq 4 \quad \text{and} \quad 2t - 8 \leq -4 \qquad \text{Write as a compound inequality.}$$
$$2t \geq 12 \qquad\qquad 2t \leq 4 \qquad\quad \text{Solve.}$$
$$t \geq 6 \qquad\qquad\quad t \leq 2$$

The sets described by $t \geq 6$ and $t \leq 2$ do not intersect, so the solution set is the empty set.

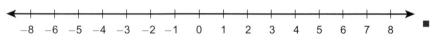

> **TIP**
>
> There are no values of t that satisfy this inequality because an absolute value is never negative.

Solving Absolute Value Inequalities (Disjunctions)

Example 2   Solve each inequality and graph the solution set.

A $\dfrac{|h + 6|}{3} \geq 4$

Solution

$$\frac{|h + 6|}{3} \geq 4$$

$$|h + 6| \geq 12 \qquad \text{Isolate the absolute value expression.}$$

$$h + 6 \leq -12 \quad \text{or} \quad h + 6 \geq 12 \qquad \text{Write as a compound inequality.}$$
$$h \leq -18 \qquad\qquad h \geq 6 \qquad\quad \text{Solve.}$$

The solution is $h \in (-\infty, -18] \cup [6, \infty)$. The graph of the solution set is:

> **REMEMBER**
>
> In a disjunction, the solution is the set of all numbers that belong to one or the other of the solution sets of the component inequalities.

B $|x - 1| > -3$

Solution

$$|x - 1| > -3$$
$$x - 1 < 3 \quad \text{or} \quad x - 1 > -3 \qquad \text{Write as a compound inequality.}$$
$$x < 4 \qquad\qquad x > -2 \qquad\quad \text{Solve.}$$

The solution is $x \in (-\infty, \infty)$.

The graph of the solution set is the entire number line:

> **THINK ABOUT IT**
>
> Any value of x will satisfy this inequality because an absolute value is always positive.

Problem Set

. . . .

Determine whether the given absolute value inequality represents a conjunction or a disjunction.

1. $|x| < 10$

2. $|2v| > 10$

3. $|5p + 1| \geq 10$

4. $|6x - 1| \leq 10$

For each absolute value inequality, do the following:

A. Write it as a compound inequality.
B. Write the solution in interval notation.
C. Graph the solution set.

5. $|x| < 5$

6. $|x| > 3$

7. $|m| \leq 2$

8. $|x| \geq 1$

Solve each absolute value inequality and graph the solution set.

9. $|4 + 2a| < 10$

10. $|3x + 1| \geq 19$

11. $|7r - 4| < 5$

12. $3|4q - 2| \leq 18$

13. $2|5x + 1| > 20$

14. $|9 - 3x| \leq 9$

15. $|12 - 2f| > 12$

16. $|9x| + 3 \geq 9$

17. $|6 - 4n| > 12$

18. $\dfrac{|x + 5|}{5} > 2$

19. $\dfrac{|t + 4|}{3} \geq 16$

20. $\dfrac{|x - 1|}{2} < 4.5$

21. $|y| + 2 > -5$

22. $|4x| + 1 \leq 9$

23. $\dfrac{|x + 3|}{10} > \dfrac{1}{10}$

24. $|3t| - 2 \geq 4$

25. $\dfrac{|g - 9|}{4} \leq 2$

26. $|2x| + 3 < -4$

27. $-|8 - 4x| < 16$

28. $-4|3z + 5| \leq 20$

Solve.

*29. Challenge A building manufacturer makes modular homes. When the materials are cut, each joist must measure no more than 0.25 inches longer or shorter than 20 feet. Write an absolute value inequality and the compound inequality whose solution set represents the range of acceptable measurements.

*30. Challenge On the highway, a driver never drives more than 10 mph faster or slower than the posted speed. If the posted speed is 55 mph, write an absolute value inequality and the compound inequality whose solution set represents the range of the driver's speed.

Inequalities in Two Variables

When the equals sign in a linear equation is replaced by an inequality symbol, the statement becomes a *linear inequality*.

> **DEFINITION**
>
> A **linear inequality** uses terms with degree zero or one and an inequality symbol to relate two variables.

The graph of a linear inequality is a region of the coordinate plane. The region is determined by a line, called the **boundary line**. The boundary line is the graph of the related equation, which uses an equals sign.

$$\text{Linear Inequality: } y \geq \frac{3}{4}x - 3$$

$$\text{Related Linear Equation: } y = \frac{3}{4}x - 3$$

The boundary line divides the plane into two **half-planes**. If the inequality is a nonstrict inequality (that is, it uses $\leq$ or $\geq$), then the boundary line is a solid line and the half-plane is a **closed half-plane**. If the inequality is a strict inequality (it uses $<$ or $>$), then the boundary line is a dashed line and the half-plane is an **open half-plane**.

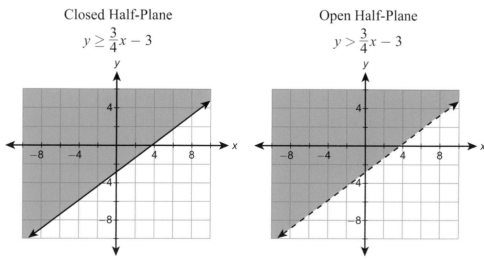

Closed Half-Plane
$$y \geq \frac{3}{4}x - 3$$

Open Half-Plane
$$y > \frac{3}{4}x - 3$$

To determine which half-plane to shade, use a *test point*. You can choose any point that is not on the boundary line.

When the inequality is written in the form such that the related equation is in slope-intercept form, then the region to be shaded may be determined without using a test point. For $>$ or $\geq$, shade above the boundary line (where the y-values on the y-axis are greater than the y-intercept). For $<$ or $\leq$, shade below the boundary line (where the y-values on the y-axis are less than the y-intercept).

Any point in the shaded region is a solution of the inequality. A point on a solid boundary line is also a solution, but a point on a dashed boundary line is not a solution.

Using the y-intercept to Graph an Inequality in Two Variables

Example 1   Graph $y < -2x + 1$.

Solution

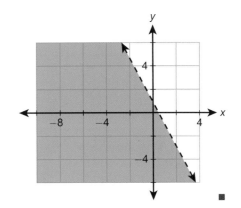

Step 1   Graph the related equation, $y = -2x + 1$. The y-intercept is 1, so first plot $(0, 1)$. Use the slope of -2 to find another point on the line by moving down 2 units and right 1 unit from that point.

Step 2   Draw a dashed line through the points because $<$ indicates that the boundary line does not contain solutions.

Step 3   Since the related linear equation is written in slope-intercept form and the inequality symbol is $<$, shade below the boundary line.   ∎

Graphing a Linear Inequality with One Variable

Example 2   Graph $x \geq 1.5$.

Solution

Step 1   Graph the related equation, $x = 1.5$. The line is a vertical line passing through $(1.5, 0)$.

Step 2   Use a solid line because $\geq$ indicates that the boundary line contains solutions.

Step 3   Choose a test point to determine which half-plane to shade.
Test-point: $(0, 0)$
$x \overset{?}{\geq} 1.5$
$0 \ngeq 1.5$

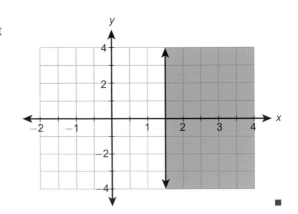

$(0, 0)$ is *not* in the solution set; the half-plane that does *not* contain the origin is shaded.
Shade to the right of the line.   ∎

Using Intercepts to Graph an Inequality in Two Variables

Example 3 Graph $2x - 5y > 10$.

Solution

Step 1 Use intercepts to find two points on the graph of the related equation.

$$2x - 5y = 10 \qquad\qquad 2x - 5y = 10$$
$$2 \cdot 0 - 5y = 10 \qquad\qquad 2x - 5 \cdot 0 = 10$$
$$-5y = 10 \qquad\qquad 2x = 10$$
$$y = -2 \qquad\qquad x = 5$$

Step 2 Draw a dashed boundary line through $(0, -2)$ and $(5, 0)$.

Step 3 Choose a test point to determine which half-plane to shade.

$$2x - 5y \overset{?}{>} 10$$
$$2 \cdot 0 - 5 \cdot 0 \overset{?}{>} 10$$
$$0 \not> 10$$

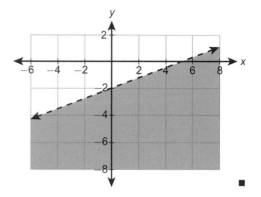

$(0, 0)$ is not in the solution set, so the half-plane that does not contain the origin is shaded. ∎

Writing Linear Inequalities from Graphs

Example 4 Write an inequality for each graph.

A

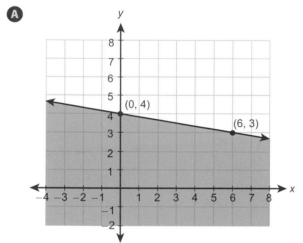

Solution

Step 1 Determine the equation of the boundary line. The y-intercept is 4 and the slope is $-\frac{1}{6}$. The equation of the boundary line is $y = -\frac{1}{6}x + 4$.

Step 2 Determine the inequality sign. Because the boundary line is solid, the inequality will be a nonstrict inequality, using either $\leq$ or $\geq$. Because the shading is below the line, use $\leq$.

Step 3 Write the inequality: $y \leq -\frac{1}{6}x + 4$. ∎

> **THINK ABOUT IT**
>
> $(0, 0)$ satisfies $y \leq -\frac{1}{6}x + 4$ because $0 \leq 4$.

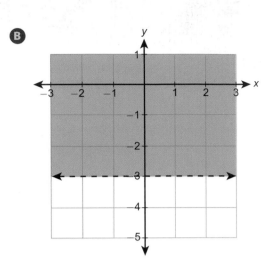

B

Solution

Step 1 Determine the equation of the boundary line. The y-value of every ordered pair is -3, so the equation is $y = -3$.

Step 2 Determine the inequality sign. Because the boundary line is dashed, the inequality will be a strict inequality, using either $<$ or $>$. Because the shading is above the line, use $>$.

Step 3 Write the inequality: $y > -3$. ■

> **REMEMBER**
>
> The slope of a horizontal line is 0. The equation of the boundary line can be written as $y = 0x - 3$.

Problem Set

Graph the inequality.

1. $y > 3x + 5$

2. $y \leq 4x + \dfrac{1}{2}$

3. $y \leq \dfrac{2}{3}x - 7$

4. $y < -\dfrac{1}{2}x - 6$

5. $y > -x + \dfrac{3}{2}$

6. $y \geq -5x + 4$

7. $y < -\dfrac{3}{5}x - 2$

8. $y \geq 5$

9. $y < -2$

10. $x < -4.5$

11. $x \geq 7$

12. $-x + 2y \geq -5$

13. $4x + y > 3$

14. $-5x + 4y < 20$

15. $6x - 6y > 24$

16. $-x - 3y \geq 8$

17. $-4x - 7y \leq 63$

18. $6x - 3y > 3$

Write an inequality for each graph.

19.

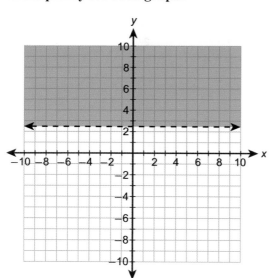

20.

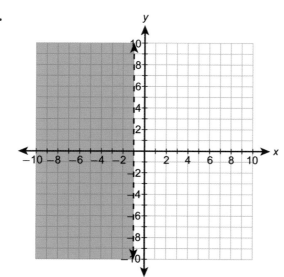

21.

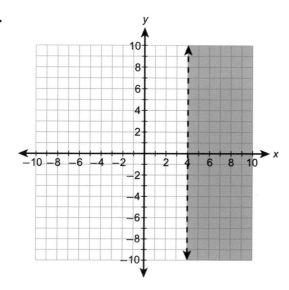

22.

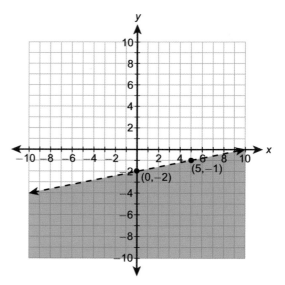

23.

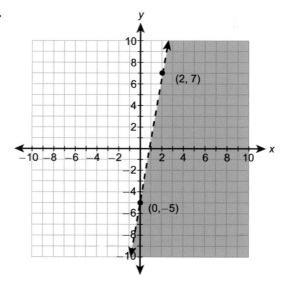

24.

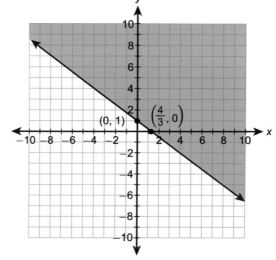

25.

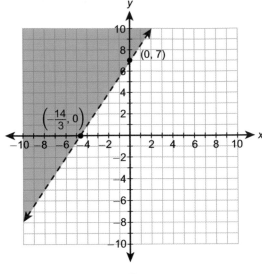

27.

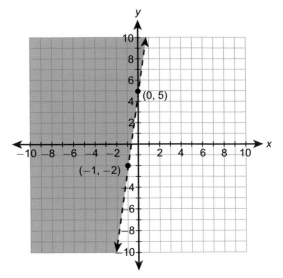

26.

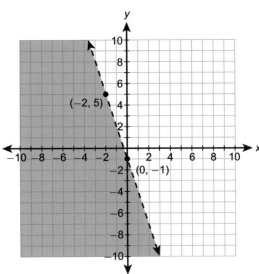

28.

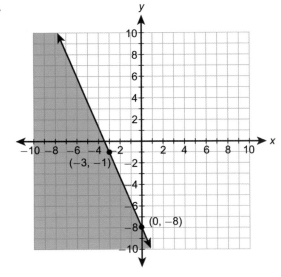

Solve.

*__29.__ **Challenge** Write and graph three separate inequalities whose solution set includes the point $(-2, 4)$. Make one of the graphs a vertical line and make another graph a horizontal line.

Systems of Linear Inequalities

A solution of a *system of linear inequalities* is any ordered pair that satisfies all the inequalities in the system.

Recall that you can solve a system of linear equations by graphing. Similarly, you can also solve a system of linear inequalities by graphing. When two or more linear inequalities are graphed on the same coordinate plane, the solutions of the system are the ordered pairs in the intersection of the shaded regions.

Solving Systems of Two Linear Inequalities

To solve a system of linear inequalities, graph each inequality in the system and then identify the overlapping region.

Example 1   Graph each system of linear inequalities. Then give one ordered pair that is a solution of the system and check your answer.

A $\begin{cases} y > 2x \\ y \le -\dfrac{1}{3}x - 1 \end{cases}$

Solution

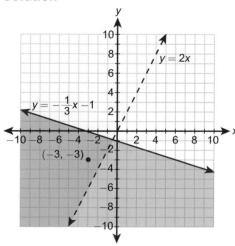

Graph $y = 2x$ with a dashed line and shade above the line. Graph $y = -\dfrac{1}{3}x - 1$ with a solid line and shade below it.

The intersection of the half-planes is the green shaded region. The solutions are the ordered pairs in the green region. One solution is the ordered pair $(-3, -3)$. You can verify that $(-3, -3)$ satisfies both inequalities.

THINK ABOUT IT

The ordered pair tested is just one of infinitely many solutions.

Check

Substitute $(-3, -3)$ in $y > 2x$.   Substitute $(-3, -3)$ in $y \leq -\frac{1}{3}x - 1$.

$$y > 2x$$ $$y \leq -\frac{1}{3}x - 1$$

$$-3 \overset{?}{>} 2(-3)$$ $$-3 \overset{?}{\leq} -\frac{1}{3}(-3) - 1$$

$$-3 > -6 \checkmark$$ $$-3 \leq 0 \checkmark$$

The ordered pair $(-3, -3)$ satisfies both inequalities, so it is a solution of the system. ■

B $\begin{cases} y \geq -3x + 5 \\ y \leq -3x - 1 \end{cases}$

Solution

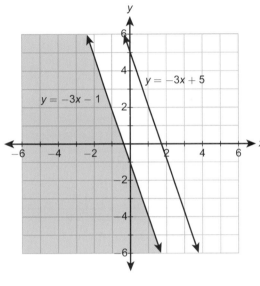

The boundary lines are parallel, and both are graphed with solid lines. One is shaded above the line, and the other is shaded below. The shaded areas do not overlap; therefore, this system of linear inequalities has *no solution*. ■

C $\begin{cases} y < 4 \\ y \geq -2 \end{cases}$

Solution

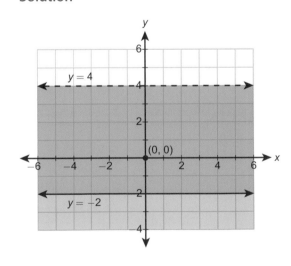

The boundary lines are parallel, but the shading is in opposite directions, creating an overlapping region. This region contains the solutions of the system. One solution is $(0, 0)$. ■

Solving Systems of Three or More Linear Inequalities

When a system has three or more inequalities, graph each inequality on the same coordinate plane. Be careful to identify the overlapping regions correctly.

Example 2   Graph each system of linear inequalities. Identify the overlapping shaded regions representing the solution of the system.

(A)
$$\begin{cases} y < 2x - 4 \\ y \le 2 \\ y > \dfrac{4}{5}x - 4 \end{cases}$$

Solution   Graph $y = 2x - 4$ with a dashed line and use small arrows to show which half-plane should be shaded. Draw the arrows below the line. Graph $y = 2$ with a solid line and draw small arrows below the line. Graph $y = \dfrac{4}{5}x - 4$ with a dashed line and draw small arrows above the line.

The solution is the shaded triangular region.

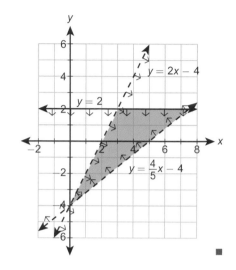

(B)
$$\begin{cases} x \ge 0 \\ y \ge 0 \\ y \le x + 3 \\ y < -2x + 12 \end{cases}$$

Solution   The first two inequalities, $x \ge 0$ and $y \ge 0$, describe Quadrant I of a coordinate graph and the adjoining sections of the x- and y-axes.

Graph the line $y = x + 3$ with a solid line and draw small arrows below the line. Graph the line $y = -2x + 12$ with a dashed line and draw small arrows below the line.

The solutions of the system are found in the region bounded by the x- and y-axes and the lines $y = x + 3$ and $y = -2x + 12$. Note that $(0, 0)$ and $(0, 3)$ are solutions of the system because they represent the intersections of solid lines. However, $(6, 0)$ and $(3, 6)$ are not solutions of the system because they represent the intersections of solid lines and dashed lines.

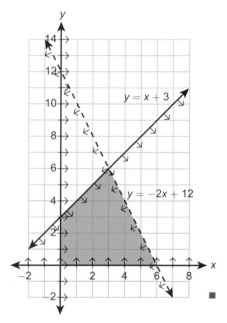

Writing Systems of Linear Inequalities from Graphs

You can write a system of linear inequalities from a graph by determining the equation for each boundary line.

Example 3   Write the system of inequalities shown by the graph.

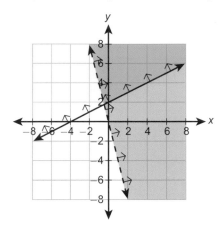

Solution

Step 1   Determine the equations of the boundary lines.

The y-intercept of the solid line is 2 and its slope is $\frac{1}{2}$. The equation of the boundary line is $y = \frac{1}{2}x + 2$.

The y-intercept of the dashed line is -1 and its slope is -4. The equation of the boundary line is $y = -4x - 1$.

Step 2   Determine the inequality signs.

Because the boundary line of $y = \frac{1}{2}x + 2$ is solid, the inequality will be a nonstrict inequality, using either $\leq$ or $\geq$. The shading is above the line, so use $\geq$.

Because the boundary line of $y = -4x - 1$ is dashed, the inequality will be a strict inequality, using $<$ or $>$. The shading is above the line, so use $>$.

Step 3   Write the system of linear inequalities: $\begin{cases} y \geq \frac{1}{2}x + 2 \\ y > -4x - 1. \end{cases}$ ∎

Problem Set

Determine whether the ordered pair is a solution of the system.

1.   ordered pair: $(1, 9)$

   system: $\begin{cases} x < 4 \\ y > 2 \end{cases}$

2.   ordered pair: $(2, -4)$

   system: $\begin{cases} x \leq 1 \\ y \leq 6 \end{cases}$

3.   ordered pair: $(-6, 12)$

   system: $\begin{cases} y < 12 \\ y > x - 8 \end{cases}$

4.   ordered pair: $(10, 4)$

   system: $\begin{cases} y \leq \frac{1}{2}x \\ y \leq 4x - 5 \end{cases}$

5.   ordered pair: $(7, 5)$

   system: $\begin{cases} y > 6x - 3 \\ y \geq -8x + 5 \end{cases}$

6.   ordered pair: $\left(-\frac{2}{3}, \frac{3}{4}\right)$

   system: $\begin{cases} y \geq x - \frac{5}{6} \\ y > -\frac{3}{5}x \end{cases}$

Graph each system of linear inequalities.

7. $\begin{cases} x > 2 \\ x \le -4 \end{cases}$

8. $\begin{cases} y \ge 4 \\ y \le -6 \end{cases}$

9. $\begin{cases} y > x - 3 \\ y \ge 5 \end{cases}$

10. $\begin{cases} x > 10 \\ y > -3x \end{cases}$

11. $\begin{cases} y > 3x + 7 \\ y > 3x \end{cases}$

12. $\begin{cases} x + y \le 7 \\ y > -4x + 2 \end{cases}$

13. $\begin{cases} 2x - y > -12 \\ y \le -\dfrac{1}{2}x \end{cases}$

14. $\begin{cases} y - x > -12 \\ y \le -5x \end{cases}$

15. $\begin{cases} 4x + 10y \le 20 \\ y \ge 0 \\ x \ge 0 \end{cases}$

16. $\begin{cases} 3x - 5y \ge -15 \\ 6x + y < -2 \\ y \ge 0 \end{cases}$

17. $\begin{cases} x + y \le -9 \\ x - y \le -15 \\ x \le 0 \\ y \le 0 \end{cases}$

18. $\begin{cases} 4x - y > -3 \\ 2y \le -6x + 18 \\ x > 0 \\ y > 0 \end{cases}$

19. $\begin{cases} x > 10 \\ y > -4 \\ y < 1 \end{cases}$

20. $\begin{cases} y < 1 \\ y \ge 6 \\ y < -x \end{cases}$

21. $\begin{cases} x - y < 4 \\ x - y \ge -7 \\ y > 2x \end{cases}$

22. $\begin{cases} x - y > 8 \\ 4x + y \le 9 \\ y \le -6x - 1 \end{cases}$

Write the system of linear inequalities represented by each graph.

23.

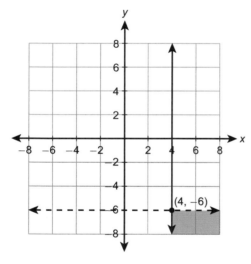

25.

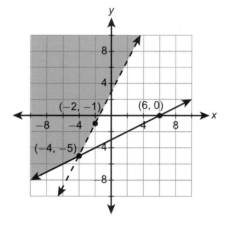

24.

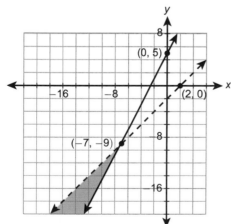

26.

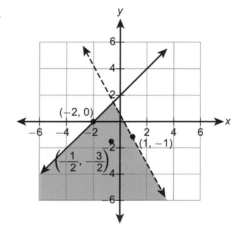

27.

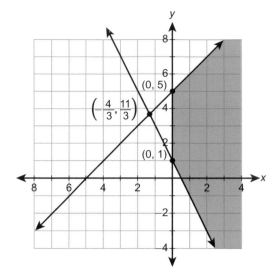

28.

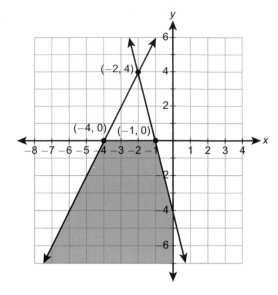

Solve.

*29. Challenge A rectangular field has a perimeter of at least 80 meters. The length of the field is no more than three times its width.

   A. Write and graph a system of linear inequalities to represent the problem.

   B. Use your graph to determine three possible dimensions of the field.

*30. Challenge Demetrius works two jobs. He earns $10 per hour at one job and $8 per hour at the other job. He wants to earn at least $320 per week. He works no more than 40 hours in a week.

   A. Write and graph a system of linear inequalities to represent the problem.

   B. Use your graph to determine the number of hours he can work at each job.

Linear Programming

Systems of linear inequalities are used in *linear programming.*

> **DEFINITION**
>
> **Linear programming** is the process of maximizing or minimizing a linear function subject to a set of conditions, called **constraints,** that are linear inequalities.

TIP

The word *feasible* means "possible to achieve." Ordered pairs outside the feasible region do not satisfy all of the constraints, so they are not possible solutions to the problem.

Each constraint in a linear programming problem is a linear inequality. The set of constraints that must be satisfied forms a system of linear inequalities. The graph of the solutions forms the **feasible region**. The feasible region is the set of all the ordered pairs that satisfy the constraints and are possible solutions to the problem.

Determining a Feasible Region

Example 1   Determine and graph the feasible region in each situation.

A A party planner needs to rent at least 30 chairs and at least 8 tables for one day. The daily rental rates are \$2 per chair and \$6 per table. The planner can spend no more than a total of \$150 on these rentals. Given these constraints, find one possible combination of the number of chairs and the number of tables the planner can rent.

Solution

Step 1   Write the constraints. Let c represent the number of chairs and t represent the number of tables.

$$\begin{cases} c \geq 30 & \text{at least 30 chairs} \\ t \geq 8 & \text{at least 8 tables} \\ 2c + 6t \leq 150 & \text{total that can be} \\ & \text{spent on rentals} \end{cases}$$

Step 2   Graph each inequality.

Step 3   Shade the region where all three inequalities intersect. The feasible region is *bounded* because the boundary lines form a closed figure. Because the numbers of tables and chairs must be whole numbers, there are several solutions, but not an infinite number of solutions. One solution is 36 chairs and 10 tables.

> **TIP**
>
> *At least* means greater than or equal to.
>
> *No more than* means less than or equal to.

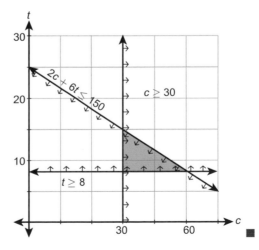

B For a school carnival to operate smoothly and make a profit, there must be at least 60 volunteers and 200 customers. Also, the number of customers must be no more than 10 times the number of volunteers. Given these constraints, find one possible combination of the number of volunteers and the number of customers that need to be at the carnival.

Solution

Step 1 Write the constraints. Let v represent the number of volunteers and c represent the number of customers.

$$\begin{cases} v \geq 60 \\ c \geq 200 \\ c \geq 10v \end{cases}$$

Step 2 Graph each inequality.

Step 3 Shade the region where all three solution sets intersect. Although the number of people must be a whole number, the feasible region is *unbounded* and there are an infinite number of solutions. One solution is 80 volunteers and 500 customers.

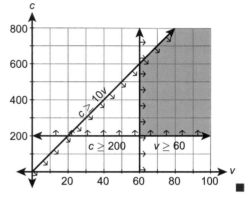

Finding an Optimal Solution: Maximum Profit

Once you know a feasible region, you can find the **optimal**, or best, **solution** for the problem. An optimal solution is a solution that maximizes or minimizes the *objective*.

> **DEFINITION**
>
> An **objective function** is a linear function that models a quantity that is to be optimized in a linear programming problem.

An optimal solution to a linear programming problem will always occur at one of the corner points, called **vertex points**, of the feasible region. The maximum and minimum values of the objective function will always occur at vertex points.

Example 2 A school's poetry club can sell at most 80 tickets to a poetry reading. Regular adult tickets will cost $10, and senior citizen tickets will cost $6. What is the maximum profit the club can make on the ticket sales?

Solution

Step 1 Write the constraints as inequalities. Let c represent the number of senior citizen tickets sold and a represent the number of regular adult tickets sold. Neither number of tickets to be sold can be negative. *At most* means less than or equal to, so 80 or fewer tickets can be sold in all.

$$\begin{cases} c \geq 0 \\ a \geq 0 \\ c + a \leq 80 \end{cases}$$

Step 2 Write the objective function. Let P represent profit. The profit for a senior citizen ticket is $6 and the profit for a regular adult ticket is $10. The objective function is given by $P = 6c + 10a$.

Step 3 Graph the feasible region. Determine the coordinates of the vertices of the feasible region. The vertices are at the intersections of the graphs of the constraints. The vertices are at $(0, 0)$, $(80, 0)$, and $(0, 80)$.

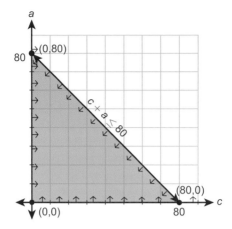

Step 4 Evaluate the profit function $P = 6c + 10a$ at the vertices of the feasible region.

Vertex	$6c + 10a$	P
$(0, 0)$	$6 \cdot 0 + 10 \cdot 0$	0
$(80, 0)$	$6 \cdot 80 + 10 \cdot 0$	480
$(0, 80)$	$6 \cdot 0 + 10 \cdot 80$	800

Step 5 The maximum profit will occur if $c = 0$ and $a = 80$. This is the case in which all regular adult tickets are sold and no senior citizen tickets are sold. The maximum profit is $800. ∎

Finding an Optimal Solution by Using a System of Equations

Example 3 A company can make up to 24 stained and 30 unstained picture frames in one day. However, the inspector can only inspect a total of up to 40 frames each day. All frames must be inspected. The company makes a profit of $12 on the stained frames and $8 on the unstained frames. To make the most profit, what number of each type of frame should the company make per day? What is the maximum daily profit?

Solution

Step 1 Write the constraints. Let s represent the number of stained frames and u represent the number of unstained frames.

$$\begin{cases} s \geq 0 \\ u \geq 0 \\ s \leq 24 \\ u \leq 30 \\ s + u \leq 40 \end{cases}$$
The number of frames cannot be negative.
no more than 24 stained frames
no more than 30 unstained frames
total number that can be inspected each day

Step 2 Write the objective function. The goal is to determine the number of stained and unstained frames the company should make each day to maximize profits. The profit function is $P = 12s + 8u$.

Step 3 Graph the feasible region and determine the coordinates of the vertices. To find the coordinates of some intersections, you may need to solve a system of two equations.

Step 4 Evaluate the objective function for each vertex.

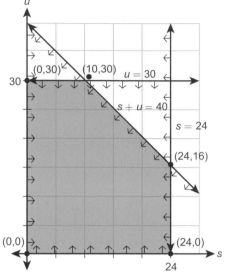

Vertex	12s + 8u	P
$(0, 0)$	$12 \cdot 0 + 8 \cdot 0$	0
$(0, 30)$	$12 \cdot 0 + 8 \cdot 30$	240
$(10, 30)$	$12 \cdot 10 + 8 \cdot 30$	360
$(24, 16)$	$12 \cdot 24 + 8 \cdot 16$	416
$(24, 0)$	$12 \cdot 24 + 8 \cdot 0$	288

Step 5 Because the value of P is greatest at $(24, 16)$, the maximum daily profit of \$416 occurs when the company makes 24 stained and 16 unstained frames. ■

Finding an Optimal Solution: Minimum Cost

An objective function may also describe the costs required to produce products. Linear programming can be used to determine the minimum cost possible given certain constraints on the variables.

Example 4 Sonya is a jewelry artist who makes necklaces and bracelets. Materials cost \$2 for each bracelet and \$4 for each necklace. She will make at least 5 necklaces. She plans to make no more than 10 more necklaces than bracelets. She also needs no more than 30 bracelets and necklaces. What will be the minimum cost of the materials?

Solution

Step 1 Write the constraints as inequalities. Let b represent the number of bracelets and let n represent the number of necklaces she will make.

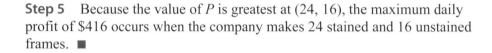

$b \geq 0$	The number of necklaces cannot
$n \geq 0$	be negative.
$n \geq 5$	at least 5 necklaces
$n \leq b + 10$	no more than 10 more necklaces than bracelets
$b + n \leq 30$	total number she makes is no more than 30

Step 2 Write the objective function. The materials needed to make a bracelet cost \$2 and the materials needed to make a necklace cost \$4. The objective function is given by $C = 2b + 4n$.

Step 3 Graph the feasible region. Determine the coordinates of the vertices of the feasible region. The vertices are at the intersections of the graphs of the constraints. They are (0, 5), (0, 10), (10, 20), and (25, 5).

Step 4 Evaluate the cost function $C = 2b + 4n$ at the vertices of the feasible region.

Vertex	$2b + 4n$	C
(0, 5)	$2 \cdot 0 + 4 \cdot 5$	20
(0, 10)	$2 \cdot 0 + 4 \cdot 10$	40
(10, 20)	$2 \cdot 10 + 4 \cdot 20$	100
(25, 5)	$2 \cdot 25 + 4 \cdot 5$	70

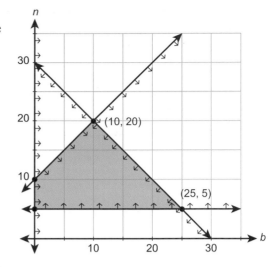

Step 5 The minimum cost occurs when $b = 0$ and $n = 5$. That is when she makes no bracelets and 5 necklaces. The minimum cost in that case is $20. ∎

Problem Set

For each problem, do the following:

A. Write inequalities to model the constraints in the problem.
B. Graph the feasible region.
C. Answer the question.

1. Stacy sells homemade baked pizzas. She uses 10 olive pieces and 15 mushroom pieces for a small pizza. She uses 15 olive pieces and 45 mushroom pieces for a large pizza. She has 60 olive pieces and 135 mushrooms pieces in stock. Given these constraints, find two possible combinations of the number of large pizzas and the number of small pizzas Stacy can sell.

2. A company manufactures its product at two locations. At Location P, producing the product takes 40 hours; at location Q, producing it takes 30 hours. The costs of producing these items are $40 at Location P and $50 at Location Q. The company's labor force can provide 7500 hours of labor each week, and resources are $9300 each week. Given these constraints, find two possible combinations of the number of products at P and the number of products at Q the company can produce.

3. Jessie needs to buy cashews and almonds for a dessert recipe. She can spend a total of $50. Each packet of cashews and almonds costs $8 and $5, respectively. She needs at most twice as many almonds as cashews. Given these constraints, find two possible combinations of the number of cashew packets and number of almond packets Jessie can buy.

4. Pizza Mania delivers 40 to 55 cheese pizzas and 25 to 45 veggie pizzas each day. The total number of deliveries has never exceeded 80 pizzas a day. Given these constraints, find two possible combinations of the number of cheese pizzas and the number of veggie pizzas Pizza Mania might deliver.

5. If Dorian rides his motorcycle at 25 kilometers per hour, he has to spend $2 per kilometer on gas. If he rides it at a faster speed of 40 kilometers per hour, the gas cost increases to $5 per kilometer. He has $100 to spend on gas. Given these constraints, find two possible combinations of the distance he can drive at 25 kilometers per hour and the distance he can drive at 40 kilometers per hour.

6. Suppose every gram of wheat provides 0.1 g of protein and 0.25 g of carbohydrates, and every gram of rice provides 0.05 g of protein and 0.5 g of carbohydrates. The minimum daily requirements of protein and carbohydrates for an average child are 50 g and 200 g, respectively. Given these constraints, find two possible combinations of wheat and rice a child might consume daily.

For each problem, do the following:

A. Graph the feasible region.

B. Determine the optimal solution (if any) to the problem.

7. Find the minimum value of the objective function $P = 2x + 3y$, subject to the following constraints:
$$\begin{cases} x + 2y \geq 1 \\ 2x + 2y \leq 10 \\ x \geq 0 \\ y \geq 0 \end{cases}$$

8. Find the maximum value of the objective function $P = x + 3y$, subject to the following constraints:
$$\begin{cases} x + y \geq 1 \\ 7x + 9y \leq 63 \\ 0 \leq y \leq 5 \\ 0 \leq x \leq 6 \end{cases}$$

9. Find the maximum and minimum values of the objective function $P = 5x + 7y$, subject to the following constraints:
$$\begin{cases} 2x + 3y \geq 6 \\ 3x - y \leq 15 \\ -x + y \leq 4 \\ 2x + 5y \leq 27 \\ x \geq 0 \\ y \geq 0 \end{cases}$$

10. Find the maximum value of the objective function $P = 7x + 7y$, subject to the following constraints:
$$\begin{cases} x + y \geq 2 \\ 2x + 3y \leq 6 \\ x \geq 0 \\ y \geq 0 \end{cases}$$

11. Show that there is no feasible region for the following linear constraints:
$$\begin{cases} x - 2y \geq 0 \\ 2x - y \leq -2 \\ x \geq 0 \\ y \geq 0 \end{cases}$$

For each problem, do the following:

A. Write inequalities to model the constraints in the problem.
B. Graph the feasible region.
C. Write an equation for the objective function.
D. Determine the optimal solution to the problem.

12. Juan invests $15,000 in two different ways. A government bond has a 5.5% return, and a stock investment has an expected 14% return. To minimize risk, Juan does not want to invest more than $1500 in bonds. Also, he wants to invest at least three times as much in bonds as in stocks. How should Juan invest in bonds and stocks to get the maximum return?

*13. **Challenge** To recover from an illness, Liza needs at least 15 units of vitamin supplements, 6 units of protein supplements, and 8 units of calcium supplements. These supplements are available in two brands, X and Y. One Brand X pill has 7 vitamin units, 2 protein units, and 3 calcium units, and each pill costs $7. One Brand Y pill has 5 vitamin units, 2 protein units, and 2 calcium units, and each pill costs $4. What is the number of X and Y pills Liza can buy at a minimum cost?

14. Dena and Macy earn $15 and $20 per day, respectively. Dena can stitch 6 shirts and 4 pants per day, while Macy can stitch 10 shirts and 4 pants per day. How many days should each of them work to produce at least 60 shirts and 32 pants at a minimum labor cost?

15. Jiao works at least 36 hours per week. She earns $15 per hour as a science tutor and $25 per hour as a teacher. The number of hours she works as a teacher is at least twice the number she works as a tutor. How many hours should she work at each job to earn the *least* amount of money? What is her minimum earning for one week?

16. Tom, a dealer, wishes to purchase washers and dryers. He has $5760 to invest and storage space for at most 20 items. Each washer costs $360, and each dryer costs $240. He expects to make a profit of $22 on each washer and $18 on each dryer. Assuming that he can sell all the items he purchases, how should Tom invest his money to maximize profits?

17. Auto World produces front windshield wipers and back windshield wipers. The company predicts a future demand of at least 250 pairs of front wipers and 200 pairs of back wipers each day. Auto World's production capacity is limited to producing at most 500 pairs of each kind. It needs to ship a total of at least 600 pairs of wipers each day. If each pair of front wipers results in a $3 loss, but each pair of back wipers produces a $5 profit, how many of each type should be made daily to maximize net profits?

18. Sherry's cat Willow consumes a minimum of 21 grams of fat and 3 grams of protein, and no more than 6 ounces of food total per day. Sherry purchases two brands of food, A and B, and mixes them. An ounce of brand A contains 7 grams of fat and 1 gram of protein. One ounce of brand A costs $0.15. An ounce of brand B contains 14 grams of fat and 2 grams of protein. One ounce of brand B costs $0.35. How much of each brand should Sherry mix for an optimal blend?

UNIT 5

Polynomials and Power Functions

Engineers use polynomial curves to design cars.

Engineers and artists use graphics programs to design cars, planes, and even shoes. Each surface consists of many polynomial functions.

Big Ideas

▶ You can apply the rules of arithmetic to simplify algebraic expressions. Solving an equation means finding numbers for the variable or variables that make the equation true.

▶ Expressions and equations express relationships between different entities.

▶ A function is a correspondence between two sets, the domain and the range, that assigns to each member of the domain exactly one member of the range. Functions can model many events in the physical world.

Unit Topics

▶ Foundations for Unit 5

▶ Working with Polynomials

▶ Multiplying Polynomials

▶ Factoring Patterns

▶ More Factoring Patterns

▶ Solving Polynomial Equations

▶ Power Functions

Foundations for Unit 5

Before you study polynomials and power functions, you should know how to do the following:

▶ Evaluate powers.

▶ Use the product of powers property to simplify expressions.

▶ Use the properties of exponents to simplify expressions.

Evaluating Powers

Definitions

base (in a power) a number, variable, or expression that is a factor in a power

exponent a number or variable that indicates how many times the base is used as a factor

power an expression that contains an exponent and a base, or the value of such an expression

The **power** 5^3 is read "5 to the third power," where 5 is the **base** and 3 is the **exponent**. To evaluate 5^3, write the base as a factor 3 times, as indicated by the exponent 3, and then multiply: $5^3 = 5 \cdot 5 \cdot 5 = 125$. The number 125 may also be referred to as a power because it is the value of 5^3. That is, 125 is a power of 5.

An exponent may be positive, negative, or zero. A power containing a negative exponent may be rewritten with a positive exponent by applying the property of negative exponents. When the base is a nonzero number and the exponent is any integer, $a^{-n} = \frac{1}{a^n}$. For example, $6^{-2} = \frac{1}{6^2} = \frac{1}{36}$.

REMEMBER

The **zero exponent** property states that for any nonzero number a,
$$a^0 = 1.$$
Examples:
$5^0 = 1$, $(3a^2)^0 = 1$

Example 1 Evaluate each power.

A $8^4 = 8 \cdot 8 \cdot 8 \cdot 8 = 4096$

B $\left(\frac{2}{3}\right)^2 = \frac{2}{3} \cdot \frac{2}{3} = \frac{4}{9}$

C $(-4)^3 = (-4) \cdot (-4) \cdot (-4)$
$ = 16 \cdot (-4)$
$ = -64$

D $1.8^1 = 1.8$

E $(6.25 + 2.75)^0 = 1$

TIP

The value of any nonzero base to the power 1 is the same as the base itself.

Examples:
$7^1 = 7$, $\left(\frac{3}{4}\right)^1 = \frac{3}{4}$

Problem Set A

Evaluate each power. Assume all variables are nonzero.

1. 2^3

2. $\left(\frac{1}{2}ab\right)^0$

3. $(2abc)^1$

4. $(-7)^2$

5. $\left(-\frac{4}{5}\right)^2$

6. $2^1 + y^0$

Using the Product of Powers Property

To simplify the product of two or more powers with the same base, add the exponents and keep the base the same. Follow the sign rules for addition of integers when you add the exponents. A product of powers with different bases cannot be simplified.

Example 2　Simplify each product.

A　$3^2 \cdot 10^2 \cdot 10^3$

$= 3^2 \cdot 10^{2+3}$

$= 9 \cdot 100{,}000$

$= 900{,}000$

B　$5 \cdot 5^{-2} \cdot a^2 \cdot b^6$

$= 5^{1+(-2)} \cdot a^2 \cdot b^6$

$= 5^{-1} \cdot a^2 \cdot b^6$

$= \dfrac{a^2 b^6}{5}$

C　$b^{10} \cdot b^{-2} \cdot b$

$= b^{10} \cdot b^{-2} \cdot b^1$

$= b^{10+(-2)+1}$

$= b^9$

D　$7^3 \cdot z^6 \cdot 7^{-1} \cdot y^{-4} \cdot y^5$

$= 7^3 \cdot 7^{-1} \cdot y^{-4} \cdot y^5 \cdot z^6$

$= 7^{3+(-1)} \cdot y^{-4+5} \cdot z^6$

$= 7^2 \cdot y^1 \cdot z^6$

$= 49yz^6$

> **REMEMBER**
>
> The **product of powers** property states that for any nonzero real number a and any two real numbers m and n,
>
> $$a^m \cdot a^n = a^{m+n}.$$
>
> **Example:**
>
> $4a^5 \cdot a^{-2} = 4a^{5+(-2)} = 4a^3$

Problem Set B

Use the product of powers property to simplify each product.

7. $3^7 \cdot 3^{-2} \cdot 3^5$

8. $2^5 \cdot 2^4$

9. $x^0 \cdot x^2$

10. $n^3 \cdot m^5$

11. $x^2 \cdot y^4 \cdot x^{-1}$

12. $4^{-3} \cdot 4^4$

13. $y \cdot y^{-3} \cdot y^4$

14. $(-2)^3 \cdot (-2)^2$

15. $d^{-3} \cdot f^4 \cdot d^2 \cdot f^0$

16. $x \cdot y^2 \cdot z^3$

Using the Properties of Exponents

The description **power of a power** refers to a power that is raised to another power, such as $(2^3)^2$ or $(x^{-2})^3$. To simplify a power of a power, multiply the exponents and keep the base the same.

$$(2^3)^2 = 2^{3 \cdot 2} = 2^6 \qquad (x^{-2})^3 = x^{-2 \cdot 3} = x^{-6} = \frac{1}{x^6}$$

The description **power of a product** refers to a base, which is itself a product, raised to a power. Two examples of a power of a product are $(-4 \cdot 5)^2$ and $(3yz)^4$. To simplify a power of a product, raise each factor to the power.

> **REMEMBER**
>
> The **power of a power** property states that for any nonzero real number a and two integers m and n,
> $$(a^m)^n = a^{mn}.$$
>
> The **power of a product** property states that for any two nonzero real numbers a and b and any integer m,
> $$(ab)^m = a^m \cdot b^m.$$

Example 3   Simplify each power of a product.

A $(10^3)^2 = 10^{3 \cdot 2} = 10^6 = 1{,}000{,}000$

B $5a^2(a^3)^4 = 5a^2 \cdot a^{12} = 5a^{2+12} = 5a^{14}$

C $(-2 \cdot 3)^2 = (-2)^2 \cdot 3^2$

$\qquad = -2 \cdot (-2) \cdot 3 \cdot 3$

$\qquad = 36$

D $\frac{1}{3}(2n)^3 = \frac{1}{3} \cdot 2^3 \cdot n^3 = \frac{1}{3} \cdot 2 \cdot 2 \cdot 2 \cdot n^3$

$\qquad = \frac{1}{3} \cdot 8 \cdot n^3$

$\qquad = \frac{8}{3}n^3$

Problem Set C

Use the properties of exponents to simplify.

17. $(3^2)^1$

18. $(4^{-2} \cdot 4)^3$

19. $(2m)^3$

20. $(4x^3)^2$

21. $5y(xy^3)^2$

22. $\frac{1}{2}(2a)^3$

23. $2s(s^2 \cdot t)^6$

24. $x^0(x^2y^{-5})^3$

Working with Polynomials

A polynomial is a monomial or sum of monomials.

The prefix *poly–* means "many." A polynomial can be a sum of many monomials.

DEFINITIONS

A **monomial** is a number, a variable, or the product of a number and one or more variables. A monomial can have variables with whole-number exponents. A monomial cannot have a variable in a denominator or under a radical symbol. Monomials are sometimes called **terms**.
The **coefficient** of a monomial with multiple factors is the numerical factor.
A monomial with no variable factors is called a **constant**.
A **polynomial** is a monomial or sum of monomials.

Determining Whether an Expression Is a Polynomial

Example 1   Determine which expressions are polynomials.

Expression	Solution
A $3\sqrt{x} + 17x + 1$	This is not a polynomial. It has a variable under a radical symbol. ∎
B $2x^3 - x^2 - 5$	This is a polynomial. It is a sum of monomials because $2x^3 - x^2 - 5 = 2x^3 + (-x^2) + (-5)$. ∎
C $x^{-5} + 4x^4 - 1$	This is not a polynomial. It has a variable with a negative exponent. ∎
D $\frac{2}{3}x^3 - x^0$	This is a polynomial. Note that 0 is a whole number. $\frac{2}{3}x^3 - x^0 = \frac{2}{3}x^3 - 1$ ∎

TIP

In Example 1A, $\sqrt{x} = x^{\frac{1}{2}}$, so a variable has an exponent that is not a whole number.

In Example 1C, $x^{-5} = \frac{1}{x^5}$, so there is a variable in a denominator.

REMEMBER

The whole numbers are $\{0, 1, 2, 3, \ldots\}$.

Like terms are terms that contain the same variable factors taken to the same powers.

The **degree of a monomial** is the sum of the exponents of its variable factors.

The **degree of a polynomial** is the degree of the monomial with the greatest degree.

A polynomial is in **simplified form** when it has no like terms, every term is in simplest form, and its terms are in order of decreasing degree with respect to a variable.

The **leading coefficient** of a polynomial in simplified form is the coefficient of the first term.

Monomials and Like Terms

Example 2 Which of the following are like terms?

$6x^2$ x^2y $-2xy$ $-2x^2y$ $10x^2$ $-x^2$

Solution $6x^2$, $10x^2$, and $-x^2$ are like terms.

x^2y and $-2x^2y$ are like terms.

$-2xy$ is not like any of the other terms. ∎

Example 3 Determine the degree of each monomial.

Ⓐ $-21x^2y^5z^3$

Solution Add the exponents of the variables.

$-21x^2y^5z^3$

$2 + 5 + 3 = 10$. The degree of the monomial is 10. ∎

Ⓑ $7ab$

Solution Add the exponents of the variables.

$7ab = 7a^1b^1$

$1 + 1 = 2$. The degree of the monomial is 2. ∎

Simplifying and Classifying Polynomials

Example 4 Simplify $8x + 2x^3 + 9x + 2 - 6x^2 - 5x^3$. Then identify the leading coefficient.

Solution Combine like terms:

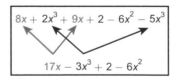

Then write the terms in order of decreasing degree. The simplified form is $-3x^3 - 6x^2 + 17x + 2$ and the leading coefficient is -3. ∎

> **THINK ABOUT IT**
>
> Combining like terms uses the distributive property.
>
> $8x + 9x = (8 + 9)x = 17x$

A polynomial can be classified by its number of terms or by its degree.

Classifying Polynomials by Number of Terms

Type	Number of Terms	Examples
Monomial	1	12 $-\dfrac{2}{5}xy^3$
Binomial	2	$a + b$ $1 - 3c^5$
Trinomial	3	$x^2 + 3x - 10$ $a^2 + 4ab + 4b^2$

TIP

Prefixes can help you remember the number of terms in monomials, binomials, and trinomials.

Mono– means "one," as in monocle or monopoly.

Bi– means "two," as in bicycle or bilingual.

Tri– means "three," as in tricycle or triathlon.

Many of the polynomials in the study of algebra are polynomials in one variable.

DEFINITION

A **polynomial in x** is a polynomial of the form
$$a_n x^n + a_{n-1} x^{n-1} + \ldots + a_2 x^2 + a_1 x + a_0$$
where the exponents are all whole numbers, the coefficients are all real numbers, and $a_n \neq 0$.

Note that the polynomial in the definition above can be written:
$$a_n x^n + a_{n-1} x^{n-1} + \ldots + a_2 x^2 + a_1 x^1 + a_0 x^0.$$

The exponents are $n, n - 1, n - 2, \ldots, 2, 1,$ and 0. The coefficients are a_n, $a_{n-1}, a_{n-2}, \ldots, a_2, a_1,$ and a_0.

Classifying Polynomials by Degree

Type	Degree	Example
Constant	0	-7
Linear	1	$9x - 12$
Quadratic	2	$x^2 + 8x + 16$
Cubic	3	$6x^3 - 2x^2 - 5$
Quartic	4	$5x^4 - 3x + 1$
Quintic	5	$-x^5 + 2x^4 - 3x^3 + 7x^2 - 10x + 1$
nth degree	n	$a_n x^n + a_{n-1} x^{n-1} + \ldots + a_1 x + a_0$

Example 5 Classify $5a^4 + a^2 - 3$ by its number of terms and by its degree.

Solution $5a^4 + a^2 - 3$ has three terms, so it is a trinomial. The term with the greatest degree is $5a^4$, and its degree is 4, so the degree of the polynomial is 4. It is a quartic trinomial. ∎

Adding and Subtracting Polynomials

To add or subtract polynomials, combine like terms. You can work either horizontally or vertically for any addition or subtraction.

THINK ABOUT IT

Try Example 6A in the vertical format and try Example 6B in the horizontal format. Decide whether you prefer one format over the other.

Example 6

A Add horizontally: $(7x + 14) + (2x^2 - 3x + 2)$.

Solution

$$
\begin{aligned}
(7x + 14) + (2x^2 - 3x + 2) &= 7x + 14 + 2x^2 - 3x + 2 \quad \text{Eliminate parentheses.}\\
&= 2x^2 + 7x - 3x + 14 + 2 \quad \text{Write in order of}\\
&\qquad\qquad\qquad\qquad\qquad\qquad \text{decreasing degree.}\\
&= 2x^2 + 4x + 16 \qquad\qquad\quad \text{Combine like terms.} \ \blacksquare
\end{aligned}
$$

B Add vertically: $(-4x^3 + 2x^2 + 9) + (7x^3 + 10x^2 - 3x - 4)$.

Solution

$$
\begin{array}{r}
-4x^3 + 2x^2 \qquad\ + 9\\
+\ 7x^3 + 10x^2 - 3x - 4\\
\hline
3x^3 + 12x^2 - 3x + 5
\end{array}
$$

Write one polynomial under the other so that like terms appear in the same columns.

Add and combine like terms. ∎

Example 7

A Subtract horizontally: $(a^2 + 3a) - (2a^2 - 5a + 1)$.

Solution To subtract polynomials, add the opposite of every term in the subtrahend. The rest of the work is the same as adding polynomials.

$$
\begin{aligned}
(a^2 + 3a) - (2a^2 - 5a + 1) &= a^2 + 3a - 2a^2 + 5a - 1\\
&= a^2 - 2a^2 + 3a + 5a - 1\\
&= -a^2 + 8a - 1 \ \blacksquare
\end{aligned}
$$

REMEMBER

minuend − subtrahend
= difference

B Subtract vertically: $(2x^4 - 10x^2 - 6x + 1) - (2x^4 + 7x^3 + 6x + 1)$.

Solution

$$
\begin{array}{r}
2x^4 \qquad\ - 10x^2 - 6x + 1\\
-\ (2x^4 + 7x^3 \qquad\ + 6x + 1)\\
\hline
\end{array}
$$

Write the second polynomial under the first polynomial so that like terms appear in the same columns.

$$
\begin{array}{r}
2x^4 \qquad\quad - 10x^2 - 6x + 1\\
+\ (-2x^4) - 7x^3 \qquad\ - 6x - 1\\
\hline
- 7x^3 - 10x^2 - 12x
\end{array}
$$

To subtract, add the opposite of every term in the second polynomial. ∎

THINK ABOUT IT

Subtraction is not commutative. You must subtract the *second* polynomial from the *first* polynomial.

Problem Set

Determine whether each expression is a polynomial. If it is not, explain why.

1. x^0

2. $-4m^6 + \dfrac{3}{5}$

3. $3z^{-3} - 4z^2 - 5$

4. $25 - 5(\sqrt{x})^3 + 6x$

Find like terms.

5. $6d, c^3, \dfrac{1}{4}d, 25c^3$

6. $-p^3, 2p^3, 14p^2, 7p^3$

7. $10y, -10x^5, 5xy, -5y, 30xy$

8. $-\dfrac{2}{3}xy, 5x^2y, 16xy, -\dfrac{2}{3}y$

Classify each polynomial by its number of terms and by its degree.

9. $-9y + 5$

10. $6m^5 + 4m^3 - 2$

11. $-3x^2 - \dfrac{1}{2}x$

12. $-\sqrt{17}y^4$

Simplify to write each polynomial in standard form.

13. $7 + 3z - 14$

14. $13x^2 - 2 + 16x - x^2$

15. $4c^2 - 3 + \dfrac{3}{5}c^3 + c^3 - 15$

16. $12x^3 - 6x^4 - \dfrac{2}{7}x + 2x^3 - \dfrac{5}{7}x + 2x^4$

For each polynomial, find the degree, leading coefficient, and constant term.

17. $3x^2y$

18. $3m + 6 - 2m^3 + m^3$

19. $-5p + 6p^5 - 4p^3 - 3p^5 + 11p + 4$

20. $\dfrac{2}{5}x^3 - 3x + 5x^2 + 5 - 4x^4 + 6x - 13x^2$

Add or subtract. Simplify.

21. $(9m - 12) + (-3m^2 + 15 - 5m)$

22. $(4 + 5x - 3x^2) - (2x + 5)$

23. $(a^3 + 4a - 3a^2) + (-5a^3 - 2a^2 - 3)$

24. $(6y - 7y^4 - 14) - (4y^3 + 3y^4 - 5y)$

25. $(z - 3z^2) - (4 - 3z)$

26. $(2x - 6 + \dfrac{3}{4}x^3) - (4x^3 + 2x^2 + 3)$

27. $(-3x^3 - 4 + 5x) + (9 - 3x + x^3)$

28. $(-5y + 14 - 2y^4 - 3y^2) - (11 - y^4 + 3y^2)$

Solve.

*29. **Challenge** Write the simplified polynomial expression that represents the sum of the perimeters of the rectangles below.

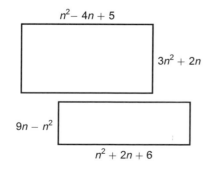

*30. **Challenge** Write the simplified polynomial expression that represents the difference of the perimeters of the isosceles triangles below.

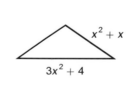
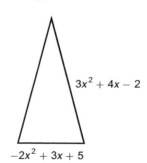

Multiplying Polynomials

To multiply polynomials, use various properties,
including the distributive property.

Multiplying Two Monomials

To multiply monomials, rearrange the factors so that the constants are
grouped together and variable factors with the same base are grouped
together. In other words, just put the constants together, the x's together,
the y's together, and so on.

Example 1 Multiply $-3x^3y^2z^6 \cdot 2x^4y$.

Solution

$$-3x^3y^2z^6 \cdot 2x^4y = -3 \cdot 2 \cdot x^3x^4 \cdot y^2y \cdot z^6 \quad \text{Commutative and Associative Properties}$$

$$= -6x^7y^3z^6 \quad \text{Product of Powers} \quad \blacksquare$$

Multiplying a Polynomial by a Monomial

The distributive property states that for any real numbers a, b, and c,
$a(b + c) = ab + ac$. The distributive property also applies when the order is
changed or when there are more than two terms in the group. For example,
$(b + c)a = ba + ca$ and $a(b + c + d) = ab + ac + ad$.

Example 2 Multiply $5a(2a^2 - 7a - 4)$.

Solution

$$5a(2a^2 - 7a - 4) = 5a \cdot 2a^2 + 5a \cdot (-7a) + 5a \cdot (-4) \quad \text{Distributive Property}$$

$$= 10a^3 - 35a^2 - 20a \quad \text{Multiply the monomials.} \quad \blacksquare$$

Multiplying a Polynomial by a Polynomial

Example 3   Multiply and simplify.

A $(3x + 2)(x - 1)$

Solution

$(3x + 2)(x - 1) = 3x(x - 1) + 2(x - 1)$
    Think of $(x - 1)$ as a single quantity. Apply the distributive property. Multiply $(x - 1)$ by $3x$ and then by 2.

$= 3x \cdot x + 3x \cdot (-1) + 2 \cdot x + 2 \cdot (-1)$
    Apply the distributive property to multiply $3x(x - 1)$. Apply the distributive property to multiply $2(x - 1)$.

$= 3x^2 - 3x + 2x - 2$
    Multiply the monomials.

$= 3x^2 - x - 2$
    Combine like terms. ∎

B $(x + 3)(x^2 - 2x - 1)$

Solution

$(x + 3)(x^2 - 2x - 1) = x(x^2 - 2x - 1) + 3(x^2 - 2x - 1)$

$= x \cdot x^2 + x \cdot (-2x) + x \cdot (-1) + 3 \cdot x^2 + 3 \cdot (-2x) + 3 \cdot (-1)$

$= x^3 - 2x^2 - x + 3x^2 - 6x - 3$

$= x^3 + x^2 - 7x - 3$ ∎

Multiplying Two Binomials Using the FOIL Method

When you apply the distributive property to multiply two polynomials, each term in one polynomial is multiplied by each term in the other polynomial. When both polynomials are binomials, you can use the FOIL method as a way to organize your steps. The letters of the word **FOIL** stand for **F**irst, **O**uter, **I**nner, and **L**ast.

THINK ABOUT IT

The FOIL method combines the distributive property and the commutative property.

Example 4   Multiply $(x + 5)(3x - 2)$.

Solution

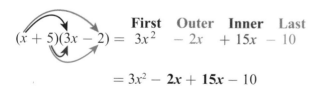

$$\begin{array}{cccc} & \textbf{First} & \textbf{Outer} & \textbf{Inner} & \textbf{Last} \\ (x + 5)(3x - 2) = & 3x^2 & - 2x & + 15x & - 10 \end{array}$$

$= 3x^2 - \mathbf{2x} + \mathbf{15x} - 10$
    Identify like terms.

$= 3x^2 + 13x - 10$
    Combine like terms. ∎

Writing Polynomial Models for Areas of Polygons

Polynomials can be used to represent areas of plane figures.

Example 5

A Write a simplified polynomial to represent the area of the rectangle.

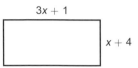

Solution Use the formula for the area of a rectangle.

$Area = length \times width$

$$A = (3x + 1)(x + 4)$$

$$= 3x^2 + 12x + x + 4 \quad \text{FOIL method}$$

$$= 3x^2 + 13x + 4 \qquad \text{Combine like terms.} \blacksquare$$

B Use two different methods to write a simplified polynomial that represents the area of the large square.

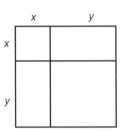

Solution

Method 1 The area of the large square is the sum of the four areas:

$x^2 + xy + xy + y^2$, or $x^2 + 2xy + y^2$.

Method 2 The length of each side of the large square is $x + y$. Use the formula for the area of a square.

$Area = side\ length \times side\ length$

$$A = (x + y)(x + y)$$

$$= x^2 + xy + xy + y^2 \quad \text{FOIL method}$$

$$= x^2 + 2xy + y^2 \qquad \text{Combine like terms.} \blacksquare$$

Problem Set

Multiply and simplify.

1. $(2xy^3z^2)(4x^3z)$

2. $(-3a^2bc)(2ab^3c)$

3. $-x^2(3x - 5)$

4. $4p(2p^2 + 3p - 1)$

5. $-6y(-3y^3 - y^2 + 2y + 3)$

6. $3xy(-2x^2 - 4xy + 5y - 3y^2)$

7. $(2y - 5)(y - 4)$

8. $(6x + 2)(2x - 3)$

9. $(3m - 1)(4m + 8)$

10. $(x + 2)(-2x^2 - x - 3)$

11. $(y^2 - 2)(4y^2 - 3y + 2)$

12. $(3x + 5)(2x^3 - 4x^2 + x - 1)$

13. $(x - 4)^2$

14. $(4y - 1)^3$

15. $(-5x + 7)^2$

16. $(-x - 4)^3$

17. $(a + b)(a^2 - ab + b^2)$

18. $(m - n)(m^2 + mn + n^2)$

Use the FOIL method to multiply. Simplify.

19. $(z + 2)(4z + 8)$

20. $(2y - 7)(y + 1)$

21. $(-4x - 2y)(3x^2 + 4)$

22. $(3x - 4)\left(\frac{1}{2}x - 6\right)$

23. $(6z^2 - z)(z + 3)$

24. $(x - 7)(\sqrt{5}x + 3\sqrt{5})$

25. $(\sqrt{2}m - 4)(3m - \sqrt{2})$

26. $(\sqrt{3}x - 2y)(\sqrt{3}x + y)$

27. $(\sqrt{8}x - 5y)(\sqrt{2}x + 6y)$

28. $(\sqrt{5}x^2 - 4xy)(\sqrt{5}x^2 - xy)$

Solve.

29. Write a simplified polynomial to represent the area of the rectangle.

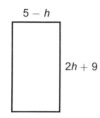

30. Write a simplified polynomial that represents the area of the large square.

*31. **Challenge** Write a polynomial expression representing the sum of the areas of 3 circles that have a radius of $5a - 2$.

*32. **Challenge** Two panoramic photographs of equal dimensions are arranged on a rectangular background. Each photograph has length $3x + 4$ and width $x - 1$. Write a polynomial expression for the area of the background surrounding the photographs.

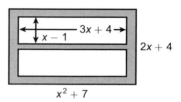

Factoring Patterns

Polynomials are written in many different forms, some of which have recognizable factoring patterns.

Factoring the Greatest Common Monomial Factor

When all the terms of a polynomial have a common factor, you can use the distributive property to factor it out. This is usually a good first thing to look for when factoring a polynomial.

Example 1 Factor the greatest common monomial factor from $16x^3 - 12x^2 + 24x$.

Solution

Step 1 Find the greatest common factor (GCF) of the polynomial. The GCF of the coefficients 16, 12, and 24 is 4, while the GCF of the variable expressions x^3, x^2, and x is x. So the GCF of the polynomial is $4x$.

Step 2 Factor out the GCF.

$16x^3 - 12x^2 + 24x = 4x(4x^2 - 3x + 6)$ ∎

Factoring Special Patterns

You can use factoring patterns of special products to factor some polynomials.

FACTORING PATTERNS

	Pattern	Example
Difference of Squares	$a^2 - b^2 = (a - b)(a + b)$	$x^2 - 16 = (x - 4)(x + 4)$
Perfect Square Trinomial	$a^2 + 2ab + b^2 = (a + b)^2$	$x^2 + 10x + 25 = (x + 5)^2$
	$a^2 - 2ab + b^2 = (a - b)^2$	$x^2 - 10x + 25 = (x - 5)^2$
Difference of Cubes	$a^3 - b^3 = (a - b)(a^2 + ab + b^2)$	$x^3 - 8 = (x - 2)(x^2 + 2x + 4)$
Sum of Cubes	$a^3 + b^3 = (a + b)(a^2 - ab + b^2)$	$x^3 + 8 = (x + 2)(x^2 - 2x + 4)$

THINK ABOUT IT
The difference of two squares is a binomial that factors into the product of two binomials.

THINK ABOUT IT
The sum of two squares cannot be factored.

Example 2 Factor.

Ⓐ $9x^2 - 121$

Solution The binomial $9x^2 - 121$ can be written as $(3x)^2 - 11^2$ and can be factored with the difference of squares pattern.

$9x^2 - 121 = (3x - 11)(3x + 11)$ ∎

Ⓑ $x^3 - 64$

Solution The binomial $x^3 - 64$ can be written as $x^3 - 4^3$ and can be factored with the difference of cubes pattern.

$x^3 - 64 = (x - 4)(x^2 + 4x + 16)$ ∎

Ⓒ $x^2 - 14x + 49$

Solution The trinomial $x^2 - 14x + 49$ can be written as $x^2 - 2 \cdot 7x + 7^2$ and can be factored with the perfect square pattern.

$x^2 - 14x + 49 = (x - 7)^2$ ∎

Ⓓ $2x^3 + 64x^2$

Solution The binomial $2x^3 + 64x^2$ has a common monomial $2x^2$ that can be factored out.

$2x^3 + 64x^2 = 2x^2(x + 32)$ ∎

Ⓔ $x^2 + 36$

Solution The binomial $x^2 + 36$ is a sum of two squares that cannot be factored. ∎

Ⓕ $x^3 + 125$

Solution The binomial $x^3 + 125$ can be written as $x^3 + 5^3$ and can be factored with the sum of cubes pattern.

$x^3 + 125 = (x + 5)(x^2 - 5x + 25)$ ∎

Factoring Trinomials of the Form $x^2 + bx + c$

When you use the FOIL method to multiply two binomials $(x + s)(x + t)$, you can write the product as follows:

$$x^2 + tx + sx + st = x^2 + (t + s)x + st.$$

So some trinomials of the form $x^2 + bx + c$ can be factored as

$$x^2 + bx + c = x^2 + (t + s)x + st$$
$$= (x + s)(x + t),$$

where $t + s = b$ and $st = c$.

You can use this pattern to help you with a guess-and-check strategy to factor trinomials of the form $x^2 + bx + c$.

> **TIP**
>
> If there are no values for *s* and *t* with product *c* and sum *b*, then the polynomial can't be factored. Any polynomial that can't be factored is a **prime polynomial**.

Example 3 Factor.

Ⓐ $x^2 + 15x + 36$

Solution In this trinomial, b and c are both positive, so s and t are both positive. Find the solution by "guessing" the factors of 36 and checking to determine which factor pair has a sum of 15.

Positive Factors of 36	Sum of the Factors
1, 36	37
2, 18	20
3, 12	15
4, 9	13
6, 6	12

So $x^2 + 15x + 36 = (x + 3)(x + 12)$. ■

Ⓑ $x^2 + 5x - 14$

Solution In this trinomial, c is negative, so s and t have opposite signs. Find the solution by "guessing" the factors of -14 and checking to determine which factor pair has a sum of 5.

Factors of -14	Sum of the Factors
1, -14	-13
-1, 14	13
-2, 7	5
2, -7	-5

So $x^2 + 5x - 14 = (x - 2)(x + 7)$. ■

Ⓒ $x^2 - 6x - 7$

Solution In this trinomial, c is negative, so s and t have opposite signs. Find the solution by "guessing" the factors of -7 and checking to determine which factor pair has a sum of -6.

Factors of -7	Sum of the Factors
1, -7	-6
-1, 7	6

So $x^2 - 6x - 7 = (x + 1)(x - 7)$. ■

D $x^2 - 13x + 22$

Solution In this trinomial, b is negative and c is positive, so s and t are both negative. Find the solution by "guessing" the factors of 22 and checking to determine which factor pair has a sum of -13.

Negative Factors of 22	Sum of the Factors
$-1, -22$	-23
$-2, -11$	-13

So $x^2 - 13x + 22 = (x - 2)(x - 11)$. ■

E $x^2 - 7x + 9$

Solution In this trinomial, b is negative and c is positive, so s and t are both negative. Write the factors of 9 and check to determine which has a sum of -7.

Factors of 9	Sum of the Factors
$-1, -9$	-10
$-3, -3$	-6

None of the factor pairs have a sum of -7, so this trinomial cannot be factored and is prime. ■

Factoring Trinomials of the Form $ax^2 + bx + c$

When a polynomial has a leading coefficient, a, other than 1, find the factors of a and the factors of c. Then use the guess-and-check strategy to find the right combination of factors of the polynomial.

Example 4 Factor.

A $3y^2 + 2y - 5$

Solution Use the factors of 3 and -5 to find all possible factors of $3y^2 + 2y - 5$.

Factors of 3	Factors of -5	Possible Factors of $3y^2 + 2y - 5$	Value of b
1, 3	1, -5	$(y + 1)(3y - 5)$	-2
		$(3y + 1)(y - 5)$	-14
	$-1, 5$	$(y - 1)(3y + 5)$	2
		$(3y - 1)(y + 5)$	14

So $3y^2 + 2y - 5 = (y - 1)(3y + 5)$. ■

B $-5r^2 + 9r + 2$

Solution

Step 1 Factor -1 from each term.

$-5r^2 + 9r + 2 = -(5r^2 - 9r - 2)$

Step 2 Factor $5r^2 - 9r - 2$.

Factors of 5	Factors of -2	Possible Factors of $5r^2 - 9r - 2$	Value of b
1, 5	1, -2	$(r + 1)(5r - 2)$	3
		$(5r + 1)(r - 2)$	-9
	$-1, 2$	$(r - 1)(5r + 2)$	-3
		$(5r - 1)(r + 2)$	9

So $-5r^2 + 9r + 2 = -(5r + 1)(r - 2)$. ■

Using Multiple Factoring Strategies

When you factor a polynomial completely, continue factoring until all factors other than monomial factors are prime. To factor completely, first look for a greatest common factor. If you find one, factor it out of the polynomial. Examine what remains. Look for a binomial (difference of squares, difference of cubes, sum of cubes) or a trinomial that can be factored.

Example 5 Factor completely.

A $4x^3 - 22x^2 - 42x$

Solution

$$4x^3 - 22x^2 - 42x = 2x(2x^2 - 11x - 21) \qquad \text{Factor out the greatest common monomial factor.}$$

$$= 2x(x - 7)(2x + 3) \qquad \text{Factor the trinomial.} ■$$

B $2x^4 - 26x^2 + 72$

Solution

$$2x^4 - 26x^2 + 72 = 2(x^4 - 13x^2 + 36) \qquad \text{Factor out the greatest common monomial factor.}$$

$$= 2(x^2 - 4)(x^2 - 9) \qquad \text{Factor the trinomial.}$$

$$= 2(x + 2)(x - 2)(x + 3)(x - 3) \qquad \text{Factor the differences of squares.} ■$$

C $-32z^2 - 48z - 18$

Solution

$$-32z^2 - 48z - 18 = -2(16z^2 + 24z + 9) \qquad \text{Factor out the greatest common monomial factor.}$$

$$= -2(4z + 3)^2 \qquad \text{Factor the perfect square trinomial.} ■$$

Problem Set

Identify the greatest common monomial factor and use it to factor the polynomial.

1. $9a^2 + 18a - 36$

2. $5x^4 - 10x^3 + 15x^2$

3. $-6c^4 - 15c^2 - 9c$

4. $6r + 9rs - 15rs^2$

5. $7m^3n - 21mn^3 + 14mn$

6. $12x^3y^2 + 24x^2y^2 - 16x^2y^3$

Factor.

7. $n^2 - 81$

8. $4x^2 - 64$

9. $144 + z^4$

10. $b^2 - 12b + 36$

11. $p^2 + 14p + 81$

12. $x^3 - 27$

13. $w^3 + 216$

14. $x^2 + 19x + 60$

15. $c^2 + 5c - 50$

16. $b^2 + 15$

17. $p^2 + 15p - 24$

18. $8y^3 + 26y^2 - 20y$

19. $3x^2 + 7x - 6$

20. $12a^2 - 8a - 15$

21. $9c^2 - 12c + 4$

22. $6t^2 + 25t - 25$

23. $6r^2 + 54r$

*24. Challenge $m^2 + 7mn + 10n^2$

Factor completely.

25. $-36n^2 + 48n - 15$

26. $8t^3 + 38t^2 - 10t$

27. $3x^4 - 60x^2 + 192$

28. $72w^2 - 24w + 2$

29. $12y^2 + 60y + 75$

*30. Challenge $4x^5 - 100x^3 + 576x$

More Factoring Patterns

Polynomials are written in many different forms, some of which are recognizable factoring patterns.

Factoring and Checking the Sum and Difference of Cube Patterns

You can check whether your factors are correct by multiplying them together.

Example 1   Factor and use multiplication to check the answer.

Ⓐ $27x^3 - 64$

Solution   The binomial $27x^3 - 64$ can be written as $(3x)^3 - 4^3$ and can be factored with the difference of cubes pattern.

$27x^3 - 64 = (3x - 4)(9x^2 + 12x + 16)$

Check

$$
\begin{array}{r}
9x^2 + 12x + 16 \\
\times \qquad 3x - \;\; 4 \\
\hline
-36x^2 - 48x - 64 \\
27x^3 + 36x^2 + 48x \qquad\quad \\
\hline
27x^3 \qquad\qquad\qquad - 64 \;\; \checkmark \;\; \blacksquare
\end{array}
$$

Ⓑ $8x^3 + 125$

Solution   The binomial $8x^3 + 125$ can be written as $(2x)^3 + 5^3$ and can be factored with the sum of cubes pattern.

$8x^3 + 125 = (2x + 5)(4x^2 - 10x + 25)$

Check

$$
\begin{array}{r}
4x^2 - 10x + \;\; 25 \\
\times \qquad\;\; 2x + \;\;\; 5 \\
\hline
20x^2 - 50x + 125 \\
8x^3 - 20x^2 + 50x \qquad\qquad \\
\hline
8x^3 \qquad\qquad\qquad\; + 125 \;\; \checkmark \;\; \blacksquare
\end{array}
$$

Factoring by Grouping

Some polynomials can be factored by grouping. With this method, a common polynomial term is factored from pairs of terms.

Example 2   Factor.

Ⓐ $x^3 + 2x^2 - 25x - 50$

Solution Group the polynomial by terms and factor out a common binomial from each group.

$$x^3 + 2x^2 - 25x - 50 = (x^3 + 2x^2) - (25x + 50) \qquad \text{Group into pairs of terms.}$$

$$= x^2(x + 2) - 25(x + 2) \qquad \text{Factor the common binomial.}$$

$$= (x^2 - 25)(x + 2) \qquad \text{Distributive Property}$$

$$= (x - 5)(x + 5)(x + 2) \qquad \text{Factor the difference of squares.} \ \blacksquare$$

B $2y^2 + 5y - 7$

Solution It doesn't look like you can group this polynomial, but if you can find a way to split the middle term, you will be able to group the polynomial by its terms.

$$2 \cdot (-7) = -14 \qquad \text{Find the product } ac.$$

$$-2, 7 \qquad \text{Find two factors of } -14 \text{ whose sum is 5.}$$

$$2y^2 - 2y + 7y - 7 \qquad \text{Rewrite } 5y \text{ as the sum of } -2y \text{ and } 7y.$$

$$= (2y^2 - 2y) + (7y - 7) \qquad \text{Group pairs of terms.}$$

$$= 2y(y - 1) + 7(y - 1) \qquad \text{Find a common binomial factor for each group.}$$

$$= (2y + 7)(y - 1) \qquad \text{Distributive Property} \ \blacksquare$$

Factoring Completely

To factor a polynomial completely, first look for a greatest common factor. If you find one, factor it out of the polynomial. Examine what remains. Look for special factors (difference of squares, difference of cubes, sum of cubes, perfect square trinomial) and try to factor by grouping. You can use the guess-and-check strategy to factor trinomials of the form $x^2 + bx + c$.

> **REMEMBER**
>
> If a polynomial cannot be factored, it is called **prime**.

Example 3 Factor completely. If the polynomial is not factorable, write *prime*.

A $20x^4 + 80x^3 - 5x^2 - 20x$

Solution

$$20x^4 + 80x^3 - 5x^2 - 20x$$

$$= 5x(4x^3 + 16x^2 - x - 4) \qquad \text{Factor the greatest common monomial factor.}$$

$$= 5x[(4x^3 + 16x^2) - (x + 4)] \qquad \text{Group into pairs of terms.}$$

$$= 5x[4x^2(x + 4) - (x + 4)] \qquad \text{Find a common binomial factor for each group.}$$

$$= 5x(4x^2 - 1)(x + 4) \qquad \text{Distributive Property}$$

$$= 5x(2x + 1)(2x - 1)(x + 4) \qquad \text{Factor the difference of squares.} \ \blacksquare$$

B $25x^4 + 16y^6$

Solution The binomial $25x^4 + 16y^6$ is prime because it has no common monomial factors and is the sum of two squares, $(5x^2)^2$ and $(4y^3)^2$. ∎

C $40a^3 + 135b^6$

Solution

$40a^3 + 135b^6 = 5(8a^3 + 27b^6)$ Factor the greatest common monomial factor.

$= 5[(2a)^3 + (3b^2)^3]$ Rewrite the factor as the sum of cubes.

$= 5[(2a + 3b^2)((2a)^2 - 2a \cdot 3b^2 + (3b^2)^2)]$ Factor the sum of cubes.

$= 5(2a + 3b^2)(4a^2 - 6ab^2 + 9b^4)$ Simplify. ∎

D $300 - 3(x - 1)^2$

Solution

$300 - 3(x - 1)^2 = 3[100 - (x - 1)^2]$ Factor the greatest common monomial factor.

$= 3[10 - (x - 1)][10 + (x - 1)]$ Factor the difference of two squares.

$= 3(10 - x + 1)(10 + x - 1)$ Simplify.

$= 3(-x + 11)(x + 9)$ Simplify. ∎

E $1 - t^6$

Solution

$1 - t^6 = (1 + t^3)(1 - t^3)$ Factor the difference of squares.

$= (1 + t)(1 - 2t + t^2)(1 - t)(1 + 2t + t^2)$ Factor the sum of cubes and the difference of cubes. ∎

Problem Set

Determine whether the polynomial is a sum or difference of cubes. If it is neither, explain why.

1. $x^3 + 8$

2. $m^6 - \dfrac{1}{27}$

3. $125c^3 - 4$

4. $64 - 8z^3$

5. $6x^3 + 3^3$

6. $81 - 27y^3$

Factor.

7. $c^9 + 125$

8. $27x^3 - 8$

9. $64 - x^3$

10. $x^3 - 1$

11. $m^9 + \dfrac{1}{8}$

12. $216x^9 + 64$

Use grouping to factor.

13. $ac - 4a + bc - 4b$

14. $2xy + xz + 4y + 2z$

15. $4x^2 - 3y + x - 12xy$

16. $x^2y - 3x^2 - 4y + 12$

Rewrite the middle term to factor. If the polynomial is not factorable, write _prime_.

17. $x^2 + 4x - 21$

18. $y^2 - 2y - 15$

19. $6x^2 - 11x - 10$

20. $3y^2 + 4y - 5$

Factor completely. If the polynomial is not factorable, write _prime_.

21. $y^3 - y^2 - 9y + 9$

22. $128(z + 2)^3 - 250$

23. $4a^3 + 24a^2 - 108a$

24. $\dfrac{1}{2}p^3 + \dfrac{1}{16}q^3$

25. $12x^2 - 16x + 24xy - 32y$

26. $36x^2 + 25y^4$

27. $3y^6 - 192$

28. $100 - 4(y + 3)^2$

*29. **Challenge** $64x^4 + 128x^3 - 100x^2 - 200x$

*30. **Challenge**
$4x^2y^2 + 4xy^2 - 24y^2 - 100x^2 - 100x + 600$

Solving Polynomial Equations

To solve a polynomial equation, set the equation equal to zero and factor completely. Then apply the zero product property to find the solutions of the equation.

> **ZERO PRODUCT PROPERTY**
>
> The **zero product property** states that if the product of two or more expressions is zero, then one or more of the expressions are equal to zero.

Solving a Polynomial Equation in Factored Form

Set each factor equal to zero to find all the solutions of the polynomial equation.

Example 1 Solve each equation.

A $(x + 1)(5x - 4) = 0$

Solution Set each factor equal to zero and solve.

$$x + 1 = 0 \qquad 5x - 4 = 0$$
$$x = -1 \qquad 5x = 4$$
$$x = \frac{4}{5}$$

The solution set is $\left\{-1, \frac{4}{5}\right\}$. ∎

> **TIP**
>
> Always be certain that the original equation is set equal to zero before solving.

B $3(2x + 1)(x - 2) = 0$

Solution For each factor containing a variable, set the factor equal to zero and solve.

$$2x + 1 = 0 \qquad x - 2 = 0$$
$$2x = -1 \qquad x = 2$$
$$x = -\frac{1}{2}$$

The solution set is $\left\{-\frac{1}{2}, 2\right\}$. ∎

Using Factoring Patterns to Solve a Polynomial Equation

You can use factoring patterns to help solve some polynomial equations, but do not try to factor and use the zero product property unless the equation has zero alone on one side.

Example 2   Use factoring and the zero product property to solve the equation.

Ⓐ $4x^2 - 16 = 9$

Solution   Set the equation equal to zero first and then factor the polynomial.

$$4x^2 - 16 = 9$$

$$4x^2 - 25 = 0 \qquad \text{Set the equation equal to zero.}$$

$$(2x - 5)(2x + 5) = 0 \qquad \text{Factor the difference of squares.}$$

Apply the zero product property.

$2x - 5 = 0$	$2x + 5 = 0$
$2x = 5$	$2x = -5$
$x = \dfrac{5}{2}$	$x = -\dfrac{5}{2}$

The solution set is $\left\{ -\dfrac{5}{2}, \dfrac{5}{2} \right\}$. ∎

Ⓑ $2x^3 + 4x^2 + 2x = 0$

Solution   Factor the polynomial completely and then solve the equation.

$$2x^3 + 4x^2 + 2x = 0$$

$$2x(x^2 + 2x + 1) = 0 \qquad \text{Factor the greatest common monomial.}$$

$$2x(x + 1)(x + 1) = 0 \qquad \text{Factor the perfect square trinomial.}$$

Apply the zero product property.

$2x = 0$	$x + 1 = 0$	$x + 1 = 0$
$x = 0$	$x = -1$	$x = -1$

The solution set is $\{-1, 0\}$. ∎

> **TIP**
>
> Because the factor $(x + 1)$ appears two times in the factored form of the equation, -1 is a solution with **multiplicity 2**.

Checking the Solutions of a Polynomial Equation

To verify that the solutions found are correct, substitute each one in the original equation. All correct solutions will make the original equation true.

Example 3   Use factoring to solve the equation and check the solutions.
$(2x + 1)^3 - (2x + 1) = 0$

Solution   Factor the polynomial completely.

$$(2x + 1)^3 - (2x + 1) = 0$$

$$(2x + 1)[(2x + 1)^2 - 1] = 0 \qquad \text{Factor the common binomial.}$$

$$(2x + 1)[(2x + 1) - 1][(2x + 1) + 1] = 0 \qquad \begin{array}{l}\text{Factor the difference of} \\ \text{squares inside the brackets.}\end{array}$$

$$(2x + 1)(2x)(2x + 2) = 0 \qquad \text{Simplify inside the brackets.}$$

Apply the zero product property.

$2x + 1 = 0$	$2x = 0$	$2x + 2 = 0$
$2x = -1$	$x = 0$	$2x = -2$
$x = -\dfrac{1}{2}$		$x = -1$

Check each solution by substituting into the original equation.

Let $x = -\dfrac{1}{2}$.

$$(2x + 1)^3 - (2x + 1) = \left(2 \cdot \left(-\frac{1}{2}\right) + 1\right)^3 - \left(2 \cdot \left(-\frac{1}{2}\right) + 1\right)$$

$$= (-1 + 1)^3 - (-1 + 1)$$

$$= 0 - 0$$

$$= 0 \checkmark$$

Let $x = 0$.

$$(2x + 1)^3 - (2x + 1) = (2 \cdot 0 + 1)^3 - (2 \cdot 0 + 1)$$

$$= 1^3 - 1$$

$$= 1 - 1$$

$$= 0 \checkmark$$

Let $x = -1$.

$$(2x + 1)^3 - (2x + 1) = (2 \cdot (-1) + 1)^3 - (2 \cdot (-1) + 1)$$

$$= (-2 + 1)^3 - (-2 + 1)$$

$$= (-1)^3 - (-1)$$

$$= -1 + 1$$

$$= 0 \checkmark$$

Each solution checks out correctly. The solution set is $\left\{-1, -\dfrac{1}{2}, 0\right\}$. ■

Problem Set

. . . .

Solve each equation.

1. $(x - 3)(x + 2) = 0$

2. $(2 - x)(4 + x) = 0$

3. $(2y + 5)(y - 3) = 0$

4. $(3s - 1)\left(2s - \dfrac{2}{3}\right) = 0$

5. $(4 - 2y)(3 - 4y) = 0$

6. $2(x + 6)(3x - 2) = 0$

7. $3\left(x + \dfrac{1}{2}\right)\left(2x - 2\dfrac{3}{4}\right) = 0$

8. $4n(2n - 5)(3n + 1.5) = 0$

9. $\left(\dfrac{1}{2}x + \dfrac{3}{4}\right)\left(\dfrac{1}{3}x - 4\right) = 0$

10. $(3t + 3.25)(t - 6)(4t + 2.5) = 0$

Use factoring and the zero product property to solve each equation.

11. $a^2 - 10 = 26$

12. $2x^2 + 3x = 0$

13. $15a^2 - 3a = 0$

14. $4x^3 + x = 0$

15. $72c^3 - 24c^2 + 2c = 0$

16. $2x^3 - 6x^2 - 8x + 24 = 0$

17. $25y^2 - 1 = 8$

18. $(3x - 4)^2 - 4x^2 = 0$

19. $3m^3 - m^2 + \dfrac{m}{12} = 0$

20. $(x - 3)^3 - (x - 3) = 0$

Use factoring to solve each equation and check the solutions.

21. $4x^2 + 3 = 4$

22. $9c^2 - 15 = 1$

23. $36x^2 = 4$

24. $12x^3 + 12x^2 + 3x = 0$

25. $12x^3 - 36x^2 + 27x = 0$

26. $(y^2 - 1)^2(y - 3)^2 = 0$

27. $\left(2x + \dfrac{1}{2}\right)^3 - \left(2x + \dfrac{1}{2}\right) = 0$

28. $\dfrac{y^2}{64} - 25 = 0$

*29. **Challenge** $\left(x - \dfrac{3}{2}\right)^2 - \left(2x + \dfrac{1}{3}\right)^2 = 0$

*30. **Challenge** $2x^5 + \dfrac{11}{2}x^4 - \dfrac{3}{2}x^3 = 0$

Power Functions

Graphs of power functions differ in shape, depending on the degree of the polynomial.

You can predict how a function will look and behave on a graph if you know its degree and leading coefficient.

Graphs of Power Functions

> **DEFINITION**
>
> A **power function** is any function that can be written in the form:
> $$f(x) = ax^n + b$$
> where n is a positive integer, a is any nonzero real number, and b is any real number.

Graphs of linear, quadratic, and cubic functions differ greatly in their appearance.

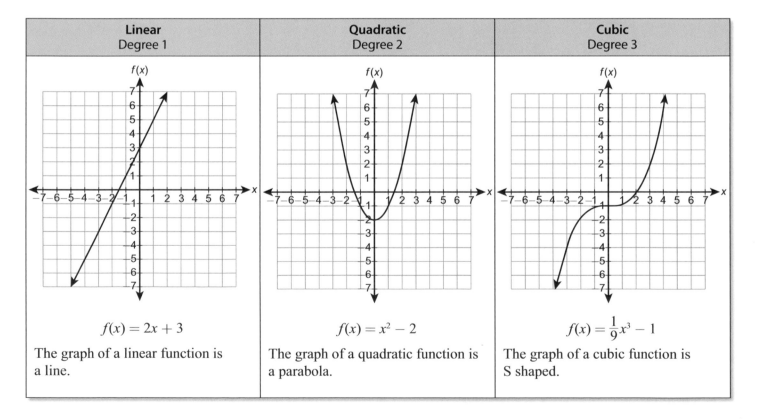

Linear Degree 1	Quadratic Degree 2	Cubic Degree 3
$f(x) = 2x + 3$	$f(x) = x^2 - 2$	$f(x) = \dfrac{1}{9}x^3 - 1$
The graph of a linear function is a line.	The graph of a quadratic function is a parabola.	The graph of a cubic function is S shaped.

Example 1 Determine whether the graph is a linear, quadratic, or cubic function.

A

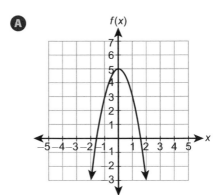

Solution The function is a parabola, so it is quadratic. ■

B

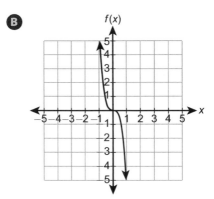

Solution The function is S shaped, so it is cubic. ■

Graphing Power Functions

Example 2

A Graph $f(x) = -x^3 + 3$.

Solution

Step 1 Make a table of values.

x	−3	−2	−1	0	1	2	3
f(x)	30	11	4	3	2	−5	−24

Step 2 Graph the function. Plot each point and join the points with a smooth curve.

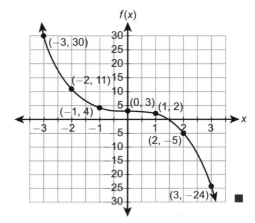

B Graph $g(x) = 4x^2 - 2$.

Solution

Step 1 Make a table of values.

x	−3	−2	−1	0	1	2	3
g(x)	34	14	2	−2	2	14	34

Step 2 Graph the function. Plot each point and join the points with a smooth curve.

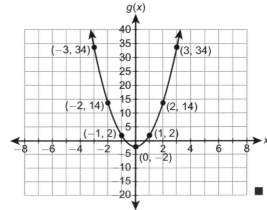

Describing the End Behavior of a Polynomial Function

Knowing what to expect for the *end behavior* of a graph can help you visualize a polynomial function.

> ## DEFINITION
>
> The **end behavior** of a function is how the function behaves when the domain values increase or decrease without bound.

The end behavior of a polynomial function depends on the degree of the function and on the sign of the leading coefficient.

End Behavior of Power Functions $f(x) = ax^n + b$	
n is even, $a > 0$ 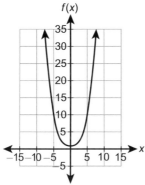 As *x* increases without bound, $f(x)$ eventually increases without bound. As *x* decreases without bound, $f(x)$ eventually increases without bound.	*n* is even, $a < 0$ 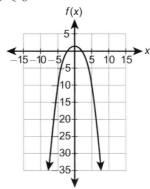 As *x* increases without bound, $f(x)$ eventually decreases without bound. As *x* decreases without bound, $f(x)$ eventually decreases without bound.
n is odd, $a > 0$ 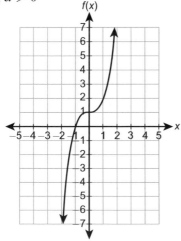 As *x* increases without bound, $f(x)$ eventually increases without bound. As *x* decreases without bound, $f(x)$ eventually decreases without bound.	*n* is odd, $a < 0$ 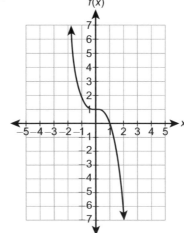 As *x* increases without bound, $f(x)$ eventually decreases without bound. As *x* decreases without bound, $f(x)$ eventually increases without bound.

Example 3 Describe the end behavior of each function.

Ⓐ $f(x) = -2x^4 + 7$

Solution The function is a quartic function and the leading coefficient is negative, so as x increases without bound, $f(x)$ eventually decreases without bound, and as x decreases without bound, $f(x)$ eventually decreases without bound. ■

Ⓑ $f(x) = x^3 - 1$

Solution The function is a cubic and the leading coefficient is positive, so as x increases without bound, $f(x)$ eventually increases without bound, and as x decreases without bound, $f(x)$ eventually decreases without bound. ■

Relating Power Functions Within a Family of Graphs

Power Function Graph Family: $f(x) = ax^n + b$

Each change in the value of a or b results in a different transformation of the parent graph, $f(x) = x^n$.

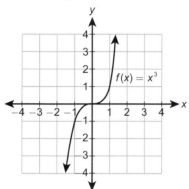

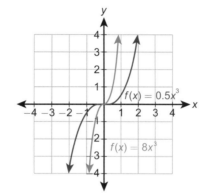

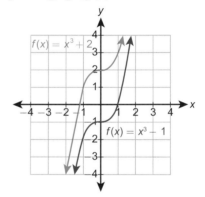

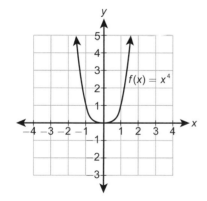

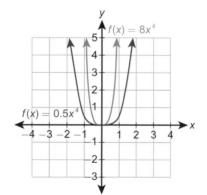

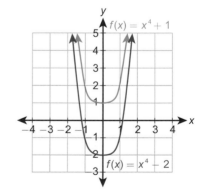

All equations of the form $f(x) = x^n$ go through the origin.

If you change only the parameter a, the graphs expand or contract while passing through the origin.

If you change only the parameter b, the graphs shift up or down on the y-axis, resulting in different y-intercepts.

Writing a Power Function when Given a Point

Example 4   Find the equation for the power function of the form $p(x) = ax^2$ that contains the point $p(-2) = 12$.

Solution

$$p(x) = ax^2$$

$$12 = a \cdot (-2)^2 \qquad \text{Substitute 12 for } p(x) \text{ and } -2 \text{ for } x.$$

$$\frac{12}{4} = a \qquad\qquad\;\; \text{Solve for } a.$$

$$3 = a$$

Substitute the value found for a into $p(x) = ax^2$. The function is $p(x) = 3x^2$. ∎

Identifying Odd and Even Functions

You can also determine whether a function is *even* or *odd*.

DEFINITIONS

A function is **even** if $f(-x) = f(x)$. The graph of an even function is symmetric about the y-axis.
A function is **odd** if $f(-x) = -f(x)$. The graph of an odd function is symmetric about the origin.

Example 5 Identify each function as even, odd, or neither.

A $f(x) = -2x^2 + 1$

Solution
Geometrically:

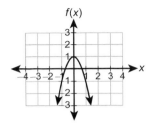

The function is symmetric about the y-axis.

Algebraically:

$$f(-x) = -2(-x)^2 + 1$$
$$= -2x^2 + 1$$
$$= f(x)$$

The function $f(x) = -2x^2 + 1$ is an even function. ■

B $f(x) = 7x^3 + 2$

Solution
Geometrically:

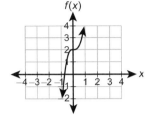

The function is not symmetric about the y-axis or the origin.

Algebraically:

$$f(-x) = 7(-x)^3 + 2$$
$$= -7x^3 + 2$$

The function $f(x) = 7x^3 + 2$ is neither even nor odd. ■

C $f(x) = 5x$

Solution
Geometrically:

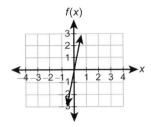

The function is symmetric about the origin.

Algebraically:

$$f(-x) = 5(-x)$$
$$= -5x$$
$$= -f(x)$$

The function $f(x) = 5x$ is an odd function. ■

Using a Table of Values to Classify a Polynomial

By finding the successive differences when given a table of values, you can determine what degree the power function has. First differences are the differences of the function values. Second differences are the differences of the first differences. Third differences are the differences of the second differences, and so on.

Linear $f(x) = 3x + 2 = 3x^1 + 2$ has 1st successive differences equal.
Quadratic $f(x) = x^2 - 4x - 5$ has 2nd successive differences equal.
Cubic $f(x) = 2x^3 + 9$ has 3rd successive differences equal.
Quartic $f(x) = 5x^4 - 3x^2 + 1$ has 4th successive differences equal.

SUCCESSIVE DIFFERENCES OF POWER FUNCTIONS

An nth power function has a constant nth successive difference.

Example 6 Determine whether the table of values represents a linear, quadratic, or cubic function.

A

x	−2	−1	0	1	2
f(x)	−8	−6	−4	−2	0

−2   −2   −2   −2

Solution The differences of successive $f(x)$ values are equal, so this table of values represents a linear function. ■

B

x	−2	−1	0	1	2
g(x)	7	4	3	4	7

3   1   −1   −3

2   2   2

Solution The successive differences of $g(x)$ values are not equal, so find the differences of the first differences. Because these second differences are equal, the table of values represents a quadratic function. ■

C

x	−4	−3	−2	−1	0	1	2	3	4
h(x)	−64	−27	−8	−1	0	1	8	27	64

−37   −19   −7   −1   −1   −7   −19   −37

−18   −12   −6   0   6   12   18

−6   −6   −6   −6   −6   −6

> **THINK ABOUT IT**
> The domain of every polynomial function is the set of real numbers.

Solution The successive differences of $h(x)$ are not equal and the second differences are not equal, so find the third differences. The third differences are equal, so the table of values represents a cubic function. ■

Problem Set

Determine whether the graph appears to be a linear, quadratic, or cubic function.

1.

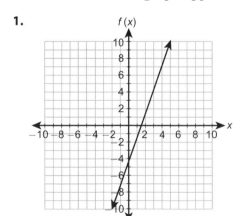

2.

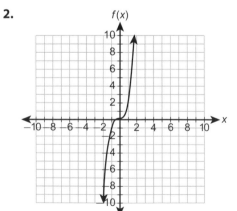

3.

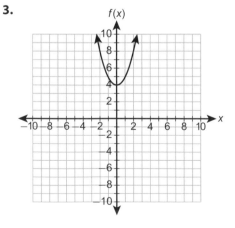

Graph each power function.

4. $f(x) = 5x^3 + 1$

5. $h(x) = -x^2 - 3$

6. $f(x) = x^2 + 6$

7. $s(x) = \frac{1}{4}x^4$

8. $m(x) = x^3 - \frac{3}{2}$

9. $f(x) = 6x^4 - 2$

10. $g(x) = 2x^5$

11. $s(x) = \frac{1}{7}x - 3$

Determine the effects each parameter has on the graph of a power function by comparing $f(x)$ and $g(x)$.

12. $f(x) = x^2$ and $g(x) = 0.25x^2$

13. $f(x) = x^3$ and $g(x) = -3x^3$

14. $f(x) = 6x$ and $g(x) = 6x - 8$

15. $f(x) = x^4$ and $g(x) = 5x^4 + 12$

Write the specific equation of the power function $p(x)$ that passes through the given point.

16. $p(x) = ax^2$ and $p(2) = 6$

17. $p(x) = ax^3$ and $p(3) = 18$

18. $p(x) = ax^4$ and $p(1) = 8$

19. $p(x) = ax$ and $p(-4) = 12$

For each function, do the following:

A. Identify the function as even, odd, or neither.

B. Describe the end behavior of the function.

20. $f(x) = -3x^3 + 4$

21. $f(x) = -6x^2 + 2$

22. $f(x) = 13x^2 - 9$

23. $f(x) = 10x + 4$

24. $f(x) = -20x^4 + 6$

25. $f(x) = 4x^3$

Determine what degree the power function has, using the table of values.

26.

x	-2	-1	0	1	2
$f(x)$	2	-4	-6	-4	2

28.

x	-2	-1	0	1	2
$h(x)$	40	5	0	-5	-40

27.

x	-2	-1	0	1	2
$g(x)$	-36	-17	2	21	40

29.

x	-2	-1	0	1	2
$f(x)$	38	-7	-10	-7	38

Solve.

*30. Challenge Your cell phone provider charges $1 for your first text message and $0.25 for each additional text message. Write the function that represents the total cost of text messaging. Determine whether this function is odd, even, or neither.

*31. Challenge A 6'1" batter hits a baseball hits a baseball over a 400' center field fence for a home run. The path of the ball, time versus ball height, can be written as a power function. Determine the end behavior of this function.

UNIT 6   Rational Equations

You can use a rational function to model the intensity of sound.

The intensity of sound is inversely proportional to the square of the distance from the sound source. For instance, if Paulina is twice as far from the stage as Ric, then she hears sound that is one-fourth the intensity Ric hears.

Big Ideas

▶ The laws of arithmetic can be used to simplify algebraic expressions and equations.

▶ Expressions and equations express relationships between different entities.

▶ A function is a correspondence between two sets, the domain and the range, that assigns to each member of the domain exactly one member of the range.

Unit Topics

▶ Foundations for Unit 6

▶ Dividing Monomials and Polynomials

▶ Operations with Rational Expressions

▶ Compound Fractions

▶ Solving Rational Equations

▶ Reciprocal Power Functions

▶ Graphing Rational Functions

Foundations for Unit 6

Before you learn about rational equations, you should know how to do the following:

▶ Add and subtract fractions.

▶ Multiply fractions.

▶ Use quotient properties of exponents to simplify expressions.

Adding and Subtracting Fractions

You can add or subtract two fractions with a common denominator by adding or subtracting the numerators of the fractions and keeping the denominator the same.

Definition

least common denominator (LCD) the least common multiple of (the smallest number that all the denominators will divide into evenly)

Example 1 Add or subtract the following fractions.

Ⓐ $\dfrac{2}{3} + \dfrac{3}{4} = \dfrac{2 \cdot 4}{3 \cdot 4} + \dfrac{3 \cdot 3}{4 \cdot 3}$

$= \dfrac{8}{12} + \dfrac{9}{12}$

$= \dfrac{17}{12}$

$= 1\dfrac{5}{12}$

Ⓑ $\dfrac{x}{z} - \dfrac{y}{z} = \dfrac{x - y}{z}$

Ⓒ $\dfrac{a}{b} + \dfrac{c}{d} = \dfrac{a \cdot d}{b \cdot d} + \dfrac{c \cdot b}{d \cdot b}$

$= \dfrac{ad}{bd} + \dfrac{bc}{bd}$

$= \dfrac{ad + bc}{bd}$

Problem Set A

Add or subtract the following fractions.

1. $\dfrac{5}{6} - \dfrac{1}{3}$

2. $\dfrac{3}{8} + \dfrac{3}{5}$

3. $\dfrac{a}{b} + \dfrac{c}{b}$

4. $\dfrac{r}{t} - \dfrac{s}{t}$

5. $\dfrac{x}{y} + \dfrac{a}{b}$

6. $\dfrac{a}{b} - \dfrac{c}{d}$

Multiplying and Dividing Fractions

To multiply two fractions, multiply the numerators and multiply the denominators.

Example 2   Multiply.

A $\dfrac{a}{b} \cdot \dfrac{c}{d} = \dfrac{a \cdot c}{b \cdot d} = \dfrac{ac}{bd}$

B $\dfrac{2}{3} \cdot \dfrac{3}{4} = \dfrac{\overset{1}{\cancel{2}} \cdot \overset{1}{\cancel{3}}}{\cancel{3} \cdot \cancel{4}} = \dfrac{1}{2}$

C $\dfrac{r}{t} \cdot \dfrac{s}{t} = \dfrac{r \cdot s}{t \cdot t} = \dfrac{rs}{t^2}$

To divide two fractions, you find the reciprocal of the divisor and then multiply the numerators and multiply the denominators.

Example 3   Divide.

A $\dfrac{7}{8} \div \dfrac{3}{4} = \dfrac{7}{8} \cdot \dfrac{4}{3} = \dfrac{7 \cdot \overset{1}{\cancel{4}}}{\underset{2}{\cancel{8}} \cdot 3}$
$= \dfrac{7}{6} = 1\dfrac{1}{6}$

B $\dfrac{a}{b} \div \dfrac{c}{d} = \dfrac{a}{b} \cdot \dfrac{d}{c}$
$= \dfrac{a \cdot d}{b \cdot c} = \dfrac{ad}{bc}$

C $\dfrac{x}{z} \div \dfrac{y}{z} = \dfrac{x}{z} \cdot \dfrac{z}{y}$
$= \dfrac{x \cdot \overset{1}{\cancel{z}}}{\underset{1}{\cancel{z}} \cdot y} = \dfrac{x}{y}$

Problem Set B

Multiply.

7. $\dfrac{3}{4} \cdot \dfrac{1}{4}$

8. $\dfrac{7}{12} \cdot \dfrac{3}{7}$

9. $\dfrac{7}{10} \cdot \dfrac{5}{6}$

10. $\dfrac{x}{y} \cdot \dfrac{t}{y}$

11. $\dfrac{u}{v} \cdot \dfrac{w}{x}$

12. $\dfrac{a}{b} \cdot \dfrac{a}{c}$

Divide.

13. $\dfrac{3}{8} \div \dfrac{1}{8}$

14. $\dfrac{5}{12} \div \dfrac{3}{5}$

15. $\dfrac{1}{2} \div \dfrac{1}{4}$

16. $\dfrac{x}{y} \div \dfrac{x}{z}$

17. $\dfrac{c}{d} \div \dfrac{e}{f}$

18. $\dfrac{r}{s} \div \dfrac{s}{r}$

Using Properties of Exponents to Simplify an Algebraic Expression

You can use properties of negative exponents and quotients to simplify expressions.

PROPERTIES OF EXPONENTS

Let a and b be nonzero real numbers. Let m and n be integers.

Property	Statement	Examples
Negative Exponent	$a^{-m} = \dfrac{1}{a^m}$	$5^{-2} = \dfrac{1}{5^2} = \dfrac{1}{25}$
Quotient of Powers	$\dfrac{a^m}{a^n} = a^{m-n}$	$\dfrac{2^5}{2^2} = 2^{5-2} = 2^3 = 8$
Power of a Quotient	$\left(\dfrac{a}{b}\right)^m = \dfrac{a^m}{b^m}$	$\left(\dfrac{2}{3}\right)^3 = \dfrac{2^3}{3^3} = \dfrac{8}{27}$

Example 4   Simplify each expression.

Ⓐ $2^{-3} = \dfrac{1}{2^3}$

$\qquad = \dfrac{1}{8}$

Ⓑ $\dfrac{3^7}{3^5} = 3^{7-5}$

$\qquad = 3^2$

Ⓒ $\left(\dfrac{3}{4}\right)^4 = \dfrac{3^4}{4^4}$

$\qquad = \dfrac{81}{256}$

Ⓓ $xy^{-3} = x \cdot \dfrac{1}{y^3}$

$\qquad = \dfrac{x}{y^3}$

Ⓔ $\dfrac{z^a}{z^b} = z^{a-b}$

Ⓕ $\left(\dfrac{ab}{c}\right)^2 = \dfrac{(ab)^2}{c^2}$

$\qquad = \dfrac{a^2b^2}{c^2}$

Problem Set C

Simplify each expression.

19. 6^{-3}

20. $\dfrac{5^6}{5^3}$

21. $\left(\dfrac{2}{3}\right)^5$

22. $a^{-3}b$

23. $\dfrac{c^x}{c^y}$

24. $\left(\dfrac{r}{st}\right)^3$

Dividing Monomials and Polynomials

A *ratio* is a comparison of two quantities, often written as a fraction. If the quantities are represented by polynomials, the ratio is a *rational expression*.

DEFINITION

A **rational expression** is a ratio whose numerator and denominator are polynomials, and the denominator is nonzero.

Finding Restrictions on the Domain of a Rational Expression

To find the domain of a rational expression, find the values of the variables that make the denominator equal to 0. These values are excluded from the domain.

Example 1 Find the domain restrictions for each expression.

A $\dfrac{x^4y}{3xy^5}$

Solution $3xy^5 = 0$ when $x = 0$ or $y = 0$.

The domain restrictions are $x \neq 0$ and $y \neq 0$. ■

B $\dfrac{3x^3 - 7x}{4 - 3x}$

Solution

$4 - 3x = 0$

$\quad 4 = 3x$

$\quad \dfrac{4}{3} = x$

The domain restriction is $x \neq \dfrac{4}{3}$. ■

C $\dfrac{x^2 + 10x - 5}{x^2 + 2x - 48}$

Solution

$\qquad x^2 + 2x - 48 = 0$

$\qquad (x + 8)(x - 6) = 0$

$x + 8 = 0 \qquad\qquad \text{or} \qquad\qquad x - 6 = 0$

$\quad x = -8 \qquad\qquad\qquad\qquad\qquad x = 6$

The domain restrictions are $x \neq -8$ and $x \neq 6$. ■

Simplifying Rational Expressions

Simplifying a rational expression is similar to simplifying a fraction. Identify and divide out any factors you find in the numerator and denominator. Be careful, though; both the numerator and denominator must be written as products of factors. You can't divide out a factor in the denominator with a term that is being added in the numerator.

Example 2   Find the domain restrictions and simplify each expression.

A $\dfrac{8x^2y^5}{24xy^7}$

Solution   The domain restrictions are $x \neq 0$ and $y \neq 0$.

$\dfrac{8x^2y^5}{24xy^7} = \dfrac{8xy^5 \cdot x}{8xy^5 \cdot 3y^2}$ Factor the greatest common factor from the numerator and denominator.

$= \dfrac{\overset{1}{\cancel{8xy^5}} \cdot x}{\underset{1}{\cancel{8xy^5}} \cdot 3y^2}$ Divide out the common factor.

$= \dfrac{x}{3y^2}$ Simplify. ∎

B $\dfrac{8a^2 - 20a + 16}{4a}$

Solution   To find the restrictions on the domain, set $4a = 0$ and solve. The domain restriction is $a \neq 0$.

$\dfrac{8a^2 - 20a + 16}{4a} = \dfrac{8a^2}{4a} - \dfrac{20a}{4a} + \dfrac{16}{4a}$ Divide each term of the polynomial by the monomial.

$= \dfrac{\overset{2a}{\cancel{8a^2}}}{\underset{1}{\cancel{4a}}} - \dfrac{\overset{5}{\cancel{20a}}}{\underset{1}{\cancel{4a}}} + \dfrac{\overset{4}{\cancel{16}}}{\underset{a}{\cancel{4a}}}$ Divide out common factors.

$= 2a - 5 + \dfrac{4}{a}$ Simplify. ∎

C $\dfrac{(x + 1)(x + 3)}{(x + 1)(x + 2)}$

Solution   To find the restrictions on the domain, set $(x + 1)(x + 2) = 0$ and solve. The domain restrictions are $x \neq -1$ and $x \neq -2$.

$\dfrac{(x + 1)(x + 3)}{(x + 1)(x + 2)} = \dfrac{\overset{1}{\cancel{(x + 1)}}(x + 3)}{\underset{1}{\cancel{(x + 1)}}(x + 2)}$ Divide out the common factor.

$= \dfrac{x + 3}{x + 2}$ Simplify. ∎

A rational expression is in simplest form when the numerator and denominator have no common factors other than 1.

TIP

In Example 2A, you can find the greatest common factor of the numerator and denominator with the same strategies that you use to find the greatest common monomial factor in the polynomial $8x^2y^5 + 24xy^7$.

D $\dfrac{3x^2 + 16x - 12}{x^2 + 2x - 24}$

Solution   To find the domain restrictions, set $x^2 + 2x - 24 = 0$ and solve.

$$x^2 + 2x - 24 = 0$$

$$(x - 4)(x + 6) = 0$$

$x - 4 = 0$ or $x + 6 = 0$

$x = 4$ $x = -6$

The domain restrictions are $x \neq 4$ and $x \neq -6$.

$$\dfrac{3x^2 + 16x - 12}{x^2 + 2x - 24} = \dfrac{(3x - 2)(x + 6)}{(x - 4)(x + 6)} \quad \text{Factor the trinomials.}$$

$$= \dfrac{(3x - 2)(x + \cancel{6})^{1}}{(x - 4)(x + \cancel{6})_{1}} \quad \text{Divide out the common factor.}$$

$$= \dfrac{3x - 2}{x - 4} \quad \text{Simplify.} \ \blacksquare$$

E $\dfrac{5x^2 - 20x}{4 - x}$

Solution   To find the restrictions on the domain, set $4 - x = 0$ and solve.

$$4 - x = 0$$

$$4 = x$$

The domain restriction is $x \neq 4$.

$$\dfrac{5x^2 - 20x}{4 - x} = \dfrac{5x(x - 4)}{4 - x} \quad \text{Factor the numerator.}$$

$$= \dfrac{5x(x - 4)}{-1(x - 4)} \quad \begin{array}{l} x - 4 \text{ and } 4 - x \text{ are opposites. Rewrite } 4 - x \\ \text{in the denominator as } -1(x - 4). \end{array}$$

$$= \dfrac{5x(x - \cancel{4})^{1}}{-1(x - \cancel{4})_{1}} \quad \text{Divide out the common factor.}$$

$$= -5x \quad \text{Simplify.} \ \blacksquare$$

> **TIP**
>
> To demonstrate that $x - 4$ and $4 - x$ are opposites, choose a value for x.
>
> Let $x = 7$.
>
> Then $x - 4 = 7 - 4 = 3$ and $4 - x = 4 - 7 = -3$.
>
> In general, binomial factors of the forms $(a - b)$ and $(b - a)$ are opposites of each other, and $\dfrac{a - b}{b - a} = -1$.

Problem Set

Find the domain restrictions for each expression.

1. $\dfrac{x^2 y^5}{5x^3 y^2}$

2. $\dfrac{3ab^2}{a^3 b^3}$

3. $\dfrac{2t^3 - 3}{5 + 2t}$

4. $\dfrac{2v(2v^3 + 3)}{5v - 4}$

5. $\dfrac{d^2(d^3 - 7)}{3d + 6}$

6. $\dfrac{(y - 3)(y + 3)}{2(2 - y)}$

7. $\dfrac{x^2 + 4x - 3}{x^2 + 2x - 8}$

8. $\dfrac{a^2 - 5a + 2}{a^2 - 7a + 6}$

9. $\dfrac{r^2 - r + 3}{r^2 + r - 12}$

For each expression, do the following:

A. Find the domain restrictions.

B. Simplify the expression.

10. $\dfrac{10x^4y^7}{5x^3y^5}$

11. $\dfrac{2p^2q^9}{14p^5q^3}$

12. $\dfrac{3a^6b^8}{18a^4b^7}$

13. $\dfrac{(x-2)(x+5)}{(x-3)(x-2)}$

14. $\dfrac{(2-g)(g+4)}{(g+4)(5-g)}$

15. $\dfrac{(3-n)(5+n)}{(n-3)(5+n)}$

16. $\dfrac{3x^2+6x-9}{3x}$

17. $\dfrac{4t^2-12t+16}{4t}$

18. $\dfrac{5p^2+15p+20}{5p}$

19. $\dfrac{2r^3+3r^2+5r}{r}$

20. $\dfrac{6m^4+3m^2-12m}{6m}$

21. $\dfrac{14f^5+28f^3+7f}{7f}$

22. $\dfrac{s^2+4s+4}{s^2-2s-8}$

23. $\dfrac{a^2+a-6}{a^2-9}$

24. $\dfrac{q^2+6q-7}{q^2-9q+8}$

25. $\dfrac{v^2+2v-15}{v-3}$

26. $\dfrac{c^2-11c+18}{c-2}$

27. $\dfrac{h^2+9h+20}{h+4}$

*28. Challenge $\dfrac{3x^2yz^3-6x^2y^2z^3}{3yz^3-6y^2z^3}$

*29. Challenge $\dfrac{c^2-3c-10}{(c-5)\sqrt{c+2}}$

Solve.

*30. Challenge The vertical asymptote of the graph of an equation is where the denominator equals zero after the equation has been simplified. The following equations are related to the expressions in Problems 22, 23, and 24. What are the equations of the asymptotes?

A. $y=\dfrac{x^2+4x+4}{x^2-2x-8}$

B. $y=\dfrac{x^2+x-6}{x^2-9}$

C. $y=\dfrac{x^2+6x-7}{x^2-9x+8}$

Operations with Rational Expressions

As with numbers, rational expressions can be added, subtracted, multiplied, or divided.

Adding or Subtracting Rational Expressions with Like Denominators

To add or subtract rational expressions with like denominators, add or subtract the numerators. Keep the same common denominator.

Example 1 Add.

$$\frac{x^2 + 2x}{x - 3} + \frac{x^2 - 3x - 15}{x - 3}$$

Solution

$$\frac{x^2 + 2x}{x - 3} + \frac{x^2 - 3x - 15}{x - 3} = \frac{(x^2 + 2x) + (x^2 - 3x - 15)}{x - 3} \quad \text{Add the numerators.}$$

$$= \frac{2x^2 - x - 15}{x - 3} \quad \text{Combine like terms.}$$

$$= \frac{(2x + 5)(x - 3)}{x - 3} \quad \text{Factor and reduce if possible.}$$

$$= 2x + 5 \quad \text{Simplify.} \blacksquare$$

Adding or Subtracting Rational Expressions with Unlike Denominators

To add or subtract rational expressions with unlike denominators, first rewrite the expressions with a common denominator, preferably the least common denominator. Then add or subtract.

> **DEFINITION**
>
> The **least common denominator (LCD)** of two rational expressions is the least common multiple of the denominators.

> **TIP**
>
> **How to Find the Least Common Denominator**
>
> **Step 1** Fully factor each denominator.
>
> **Step 2** Write each factor the greatest number of times it appears in any one denominator.
>
> **Step 3** Multiply the factors described in Step 2; the LCD is the product of those factors.

Example 2 Subtract.

Ⓐ $\dfrac{7x + 3}{(x + 1)(x - 3)} - \dfrac{5}{x + 1}$

Solution

$\dfrac{7x + 3}{(x + 1)(x - 3)} - \dfrac{5}{x + 1}$ The denominators are in factored form.

The LCD is $\underset{\substack{(x + 1)\text{ appears}\\ \text{once in the first}\\ \text{and second}\\ \text{denominator.}}}{\underbrace{x + 1}} \cdot \underset{\substack{(x - 3)\text{ appears}\\ \text{once in the first}\\ \text{denominator.}}}{\underbrace{x - 3}}.$ Write the LCD by writing each factor the greatest number of times it appears in any denominator.

$= \dfrac{7x + 3}{(x + 1)(x - 3)} - \dfrac{5}{x + 1} \cdot \dfrac{x - 3}{x - 3}$ The first ratio has the LCD. Multiply the second ratio by 1. For the appropriate form of 1, decide what factor(s) would be needed to get the LCD.

$= \dfrac{7x + 3}{(x + 1)(x - 3)} - \dfrac{5x - 15}{(x + 1)(x - 3)}$ Expand the second numerator.

$= \dfrac{(7x + 3) - (5x - 15)}{(x + 1)(x - 3)}$ Subtract the numerators.

$= \dfrac{2x + 18}{(x + 1)(x - 3)}$ Simplify the numerator.

$= \dfrac{2(x + 9)}{(x + 1)(x - 3)}$ You can factor out a 2, but no factors can be divided out. The last expression is in simplified form. ■

Ⓑ $\dfrac{8}{5a^3 + 25a^2} - \dfrac{a + 2}{a^3 + 10a^2 + 25a}$

Solution

$\dfrac{8}{5a^3 + 25a^2} - \dfrac{a + 2}{a^3 + 10a^2 + 25a}$

$= \dfrac{8}{5a^2(a + 5)} - \dfrac{a + 2}{a(a + 5)(a + 5)}$ Factor the denominators so you can find the LCD.

The LCD is $\underset{\substack{5\text{ appears once}\\ \text{in the first}\\ \text{denominator.}}}{\underbrace{5}} \cdot \underset{\substack{a\text{ appears twice (2nd}\\ \text{power) in the first}\\ \text{denominator and once}\\ \text{in the second.}}}{\underbrace{a^2}} \cdot \underset{\substack{(a + 5)\text{ appears}\\ \text{twice in the second}\\ \text{denominator.}}}{\underbrace{(a + 5)(a + 5)}}$ Write the LCD by writing each factor the greatest number of times it appears in any denominator.

$= \dfrac{8}{5a^2(a + 5)} \cdot \dfrac{a + 5}{a + 5} - \dfrac{a + 2}{a(a + 5)(a + 5)} \cdot \dfrac{5a}{5a}$ Multiply each ratio by 1. To determine the appropriate form of 1 for each ratio, decide what factor(s) would be needed to get the LCD as the denominator.

$= \dfrac{8a + 40}{5a^2(a + 5)(a + 5)} - \dfrac{5a^2 + 10a}{5a^2(a + 5)(a + 5)}$ Expand the numerators.

$= \dfrac{(8a + 40) - (5a^2 + 10a)}{5a^2(a + 5)(a + 5)}$ Subtract the numerators.

$= \dfrac{-5a^2 - 2a + 40}{5a^2(a + 5)(a + 5)}$ Simplify the numerator to get $-5a^2 - 2a + 40$, which cannot be factored. So no factors can be divided out, and the last expression is in simplified form. ■

Multiplying Rational Expressions

To multiply rational expressions, multiply the numerators and multiply the denominators. Divide out common factors to simplify.

Example 3 Multiply.

Ⓐ $\dfrac{3h}{(h-7)(h-2)} \cdot \dfrac{h-7}{h(h+8)}$

> **TIP**
>
> $\dfrac{3}{(h-2)(h+8)}$ and $\dfrac{3}{h^2+6h-16}$ are both in simplified form. Recognizing that they are equal can be helpful when you work with rational functions.

Solution

$\dfrac{3h}{(h-7)(h-2)} \cdot \dfrac{h-7}{h(h+8)} = \dfrac{3h(h-7)}{(h-7)(h-2)(h)(h+8)}$

The polynomials are in factored form, so multiply the numerators and the denominators.

$= \dfrac{3\cancel{h}(h-7)}{(h-7)(h-2)(\cancel{h})(h+8)}$

Divide out common factors.

$= \dfrac{3}{(h-2)(h+8)}$

Simplify.

$= \dfrac{3}{h^2+6h-16}$

Alternate simplified form ■

Ⓑ $\dfrac{2x^2-10x}{x^2-2x-8} \cdot \dfrac{x+2}{6x^3-30x^2}$

Solution

$\dfrac{2x^2-10x}{x^2-2x-8} \cdot \dfrac{x+2}{6x^3-30x^2} = \dfrac{2x(x-5)}{(x+2)(x-4)} \cdot \dfrac{x+2}{6x^2(x-5)}$

Factor the polynomials.

$= \dfrac{2x(x-5)(x+2)}{(x+2)(x-4)(6x^2)(x-5)}$

Multiply the numerators and the denominators.

$= \dfrac{2\cancel{x}(x-5)(x+2)}{(x+2)(x-4)(2\cancel{x} \cdot 3x)(x-5)}$

Divide out common factors. To identify the greatest common monomial factor, write $6x^2$ as $2x \cdot 3x$.

$= \dfrac{1}{(3x)(x-4)}$

Simplify.

$= \dfrac{1}{3x^2-12x}$

Alternate simplified form ■

Dividing Rational Expressions

To divide by a rational expression, multiply by its reciprocal.

Example 4 Divide.

Ⓐ $\dfrac{5(x-2)}{(x+12)(x+3)} \div \dfrac{15(x-2)}{x(x+12)}$

Solution Write the division problem as multiplying by a reciprocal.

$\dfrac{5(x-2)}{(x+12)(x+3)} \div \dfrac{15(x-2)}{x(x+12)} = \dfrac{5(x-2)}{(x+12)(x+3)} \cdot \dfrac{x(x+12)}{15(x-2)}$

Multiply by the reciprocal of the divisor.

$= \dfrac{\cancel{5}(x-2)(x)(x+12)}{(x+12)(x+3)(\underset{3}{\cancel{15}})(x-2)}$

Multiply numerators and denominators. Divide out common factors.

$= \dfrac{x}{3(x+3)}$ or $\dfrac{x}{3x+9}$

Simplify. ■

B $\dfrac{p^2 - 16}{4p^2 + 4p + 1} \div \dfrac{2p^2 - 7p - 4}{6p^2 + 3p}$

Solution Write the division problem as multiplying by a reciprocal.

$$\dfrac{p^2 - 16}{4p^2 + 4p + 1} \div \dfrac{2p^2 - 7p - 4}{6p^2 + 3p} = \dfrac{p^2 - 16}{4p^2 + 4p + 1} \cdot \dfrac{6p^2 + 3p}{2p^2 - 7p - 4}$$ Multiply by the reciprocal of the divisor.

$$= \dfrac{(p + 4)(p - 4)}{(2p + 1)(2p + 1)} \cdot \dfrac{3p(2p + 1)}{(p - 4)(2p + 1)}$$ Factor.

$$= \dfrac{(p + 4)(p - 4)(3p)(2p + 1)}{(2p + 1)(2p + 1)(p - 4)(2p + 1)}$$ Multiply numerators and denominators. Divide out common factors.

$$= \dfrac{3p(p + 4)}{(2p + 1)^2} \ \text{ or } \ \dfrac{3p^2 + 12p}{4p^2 + 4p + 1}$$ Simplify. ■

Problem Set

Add or subtract the expressions and simplify.

1. $\dfrac{x - 3x^2 + 1}{2x - 1} + \dfrac{5x^2 + 6}{2x - 1}$

2. $\dfrac{5t^2 - 5}{3t + 1} - \dfrac{3t + 2}{3t + 1}$

3. $\dfrac{q^2 - q - 1}{q^3} - \dfrac{2q^2 + 2q - 1}{q^3}$

4. $\dfrac{6y + 1 - 3y^2}{y^2 - 5} + \dfrac{4y^3 + 5y^2}{y^2 - 5}$

5. $\dfrac{4b^2 - 3b}{3b - 5} - \dfrac{2b^2 + 17b - 4}{3b - 5}$

6. $\dfrac{x}{3x + 8} + \dfrac{x + 1}{x - 3}$

7. $\dfrac{4x}{5x - 4} - \dfrac{3x}{x + 2}$

8. $\dfrac{5}{x - 1} - \dfrac{2x}{(x - 1)(2x + 3)}$

9. $\dfrac{x - 5}{(x + 4)(x - 4)} + \dfrac{2}{(x - 4)(x - 2)}$

10. $\dfrac{a}{4a^2 + 16a} + \dfrac{a - 1}{8a^2 + 12a}$

11. $\dfrac{12}{x^3 + x} - \dfrac{3x - 2}{10x^3 + 10x}$

12. $\dfrac{4}{3v - 15v^2} - \dfrac{3v}{2 - 20v + 50v^2}$

13. $\dfrac{x + 3}{3x^2 + 6x} + \dfrac{x - 4}{3x^2 - 12x}$

14. $\dfrac{z - 2}{2z^2 + 9z - 5} - \dfrac{6z}{12z^3 - 6z^2}$

Multiply or divide the expressions and simplify. Assume that no denominator equals zero.

15. $\dfrac{x^2(x - 1)}{(x + 5)(x - 3)} \cdot \dfrac{x + 5}{x(x - 1)}$

16. $\dfrac{4n(n + 3)}{n - 2} \cdot \dfrac{n - 2}{4n^2}$

17. $\dfrac{5x(x - 3)}{x^2 + 1} \div \dfrac{x - 3}{x^2 + 1}$

18. $\dfrac{4c^3}{(c + 3)(c - 2)} \div \dfrac{2c}{(c - 2)}$

19. $\dfrac{3(w^2 - 4)}{w - 2} \cdot \dfrac{6w}{w + 2}$

20. $\dfrac{y^2(y - 1)}{y(y + 4)} \div \dfrac{y(y - 1)}{4y}$

21. $\dfrac{(x - 4)}{x^2} \div \dfrac{9(x - 4)}{x^3(3x - 2)}$

22. $\dfrac{4r - r^2}{r^2 - r - 2} \cdot \dfrac{r + 1}{24r - 6r^2}$

23. $\dfrac{d^2 - 25}{6d - 2} \div \dfrac{d^2 - 2d - 15}{18d^2 - 6d}$

24. $\dfrac{3b^2 - b - 2}{3b^2 - 9b} \div \dfrac{15b + 10}{6(b^2 - 5b + 6)}$

25. $\dfrac{6x^2 - 6x}{12x^3 + 8x^2} \div \dfrac{2x^2 - 2x}{3x^3 + 2x^2}$

26. $\dfrac{3g}{21g + 42} \cdot \dfrac{7g^2 - 35g}{g^3 - 5g^2}$

27. $\dfrac{(3x - 1)^2}{6x^2 + 12x} \cdot \dfrac{4x^2 + 8x}{24x^2 - 8x}$

28. $\dfrac{y^2 - 3y - 10}{6y - 3} \div \dfrac{3y - 15}{12y^3 - 6y^2}$

Simplify. Assume that no denominator equals zero.

***29.** **Challenge** $\dfrac{k + 1}{k^2 + 6k + 9} + \dfrac{4}{k + 3} - \dfrac{(-6)}{k - 1}$

***30.** **Challenge** $\dfrac{a^2 - 3a + 2}{2a} \div \dfrac{a - 2}{a + 3} \cdot \dfrac{4a^3 - 8a^2}{a^2 + a - 6}$

Compound Fractions

A compound event involves two or more actions. Similarly, a *compound fraction* has two or more operations.

TIP

A compound fraction can contain numerical fractions, rational expressions, or both.

Examples:

$$\frac{\frac{1}{b}+3}{\frac{2}{b-5}}, \quad \frac{\frac{1}{4}-x}{\frac{1}{8}}, \quad \frac{\frac{1}{2}}{\frac{2}{5}}$$

DEFINITION

A **compound fraction** is a fraction that has a fraction in the numerator and/or denominator.

Simplifying a Compound Fraction

To simplify a compound fraction, either multiply the numerator and the denominator of the compound fraction by a common denominator of the fractions within the fraction (the LCD method) or divide the numerator of the compound fraction by the denominator (the division method).

REMEMBER

The LCD is the least common denominator of two or more fractions.

Example 1 Simplify each expression.

 $\dfrac{\frac{2}{3}}{\frac{3}{5}}$

Solution

LCD Method

$$\frac{\frac{2}{3}}{\frac{3}{5}} = \frac{\frac{2}{3}\cdot 15}{\frac{3}{5}\cdot 15} = \frac{\frac{2}{\cancel{3}}\cdot \overset{5}{\cancel{15}}}{\frac{3}{\cancel{5}}\cdot \underset{1}{\cancel{15}}^{3}} = \frac{10}{9} = 1\frac{1}{9}$$

Division Method

$$\frac{\frac{2}{3}}{\frac{3}{5}} = \frac{2}{3} \div \frac{3}{5} = \frac{2}{3}\cdot\frac{5}{3} = \frac{10}{9} = 1\frac{1}{9} \quad \blacksquare$$

B $\dfrac{\frac{a}{b}}{\frac{c}{d}}$

Solution

LCD Method

$$\frac{\frac{a}{b}}{\frac{c}{d}} = \frac{\frac{a}{b}\cdot bd}{\frac{c}{d}\cdot bd} = \frac{\frac{a}{\cancel{b}}\cdot \overset{d}{\cancel{bd}}}{\frac{c}{\cancel{d}}\cdot \underset{1}{\cancel{bd}}^{b}} = \frac{ad}{bc}$$

Division Method

$$\frac{\frac{a}{b}}{\frac{c}{d}} = \frac{a}{b} \div \frac{c}{d} = \frac{a}{b}\cdot\frac{d}{c} = \frac{ad}{bc} \quad \blacksquare$$

Example 2 Simplify each expression.

A $\dfrac{\frac{1}{2} + 5}{3 + \frac{1}{4}}$

Solution

$\dfrac{\frac{1}{2} + 5}{3 + \frac{1}{4}} = \dfrac{\left(\frac{1}{2} + 5\right) \cdot 4}{\left(3 + \frac{1}{4}\right) \cdot 4}$ Multiply the numerator and denominator by the LCD: 4.

$= \dfrac{\frac{1}{2} \cdot 4 + 5 \cdot 4}{3 \cdot 4 + \frac{1}{4} \cdot 4}$ Distribute 4.

$= \dfrac{2 + 20}{12 + 1}$ Simplify.

$= \dfrac{22}{13}$ Simplify.

$= 1\dfrac{9}{13}$ Simplify. ∎

B $\dfrac{5 + \frac{1}{2a}}{\frac{3}{2a}}$

Solution

$\dfrac{5 + \frac{1}{2a}}{\frac{3}{2a}} = \left(5 + \dfrac{1}{2a}\right) \div \dfrac{3}{2a}$ Rewrite as division.

$= \left(\dfrac{5 \cdot 2a}{2a} + \dfrac{1}{2a}\right) \div \dfrac{3}{2a}$ Rewrite the first fraction of the dividend using the LCD: $2a$.

$= \left(\dfrac{10a}{2a} + \dfrac{1}{2a}\right) \div \dfrac{3}{2a}$ Simplify.

$= \left(\dfrac{10a + 1}{2a}\right) \div \dfrac{3}{2a}$ Simplify.

$= \dfrac{10a + 1}{2a} \cdot \dfrac{2a}{3}$ Division is the same as multiplication by the reciprocal of the divisor.

$= \dfrac{10a + 1}{\overset{}{\underset{1}{2a}}} \cdot \dfrac{\overset{1}{2a}}{3}$ Divide out the common factor.

$= \dfrac{10a + 1}{3}$ Simplify. ∎

Using an LCD to Simplify a Compound Algebraic Fraction

To simplify a compound fraction with variables, multiply the numerator
and denominator by the LCD of all fractions that appear in the numerator
or denominator. Then simplify. Use this method when there is addition or
subtraction in a fraction of the numerator and/or denominator.

Example 3 Simplify.

$$\dfrac{\dfrac{1}{x-3}+\dfrac{3}{x}}{\dfrac{2}{x-3}}$$

Solution

$$\dfrac{\dfrac{1}{x-3}+\dfrac{3}{x}}{\dfrac{2}{x-3}}=\dfrac{\dfrac{1}{x-3}+\dfrac{3}{x}}{\dfrac{2}{x-3}}\cdot\dfrac{x(x-3)}{x(x-3)}$$
Multiply the numerator
and denominator by the
LCD: $x(x-3)$.

$$=\dfrac{\dfrac{1}{x-3}\cdot x(x-3)+\dfrac{3}{x}\cdot x(x-3)}{\dfrac{2}{(x-3)}\cdot x(x-3)}$$
Distribute $x(x-3)$.

$$=\dfrac{\dfrac{1}{\cancel{(x-3)}}\cdot x\cancel{(x-3)}+\dfrac{3}{\cancel{x}}\cdot\cancel{x}(x-3)}{\dfrac{2}{\cancel{(x-3)}}\cdot\cancel{x}\cancel{(x-3)}}$$
Divide out common
factors.

$$=\dfrac{x+3(x-3)}{2x}$$
Simplify.

$$=\dfrac{4x-9}{2x}$$
Simplify. ∎

Problem Set

Simplify.

1. $\dfrac{\dfrac{1}{2}}{\dfrac{3}{4}}$

2. $\dfrac{\dfrac{4}{5}}{\dfrac{1}{20}}$

3. $\dfrac{\dfrac{9}{10}}{15}$

4. $\dfrac{\dfrac{7}{8}}{\dfrac{-12}{23}}$

5. $\dfrac{\dfrac{5}{18}}{\dfrac{1}{6}}$

6. $\dfrac{\dfrac{x}{y}}{\dfrac{a}{b}}$

7. $\dfrac{\dfrac{1}{x}}{\dfrac{2}{y}}$

8. $\dfrac{\dfrac{11}{12}}{\dfrac{-3}{x}}$

9. $\dfrac{\dfrac{2a}{b}}{\dfrac{4b}{6a}}$

10. $\dfrac{-\dfrac{3x}{9y}}{-\dfrac{9x}{3y}}$

11. $\dfrac{2 + \dfrac{1}{3}}{4 + \dfrac{1}{5}}$

12. $\dfrac{6 - \dfrac{1}{4}}{3 + \dfrac{1}{2}}$

13. $\dfrac{\dfrac{1}{6} + \dfrac{1}{7}}{\dfrac{1}{2} - \dfrac{1}{3}}$

14. $\dfrac{\dfrac{1}{3} + \dfrac{1}{12}}{2 - \dfrac{1}{6}}$

15. $\dfrac{\dfrac{1}{4} + \dfrac{1}{8}}{\dfrac{1}{2} - \dfrac{3}{16}}$

16. $\dfrac{6 + \dfrac{1}{x}}{\dfrac{4}{3x}}$

17. $\dfrac{\dfrac{1}{x} - 10}{1 + \dfrac{3}{2x}}$

18. $\dfrac{\dfrac{2}{5a}}{\dfrac{3}{a} - 10}$

19. $\dfrac{8 - \dfrac{4}{y}}{\dfrac{6}{5y} - 3}$

20. $\dfrac{\dfrac{3}{7x} + 1}{9 - \dfrac{2}{3x}}$

21. $\dfrac{\dfrac{2}{x} + \dfrac{1}{x + 2}}{\dfrac{3}{x + 2}}$

22. $\dfrac{\dfrac{5}{x - 4}}{\dfrac{3}{x - 4} - \dfrac{2}{x}}$

23. $\dfrac{\dfrac{1}{y - 1} - 5}{1 + \dfrac{1}{1 - y}}$

24. $\dfrac{\dfrac{2}{y + 3} - 6}{6 - \dfrac{3}{y + 2}}$

25. $\dfrac{\dfrac{1}{x + 5} + \dfrac{2}{y}}{\dfrac{5}{y(x + 5)}}$

26. $\dfrac{\dfrac{3}{4a + 1} - \dfrac{2}{b}}{3 + \dfrac{5}{4a + 1}}$

27. $\dfrac{5 - \dfrac{2}{x + 1}}{\dfrac{3}{y + 1} - 7}$

28. $\dfrac{\dfrac{6}{x + 2} + \dfrac{9}{x + 3}}{4 + \dfrac{10}{x + 3}}$

*29. Challenge $\dfrac{\dfrac{3}{x} + \dfrac{2}{3x} - \dfrac{4}{9x}}{1 + \dfrac{5}{x} + \dfrac{10}{9x}}$

*30. Challenge

$\dfrac{\dfrac{2}{x + 1} - \dfrac{3}{x + 2}}{\dfrac{1}{x - 2} + \dfrac{2}{x^2 - x - 2}}$

Solving Rational Equations

A *rational equation* is an equation that contains one or more rational expressions.

Solving Rational Equations

METHODS OF SOLVING RATIONAL EQUATIONS

LCD method
Multiply both sides of the equation by the least common denominator (LCD) of the rational expressions. Then solve the resulting equation. This method works for any rational equation.

Cross-multiplication method
If the equation is in a form that looks like $\frac{a}{b} = \frac{c}{d}$, you can cross-multiply, then solve the resulting equation. The method of cross-multiplying is based on the following property: $\frac{a}{b} = \frac{c}{d}$ if and only if $ad = bc$.

Because rational equations have variables in denominators, you have to be careful with the domain. Any value of the variable that makes a denominator equal zero cannot be a solution, and therefore must be excluded. It's a good idea to start by identifying those values that must be excluded before you begin to solve the equation.

TIP

If you forget to identify the values that must be excluded, you should discover them when you check your solutions anyway.

Example 1 Solve and check.

$$\frac{15}{x-6} = \frac{5}{x}$$

TIP

A rational equation is a proportion if it has the form $\frac{a}{b} = \frac{c}{d}$, where $\frac{a}{b}$ and $\frac{c}{d}$ are rational expressions.

Solution To find the restrictions on the domain, set the denominators equal to zero and solve. The domain restrictions are $x \neq 0$ and $x \neq 6$.

Now solve the equation.

$$\frac{15}{x-6} = \frac{5}{x}$$

$15x = 5(x - 6)$ Cross-multiply.

$15x = 5x - 30$ Distribute the 5.

$10x = -30$ Subtract $5x$.

$x = -3$ Divide by 10.

Check

$$\frac{15}{x-6}=\frac{5}{x}$$

$$\frac{15}{-3-6}\overset{?}{=}\frac{5}{-3}$$ Substitute -3 for x in the original equation.

$$\frac{15}{-9}\overset{?}{=}\frac{5}{-3}$$

$$-\frac{5}{3}=-\frac{5}{3}\;\checkmark$$ Substituting -3 results in a true statement.

$x=-3$ is not in the domain restrictions, so the solution set is $\{-3\}$. ∎

Solving Rational Equations and Checking for Extraneous Solutions

The zero product property can be used to identify domain restrictions or solve more complicated equations.

ZERO PRODUCT PROPERTY

For any real numbers a and b, $ab = 0$ if and only if $a = 0$ or $b = 0$.

Example 2   Solve and check.

A $\dfrac{3}{x^2+5x+6}+\dfrac{x-1}{x+2}=\dfrac{7}{x+3}$

Solution

First identify values of x that must be excluded from the domain.

$$\frac{3}{x^2+5x+6}+\frac{x-1}{x+2}=\frac{7}{x+3}$$ Original equation

$$\frac{3}{(x+2)(x+3)}+\frac{x-1}{x+2}=\frac{7}{x+3}$$ Factor the first denominator.

If $x=-2$, then $x+2=0$, which makes two denominators equal zero.
If $x=-3$, then $x+3=0$, which makes two denominators equal zero.
So -2 and -3 must be excluded as possible solutions.

Now solve the equation.

$$\frac{3}{(x+2)(x+3)}+\frac{x-1}{x+2}=\frac{7}{x+3}$$ Keep denominators in factored form to help identify the LCD.

$$(x+2)(x+3)\left[\frac{3}{(x+2)(x+3)}+\frac{x-1}{x+2}\right]=(x+2)(x+3)\left(\frac{7}{x+3}\right)$$ Multiply both sides of the equation by the LCD.

$$\cancel{(x+2)}\cancel{(x+3)}\frac{3}{\cancel{(x+2)}\cancel{(x+3)}}+(x+2)(x+3)\frac{x-1}{\cancel{x+2}}=(x+2)\cancel{(x+3)}\frac{7}{\cancel{x+3}}$$ Distribute the LCD to every term.

$$3+(x+3)(x-1)=(x+2)\cdot 7$$ Divide out common factors.

$$3+x^2+2x-3=7x+14$$ Multiply binomials. Distribute 7.

$$x^2+2x=7x+14$$ Simplify.

$$x^2-5x-14=0$$ Add $-7x-14$ to get 0 on one side.

$$(x-7)(x+2)=0$$ Factor the trinomial.

$$x-7=0 \quad \text{or} \quad x+2=0$$ Apply the zero product property.
$$x=7 \qquad\qquad x=-2$$

REMEMBER

See how to apply the property with this example.
$(x-4)(x+1)=0$
$(x-4)=0$ or $(x+1)=0$
$\quad x=4 \qquad\qquad x=-1$

So the solutions to the equation are $x=4$ and $x=-1$.

Check

Substitute 7 for x:

$$\frac{3}{x^2 + 5x + 6} + \frac{x-1}{x+2} = \frac{7}{x+3}$$

$$\frac{3}{7^2 + 5 \cdot 7 + 6} + \frac{7-1}{7+2} \stackrel{?}{=} \frac{7}{7+3}$$

$$\frac{3}{49 + 35 + 6} + \frac{6}{9} \stackrel{?}{=} \frac{7}{10}$$

$$\frac{3}{90} + \frac{60}{90} \stackrel{?}{=} \frac{63}{90}$$

$$\frac{63}{90} = \frac{63}{90} \checkmark$$

So 7 is a solution.

The solution set is $\{7\}$. ∎

Substitute -2 for x:

$$\frac{3}{x^2 + 5x + 6} + \frac{x-1}{x+2} = \frac{7}{x+3}$$

$$\frac{3}{(-2)^2 + 5 \cdot (-2) + 6} + \frac{-2-1}{-2+2} \stackrel{?}{=} \frac{7}{-2+3}$$

$$\frac{3}{0} + \frac{-3}{0} \neq \frac{7}{1}$$

Here, -2 is called an **extraneous solution** because it does not make the original equation true. Recall that -2 was identified as a value that must be excluded as a possible solution anyway.

B $\quad \dfrac{10}{n} = \dfrac{n+9}{n-4} - 3$

Solution First note that 0 and 4 must be excluded as possible solutions because each value makes a denominator equal zero. Solve the equation.

$$\frac{10}{n} = \frac{n+9}{n-4} - 3$$

$$n(n-4)\frac{10}{n} = n(n-4)\frac{n+9}{n-4} + n(n-4)(-3)$$

$$\cancel{n}(n-4)\frac{10}{\cancel{n}} = n\cancel{(n-4)}\frac{n+9}{\cancel{n-4}} + n(n-4)(-3)$$

$$(n-4)10 = n(n+9) - 3n(n-4)$$

$$10n - 40 = n^2 + 9n - 3n^2 + 12n$$

$$2n^2 - 11n - 40 = 0$$

$$(2n+5)(n-8) = 0$$

Apply the zero product property:

$$2n + 5 = 0 \qquad \text{or} \qquad n - 8 = 0$$

$$n = -\frac{5}{2} \qquad\qquad\qquad n = 8$$

Check

Substitute $-\dfrac{5}{2}$ for n:

$$\frac{10}{n} = \frac{n+9}{n-4} - 3$$

$$\frac{10}{-\frac{5}{2}} \stackrel{?}{=} \frac{-\frac{5}{2}+9}{-\frac{5}{2}-4} - 3$$

$$\frac{10}{-\frac{5}{2}} \stackrel{?}{=} \frac{\frac{13}{2}}{-\frac{13}{2}} - 3$$

$$\frac{10}{1} \cdot \left(-\frac{2}{5}\right) \stackrel{?}{=} \frac{13}{2} \cdot \left(-\frac{2}{13}\right) - 3$$

$$-4 \stackrel{?}{=} -1 - 3$$

$$-4 = -4 \checkmark$$

Substitute 8 for n:

$$\frac{10}{n} = \frac{n+9}{n-4} - 3$$

$$\frac{10}{8} \stackrel{?}{=} \frac{8+9}{8-4} - 3$$

$$\frac{5}{4} \stackrel{?}{=} \frac{17}{4} - \frac{12}{4}$$

$$\frac{5}{4} = \frac{5}{4} \checkmark$$

The solution set is $\left\{-\dfrac{5}{2}, 8\right\}$. ∎

Solving a Rate Problem

Example 3   It takes 6 hours for pump A to fill a tank. It takes 4 hours for pump A and pump B together to fill the same tank. How long would it take pump B alone to fill the tank?

Solution   Pump A alone can fill the tank in 6 hours, so it fills $\frac{1}{6}$ of the tank each hour. Pumps A and B together can fill the tank in 4 hours, so they fill $\frac{1}{4}$ of the tank each hour. Let x be the number of hours it takes pump B to fill the tank alone. Then pump B alone fills $\frac{1}{x}$ of the tank each hour.

Now reason as follows:

Pump A fills $\frac{1}{6}$ of the tank in 1 hour, $\frac{2}{6}$ of the tank in 2 hours, $\frac{3}{6}$ of the tank in 3 hours, and so on.

Pump B fills $\frac{1}{x}$ of the tank in 1 hour, $\frac{2}{x}$ of the tank in 2 hours, $\frac{3}{x}$ of the tank in 3 hours, and so on.

Write an equation:

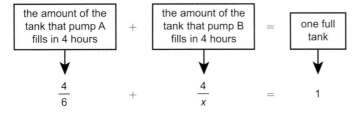

Solve the equation:

$$\frac{4}{6} + \frac{4}{x} = 1$$

$$6x \cdot \frac{4}{6} + 6x \cdot \frac{4}{x} = 6x \cdot 1 \qquad \text{Multiply both sides by the LCD.}$$

$$\cancel{6}x \cdot \frac{4}{\cancel{6}} + 6\cancel{x} \cdot \frac{4}{\cancel{x}} = 6x \cdot 1 \qquad \text{Divide out common factors.}$$

$$4x + 24 = 6x \qquad \text{Solve the resulting equation.}$$

$$24 = 2x$$

$$12 = x$$

> **THINK ABOUT IT**
> For the equation $\frac{4}{6} + \frac{4}{x} = 1$, the value 0 must be excluded as a possible solution.

Substitute 12 for x in the original equation to verify that 12 is the solution. It would take 12 hours for pump B to fill the tank alone. ■

Solving a Work Problem

Example 4   Mario can finish all the house chores twice as fast as his sister Ana. Together they can do the job in 2 hours. How long would it take each of them working alone?

Solution   Let x be the number of hours it takes Mario to do the chores alone. Mario does the job twice as fast as Ana, so Ana would take $2x$ hours to do the chores by herself. Then Mario does $\frac{1}{x}$ of the chores each hour, and Ana can do $\frac{1}{2x}$ of the chores each hour. Mario and Ana together can finish the chores in 2 hours, so together they can do $\frac{1}{2}$ of the job each hour.

Write an equation that combines Mario's and Ana's labor for each hour:

$$\frac{1}{x} + \frac{1}{2x} = \frac{1}{2}$$

Solve the equation:

$$\frac{1}{x} + \frac{1}{2x} = \frac{1}{2}$$

$$2x \cdot \frac{1}{x} + 2x \cdot \frac{1}{2x} = 2x \cdot \frac{1}{2} \qquad \text{Multiply both sides by the LCD.}$$

$$2x \cdot \frac{1}{\cancel{x}} + \cancel{2x} \cdot \frac{1}{\cancel{2x}} = \cancel{2}x \cdot \frac{1}{\cancel{2}} \qquad \text{Divide out common factors.}$$

$$2 + 1 = x \qquad\qquad \text{Solve the resulting equation.}$$

$$3 = x$$

Substitute 3 for x in the original equation to verify that 3 is the solution.

It would take 3 hours for Mario to do all the house chores alone, and it would take twice as long, or 6 hours, for Ana to do the job alone. ∎

Problem Set

Solve and check.

1. $\dfrac{8}{h+4} = \dfrac{6}{h}$

2. $\dfrac{p}{p-7} = \dfrac{5}{6}$

3. $\dfrac{-3x}{6} = \dfrac{x-7}{12}$

4. $\dfrac{y}{-12} = \dfrac{y+1}{3}$

5. $\dfrac{10}{a+3} = \dfrac{-2}{5a}$

6. $\dfrac{k-3}{2k} = \dfrac{4}{17}$

7. $\dfrac{4}{x} = \dfrac{x-1}{x+2} - 2$

8. $\dfrac{w+3}{w} = \dfrac{w-7}{8} - 1$

9. $\dfrac{-1}{q+3} = \dfrac{4}{q} + 1$

10. $\dfrac{t+7}{t-2} = \dfrac{5}{t} + 3$

11. $\dfrac{n-4}{n-4} = 2 - \dfrac{7}{n}$

12. $\dfrac{x+3}{x-5} - 2 = \dfrac{9}{x}$

13. $\dfrac{-28}{c^2+6c+5} + \dfrac{c-2}{c+5} = \dfrac{1}{c+1}$

14. $\dfrac{7}{x^2+9x+8} + \dfrac{x-3}{x+8} = \dfrac{2}{x+1}$

15. $\dfrac{1}{r-2} - \dfrac{r+1}{r^2-4} = \dfrac{1}{r-2}$

16. $\dfrac{-3}{b^2+5b+4} + \dfrac{b}{b+1} = \dfrac{7}{b+4}$

17. $\dfrac{g-4}{2g^2+5g-3} - \dfrac{1}{g+3} = \dfrac{g+2}{2g-1}$

18. $\dfrac{z^2}{z^2-25} - \dfrac{2}{3z+15} = \dfrac{z+1}{z+5}$

For each problem, do the following:

A. **Define a variable and write an equation that models the problem.**
B. **Solve the equation.**
C. **Answer the question.**

19. It takes 10 hours for Arturo to build a fence. It takes 6 hours for Sun and Arturo together to build the same fence. How long would it take Sun alone to build the fence?

20. Skyler can complete the shopping twice as fast as her brother Blaze. Together they can do the shopping in 3 hours. How long would it take each of them working alone?

21. Julio can stain the deck three times faster than his cousin Samuel. Together they can stain the deck in 3 hours. How long would it take each of them working alone?

22. It takes 5 hours for Lena to paint a room. It takes 3 hours for Lena and Gustov together to paint the same room. How long would it take Gustov alone to paint the room?

23. It takes Company A 12 hours to install a heat pump. It takes 9 hours if Company A and Company B work together. How long would it take Company B alone to install the heat pump?

24. Brooks can mow the lawn twice as fast as his sister Katrina. Together they can do the job in 2.5 hours. How long would it take each of them working alone?

25. It takes Repair Works 20 hours to fix a car. It takes 15 hours if Repair Works and Brakes & Things, Inc., work together. How long would it take Brakes & Things alone to fix the same car?

26. Deni can clean the pool four times as fast as her sister Lamur. Together they can do the job in 3 hours. How long would it take each of them working alone?

27. It takes the local church 18 hours to deliver food baskets. It takes 8 hours if the church and scouts work together. How long would it take the scouts alone to deliver the food baskets?

28. Yahir can assemble a book three times faster than Malia. Together they can do the job in 2 hours. How long would it take each of them working alone?

*29. **Challenge** Planet Ink Co. manufactures 500 books in 5 hours. Perry's Printers can do the same job in 3 hours. If Perry's Printers begins production 1 hour after Planet Ink has begun, how many hours will it take to produce 500 books?

*30. **Challenge** Taniyah can complete a project in 15 hours. Her sister, Reanna, can complete the same project in 10 hours. If Taniyah works alone for 1 hour and then Reanna works alone for 2 hours, how many additional hours are needed to finish the project if the sisters then work together?

Reciprocal Power Functions

A **power function** is a function of the form $f(x) = ax^n$, where $a \neq 0$ and n is a positive integer.

The functions $f(x) = x$, $g(x) = x^2$, and $h(x) = x^3$ are power functions.

Graphing a Reciprocal Function

> **DEFINITION OF RECIPROCAL POWER FUNCTION**
>
> A **reciprocal power function** is a power function that has the power of x in the denominator of a rational function. The functions $f(x) = \frac{1}{x}$, $g(x) = \frac{1}{x^2}$, and $h(x) = \frac{1}{x^3}$ are reciprocal power functions.

Example 1   Graph $f(x) = \frac{1}{x}$.

Solution   Use a table to find several ordered pairs in the function. Include some fractional values between $x = -1$ and $x = 1$ so that you know what happens on either side of and near $x = 0$, where $f(x)$ is undefined.

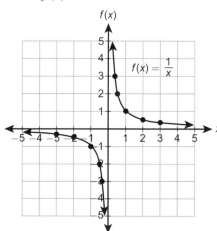

x	$f(x) = \frac{1}{x}$
-3	$-\frac{1}{3}$
-2	$-\frac{1}{2}$
-1	-1
$-\frac{1}{2}$	-2
$-\frac{1}{3}$	-3
0	undefined
$\frac{1}{3}$	3
$\frac{1}{2}$	2
1	1
2	$\frac{1}{2}$
3	$\frac{1}{3}$

The two distinct sections of the graph are called *branches*. The function $f(x) = \frac{1}{x}$ is not defined for $x = 0$, so zero is excluded from the domain of the function. Notice that the graph gets closer and closer to the x-axis as the x-values approach positive infinity and negative infinity. Also, the graph gets closer and closer to the y-axis as the x-values get closer to zero. ∎

> **THINK ABOUT IT**
>
> "$f(x)$ approaches b" means the values of $f(x)$ get closer and closer to b.
>
> "$f(x)$ approaches ∞" means the values of $f(x)$ increase without bound.
>
> "$f(x)$ approaches $-\infty$" means the values of $f(x)$ decrease without bound.

This graph is called a rectangular hyperbola.

DEFINITION OF HORIZONTAL AND VERTICAL ASYMPTOTES

The line $y = b$ is a **horizontal asymptote** of the graph of the function f if $f(x)$ approaches b as x approaches ∞ or $-\infty$.

The line $x = a$ is a **vertical asymptote** of the graph of the function f if $f(x)$ approaches ∞ or $-\infty$ as x approaches a, either from the left or the right.

So, for $f(x) = \frac{1}{x}$, the x-axis (or $y = 0$) is a *horizontal asymptote*, and the y-axis (or $x = 0$) is a *vertical asymptote*.

Finding the Domain and Range of a Reciprocal Power Function

Example 2   Determine the domain and range of each function.

Ⓐ $f(x) = \dfrac{3}{x^2}$

Ⓑ $g(x) = \dfrac{5}{2x^3}$

Solution   Find domain restrictions by setting the denominator equal to zero. Find the range by graphing.

Ⓐ **Domain:** $x^2 = 0$

$$x = 0$$

If $x = 0$, then the denominator equals 0. So the domain is the set of all real numbers except 0. In set notation, the domain is:

$\{x \mid x \in \mathbb{R} \text{ and } x \neq 0\}$.

Range: Since x is squared, $f(x)$ can never be negative and $f(x)$ cannot equal 0. So the range is the set of all real numbers greater than 0, $\{f(x) \mid f(x) > 0\}$. ∎

Ⓑ **Domain:** $2x^3 = 0$

$$x^3 = 0$$
$$x = 0$$

The domain is the set of all real numbers except 0. In set notation, the domain is:

$\{x \mid x \in \mathbb{R} \text{ and } x \neq 0\}$.

Range: Since x is cubed, $g(x)$ can be negative or positive and $g(x)$ cannot equal 0. So the range is the set of all real numbers except 0, $\{g(x) \mid g(x) \in \mathbb{R} \text{ and } g(x) \neq 0\}$. ∎

All reciprocal power functions of the form $f(x) = \frac{a}{x^n}$, where n is even, have the same domain and range. The domain is $\{x \mid x \in \mathbb{R} \text{ and } x \neq 0\}$. When a is positive, the range is $\{f(x) \mid f(x) > 0\}$, and when a is negative, the range is $\{f(x) \mid f(x) < 0\}$.

All reciprocal power functions of the form $f(x) = \frac{a}{x^n}$, where n is odd, have the same domain, $\{x \mid x \in \mathbb{R} \text{ and } x \neq 0\}$, and range, $\{f(x) \mid f(x) \in \mathbb{R} \text{ and } f(x) \neq 0\}$.

The Reciprocal Power Function Family of Graphs

Equations of the form $f(x) = \frac{a}{x^n}$ are reciprocal power functions with a horizontal asymptote at $y = 0$ and a vertical asymptote at $x = 0$.

Reciprocal Power Function Graph Family: $f(x) = \frac{a}{x^n}$

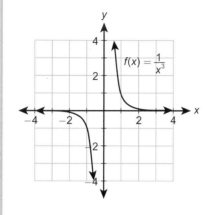

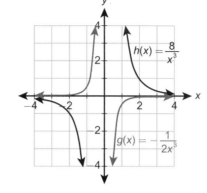

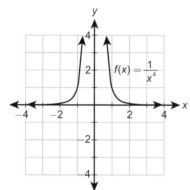

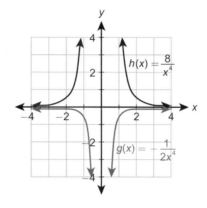

Graphs of the parent functions

If you change the parameter a, you get curves that vary in their distance from the origin.

A negative a-value will reflect the graph across the x-axis.

Reciprocal power functions with odd powers have the same general shape, and reciprocal power functions with even powers have the same general shape. All reciprocal power functions have the x- and y-axes as asymptotes.

Graphing a Simple Reciprocal Power Function

Example 3 Graph both on the same coordinate system. Compare the two graphs.

Ⓐ $f(x) = \dfrac{1}{x^2}$

Ⓑ $g(x) = \dfrac{1}{3x^2}$

Solution In both graphs, the domain is the set of all real numbers except 0: $\{x \mid x \in \mathbb{R} \text{ and } x \neq 0\}$

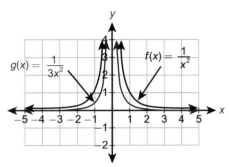

Each graph has two branches, one for positive x-values and one for negative x-values. Each graph has a vertical asymptote whose equation is $x = 0$ and a horizontal asymptote whose equation is $y = 0$. ∎

Finding the Equation from the Graph

Example 4 Find the equation for the reciprocal power function of the form $f(x) = \dfrac{a}{x^2}$ that has the following graph.

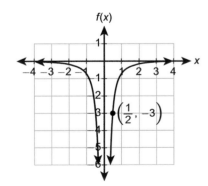

Solution

$f(x) = \dfrac{a}{x^2}$ Start with the general form of the equation.

$-3 = \dfrac{a}{\left(\frac{1}{2}\right)^2}$ Because the range is $y < 0$, and because $x^2 > 0$, notice that the value of a must be negative. To find the value of a, substitute the coordinates of the given point and solve.

$-\dfrac{3}{4} = a$ Substitute this value of a in the general form of the equation.

$f(x) = -\dfrac{3}{4x^2}$ Write the equation of the function. ■

Problem Set

Find the domain and range of each function.

1. $f(x) = \dfrac{4}{x}$

2. $g(a) = \dfrac{5}{a^9}$

3. $s(q) = \dfrac{6}{q^8}$

Graph each function.

4. $f(x) = \dfrac{1}{x^3}$

5. $M(p) = \dfrac{1}{5p^2}$

6. $N(d) = \dfrac{1}{3d^5}$

7. $V(u) = \dfrac{1}{6u}$

8. $S(r) = \dfrac{1}{8r^4}$

9. $f(x) = \dfrac{4}{x^2}$

10. $g(v) = \dfrac{9}{v^3}$

11. $M(y) = \dfrac{3}{4y^6}$

12. $N(r) = \dfrac{4}{r^4}$

13. $g(t) = \dfrac{2}{t}$

14. $P(c) = \dfrac{3}{5c^3}$

15. $f(a) = \dfrac{2}{3a^5}$

Find the equation of the function shown in the graph, given the parent function.

16. $f(x) = \dfrac{a}{x^5}$

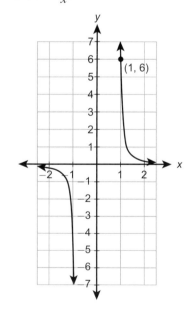

17. $g(x) = \dfrac{a}{x^2}$

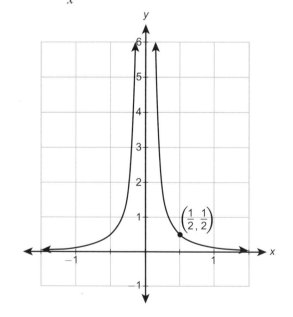

18. $k(x) = \dfrac{a}{x^3}$

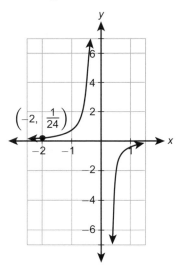

$\left(-2, \dfrac{1}{24}\right)$

21. $f(x) = \dfrac{a}{x^6}$

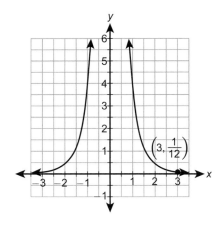

$\left(3, \dfrac{1}{12}\right)$

19. $T(x) = \dfrac{a}{x}$

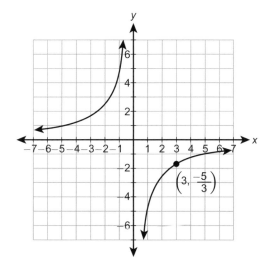

$\left(3, \dfrac{-5}{3}\right)$

22. $z(x) = \dfrac{a}{x}$

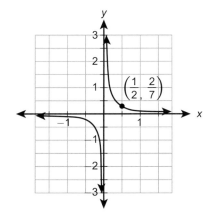

$\left(\dfrac{1}{2}, \dfrac{2}{7}\right)$

20. $b(x) = \dfrac{a}{x^4}$

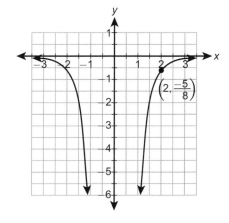

$\left(2, \dfrac{-5}{8}\right)$

23. $f(x) = \dfrac{a}{x^2}$

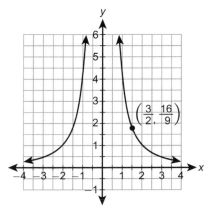

$\left(\dfrac{3}{2}, \dfrac{16}{9}\right)$

24. $V(x) = \dfrac{a}{x^3}$

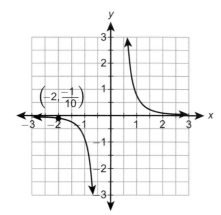

$\left(-2, \dfrac{-1}{10}\right)$

26. $m(x) = \dfrac{a}{x^4}$

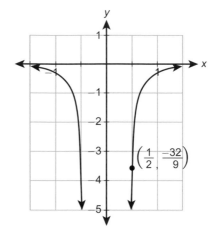

$\left(\dfrac{1}{2}, \dfrac{-32}{9}\right)$

25. $h(x) = \dfrac{a}{x}$

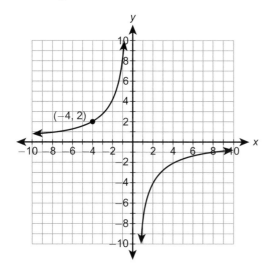

$(-4, 2)$

27. $f(x) = \dfrac{a}{x^2}$

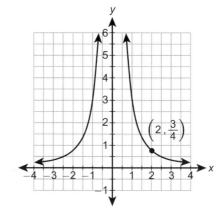

$\left(2, \dfrac{3}{4}\right)$

Solve.

*28. **Challenge** What happens to the graph as the value of a decreases for the reciprocal power function $f(x) = \dfrac{a}{x^{20}}$?

*29. **Challenge** Graph two reciprocal power functions that contain the point (2, 10). Compare the two graphs.

Graphing Rational Functions

Any function that can be written as the quotient of two polynomials can be called a rational function.

Finding the Domain of a Rational Function

Many rational functions have restricted domains because an expression is undefined if its denominator equals 0.

Example 1 Determine the domain of each rational function.

A $f(x) = \dfrac{x + 5}{x^2 - 3x - 28}$

Solution Find domain restrictions by setting the denominator equal to 0.

$$x^2 - 3x - 21 = 0$$
$$(x - 7)(x + 4) = 0$$
$$x - 7 = 0 \qquad \text{or} \qquad x + 4 = 0$$

If $x = 7$ or $x = -4$, then the denominator equals 0. So the domain is the set of all real numbers *except* 7 and -4. You can state this in set notation: $\{x \in \mathbb{R}, x \neq 7 \text{ and } x \neq -4\}$. ■

B $g(x) = \dfrac{2}{x^2 + 1}$

Solution Find domain restrictions by setting the denominator equal to 0.

$$x^2 + 1 = 0$$
$$x^2 = -1$$

The equation $x^2 = -1$ has no real solution, so there are no restrictions on the domain. The domain is the set of all real numbers. In set notation, this is $\{x \mid x \in \mathbb{R}\}$. ■

The Rational Function Family of Graphs

Equations of the form $f(x) = \dfrac{a}{x-h} + k$ are rational functions with one horizontal asymptote at $y = k$ and one vertical asymptote at $x = h$.

Rational Function Graph Family: $f(x) = \dfrac{a}{x-h} + k$

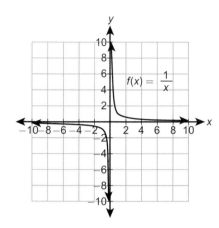

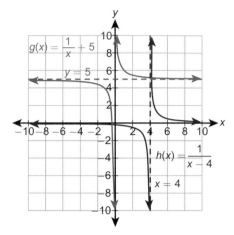

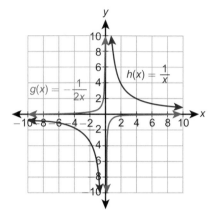

Graph of the parent function

If you change only the parameter h, the vertical asymptote shifts h units to the left or right.

If you change only the parameter k, the horizontal asymptote shifts k units up or down.

If you change only the parameter a, you get curves that vary in their distance from the origin.

A negative a-value will reflect the graph across the x-axis.

Graphing Rational Functions in the Family $f(x) = \dfrac{a}{x-h} + k$

Example 2 Graph each function.

A $y = \dfrac{1}{x+6}$

Solution If x is close to -6, then $\dfrac{1}{x+6}$ is far from 0. If x is far from -6, then $\dfrac{1}{x+6}$ is close to 0. The domain of $y = \dfrac{1}{x+6}$ is $\{x \mid x \in \mathbb{R}, x \neq -6\}$. The range of $y = \dfrac{1}{x+6}$ is $\{y \mid y \in \mathbb{R}, y \neq 0\}$.

The line $x = -6$ is a vertical asymptote. The line $y = 0$ is a horizontal asymptote.

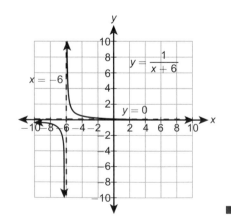

THINK ABOUT IT

$\dfrac{1}{\text{little}} = \text{big}$

$\dfrac{1}{\text{big}} = \text{little}$

B $f(x) = \frac{4}{x} - 3$

Solution The domain of $f(x) = \frac{4}{x} - 3$ is $\{x \mid x \in \mathbb{R}, x \neq 0\}$ because the denominator cannot equal 0.

The range of $f(x) = \frac{4}{x} - 3$ is $\{y \mid y \in \mathbb{R}, y \neq -3\}$ because $\frac{4}{x}$ can never be 0, so $\frac{4}{x} - 3$ can never be -3.

Since 4 is greater than 1, the curve of the graph is farther away from the intersection of the asymptotes.

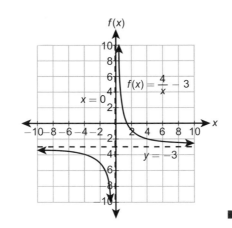

C $f(x) = \frac{2}{x - 3} + 1$

Solution The domain is $\{x \mid x \in \mathbb{R}, x \neq 3\}$ because 3 is a zero of the denominator.

The range of $f(x) = \frac{2}{x - 3} + 1$ is $\{y \mid y \in \mathbb{R}, y \neq 1\}$ because $\frac{2}{x - 3}$ can never be 0, so $\frac{2}{x - 3} + 1$ can never be 1.

The lines $x = 3$ and $y = 1$ are asymptotes.

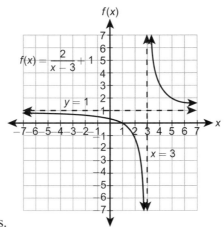

TIP

A "zero of the denominator" is just a zero of the polynomial that is in the denominator.

Finding the Equation when Given a Graph of a Rational Function in the Family $f(x) = \frac{a}{x - h} + k$

Example 3 Find the equation in the family $f(x) = \frac{a}{x - h} + k$ for the graph of each function.

A

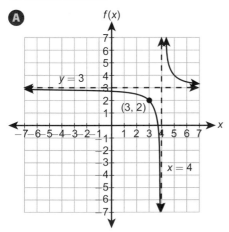

Solution

Step 1 There is a horizontal asymptote at $y = 3$ and a vertical asymptote at $x = 4$. The equation of the graph so far is $f(x) = \frac{a}{x - 4} + 3$.

Step 2 Substitute the point $(3, 2)$ into the equation.

$2 = \frac{a}{3 - 4} + 3$ Substitute.

$2 = -a + 3$ Simplify.

$a = 1$ Solve.

The equation of the graph is

$f(x) = \frac{1}{x - 4} + 3.$ ∎

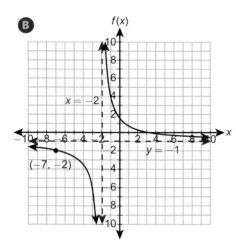

B

Solution

Step 1 There is a horizontal asymptote at $y = -1$ and a vertical asymptote at $x = -2$. So the equation of the graph so far is $f(x) = \dfrac{a}{x+2} - 1$.

Step 2 Substitute the point $(-7, -2)$ into the equation.

$$-2 = \dfrac{a}{-7+2} - 1 \qquad \text{Substitute.}$$

$$-1 = -\dfrac{a}{5} \qquad \text{Simplify.}$$

$$5 = a \qquad \text{Solve.}$$

The equation of the graph is

$$f(x) = \dfrac{5}{x+2} - 1. \quad \blacksquare$$

Graphing Rational Functions Not in the Family $f(x) = \dfrac{a}{x-h} + k$

Example 4 Graph each function.

A $y = \dfrac{x^2 - 9}{x + 3}$

Solution Factor and identify the zeros of the numerator and denominator.

$$y = \dfrac{x^2 - 9}{x+3} = \dfrac{(x+3)(x-3)}{x+3} \quad \longleftarrow \quad \text{The zeros are } x = -3 \text{ and } x = 3.$$
$$\longleftarrow \quad \text{The zero is } x = -3.$$

For this function, -3 is a zero of both the numerator and denominator, so there is a hole at $x = -3$. Meanwhile, 3 is a zero of only the numerator, so the x-intercept is 3, and $(3, 0)$ is on the graph. There are no zeros of only the denominator, so there is no vertical asymptote. The degree of the numerator is greater than the degree of the denominator $(2 > 1)$, so there is no horizontal asymptote. If you divide out the common factor $x + 3$, you get the linear function $f(x) = x - 3$. So, to graph $y = \dfrac{x^2 - 9}{x + 3}$, you can graph $f(x) = x - 3$, but you must put an open dot at $(-3, -6)$.

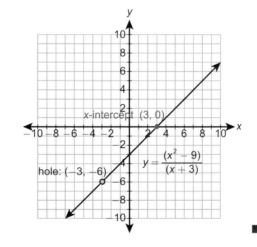

$\blacksquare$

B $f(x) = \dfrac{1}{(x-3)^2}$

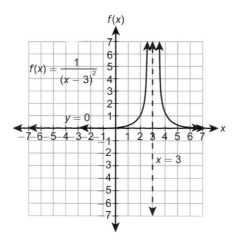

$f(x) = \dfrac{1}{(x-3)^2}$

$y = 0$

$x = 3$

Solution If x is close to 3, then $\dfrac{1}{(x-3)^2}$ is far from 0. If x is far from 3, then $\dfrac{1}{(x-3)^2}$ is close to 0. The domain of $f(x) = \dfrac{1}{(x-3)^2}$ is $\{x \mid x \in \mathbb{R}, x \neq 3\}$. The range is $\{y \mid y \in \mathbb{R}, y > 0\}$.

Identify the zeros. Because $(x-3)$ is in the denominator, the zero is $x = 3$.

There is one vertical asymptote, at $x = 3$.

The degree of the numerator is 0 and the degree of the denominator is 2. Because $0 < 2$, the x-axis, $y = 0$, is the horizontal asymptote. ∎

Problem Set

Determine the domain of each rational function.

1. $p(x) = \dfrac{x+4}{(x-2)(x+1)}$

2. $f(x) = \dfrac{x}{x^2-9}$

3. $k(x) = \dfrac{x+1}{x^2+4}$

4. $T(x) = \dfrac{x-8}{x^2+8x+16}$

Identify the equations of the asymptotes of each rational function.

5. $h(x) = \dfrac{4}{x-5}$

6. $m(x) = \dfrac{2}{x+1} + 3$

7. $f(x) = \dfrac{7}{x-2} + 4$

8. $g(x) = \dfrac{1}{(x-2)^2}$

For each problem, do the following:

A. Graph the function. Label asymptotes clearly.
B. Write the domain and range.

9. $f(x) = \dfrac{3}{x}$

10. $w(x) = \dfrac{1}{x-7} + 2$

11. $q(x) = \dfrac{3}{x+4} - 1$

12. $b(x) = \dfrac{6}{x-5} - 3$

13. $f(x) = \dfrac{5}{x+8} + 4$

14. $h(x) = \dfrac{9}{x} - 7$

Find the equation in the family $f(x) = \dfrac{1}{x - h} + k$ **for the graph of each function.**

15.

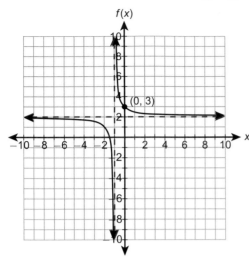

16.

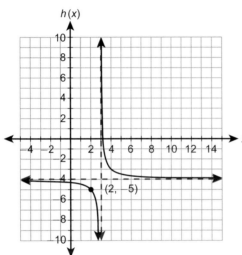

17.

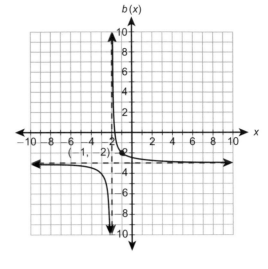

18.

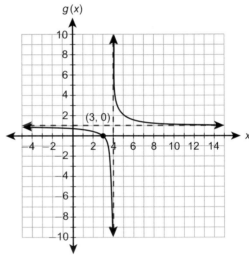

Find the equation in the family $f(x) = \dfrac{a}{x - h} + k$ **for the graph of each function.**

19.

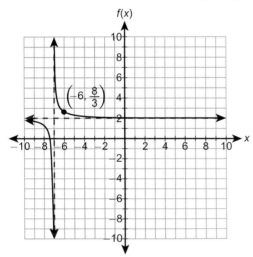

20.

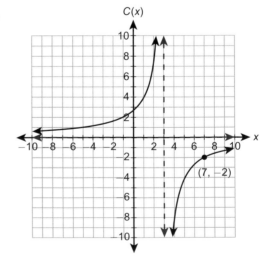

21.

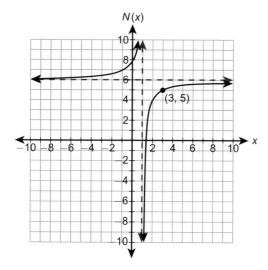

$N(x)$

$(3, 5)$

22.

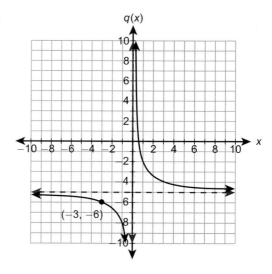

$q(x)$

$(-3, -6)$

Graph each function.

23. $g(x) = \dfrac{x^2 - 16}{x + 4}$

24. $f(x) = \dfrac{1}{(x + 2)^2}$

25. $q(x) = \dfrac{x^2 - 6x - 7}{x - 7}$

26. $c(x) = \dfrac{1}{(x - 3)(x + 3)}$

27. $h(x) = \dfrac{x + 1}{x^2 + 9x + 8}$

28. $f(x) = \dfrac{1}{x^2 - 13x + 42}$

Solve.

****29.** **Challenge** Jimi is taking a road trip during which he will drive 500 miles. He has allowed 2 hours for rest. As Jimi drives, his speed will vary and therefore his travel time will also vary.

   A. Write a rational function to describe Jimi's travel, where time is a function of rate and distance.

   B. Graph the function.

   C. Identify an appropriate domain and range for this situation. Explain your reasoning.

****30.** **Challenge** Chance the gardener is planning a flower garden in the shape of a trapezoid. He has 200 square feet to work with, and one base of the trapezoid must be 10 feet. The trapezoid area formula is $A = \dfrac{1}{2}h(b_1 + b_2)$.

   A. Write a rational function for height in terms of area and base.

   B. Graph the function.

   C. Identify an appropriate domain and range for this situation. Explain your reasoning.

UNIT 7   Radicals and Complex Numbers

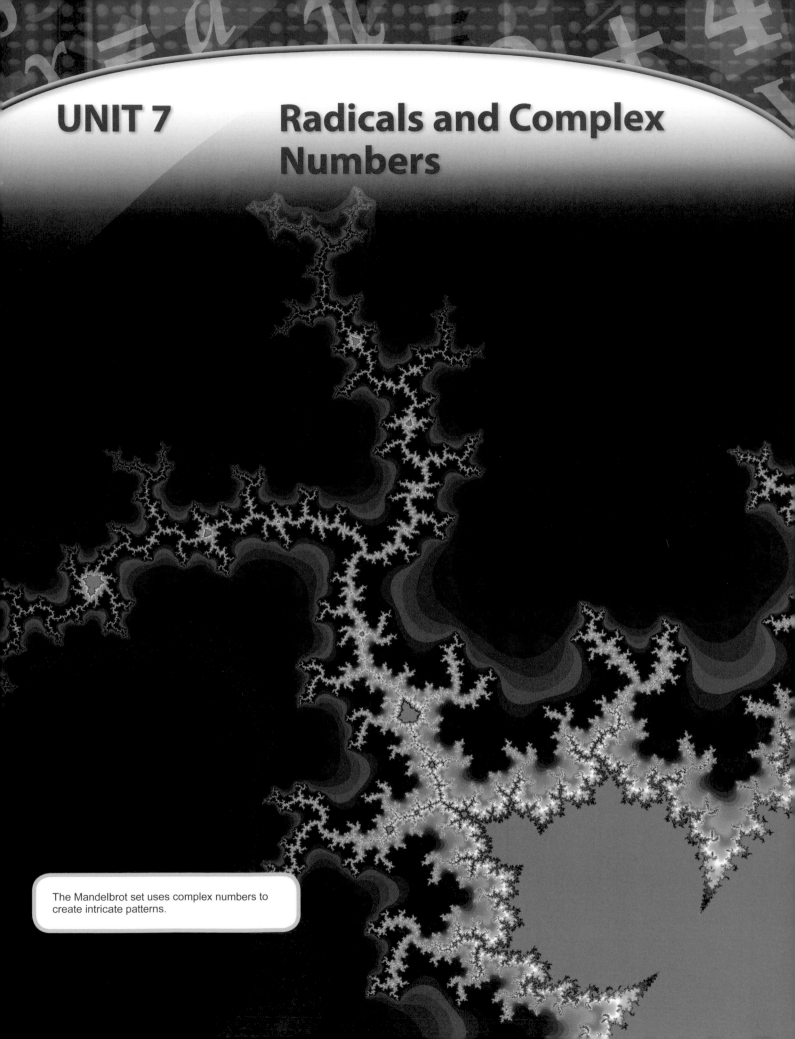

The Mandelbrot set uses complex numbers to create intricate patterns.

Some mathematicians, such as Benoit Mandelbrot, have found that powers of complex numbers can be used to create beautiful images.

Big Ideas

▶ All numbers obey the laws of arithmetic. You can use the laws of arithmetic to simplify algebraic expressions and equations.

▶ If you use a mathematical model to represent a certain situation, you can use the model to solve other problems that you might not be able to solve otherwise. Algebraic equations can capture key relationships among quantities in the world.

Unit Topics

▶ Foundations for Unit 7

▶ Simplifying Radical Expressions

▶ Fractional Exponents and Higher Roots

▶ Solving Radical Equations

▶ Graphing Radical Functions

▶ Imaginary Numbers

▶ Complex Numbers

▶ Multiplying and Dividing Complex Numbers

▶ Solving Equations with Complex Solutions

Foundations for Unit 7

Before you study radicals and complex numbers, you should know how to do the following:

▶ Find the square roots of integers, fractions, and decimals.

▶ Understand the difference between a square root and the principal square root.

▶ Use the square root property to solve quadratic equations.

Finding Square Roots

Definitions

square root a factor of a number that when multiplied by itself results in the number

principal square root the positive square root of a number

Example 1 Find the square roots of each number.

A The square roots of 121 are $+11$ and -11 because $11^2 = 121$ and $(-11)^2 = 121$.

B The square roots of 1.44 are $+1.2$ and -1.2 because $1.2^2 = 1.44$ and $(-1.2)^2 = 1.44$.

C The square roots of $\frac{4}{9}$ are $+\frac{2}{3}$ and $-\frac{2}{3}$ because $\left(\frac{2}{3}\right)^2 = \frac{4}{9}$ and $\left(-\frac{2}{3}\right)^2 = \frac{4}{9}$.

D The square roots of 0.36 are $+0.6$ and -0.6 because $0.6^2 = 0.36$ and $(-0.6)^2 = 0.36$.

E The square roots of 625 are $+25$ and -25 because $25^2 = 625$ and $(-25)^2 = 625$.

F The square root of -64 is undefined because you cannot multiply a real number by itself and have the result be negative.

Example 2 Simplify each expression.

A $\sqrt{\dfrac{25}{36}} = \dfrac{5}{6}$

because $\dfrac{5}{6} \cdot \dfrac{5}{6} = \dfrac{5 \cdot 5}{6 \cdot 6} = \dfrac{25}{36}$.

B $-\sqrt{0.81} = -0.9$

because $0.9^2 = 0.81$ and because the negative sign is outside the radical symbol.

C $\sqrt{\dfrac{1}{49}} = \dfrac{1}{7}$

because $\dfrac{1}{7} \cdot \dfrac{1}{7} = \dfrac{1 \cdot 1}{7 \cdot 7} = \dfrac{1}{49}$.

D $\sqrt{-100} =$ undefined

because you cannot multiply a real number by itself and have the result be negative.

E $\sqrt{1296} = 36$

because $36^2 = 1296$.

F $\pm\sqrt{400} = \pm 20$

because $20^2 = 400$ and $(-20)^2 = 400$.

> **THINK ABOUT IT**
>
> For real numbers, the square root of a negative number is undefined because you cannot multiply a real number by itself and have the result be negative.

Problem Set A

Find the square roots of each number.

1. 324
2. $\dfrac{121}{225}$
3. 2.56
4. 0.0196
5. $\dfrac{289}{361}$
6. -4900
7. 3600
8. $\dfrac{49}{81}$
9. 2304
10. 0.0441

Simplify each expression.

11. $-\sqrt{36}$
12. $\pm\sqrt{\dfrac{49}{121}}$
13. $\sqrt{-81}$
14. $\sqrt{\dfrac{169}{256}}$
15. $\sqrt{1024}$

Solving Simple Quadratic Equations

Some quadratic equations can be solved using the square root property.

SQUARE ROOT PROPERTY

If $x^2 = a$, then $x = +\sqrt{a}$ or $x = -\sqrt{a}$.

NOTATION

The square root property is sometimes written, "If $x^2 = a$, then $x = \pm\sqrt{a}$."

Example 3 Solve each equation.

A $4z^2 = 25$

$\dfrac{4z^2}{4} = \dfrac{25}{4}$

$z^2 = \dfrac{25}{4}$

$z = \pm\dfrac{5}{2}$

B $m^2 - 9 = 16$

$m^2 = 25$

$m = \pm 5$

C $(x - 3)^2 = 144$

$x - 3 = \pm 12$

$x = 3 + 12$ or $x = 3 - 12$

$x = 15$ $x = -9$

Problem Set B

Solve each equation.

16. $s^2 = 675$

17. $64x^2 = 225$

18. $4e^2 = 100$

19. $49c^2 = 36$

20. $81y^2 = 1$

21. $x^2 - 3 = 13$

22. $y^2 + 5 = 30$

23. $c^2 + 8 = 72$

24. $n^2 - 7 = 42$

25. $25x^2 - 8 = 92$

26. $(x - 2)^2 = 256$

27. $(c + 4)^2 = 64$

28. $(t + 9)^2 = 81$

29. $(x - 5)^2 = 400$

30. $2(t - 7)^2 = 200$

Simplifying Radical Expressions

A square root expression is in **simplified radical form** if the radicand is not a fraction, there are no radicals in the denominator, and none of the factors is a perfect square other than 1.

Simplified Radical Form

You can use properties of radicals to simplify expressions.

PRODUCT PROPERTY OF RADICALS

For real numbers $a \geq 0$ and $b \geq 0$,
$$\sqrt{ab} = \sqrt{a} \cdot \sqrt{b}.$$

QUOTIENT PROPERTY OF RADICALS

For real numbers $a \geq 0$ and $b > 0$,
$$\sqrt{\frac{a}{b}} = \frac{\sqrt{a}}{\sqrt{b}}.$$

Example 1 Write each expression in simplified radical form.

Ⓐ $\sqrt{80}$

Solution

$$\sqrt{80} = \sqrt{16 \cdot 5} \qquad \text{Use a perfect square to factor the radicand.}$$
$$= \sqrt{16} \cdot \sqrt{5} \qquad \text{Product Property of Radicals}$$
$$= 4\sqrt{5} \qquad \text{Simplify.} \ \blacksquare$$

Ⓑ $\sqrt{\frac{2}{9}}$

Solution

$$\sqrt{\frac{2}{9}} = \frac{\sqrt{2}}{\sqrt{9}} \qquad \text{Quotient Property of Radicals}$$
$$= \frac{\sqrt{2}}{3} \qquad \text{Simplify.} \ \blacksquare$$

C $\sqrt{15}$

Solution $\sqrt{15}$ is in simplified radical form because the radicand is not a fraction, there are no radicals in the denominator, and none of the factors (1, 3, 5, or 15) is a perfect square other than 1. ∎

Rationalizing a Denominator

When a radical is in the denominator of a fraction, you can simplify it by multiplying both the numerator and denominator by the radical. This is called rationalizing the denominator.

Example 2 Write $\dfrac{3}{\sqrt{5}}$ in simplified radical form.

Solution

$$\dfrac{3}{\sqrt{5}} = \dfrac{3}{\sqrt{5}} \cdot \dfrac{\sqrt{5}}{\sqrt{5}} \qquad \text{Multiply the numerator and denominator by } \sqrt{5}.$$

$$= \dfrac{3\sqrt{5}}{\sqrt{5 \cdot 5}} \qquad \text{Product Property of Radicals}$$

$$= \dfrac{3\sqrt{5}}{\sqrt{25}} \qquad \text{Simplify.}$$

$$= \dfrac{3\sqrt{5}}{5} \qquad \text{Simplify.} \quad ∎$$

Simplifying Algebraic Expressions

Here are four examples of how you can use the product property of radicals to simplify the square root of a power of a variable.

Let $x \geq 0$:

$$\sqrt{x^2} = x$$

$$\sqrt{x^3} = \sqrt{x^2 \cdot x} = \sqrt{x^2} \cdot \sqrt{x} = x\sqrt{x}$$

$$\sqrt{x^4} = \sqrt{(x^2)^2} = x^2$$

$$\sqrt{x^5} = \sqrt{x^4 \cdot x} = \sqrt{x^4} \cdot \sqrt{x} = x^2\sqrt{x}$$

Example 3 Write each expression in simplified radical form. Assume all variables are positive.

A $\sqrt{27x^2y^3}$

Solution

$$\sqrt{27x^2y^3} = \sqrt{9 \cdot 3 \cdot x^2 \cdot y^2 \cdot y} \qquad \text{Factor the radicand.}$$

$$= \sqrt{9} \cdot \sqrt{3} \cdot \sqrt{x^2} \cdot \sqrt{y^2} \cdot \sqrt{y} \qquad \text{Product Property of Radicals}$$

$$= 3\sqrt{3} \cdot xy\sqrt{y} \qquad \text{Simplify.}$$

$$= 3xy\sqrt{3y} \qquad \text{Simplify.} \quad ∎$$

B $\dfrac{a}{\sqrt{a^3}}$

Solution

$\dfrac{a}{\sqrt{a^3}} = \dfrac{a}{\sqrt{a^2 \cdot a}}$ Factor the denominator.

$= \dfrac{a}{\sqrt{a^2} \cdot \sqrt{a}}$ Product Property of Radicals

$= \dfrac{a}{a\sqrt{a}}$ Simplify.

$= \dfrac{1}{\sqrt{a}} \cdot \dfrac{\sqrt{a}}{\sqrt{a}}$ Multiply the numerator and denominator by $\sqrt{a}$.

$= \dfrac{\sqrt{a}}{a}$ Simplify. ■

C $\sqrt{7hg}$

Solution $\sqrt{7hg}$ is in simplified radical form because the radicand is not a fraction, there are no radicals in the denominator, and none of the factors is a perfect square other than 1. ■

Simplifying Radical Expressions Containing Binomial Denominators

You can also use the difference of squares pattern to rationalize a denominator. When the denominator of a fraction is a binomial expression that includes a radical, multiply both the numerator and denominator by the conjugate.

> **DEFINITION**
>
> The **conjugate** of $a + \sqrt{b}$ is $a - \sqrt{b}$.

Example 4   Simplify each expression. Assume all variables are positive.

A $\dfrac{5}{3 + \sqrt{2}}$

Solution   Multiply the numerator and denominator by the conjugate to rationalize the denominator.

$\dfrac{5}{3 + \sqrt{2}} = \dfrac{5}{3 + \sqrt{2}} \cdot \dfrac{3 - \sqrt{2}}{3 - \sqrt{2}}$ Multiply the numerator and denominator by the conjugate of the denominator.

$= \dfrac{15 - 5\sqrt{2}}{9 + 3\sqrt{2} - 3\sqrt{2} - (\sqrt{2})^2}$ Distributive Property and FOIL

$= \dfrac{15 - 5\sqrt{2}}{9 - 2}$ Simplify.

$= \dfrac{15 - 5\sqrt{2}}{7}$ Simplify. ■

B $\dfrac{2}{x + \sqrt{7y}}$

Solution

$$\dfrac{2}{x + \sqrt{7y}} = \dfrac{2}{x + \sqrt{7y}} \cdot \dfrac{x - \sqrt{7y}}{x - \sqrt{7y}}$$

Multiply the numerator and denominator by the conjugate of the denominator.

$$= \dfrac{2x - 2\sqrt{7y}}{x^2 - x\sqrt{7y} + x\sqrt{7y} - \left(\sqrt{7y}\right)^2}$$

Distributive Property and FOIL

$$= \dfrac{2x - 2\sqrt{7y}}{x^2 - 7y}$$

Simplify. ∎

Multiplying Radical Expressions

To multiply radical expressions, use the product property of radicals.

Example 5 Multiply. Assume all variables are positive.

A $\sqrt{8} \cdot \sqrt{32}$

Solution

$$\sqrt{8} \cdot \sqrt{32} = \sqrt{8 \cdot 32}$$ Product Property of Radicals

$$= \sqrt{256}$$ Multiply.

$$= \sqrt{16^2}$$ Identify that $256 = 16^2$.

$$= 16$$ Simplify. ∎

B $\sqrt{2r^3s^9} \cdot 4\sqrt{8r^5s^2}$

Solution

$$\sqrt{2r^3s^9} \cdot 4\sqrt{8r^5s^2} = 4\sqrt{2r^3s^9 \cdot 8r^5s^2}$$ Product Property of Radicals

$$= 4\sqrt{16r^8s^{11}}$$ Product of Powers Property

$$= 4\sqrt{16r^8s^{10}s}$$ Product of Powers Property

$$= 4\sqrt{4^2 \cdot (r^4)^2 \cdot (s^5)^2 \cdot s}$$

$$= 4 \cdot 4 \cdot r^4 \cdot s^5 \cdot \sqrt{s}$$ Simplify.

$$= 16r^4s^5\sqrt{s}$$ Simplify. ∎

C $(\sqrt{2} + 3\sqrt{3})(\sqrt{2} + \sqrt{5})$

Solution   Use the FOIL method to multiply two binomials.

$$(\sqrt{2} + 3\sqrt{3})(\sqrt{2} + \sqrt{5}) = (\sqrt{2})^2 + \sqrt{2} \cdot \sqrt{5} + 3\sqrt{3} \cdot \sqrt{2} + 3\sqrt{3} \cdot \sqrt{5}$$

$$= 2 + \sqrt{10} + 3\sqrt{6} + 3\sqrt{15} \ \blacksquare$$

Adding and Subtracting Radical Expressions

Like radicals have the same index and radicand. You can use the distributive property to add or subtract like radicals.

Example 6

A Add $8\sqrt{6} + \sqrt{5} + \sqrt{6}$.

Solution

$$8\sqrt{6} + \sqrt{5} + \sqrt{6} = 8\sqrt{6} + \sqrt{6} + \sqrt{5}$$
$$= (8 + 1)\sqrt{6} + \sqrt{5}$$
$$= 9\sqrt{6} + \sqrt{5} \quad \blacksquare$$

B Subtract $5\sqrt{12} - 3\sqrt{48}$.

Solution

$$5\sqrt{12} - 3\sqrt{48} = 5\sqrt{4 \cdot 3} - 3\sqrt{16 \cdot 3}$$
$$= 5\sqrt{4} \cdot \sqrt{3} - 3\sqrt{16} \cdot \sqrt{3}$$
$$= 10\sqrt{3} - 12\sqrt{3}$$
$$= (10 - 12)\sqrt{3}$$
$$= -2\sqrt{3} \quad \blacksquare$$

C Simplify $\sqrt{48t^5} - \sqrt{3t^5} - \sqrt{3t}$. Assume all variables are positive.

Solution

$$\sqrt{48t^5} - \sqrt{3t^5} - \sqrt{3t} = \sqrt{16t^4} \cdot \sqrt{3t} - \sqrt{t^4} \cdot \sqrt{3t} - \sqrt{3t}$$
$$= 4t^2\sqrt{3t} - t^2\sqrt{3t} - \sqrt{3t}$$
$$= (4t^2 - t^2)\sqrt{3t} - \sqrt{3t}$$
$$= 3t^2\sqrt{3t} - \sqrt{3t} \text{ or } (3t^2 - 1)\sqrt{3t} \quad \blacksquare$$

TIP

$(3t^2 - 1)\sqrt{3t}$ is an alternate simplified form of $3t^2\sqrt{3t} - \sqrt{3t}$.

Problem Set

Write each expression in simplified radical form. Assume all variables are positive.

1. $\sqrt{50}$

2. $\sqrt{48}$

3. $\sqrt{33}$

4. $\sqrt{108}$

5. $\dfrac{1}{\sqrt{10}}$

6. $\sqrt{\dfrac{3}{16}}$

7. $\sqrt{\dfrac{7}{64}}$

8. $\dfrac{2}{\sqrt{13}}$

9. $\sqrt{\dfrac{5}{49}}$

10. $\sqrt{90xz^6}$

11. $\sqrt{20ab^3}$

12. $\sqrt{75u^9v^8}$

13. $\sqrt{19x^4y}$

14. $\sqrt{8x^{12}y^7}$

15. $\sqrt{5a^{11}b^{13}}$

16. $\sqrt{\dfrac{x^7}{x^4}}$

17. $\dfrac{2b}{\sqrt{b^{20}}}$

18. $\sqrt{\dfrac{t^2}{t^{14}}}$

19. $\sqrt{\dfrac{m^4}{m^6}}$

20. $\dfrac{4k}{\sqrt{k^4}}$

21. $\dfrac{n^2}{\sqrt{n^7}}$

22. $\dfrac{a}{\sqrt{a^5}}$

23. $\sqrt{\dfrac{x^{10}}{x}}$

24. $\dfrac{g^3}{\sqrt{g^3}}$

Multiply. Write each expression in simplified radical form. Assume all variables are positive.

25. $\sqrt{12} \cdot \sqrt{27}$

26. $\sqrt{98} \cdot \sqrt{32}$

27. $\sqrt{50} \cdot \sqrt{128}$

28. $\sqrt{45} \cdot \sqrt{96}$

29. $\sqrt{80} \cdot \sqrt{45}$

30. $\sqrt{3x^2y^3} \cdot 2\sqrt{72x^3y^4}$

31. $\sqrt{5hg^4} \cdot 5\sqrt{63h^5g^5}$

32. $\sqrt{7p^3q^6} \cdot 3\sqrt{200p^7q}$

33. $2\sqrt{6x^5y^2} \cdot 5\sqrt{160x^8y^3}$

34. $3\sqrt{7x^6y^3} \cdot 4\sqrt{32x^4y^5}$

35. $(\sqrt{3} + 2\sqrt{2})(\sqrt{3} + \sqrt{5})$

36. $(\sqrt{7} + 3\sqrt{5})(\sqrt{7} - \sqrt{3})$

37. $(\sqrt{11} - 3\sqrt{3})(\sqrt{11} - 6\sqrt{3})$

38. $(7\sqrt{13} - 8\sqrt{3})(\sqrt{11} + 4\sqrt{7})$

39. $(\sqrt{15} - 3\sqrt{14})(\sqrt{13} - 2\sqrt{7})$

Add or subtract. Write each expression in simplified radical form. Assume all variables are positive.

40. $\sqrt{3} + 2\sqrt{3} + \sqrt{7}$

41. $\sqrt{11} - 3\sqrt{11} + \sqrt{13}$

42. $4\sqrt{17} + 4\sqrt{13} - \sqrt{17}$

43. $5\sqrt{19} - 6\sqrt{3} + 4\sqrt{19}$

44. $-6\sqrt{15} - 7\sqrt{15} - 12\sqrt{15}$

45. $2\sqrt{18} - 5\sqrt{32}$

46. $6\sqrt{27} + 11\sqrt{75}$

47. $-9\sqrt{48} - 8\sqrt{12}$

48. $12\sqrt{243} + 18\sqrt{147}$

49. $-13\sqrt{640} - 20\sqrt{490}$

50. $\sqrt{72x^3} - \sqrt{2x^3} - \sqrt{2x}$

51. $\sqrt{45x^2} + \sqrt{5x^2} + 4\sqrt{5}$

52. $\sqrt{7x^3} + 8\sqrt{28x^7} - \sqrt{7x^3}$

53. $3\sqrt{2x^5} - 5\sqrt{162x^5} - 8\sqrt{200x}$

Simplify each expression. Assume all variables are positive.

54. $\dfrac{3}{1 + \sqrt{3}}$

55. $\dfrac{4}{2 - \sqrt{5}}$

56. $\dfrac{7}{3 + \sqrt{10}}$

57. $\dfrac{2}{9 - \sqrt{7}}$

58. $\dfrac{6}{g + \sqrt{17g}}$

59. $\dfrac{9}{8n - 4\sqrt{3n}}$

60. $\dfrac{5}{x + \sqrt{6x}}$

61. $\dfrac{2}{a - \sqrt{3a}}$

62. $\dfrac{-1}{y + \sqrt{13x}}$

63. $\dfrac{11}{x - \sqrt{23xy}}$

64. $\dfrac{9}{s - 2\sqrt{17t}}$

65. $\dfrac{-2}{3m - \sqrt{3n}}$

***66. Challenge** $\dfrac{4}{\sqrt{3}} + \sqrt{12}$

***67. Challenge** $\dfrac{4 - \sqrt{2xy}}{6 + \sqrt{2xy}} - \dfrac{4 + \sqrt{2xy}}{6 - \sqrt{2xy}}$

Fractional Exponents and Higher Roots

An expression that contains a radical sign, $\sqrt{}$, is a **radical expression**.

Examples of radical expressions are $\sqrt{3x}$, $\sqrt[4]{x^2y^3}$, and $\sqrt[5]{32}$.

DEFINITIONS

If a and b are real numbers, n is a positive integer, and $a^n = b$, then a is an **nth root** of b.

The nth root of b is written $\sqrt[n]{b}$, where n is the **index** of the radical and b is the **radicand**. The index is always an integer greater than 1, and the radicand can be a real number or an algebraic expression.

Finding Real *n*th Roots

REAL *n*TH ROOTS OF *b*

	n is even	*n* is odd
$b > 0$	two real roots (one positive and one negative)	one real root
$b < 0$	no real roots	one real root
$b = 0$	one real root, $\sqrt[n]{0} = 0$	

Example 1

A Find the cube roots of -64.

Solution The cube root means that n is 3. Since n is odd and $b < 0$, there is one real root: $(-4)^3 = -64$. So the cube root of -64 is -4. ∎

B Find the fourth roots of -625.

Solution Since n is even and $b < 0$, there are no real roots. ∎

C Find the fourth roots of 81.

Solution Since n is even and $b > 0$, there are two real roots: $(-3)^4 = 81$ and $3^4 = 81$. So the fourth roots of 81 are ± 3. ∎

Radicals and Rational Exponent Form

DEFINITION

For any positive integer n, and any real number b,

$$\sqrt[n]{b} = b^{\frac{1}{n}},$$

except when $b < 0$ and n is even.

PROPERTIES OF RADICALS AND RATIONAL EXPONENTS

For any positive integers m and n, and any real number b,

$$\sqrt[n]{b^m} = \left(\sqrt[n]{b}\right)^m = b^{\frac{m}{n}},$$

except when $b < 0$ and n is even.

Example 2 Write each expression in rational exponent form. Assume all variables are positive.

A $\sqrt[3]{5}$

Solution

$\sqrt[3]{5} = 5^{\frac{1}{3}}$ ∎

B $\left(\sqrt{x+1}\right)^3$

Solution

$\left(\sqrt{x+1}\right)^3 = \sqrt[2]{(x+1)^3} = (x+1)^{\frac{3}{2}}$ ∎

REMEMBER

Assume that the index of a radical expression is 2 whenever no index is written.

Example 3 Write each expression in radical form.

A $2^{\frac{3}{4}}$

Solution

$2^{\frac{3}{4}} = \sqrt[4]{2^3} = \sqrt[4]{8}$ ∎

B $(4m)^{\frac{2}{3}}$

Solution

$(4m)^{\frac{2}{3}} = \sqrt[3]{(4m)^2} = \sqrt[3]{16m^2}$ ∎

Simplifying a Radical Expression

The properties of exponents given for integer exponents may also be applied to fractional exponents, but be careful with even roots.

PROPERTIES OF nTH ROOTS OF nTH POWERS

For any real number b and positive integer n,

$$\text{if } n \text{ is even, then } \sqrt[n]{b^n} = |b|,$$
$$\text{if } n \text{ is odd, then } \sqrt[n]{b^n} = b.$$

PRODUCT AND QUOTIENT PROPERTIES OF RADICALS

For any real numbers a and b, where the following roots are represented by real numbers,

$$\sqrt[n]{ab} = \sqrt[n]{a}\,\sqrt[n]{b} \qquad \text{Product Property of Radicals}$$

$$\sqrt[n]{\frac{a}{b}} = \frac{\sqrt[n]{a}}{\sqrt[n]{b}}, \ (b \neq 0) \qquad \text{Quotient Property of Radicals}$$

REMEMBER

Properties of Exponents

If a and b are nonzero real numbers and m and n are integers, then

$a^m \cdot a^n = a^{(m+n)}$ Product of Powers

$\dfrac{a^m}{a^n} = a^{(m-n)}$ Quotient of Powers

$(ab)^n = a^n b^n$ Power of a Product

$\left(\dfrac{a}{b}\right)^n = \dfrac{a^n}{b^n}$ Power of a Quotient

$(a^m)^n = a^{mn}$ Power of a Power

Example 4   Simplify each expression.

Ⓐ $\sqrt[4]{(-16)^4}$

Solution

$\sqrt[4]{(-16)^4} = |-16|$ Simplify.

$= 16$ Definition of Absolute Value ∎

Ⓑ $\sqrt[3]{128}$

Solution

$\sqrt[3]{128} = \sqrt[3]{64 \cdot 2}$ Factor 128.

$= \sqrt[3]{64} \cdot \sqrt[3]{2}$ Product Property of Radicals

$= 4\sqrt[3]{2}$ Simplify. ∎

Ⓒ $\sqrt[3]{2^6}$

Solution

$\sqrt[3]{2^6} = \sqrt[3]{(2^2)^3}$ Power of a Power Property

$= 2^2$ Simplify.

$= 4$ Simplify. ∎

Ⓓ $\sqrt[3]{\dfrac{27}{125}}$

Solution

$\sqrt[3]{\dfrac{27}{125}} = \dfrac{\sqrt[3]{27}}{\sqrt[3]{125}}$ Quotient Property of Radicals

$= \dfrac{3}{5}$ Simplify. ∎

> **REMEMBER**
>
> A radical expression is in **simplified radical form** if the radicand is not a fraction, there are no radicals in the denominator, and no factor is a perfect nth power.

You can use properties of radicals or fractional exponents to simplify expressions.

Example 5   Simplify each expression. Assume all variables are positive.

Ⓐ $(-32)^{\frac{3}{5}}$

Solution

$(-32)^{\frac{3}{5}} = \left(\sqrt[5]{-32}\right)^3 = (-2)^3 = -8$ ∎

Ⓑ $(x^5)^{\frac{1}{4}} \cdot x^{\frac{3}{4}}$

Solution

$(x^5)^{\frac{1}{4}} \cdot x^{\frac{3}{4}} = x^{\frac{5}{4}} \cdot x^{\frac{3}{4}} = x^{\frac{8}{4}} = x^2$ ∎

Example 6   Write each expression in simplified radical form. Assume all variables are positive.

Ⓐ $\sqrt[4]{32x^{10}y^4}$

Solution

$\sqrt[4]{32x^{10}y^4} = \sqrt[4]{2^5x^{10}y^4}$ Write 32 as a power of 2.

$= \sqrt[4]{2^4x^8y^4} \cdot \sqrt[4]{2x^2}$ Product Property of Radicals

$= 2x^2y\sqrt[4]{2x^2}$ Simplify. ∎

Ⓑ $\sqrt[8]{a^6b^4}$

Solution

$\sqrt[8]{a^6b^2} = (a^6b^2)^{\frac{1}{8}}$ Property of Radicals

$= a^{\frac{6}{8}} b^{\frac{2}{8}}$ Power of a Product

$= a^{\frac{3}{4}} b^{\frac{1}{4}}$ Simplify.

$= \sqrt[4]{a^3b}$ Property of Radicals ∎

Problem Set

Find the indicated roots of each expression.

1. Find the cube roots of 27.
3. Find the fifth roots of 32.
5. Find the fifth roots of -243.

2. Find the fourth roots of 625.
4. Find the fourth roots of -16.
6. Find the cube roots of 216.

Write each expression in rational exponent form.

7. $\sqrt[4]{17}$
9. $\left(\sqrt{x-2}\right)^3$
11. $\left(\sqrt[4]{t^2+4}\right)^3$

8. $\sqrt[3]{20}$
10. $\left(\sqrt[3]{5-y}\right)^4$
12. $\left(\sqrt[7]{2r^3+9}\right)^5$

Write each expression in radical form.

13. $5^{\frac{2}{3}}$
15. $(8a)^{\frac{2}{3}}$
17. $(3ab)^{\frac{2}{5}}$

14. $6^{\frac{3}{5}}$
16. $(5xy^2)^{\frac{3}{4}}$
18. $(4p^2q)^{\frac{8}{3}}$

Write each expression in simplified radical form. Assume all variables are positive.

19. $\sqrt[3]{(-27)^3}$
24. $\dfrac{y^3}{y^{\frac{3}{4}}}$
28. $\sqrt[8]{p^{20}q^{29}r^{11}}$

20. $\sqrt[4]{\dfrac{16}{81}}$
25. $\sqrt[4]{81h^8g^5}$
*29. **Challenge** $\sqrt[3]{\dfrac{8x^3y^8z^4}{27a^9b^{18}}}$

21. $\sqrt[4]{3^7}$
26. $\sqrt[3]{192x^6y^8}$
*30. **Challenge** $\dfrac{3 \cdot \sqrt[5]{2048x^{10}y^9z^{16}}}{5 \cdot \sqrt[4]{1296x^4y^8z^{12}}}$

22. $243^{\frac{2}{5}}$
27. $\sqrt[10]{x^2y^6}$

23. $(x^4)^{\frac{1}{3}} \cdot x^{\frac{2}{3}}$

Solving Radical Equations

A **radical equation** has at least one radical expression with a variable in the radicand.

EXPONENTIAL PROPERTY OF EQUALITY

If $a = b$ and n is a positive integer, then $a^n = b^n$.

SOLVING RADICAL EQUATIONS

Step 1   Isolate the radical on one side of the equation.
Step 2   Raise both sides of the equation to the same power to eliminate the radical.
Step 3   Solve the equivalent equation.
Step 4   Check each solution by substituting into the original equation.

THINK ABOUT IT

Raising to the nth power is the inverse operation of taking the nth root.

The power of a power property, $(a^m)^n = a^{mn}$, makes it possible to use the exponential property of equality to solve radical equations.

Example 1   Solve and check.

A $\sqrt{x + 12} = 8$

Solution

$\sqrt{x + 12} = 8$

$(\sqrt{x + 12})^2 = 8^2$ Square both sides of the equation.

$x + 12 = 64$ Simplify.

$x = 52$ Subtract 12 from both sides.

► Check

Substitute 52 for x:

$\sqrt{52 + 12} \overset{?}{=} 8$

$\sqrt{64} \overset{?}{=} 8$

$8 = 8$ ✓ ∎

B $-5\sqrt[3]{a - 1} = 25$

Solution

$-5\sqrt[3]{a - 1} = 25$

$\sqrt[3]{a - 1} = -5$ Isolate the radical.

$(\sqrt[3]{a - 1})^3 = (-5)^3$ Cube both sides of the equation.

$a - 1 = -125$ Simplify.

$a = -124$ Add 1 to both sides.

► Check

Substitute -124 for x:

$-5\sqrt[3]{-124 - 1} \overset{?}{=} 25$

$-5\sqrt[3]{-125} \overset{?}{=} 25$

$-5(-5) \overset{?}{=} 25$

$25 = 25$ ✓ ∎

REMEMBER

The third root of a negative number is negative.

Identifying an Extraneous Solution

Raising each side of an equation to a power can create extraneous solutions. Always check your solutions to be certain each one satisfies the original equation.

Example 2   Solve $x + 1 = \sqrt{5x + 11}$.

Solution

$$x + 1 = \sqrt{5x + 11}$$

$(x + 1)^2 = (\sqrt{5x + 11})^2$ Square both sides of the equation.

$x^2 + 2x + 1 = 5x + 11$ Simplify.

$x^2 - 3x - 10 = 0$ Set equal to 0.

$(x - 5)(x + 2) = 0$ Factor.

$x = 5$ or $x = -2$ Zero Product Property

Check

Substitute 5 for x:

$5 + 1 \overset{?}{=} \sqrt{5 \cdot 5 + 11}$

$6 \overset{?}{=} \sqrt{36}$

$6 = 6 \checkmark$

Substitute –2 for x:

$-2 + 1 \overset{?}{=} \sqrt{5(-2) + 11}$

$-1 \neq \sqrt{1}$

> **REMEMBER**
>
> An extraneous solution is an apparent solution that does not satisfy the original equation.

The solution $x = -2$ is extraneous. The only solution is $x = 5$. ■

Solving a Radical Equation with Two Radicals

Example 3   Solve $\sqrt{3m - 2} = \sqrt{m + 10}$.

Solution

$$\sqrt{3m - 2} = \sqrt{m + 10}$$

$(\sqrt{3m - 2})^2 = (\sqrt{m + 10})^2$ Square both sides of the equation.

$3m - 2 = m + 10$ Simplify.

$2m = 12$ Subtraction and Addition Properties of Equality

$m = 6$ Division Property of Equality ■

When squaring an equation with radicals on both sides is not enough to clear all variables from radical expressions, isolate the radical, square both sides again, and simplify.

Example 4 Solve $\sqrt{x+13} = \sqrt{12-x} - 1$.

Solution

$$\sqrt{x+13} = \sqrt{12-x} - 1$$

$(\sqrt{x+13})^2 = (\sqrt{12-x} - 1)^2$ Square both sides of the equation.

$x + 13 = 12 - x - 2\sqrt{12-x} + 1$ Use the binomial square pattern on the right side.

$2x = -2\sqrt{12-x}$ Simplify.

$-x = \sqrt{12-x}$ Isolate the radical.

$(-x)^2 = (\sqrt{12-x})^2$ Square both sides of the equation.

$x^2 = 12 - x$ Simplify.

$x^2 + x - 12 = 0$ Set equal to 0.

$(x+4)(x-3) = 0$ Factor.

$x = -4$ or $x = 3$ Zero Product Property

Check

Substitute -4 for x:

$$\sqrt{-4+13} \overset{?}{=} \sqrt{12-(-4)} - 1$$

$$\sqrt{9} \overset{?}{=} \sqrt{16} - 1$$

$$3 = 3 \checkmark$$

Substitute 3 for x:

$$\sqrt{3+13} \overset{?}{=} \sqrt{12-3} - 1$$

$$\sqrt{16} \overset{?}{=} \sqrt{9} - 1$$

$$4 \neq 2$$

The solution $x = 3$ is extraneous. The only solution is $x = -4$. ∎

Problem Set

Solve.

1. $\sqrt{c+5} = 7$

2. $\sqrt{z-4} = 6$

3. $-2\sqrt[3]{x+3} = 8$

4. $-3\sqrt{6-x} = 12$

5. $-2\sqrt{a+3} = -10$

6. $3\sqrt{x-6} = 20$

7. $6\sqrt[4]{2a+3} = 24$

8. $-15\sqrt[3]{3a+1} = 30$

9. $\sqrt{4z+3} = \sqrt{z+6}$

10. $\sqrt{x} - \sqrt{2x-5} = 0$

11. $\sqrt{3s+1} = \sqrt{-2s+4}$

12. $\sqrt{7m-1} + \sqrt{3m-8} = 0$

13. $4 - \sqrt{6x-2} = 0$

14. $\sqrt{-5f-4} - f = 0$

15. $\sqrt{2x+6} = x+3$

16. $x - \sqrt{8g+1} = 4$

17. $-\sqrt{2-4x} = -\sqrt{3-8x}$

18. $\sqrt{8c-4} = 2\sqrt{3c-7}$

19. $b + \sqrt{5b-1} = 5$

20. $3\sqrt{3x+1} = -\sqrt{6+2x}$

21. $5\sqrt{6-x} = 4\sqrt{9-x}$

22. $c - 1 = \sqrt{3-2c}$

23. $\sqrt{x+7} = \sqrt{6-x} + 1$

24. $\sqrt{8b-4} = \sqrt{6b-5} - 1$

25. $\sqrt{2x-2} - \sqrt{x} = 1$

26. $\sqrt{2r} = 2 + \sqrt{r-2}$

27. $\sqrt{4g+1} = 2 + \sqrt{g-1}$

Solve.

*28. **Challenge** In a right triangle, the length of one leg a is 7 inches more than the length of the other leg b. If the hypotenuse c measures 17 inches, use $c = \sqrt{a^2 + b^2}$ to find the lengths of both legs.

*29. **Challenge** Heron's formula states that the area A of a triangle whose sides have lengths a, b, and c is $A = \sqrt{s(s - a)(s - b)(s - c)}$, where s is the semiperimeter of the triangle: $s = \dfrac{a + b + c}{2}$. If the sides of a triangle have lengths 4 cm, 5 cm, and 7 cm, what is the area of the triangle expressed in simplest radical form?

Graphing Radical Functions

A **radical function** of the form $f(x) = a\sqrt[n]{x - h} + k$, where n is an integer greater than 1, is in a family of functions whose parent function is $f(x) = \sqrt[n]{x}$.

Graphing a Square Root Function

If $n = 2$, the family contains square root functions.

Example 1 Graph $f(x) = \sqrt{x}$.

Solution Use a table to find several ordered pairs of the function. Include only nonnegative values for x because $\sqrt{x}$ is undefined if x is negative. For convenience, choose perfect squares for x.

THINK ABOUT IT

Every positive real number has two square roots. For example, the two square roots of 9 are 3 and -3. But the $\sqrt{}$ symbol indicates only the *principal* (nonnegative) square root. Therefore, $\sqrt{9} = 3$.

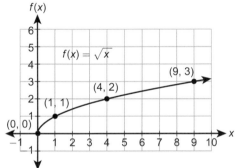

x	f(x)
0	0
1	1
4	2
9	3
16	4

Domain: $\{x \mid x \geq 0\}$

Range: $\{y \mid y \geq 0\}$

The graph looks like the top half of a sideways parabola. ■

Graphing a Cube Root Function

If $n = 3$, the family contains cube root functions.

Example 2 Graph $f(x) = \sqrt[3]{x}$.

Solution Use a table to find several ordered pairs of the function. Negative numbers have cube roots, so include negative values for x. For convenience, choose integer values for x that have integer cube roots.

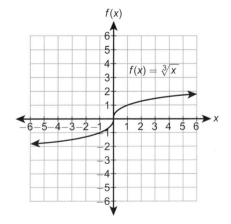

x	f(x)
−27	−3
−8	−2
−1	−1
0	0
1	1
8	2
27	3

Domain: $\{x \mid x \in \mathbb{R}\}$

Range: $\{y \mid y \in \mathbb{R}\}$ ■

Graphing Families of *n*th Root Functions

Every radical function of the form $f(x) = a\sqrt[n]{x - h} + k$ is a transformation of a parent function $f(x) = \sqrt[n]{x}$.

Square Root Function Graph Family: $f(x) = a\sqrt{x - h} + k$

Each change in the value of a, h, or k results in a different transformation of the parent graph, $f(x) = \sqrt{x}$.

Changing only the parameter a causes the parent function to reflect, stretch, or compress.

Changing only the parameter k causes the parent function to shift up or down on the y-axis.

Changing only the parameter h causes the parent function to shift left or right on the x-axis.

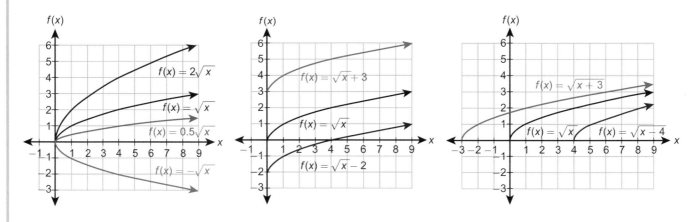

Cube Root Function Graph Family: $f(x) = a\sqrt[3]{x - h} + k$

Each change in the value of a, h, or k results in a different transformation of the parent graph, $f(x) = \sqrt[3]{x}$.

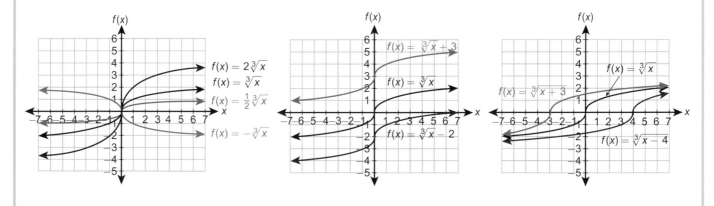

All graphs of functions with even roots look similar, and all graphs of functions with odd roots look similar. The only way to tell the graphs apart is to look at specific ordered pairs.

To transform the graph of $f(x) = \sqrt[n]{x}$ by changing more than one parameter, *first* decide whether or not to reflect it across the x-axis. *Then* apply each transformation to the graph obtained from the previous transformation.

Graphing a Square Root Function and Identifying the Domain and Range

Example 3   For the function $g(x) = -3\sqrt{x+1} - 2$, do the following:

Ⓐ Graph the function.

Ⓑ Identify the function's domain and range.

Solution

Ⓐ

Step 1   Describe how to obtain the graph by transforming the graph of $f(x) = \sqrt{x}$.

$g(x) = -3\sqrt{x+1} - 2$ is in the form $g(x) = a\sqrt{x-h} + k$, with $a = -3$, $h = -1$, and $k = -2$.

$a < 0$	Reflect the graph of $f(x) = \sqrt{x}$ across the x-axis.
$a = -3$	Stretch vertically by a factor of 3.
$h = -1$	Translate 1 unit to the left.
$k = -2$	Translate 2 units down.

Step 2   Make a table of values. Then plot points and sketch the graph. If you choose x-values so that $x + 1$ is a perfect square, then calculating corresponding y-values becomes easy. For example, $g(8) = -3\sqrt{8+1} - 2 = -3\sqrt{9} - 2 = -3 \cdot 3 - 2 = -11$.

x	g(x)
−1	−2
0	−5
3	−8
8	−11

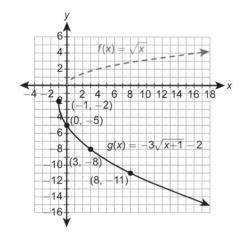

> **TIP**
>
> You might prefer to plot points and sketch the graph first, and then use the transformation description to check that your graph is reasonable.

B Domain: The radicand is $x + 1$. The radicand in a square root expression must be nonnegative, so solve the inequality $x + 1 \geq 0$. The solution set of $x + 1 \geq 0$ is given by $x \geq -1$. The domain, then, is $\{x \mid x \geq -1\}$.

Range: $\sqrt{x + 1} \geq 0$, so $-3\sqrt{x + 1} \leq 0$, and $-3\sqrt{x + 1} - 2 \leq -2$. The range is $\{y \mid y \leq -2\}$.

Verify that the domain and range are reasonable, based on the graph. ∎

REMEMBER

The radicand is the expression under the radical symbol.

Graphing a Cube Root Function and Identifying the Domain and Range

Example 4 For the function $g(x) = \frac{1}{2}\sqrt[3]{x - 1} + 3$, do the following:

A Graph the function.

B Identify the function's domain and range.

Solution

A

Step 1 Describe how to obtain the graph by transforming the graph of $f(x) = \sqrt[3]{x}$.

$g(x) = \frac{1}{2}\sqrt[3]{x - 1} + 3$ is in the form $f(x) = a\sqrt[3]{x - h} + k$, with $a = \frac{1}{2}$, $h = 1$, and $k = 3$.

$a = \frac{1}{2}$ Compress the graph of $f(x) = \sqrt[3]{x}$ vertically by a factor of $\frac{1}{2}$.

$h = 1$ Translate 1 unit to the right.

$k = 3$ Translate 3 units up.

Step 2 Make a table of values. Then plot points and sketch the graph.

x	g(x)
−7	2
0	2.5
1	3
2	3.5
9	4

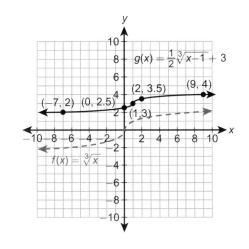

TIP

If you choose x-values for your table that make $x - 1$ an integer whose cube root is an integer, then corresponding function values are easy to calculate. For example,

$$g(-7) = \frac{1}{2}\sqrt[3]{-7 - 1} + 3$$
$$= \frac{1}{2}\sqrt[3]{-8} + 3$$
$$= \frac{1}{2} \cdot (-2) + 3 = 2$$

B Domain: The index of the radical is 3, an odd integer. So the radicand $x - 1$ can be positive, negative, or zero. $\sqrt[3]{x - 1}$ is defined for all real values of x. The domain is $\{x \mid x \in \mathbb{R}\}$.

Range: x can be any real number, so all of the following expressions can be any real number: $x - 1, \sqrt[3]{x - 1}, \frac{1}{2}\sqrt[3]{x - 1}$, and $\frac{1}{2}\sqrt[3]{x - 1} + 3$. The range is $\{y \mid y \in \mathbb{R}\}$. ■

Problem Set

For each function, do the following:

A. Determine the domain.
B. Determine the range.
C. Graph the function.

1. $f(x) = -\sqrt{x}$

2. $f(x) = 4\sqrt[3]{x}$

3. $f(x) = 3\sqrt{x} - 1$

4. $f(x) = 2\sqrt{x + 4} - 3$

5. $f(x) = -\sqrt[3]{x + 5} + 4$

6. $f(x) = \frac{3}{4}\sqrt{3x - 1} - 6$

7. $f(x) = \sqrt{5x}$

8. $f(x) = 2\sqrt[3]{x} + 4$

9. $f(x) = 5\sqrt{x - 1} + 2$

10. $f(x) = 4\sqrt[3]{x + 2} + 5$

11. $f(x) = -\sqrt{x - 3} - 1$

12. $f(x) = -2\sqrt[3]{x + 7} - 6$

Describe how to obtain the graph of each function by transforming the graph of $f(x) = \sqrt{x}$.

13. $g(x) = -\sqrt{x} + 10$

14. $g(x) = \sqrt{7x} - 4$

15. $g(x) = 8\sqrt{x + 5} + 9$

16. $g(x) = -\sqrt{x + 11} - 4$

17. $g(x) = 6\sqrt{x - 3} + 12$

18. $g(x) = -\frac{1}{5}\sqrt{x + 2} + 3$

Write the equation of each graph of a radical function using the form $f(x) = a\sqrt{x - h} + k$ or $f(x) = a\sqrt[3]{x - h} + k$.

19.

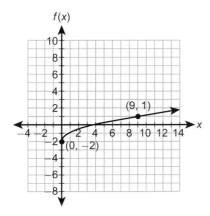

20.

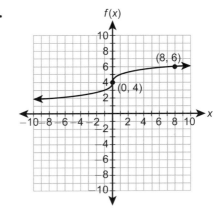

21.

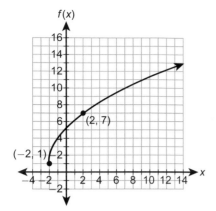

22.

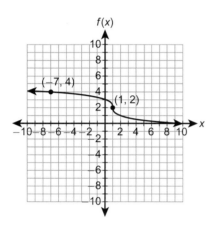

23.

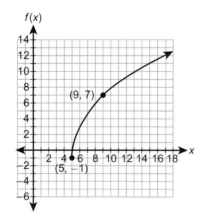

24.

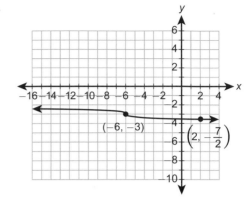

25.

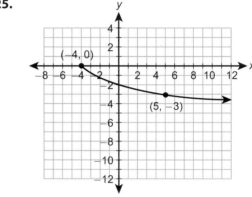

26.

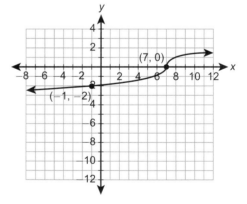

Solve.

*27. **Challenge** $S = 2\pi\sqrt{\dfrac{L}{32}}$ represents the swing of a pendulum, where S is the time in seconds it takes the pendulum to swing back and forth, and L is the pendulum length in feet. Graph the function and determine the time it takes for a 10-foot pendulum to complete one swing (back and forth).

*28. **Challenge** $S = 356\sqrt{d}$ represents the speed S (km/hr) that a tsunami can travel, where d is the average depth of water (km). Graph the function, determine the domain and range, and find the average depth of water if a tsunami is traveling at 200 km/hr.

Imaginary Numbers

An equation such as $x^2 = -1$ has no real-number solutions because the square of a real number is never negative.

Expanding the number system to include imaginary numbers makes it possible to solve this equation.

> **DEFINITIONS**
>
> i is the **imaginary unit** where $i^2 = -1$ and $i = \sqrt{-1}$.
> Any number that can be written in the form ai, where a is any real number, is called an **imaginary number**.

Simplifying Imaginary Numbers

To simplify an expression with imaginary numbers, follow the same rules you have used to put expressions into simplified radical form. The key difference is that any time you see a negative radicand, you should isolate the imaginary unit.

Example 1 Simplify each expression.

A $\sqrt{-36}$

Solution

$$\sqrt{-36} = \sqrt{36 \cdot (-1)}$$
$$= \sqrt{36} \cdot \sqrt{-1}$$
$$= 6i \ \blacksquare$$

B $3\sqrt{-50}$

Solution

$$3\sqrt{-50} = 3\sqrt{25 \cdot (-1) \cdot 2}$$
$$= 3\sqrt{25} \cdot \sqrt{-1} \cdot \sqrt{2}$$
$$= 3 \cdot 5i\sqrt{2}$$
$$= 15i\sqrt{2} \ \blacksquare$$

> **THINK ABOUT IT**
>
> The i is usually written to the left of the radical. This makes it clear that the i is not under the radical. For example, $\sqrt{2} \cdot i$ might be confused with $\sqrt{2i}$, so it is written $i\sqrt{2}$.

Performing Operations with Imaginary Numbers

The commutative and associative properties of addition and multiplication, as well as the distributive property, hold for imaginary numbers.

Operations with Imaginary Numbers Let x, y, a, and b be real numbers, $a \neq 0$, and $y \neq 0$.	
Addition	$xi + yi = (x + y)i$
Subtraction	$xi - yi = (x - y)i$
Multiplication of Two Imaginary Numbers	$(xi)(yi) = xy(i^2) = xy(-1) = -xy$
Multiplication of a Real Number and an Imaginary Number	$a(xi) = (ax)i$
Division of Two Imaginary Numbers	$\dfrac{xi}{yi} = \dfrac{x}{y}$
Division of a Real Number and an Imaginary Number	$\dfrac{bi}{a} = \dfrac{b}{a}i$

THINK ABOUT IT

Imaginary numbers can be graphed on a number line just as real numbers can.

Example 2 Simplify each expression.

(A) $15i + 25i$

Solution

$$15i + 25i = i \cdot (15 + 25)$$
$$= i \cdot 40$$
$$= 40i \ \blacksquare$$

(B) $-0.7i - i$

Solution

$$-0.7i - i = i \cdot (-0.7 - 1)$$
$$= i \cdot (-1.7)$$
$$= -1.7i \ \blacksquare$$

(C) $-5i \cdot 15i$

Solution

$$-5i \cdot 15i = -5 \cdot 15 \cdot i \cdot i$$
$$= -75i^2$$
$$= -75 \cdot (-1)$$
$$= 75 \ \blacksquare$$

(D) $\dfrac{21i}{-7}$

Solution

$$\frac{21i}{-7} = \frac{21}{-7} \cdot i$$
$$= -3i \ \blacksquare$$

Showing that Imaginary Numbers Are or Are Not Closed Under a Given Operation

The set of imaginary numbers is closed under the operations of addition and subtraction, but is not closed under the operations of multiplication and division.

Example 3

(A) Explain why the set of imaginary numbers is closed under addition.

Solution If ai and bi are any two imaginary numbers, then the distributive property lets us write $ai + bi$ as $(a + b)i$. Because the real numbers are closed under addition, $a + b$ is a real number (call it d), so we can write the sum as di. This is a product of a real number and the imaginary unit, so di is an imaginary number. $\blacksquare$

REMEMBER

A set of numbers is said to be **closed** under an operation if the results of the operation on elements of the set are also elements of the set.

B Show that the set of imaginary numbers is not closed under multiplication.

Solution By counterexample, $(2i)(3i) = 6i^2 = 6(-1) = -6$.
Since -6 is not an imaginary number, the set of imaginary numbers is not closed under multiplication. ∎

Simplifying Powers of *i*

The properties of exponents are useful when you simplify powers of *i*.

POWERS OF *i*	
$i^1 = i$	$i^5 = i^4 \cdot i = 1 \cdot i = i$
$i^2 = -1$	$i^6 = i^5 \cdot i = i \cdot i = i^2 = -1$
$i^3 = i^2 \cdot i = -1 \cdot i = -i$	$i^7 = i^6 \cdot i = -1 \cdot i = -i$
$i^4 = i^2 \cdot i^2 = -1 \cdot (-1) = 1$	$i^8 = i^4 \cdot i^4 = 1 \cdot 1 = 1$

The properties of exponents can also help show why the powers of *i* repeat in the pattern $i, -1, -i, 1$. When the exponent is a multiple of 4, the result will always be 1. When the exponent is a multiple of 4 with a remainder of 1, 2, or 3, the result will be i, -1, or $-i$, respectively.

Example 4 Simplify i^{15}.

Solution

$$i^{15} = i^{12} \cdot i^3 \qquad \text{Product of Powers Property}$$
$$= (i^4)^3 \cdot i^3 \qquad \text{Power of a Power Property}$$
$$= 1^3 \cdot (-i) \qquad \text{Powers of } i$$
$$= -i \qquad \text{Simplify.} \ \blacksquare$$

> **THINK ABOUT IT**
> Every integer power of *i* is equal to i, -1, $-i$, or 1.

Rationalizing an Imaginary Denominator

Simplify a fraction with an imaginary number in the denominator just as you would simplify a fraction that has a radical in the denominator. Multiply the numerator and denominator by the radical that is in the denominator.

Example 5 Simplify $\dfrac{3}{4i^7}$.

Solution

$$\frac{3}{4i^7} = \frac{3}{4(-i)} \qquad \text{Powers of } i$$
$$= \frac{3}{-4i} \cdot \frac{i}{i} \qquad \text{Rationalize the denominator.}$$
$$= \frac{3i}{-4i^2} \qquad \text{Multiply the numerators and denominators.}$$
$$= \frac{3i}{4} \qquad \text{Definition of } i^2 \ \blacksquare$$

> **THINK ABOUT IT**
> An expression is not simplified if *i* is in the denominator because *i* represents a radical ($i = \sqrt{-1}$).

Problem Set

· ·

Simplify.

  1. $\sqrt{-25}$

  2. $\sqrt{-49}$

  3. $\sqrt{-121}$

  4. $5\sqrt{-48}$

  5. $3\sqrt{-20}$

  6. $2\sqrt{-18}$

Perform the operation and simplify.

  7. $12i + 33i$

  8. $9i + 21i$

  9. $-i + 2.1i$

  10. $10i - 15i$

  11. $2i - 0.2i$

  12. $i - 3.4i$

  13. $-2i \cdot 14i$

  14. $3i \cdot 8i$

  15. $-4i \cdot (-5i)$

  16. $\dfrac{30i}{5}$

  17. $\dfrac{-24i}{3}$

  18. $\dfrac{-56i}{7i}$

Explain why each statement is true.

  19.   The set of imaginary numbers is closed under subtraction.

  20.   The set of imaginary numbers is not closed under division.

Simplify.

  21. i^{12}

  22. $-i^{32}$

  23. i^{21}

  24. $\dfrac{4i^4}{5i^3}$

  25. $\dfrac{8i^9}{4i^7}$

  26. $\dfrac{4i^4}{16i^4}$

  27. $\dfrac{-18i^5}{-3i^3}$

  ***28.**   **Challenge** $\dfrac{18}{3i^{13}}$

  ***29.**   **Challenge** $\dfrac{4}{16i^{24}}$

Answer the question.

  ***30.**   **Challenge** Consider the operation of exponentiation, z^a, where z is an imaginary number and a is any whole number. For what values of a is z^a closed under the set of imaginary numbers?

Complex Numbers

Complex numbers are numbers that contain a real part and an imaginary part.

DEFINITION

If a and b are real numbers, a **complex number** is any number of the form $a + bi$, where a is the real part and b is the imaginary part.

REMEMBER

$i = \sqrt{-1}$

Pure imaginary numbers are complex numbers of the form $0 + bi$. Every real number is a complex number of the form $a + 0i$. This means the set of real numbers and the set of imaginary numbers are both subsets of the set of complex numbers. The diagram below shows the relationship among sets of numbers.

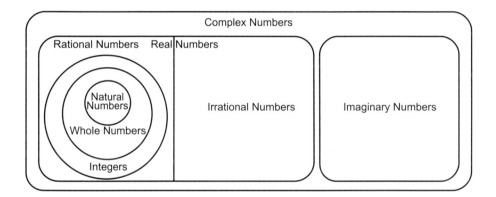

THINK ABOUT IT

The complex numbers are a superset of the real numbers.

For two complex numbers to be equal, the real parts must be equal *and* the imaginary parts must be equal.

DEFINITION

Two **complex numbers are equal** if and only if their real parts are equal and their imaginary parts are equal. In other words,

$$a + bi = c + di \text{ if and only if } a = c \text{ and } b = d.$$

The set of complex numbers are denoted $\mathbb{C}$.

Adding and Subtracting Complex Numbers

The commutative and associative properties of addition and multiplication, as well as the distributive property, hold for complex numbers.

ADDING AND SUBTRACTING COMPLEX NUMBERS

Let a, b, c, and d be real numbers.

Addition

To add complex numbers, add the real parts and then add the imaginary parts.

$$(a + bi) + (c + di) = (a + c) + (b + d)i$$

Subtraction

To subtract complex numbers, subtract the real parts and then subtract the imaginary parts.

$$(a + bi) - (c + di) = (a - c) + (b - d)i$$

CLOSURE PROPERTIES FOR THE COMPLEX NUMBERS

The set of complex numbers is closed under addition, subtraction, multiplication, and division.

Example 1   Add or subtract, and then simplify.

A $(3 + 7i) + (-9 - 4i)$

Solution

$$(3 + 7i) + (-9 - 4i) = (3 + (-9)) + (7 + (-4))i$$
$$= -6 + 3i \ \blacksquare$$

B $(-5 - 2i) - (8 + 11i)$

Solution

$$(-5 - 2i) - (8 + 11i) = (-5 - 8) + (-2 - 11)i$$
$$= -13 - 13i \ \blacksquare$$

The Complex Plane

DEFINITIONS

The **complex plane** is used to graph a complex number. Every complex number can be graphed on this plane. The horizontal axis is the **real axis**, and the vertical axis is the **imaginary axis**. Every complex number $a + bi$ is graphed using the ordered pair (a, b).

Example 2   Graph each point on the complex plane.

A $3 + 2i$

Solution   Start at the origin and move 3 units to the right along the real axis. Then move 2 units up along the imaginary axis. ■

B $5 - 3i$

Solution   Start at the origin and move 5 units to the right along the real axis. Then move 3 units down along the imaginary axis. ■

C $-2 + 2i$

Solution   Start at the origin and move 2 units to the left along the real axis. Then move 2 units up along the imaginary axis. ■

D 6

Solution   Start at the origin and move 6 units to the right along the real axis. There is no imaginary part to this number, so the point lies on the real axis. ■

E $-4i$

Solution   Start at the origin and move 4 units down the imaginary axis. There is no real part to this number, so the point lies on the imaginary axis. ■

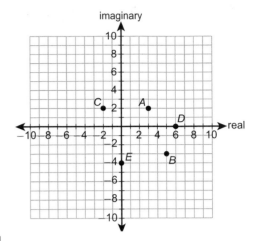

Example 3   Name the complex number represented by each point on the complex plane.

Solution   Point M lies 5 units to the right along the real axis and 2 units down along the imaginary axis. Point M represents the complex number $5 - 2i$.

Point Q lies 6 units up on the imaginary axis. Point Q represents the complex number $0 + 6i$, or $6i$.

Point R lies 3 units to the left along the real axis and 4 units down along the imaginary axis. Point R represents the complex number $-3 - 4i$. ■

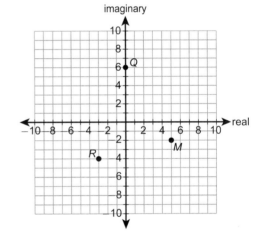

Calculating the Modulus of a Complex Number

> ### DEFINITION
>
> The **modulus** of a complex number $a + bi$, denoted by $|a + bi|$, is the distance between $a + bi$ and the origin on the complex plane. You can use the Pythagorean theorem to calculate the modulus for any complex number:
> $$|a + bi| = \sqrt{a^2 + b^2}$$
> The modulus is a distance, so it is always a nonnegative real number.

Example 4   Calculate the modulus of each complex number.

A $4 + 3i$

Solution   Use the formula $|a + bi| = \sqrt{a^2 + b^2}$.

$|4 + 3i| = \sqrt{4^2 + 3^2}$

$\qquad = \sqrt{16 + 9}$

$\qquad = \sqrt{25}$

$\qquad = 5$

The modulus of $4 + 3i$ is 5. ∎

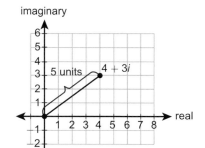

> ### NOTATION
>
> $|a + bi|$ The modulus of a complex number is also called the **absolute value** of the number.

B $2 - 5i$

Solution   Use the formula $|a + bi| = \sqrt{a^2 + b^2}$.

$|2 - 5i| = \sqrt{2^2 + (-5)^2}$

$\qquad = \sqrt{4 + 25}$

$\qquad = \sqrt{29}$

$\qquad \approx 5.4$

The modulus of $2 - 5i$ is $\sqrt{29}$, or about 5.4. ∎

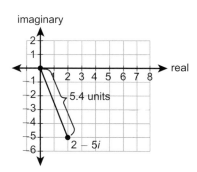

> ### TIP
>
> When the modulus is irrational, write the answer in simplified radical form. Then estimate to the nearest tenth.

Problem Set

Add or subtract, and then simplify.

1. $(4 + 3i) + (6 - 2i)$

2. $(2 - 4i) + (3 - 3i)$

3. $(-3 + 5i) + (6 + 2i)$

4. $(12 + 8i) - (7 + 4i)$

5. $(-2 + 5i) - (-2 + 9i)$

6. $(4 - 8i) - (2 + 2i)$

For each problem, do the following:

A. Graph the point on the complex plane.

B. Find the modulus. Write irrational moduli in simplified radical form, and then estimate to the nearest tenth.

7. -7

8. $8 - 6i$

9. $5i$

10. $-5 - 12i$

11. 9

12. $24 + 7i$

13. 1

14. $7 + 3i$

15. $9 + 10i$

16. $2 - 3i$

17. $-4 + 4i$

18. $-5 + 8i$

19. $-7 + 2i$

20. $1 + 4i$

21. $-1 - 2i$

Name the complex number represented by each point on the plane.

22.

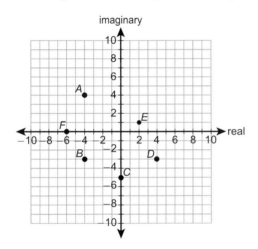

Solve.

23. **Challenge** Find the modulus of $(1 + 2i) + (2 - 3i)$.

24. **Challenge** Sketch a graph that describes all of the complex numbers with a modulus of 2.

Multiplying and Dividing Complex Numbers

You can use methods similar to those you learned for simplifying polynomials to multiply and divide complex numbers.

Multiplying Complex Numbers

Use the distributive property to multiply complex numbers.

Example 1 Multiply.

A $7i(3 + 2i)$

Solution Use the distributive property.

$$7i(3 + 2i) = 7i \cdot 3 + 7i \cdot 2i$$
$$= 21i + 14i^2$$
$$= 21i + 14(-1)$$
$$= 21i - 14$$
$$= -14 + 21i \ \blacksquare$$

> **REMEMBER**
>
> $i^2 = (\sqrt{-1})^2 = -1$

B $(8 - 3i)(4 + 7i)$

Solution Use the FOIL method.

$$(8 - 3i)(4 + 7i) = 32 + 56i - 12i - 21i^2$$
$$= 32 + 44i - 21(-1)$$
$$= 32 + 44i + 21$$
$$= 53 + 44i \ \blacksquare$$

Multiplying Complex Conjugates

> **DEFINITION**
>
> **Complex conjugates** are two complex numbers of the form $a + bi$ and $a - bi$. The expressions $a + bi$ and $a - bi$ are a **conjugate pair**.

Example 2   Multiply $(6 + 2i)(6 - 2i)$.

Solution

$$
\begin{aligned}
(6 + 2i)(6 - 2i) &= 36 - 12i + 12i - 4i^2 && \text{FOIL} \\
&= 36 - 4i^2 && \text{Simplify.} \\
&= 36 - 4(-1) && \text{Definition of } i^2 \\
&= 40 && \text{Simplify.} \ \blacksquare
\end{aligned}
$$

The product of a complex number and its conjugate is always a real number. The following proof shows this property when a and b are real numbers.

$$
\begin{aligned}
(a + bi)(a - bi) &= a^2 - abi + abi - (bi)^2 \\
&= a^2 - b^2 i^2 \\
&= a^2 - b^2 \cdot (-1) \\
&= a^2 + b^2
\end{aligned}
$$

Dividing Complex Numbers

Dividing complex numbers involves rationalizing the denominator. You can use complex conjugates to rationalize a denominator and simplify a quotient.

Example 3   Write the quotient in standard form.

$$\frac{1 + i}{2 + 3i}$$

Solution

$$
\begin{aligned}
\frac{1 + i}{2 + 3i} &= \frac{1 + i}{2 + 3i} \cdot \frac{2 - 3i}{2 - 3i} && \text{Multiply the top and bottom by the conjugate of the denominator.} \\
&= \frac{2 - 3i + 2i - 3i^2}{4 - 6i + 6i - 9i^2} && \text{FOIL} \\
&= \frac{2 - i + 3}{4 + 9} && \text{Combine like terms.} \\
&= \frac{5 - i}{4 + 9} && \text{Simplify.} \\
&= \frac{5 - i}{13} && \text{Simplify.} \ \blacksquare
\end{aligned}
$$

> **REMEMBER**
>
> $\dfrac{2 - 3i}{2 - 3i} = 1$ because the numerator and denominator of the fraction are equal.

Changing the Modulus of a Complex Number by Multiplication

When a complex number is multiplied by another number that does not have a modulus of 1, its modulus is changed. The effect of the multiplication can be demonstrated by graphing the product and examining its distance from the origin.

In the example that follows, $1 - 2i$ is the original complex number. Notice the effect on the modulus of multiplying $1 - 2i$ by 2 and then by $2i$. Lastly, compare the modulus of $1 - 2i$ to the modulus of $(1 - 2i)^2$.

Example 4 Determine the modulus of each product. Graph the results.

A $1(1 - 2i)$

Solution $1(1 - 2i) = 1 - 2i$

Step 1 Find the modulus of the original complex number.

$$|1 - 2i| = \sqrt{1^2 + (-2)^2}$$
$$= \sqrt{5}$$

Step 2 Graph the result.

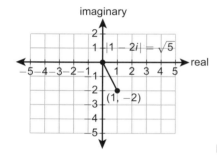

B $2(1 - 2i)$

Solution $2(1 - 2i) = 2 - 4i$

Step 1 Find the modulus of the product.

$$|2 - 4i| = \sqrt{2^2 + (-4)^2}$$
$$= \sqrt{20}$$
$$= 2\sqrt{5}$$

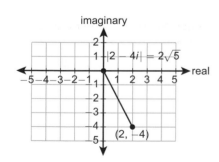

C $2i(1 - 2i)$

Solution

$$2i(1 - 2i) = 2i - 4i^2$$
$$= 2i - 4 \cdot (-1)$$
$$= 4 + 2i$$

Step 1   Find the modulus of the product.

$$|4 + 2i| = \sqrt{4^2 + 2^2}$$
$$= \sqrt{20}$$
$$= 2\sqrt{5}$$

Step 2   Graph the result.

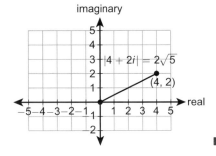

D $(1 - 2i)(1 - 2i)$

Solution $(1 - 2i)(1 - 2i) = 1 - 4i + 4i^2$
$$= 1 - 4i - 4$$
$$= -3 - 4i$$

Step 1   Find the modulus of the product.

$$|-3 - 4i| = \sqrt{(-3)^2 + (-4)^2}$$
$$= \sqrt{25}$$
$$= 5$$

Step 2   Graph the result.

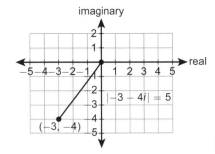

THINK ABOUT IT

The square of a complex number has a modulus that is the square of the original complex number.

The modulus of the product of two complex numbers is the product of the moduli.

Problem Set

. . . .

Multiply and simplify. Write each answer in standard form.

1. $-3i(6 + 2i)$

2. $i(4 - 7i)$

3. $-2i(-5 + 3i)$

4. $6i(-10 - 8i)$

5. $(-3 + 4i)(5 - 2i)$

6. $(7 - 5i)(2 + 6i)$

7. $(10 + 3i)(9 + i)$

8. $(12 - 5i)(7 - 3i)$

*9. **Challenge**
$(\sqrt{9} + 5i)(\sqrt{4} + 3i)$

For each problem, do the following:

A. Identify the complex conjugate.

B. Multiply the original number by its complex conjugate and simplify.

10. $5 + 3i$

11. $4 - 6i$

12. $i - \dfrac{\sqrt{3}}{2}$

13. $i + \dfrac{\sqrt{5}}{7}$

14. $7 - \sqrt{8}i$

15. $-2 + 9i$

Write each quotient in standard form.

16. $\dfrac{2 + i}{3 + 4i}$

17. $\dfrac{1 + i}{5 - 7i}$

18. $\dfrac{3 - i}{8 + 2i}$

19. $\dfrac{10 - 3i}{4 + 5i}$

20. $\dfrac{9 + 9i}{9 - 3i}$

21. $\dfrac{5 - 6i}{2 + 4i}$

22. $\dfrac{9 - 7i}{3 + 2i}$

23. $\dfrac{8 + i}{7 + 5i}$

*24. **Challenge** $\dfrac{5 - 5i}{\sqrt{8} - 3i}$

For each problem, do the following:

A. Determine the modulus of the product.

B. Graph the result.

25. $3(2 - i)$

26. $5(3 + 8i)$

27. $4i(1 - i)$

28. $2i(5 - 2i)$

29. $(5 - 6i)(3 + 3i)$

30. $(7 + 4i)(4 + 2i)$

Solving Equations with Complex Solutions

Some quadratic equations can be solved by finding the square root of each side of the equation.

Solving a Quadratic Equation with Real Solutions

The square root property says that if $x^2 = a$, then $x = \pm\sqrt{a}$. If $a > 0$, then the solutions for x are real numbers.

Example 1 Solve $4x^2 = 80$ and check the solution.

Solution

$4x^2 = 80$

$\quad x^2 = 20$ Divide both sides of the equation by 4.

$\quad x = \pm\sqrt{20}$ Take the square root of both sides.

$\quad x = \pm\sqrt{4} \cdot \sqrt{5}$ Product Property of Square Roots

$\quad x = \pm 2\sqrt{5}$ Simplify.

> **REMEMBER**
>
> The product property of square roots states that
> $$\sqrt{ab} = \sqrt{a} \cdot \sqrt{b}$$
> for real numbers $a > 0$ and $b > 0$.

Check

Substitute $2\sqrt{5}$ for x:

$4(2\sqrt{5})^2 \overset{?}{=} 80$

$\quad 4 \cdot 20 \overset{?}{=} 80$

$\quad\quad 80 = 80 \checkmark$

Substitute $-2\sqrt{5}$ for x:

$4(-2\sqrt{5})^2 \overset{?}{=} 80$

$\quad 4 \cdot 20 \overset{?}{=} 80$

$\quad\quad 80 = 80 \checkmark$ ∎

Solving a Quadratic Equation with Complex Solutions

Quadratic equations such as $x^2 = -2$ have no real-number solutions because there is no square of a real number that equals -2. Quadratic equations of this form have complex-number solutions.

> **SQUARE ROOT PROPERTY FOR IMAGINARY NUMBERS**
>
> If $d > 0$, then $x^2 = -d$ has two imaginary solutions, $x = i\sqrt{d}$ and $x = -i\sqrt{d}$.

Example 2 Solve $3x^2 + 21 = 0$ and check the solution.

Solution

$3x^2 + 21 = 0$

$\quad\quad 3x^2 = -21$ Subtract 21 from both sides.

$\quad\quad\quad x^2 = -7$ Divide both sides by 3.

$\quad\quad \sqrt{x^2} = \pm\sqrt{-7}$ Take the square root of both sides.

$\quad\quad\quad x = \pm i\sqrt{7}$ Simplify.

Check

Substitute $i\sqrt{7}$ for x:

$3(i\sqrt{7})^2 + 21 \overset{?}{=} 0$

$3(7i^2) + 21 \overset{?}{=} 0$

$3(-7) + 21 \overset{?}{=} 0$

$-21 + 21 \overset{?}{=} 0$

$\quad\quad\quad 0 = 0 ✓$

Substitute $-i\sqrt{7}$ for x:

$3(-i\sqrt{7})^2 + 21 \overset{?}{=} 0$

$3(7i^2) + 21 \overset{?}{=} 0$

$3(-7) + 21 \overset{?}{=} 0$

$-21 + 21 \overset{?}{=} 0$

$\quad\quad\quad 0 = 0 ✓$ ∎

> **TIP**
>
> When using the square root property, you can say you are "taking the square root of both sides."

Example 3 Solve $(x + 3)^2 = -5$ and check the solution.

Solution

$(x + 3)^2 = -5$

$\sqrt{(x + 3)^2} = \pm\sqrt{-5}$ Take the square root of both sides.

$\quad\quad x + 3 = \pm i\sqrt{5}$ Simplify.

$\quad\quad\quad\quad x = -3 \pm i\sqrt{5}$ Subtract 3 from both sides.

Check

Substitute $-3 + i\sqrt{5}$ for x:

$[(-3 + i\sqrt{5}) + 3]^2 \overset{?}{=} -5$

$(i\sqrt{5})^2 \overset{?}{=} -5$

$5i^2 \overset{?}{=} -5$

$5(-1) \overset{?}{=} -5$

$-5 = -5 ✓$

Substitute $-3 - i\sqrt{5}$ for x:

$[(-3 - i\sqrt{5}) + 3]^2 \overset{?}{=} -5$

$(-i\sqrt{5})^2 \overset{?}{=} -5$

$5i^2 \overset{?}{=} -5$

$5(-1) \overset{?}{=} -5$

$-5 = -5 ✓$ ∎

> **REMEMBER**
>
> The expressions $a + bi$ and $a - bi$ are a **conjugate pair**.

> **TIP**
>
> Equations with complex solutions generally occur in *conjugate pairs*.

Finding an Equation, Given the Solutions

Example 4 Find a polynomial equation in the form $p(z) = 0$ that has the given solutions.

Ⓐ $z = \pm 8i$

Solution

$$z = \pm 8i$$

$$z^2 = (\pm 8i)^2 \qquad \text{Square both sides.}$$

$$z^2 = 64 \cdot i^2 \qquad \text{Simplify.}$$

$$z^2 = -64$$

$$z^2 + 64 = 0 \qquad \text{Put the equation into the right form.} \ \blacksquare$$

Ⓑ $z = 3 \pm i\sqrt{7}$

Solution

$$z = 3 \pm i\sqrt{7}$$

$$z - 3 = \pm i\sqrt{7} \qquad \text{Subtract 3 from both sides.}$$

$$(z - 3)^2 = (\pm i\sqrt{7})^2 \qquad \text{Square both sides.}$$

$$(z - 3)^2 = 7 \cdot i^2 \qquad \text{Simplify.}$$

$$(z - 3)^2 = -7$$

$$z^2 - 6x + 16 = 0 \qquad \text{Put the equation into the right form.} \ \blacksquare$$

Problem Set

· ·

Solve and check.

1. $y^2 = 144$

2. $6a^2 = 150$

3. $3x^2 = 36$

4. $5b^2 = 50$

5. $\dfrac{c^2}{25} - 9 = -5$

6. $\dfrac{d^2}{20} + 5 = 12$

7. $-3p^2 = -213$

8. $(k - 1)^2 = 5$

9. $4(r - 1)^2 = 8$

10. $4(m + 2)^2 - 320 = 0$

11. $2(y + 2)^2 - 5 = 8$

12. $x^2 = -28$

13. $2t^2 = -76$

14. $2x^2 + 4 = -32$

15. $3b^2 + 8 = -28$

16. $6d^2 + 92 = -202$

17. $s^2 + 4s - 2 = 0$

18. $x^2 + 4x = 1$

19. $w^2 + 9w = -8$

20. $9x^2 + 12x + 4 = 5$

*21. **Challenge** $-16x^2 + 9x - 13 = 0$

Find a polynomial equation in the form $p(z) = 0$ that has the given solutions.

22. $z = \pm 2i$

23. $z = \pm 11i$

24. $z = \pm 7i$

25. $z = \pm 12i$

26. $z = \pm i\sqrt{6}$

27. $z = \pm 3i\sqrt{10}$

29. $z = \pm 2i\sqrt{5}$

29. $z = \pm 6i\sqrt{12}$

30. $z = 1 \pm i\sqrt{5}$

31. $z = -2 \pm 4i\sqrt{5}$

32. $z = 4 \pm 2i\sqrt{11}$

33. $z = -5 \pm 5i\sqrt{10}$

Quadratic Functions

Antoni Gaudi used parabolic arches in his design of Park Guell.

Antoni Gaudi (1852–1926) used parabolic arches in his architectural designs. Gaudi's parabolic arches are both beautiful and strong.

Big Ideas

▶ Expressions, equations, and inequalities express relationships between different entities.

▶ If you use a mathematical model to represent a certain situation, you can use the model to solve other problems that you might not be able to solve otherwise. Algebraic equations can capture key relationships among quantities in the world.

▶ A function is a correspondence between two sets, the domain and the range, that assigns to each member of the domain exactly one member of the range. Many functions can be described by algebraic expressions.

Unit Topics

▶ Foundations for Unit 8

▶ Graphing Quadratic Functions

▶ Properties of Quadratic Graphs

▶ Solving Quadratic Equations

▶ Quadratic Inequalities

▶ Finding a Quadratic Function from Points

▶ Applications: Quadratic Functions

Foundations for Unit 8

Before you study quadratic functions, you should know how to do the following:

▶ Determine lines of symmetry from a figure.

▶ Understand function notation and evaluate a function.

▶ Find the equation of an absolute value function from a graph.

Identifying Lines of Symmetry

Definitions

line symmetry	a figure is said to have *line symmetry* (or *reflection symmetry*) if there is at least one line such that when the figure is folded over the line, the two halves are mirror images that match up perfectly
line of symmetry	the line over which you can flip a given figure, leaving the figure unchanged; the line that divides a given figure into two congruent (mirror-image) halves

> **TIP**
>
> If you fold the graph over a line of symmetry, the two halves will match.

Example 1 Determine the equations of the lines of symmetry (if any) for each figure.

A

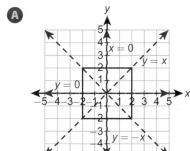

B

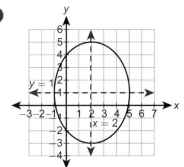

C

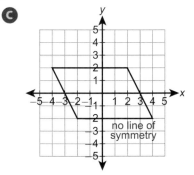

The four lines of symmetry are $y = 0$, $y = -x$, $x = 0$, and $y = x$.

The two lines of symmetry are are $y = 1$ and $x = 2$.

The figure has no lines of symmetry.

Problem Set A

Determine the equations of the lines of symmetry (if any) for each figure.

1.

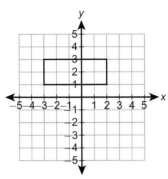

3.

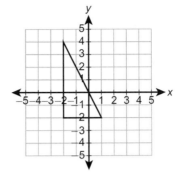

2.

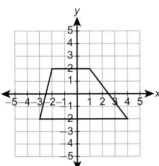

4.

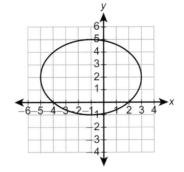

Using Function Notation and Evaluating a Function

FUNCTION NOTATIONS FOR $y = x^2$

$f:$ input $\rightarrow$ output $f(\text{input}) = \text{output}$

$f: x \rightarrow x^2$ $f(x) = x^2$

REMEMBER

A *function* is a relation in which every element of the domain is assigned to exactly one element of the range.

Example 2   Evaluate each function for the given values.

A For $f(x) = 3x - 7$, find $f(2)$ and $f(5)$.

Substitute 2 and 5 for x.

$f(2) = 3 \cdot 2 - 7 = 6 - 7 = -1$

$f(5) = 3 \cdot 5 - 7 = 15 - 7 = 8$

B For $g: a \rightarrow -a^2$, find $g(3)$ and $g(-3)$.

Substitute 3 and -3 for a.

$g(3) = -3^2 = 9$

$g(-3) = -(-3)^2 = -9$

Problem Set B

Evaluate each function for the given value.

5. For $f(x) = 2x + 5$, find $f(2)$.

6. For $h: t \to 2t^2 + 1$, find $h(7)$ and $h(-7)$.

7. For $f(x) = (x - 3)^2$, find $f(4)$ and $f(2)$.

8. For $g: b \to b^3$, find $g(2)$ and $g(-2)$.

9. For $h: x \to 2x^3 + 3$, find $h(1)$.

10. For $f(z) = 1 - z^4$, find $f(1)$ and $f(4)$.

Finding an Absolute Value Equation when Given a Graph

For an absolute value function, the parent function is $f(x) = |x|$ and the general form for functions in this family is $f(x) = a|x - h| + k$, where the point (h, k) is the coordinate of the highest or lowest point on the graph, and where a determines how wide or narrow the graph is and whether it opens up or down.

Example 3   Find an absolute value equation for each graph.

A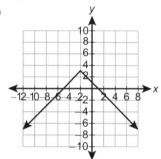

B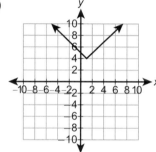

The highest point is $(-2, 3)$. The horizontal and vertical translations from the graph of the parent function, $f(x) = |x|$, reveal that the equation of the graph is $y = -|x + 2| + 3$.

The lowest point is $(1, 4)$. The horizontal and vertical translations from the graph of the parent function, $f(x) = |x|$, reveal that the equation of the graph is $y = |x - 1| + 4$.

Problem Set C

Find an absolute value equation for each graph.

11.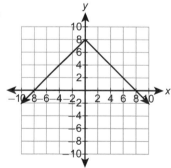

12.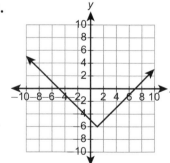

13.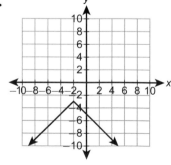

Graphing Quadratic Functions

A **quadratic function** is a second-degree polynomial function.

STANDARD FORM OF A QUADRATIC FUNCTION

The **standard form of a quadratic function** is $f(x) = ax^2 + bx + c$, where $a \neq 0$. The graph of a quadratic function is called a **parabola**.

One way to graph a quadratic function is to create a table of ordered pairs, plot the points, and then draw a smooth curve through those points. As you study the following examples, recall that y and $f(x)$ are used interchangeably.

Using a Table to Graph a Quadratic Function

Example 1   Graph each function.

A $y = x^2$

Solution

x	−2	−1	0	1	2
y	4	1	0	1	4

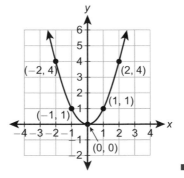

B $y = -2x^2 + 2x + 4$

Solution

x	−2	−1	0	1	2
y	−8	0	4	4	0

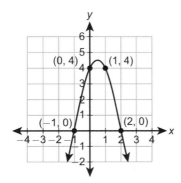

The point $(-2, -8)$ is not shown. ∎

Graphing Quadratic Functions in Standard Form

All quadratic function graphs have in common the following characteristics, which can be used to create accurate graphs.

PROPERTIES OF QUADRATIC FUNCTION GRAPHS

The graph of $f(x) = ax^2 + bx + c$ is a parabola with these characteristics:

- It opens up when $a > 0$; it opens down when $a < 0$.
- It has y-intercept c, so $(0, c)$ is a point on the graph.
- It has a vertex with x-coordinate $-\dfrac{b}{2a}$.
- It has an axis of symmetry with equation $x = -\dfrac{b}{2a}$. The axis of symmetry is the vertical line through the vertex. It separates the graph into two halves that are reflections (mirror images) of each other.

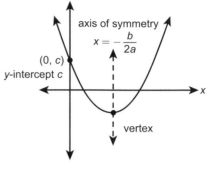

Example 2 Graph $y = 3x^2 - 12x + 6$.

Solution First identify the coefficients a, b, and c:

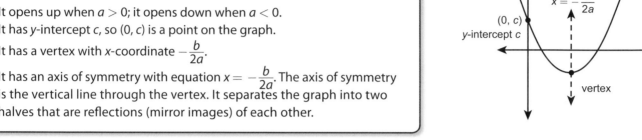

$$y = 3x^2 - 12x + 6.$$
$$\underbrace{}_{a=3}\ \underbrace{}_{b=-12}\ \underbrace{}_{c=6}$$

The leading coefficient a is positive, so the parabola opens up, not down.

The x-coordinate of the vertex is $-\dfrac{b}{2a} = -\dfrac{(-12)}{2 \cdot 3} = 2$.

TIP

The axis of symmetry is dashed because it is not part of the graph of the function.

To find the y-coordinate of the vertex, substitute 2 for x:
$y = 3x^2 - 12x + 6 = 3 \cdot 2^2 - 12 \cdot 2 + 6 = -6$. So the vertex V is $(2, -6)$, and the equation of the axis of symmetry is $x = 2$.

The y-intercept is $c = 6$, so $(0, 6)$ is a point on the graph. The reflection image of $(0, 6)$ over the axis of symmetry is $(4, 6)$, which is also on the graph.

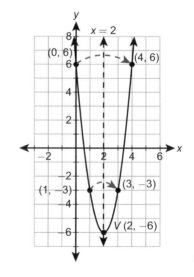

Choose any value for x and substitute it to find one more point on the parabola. If $x = 1$, then $y = 3 \cdot 1^2 - 12 \cdot 1 + 6 = -3$. So $(1, -3)$ is on the graph, and its reflection image $(3, -3)$ is also on the graph.

Draw a smooth curve through all five points, including the vertex. ∎

Determining the Number of Zeros of a Quadratic Function

Using properties of quadratic functions can help you determine where the graph of a given function crosses the x-axis.

ZEROS OF A POLYNOMIAL FUNCTION

The **zeros of a polynomial function f(x)** are the **roots** (solutions) of the equation $f(x) = 0$. The **real zeros** are the x-intercepts of the graph of $f(x)$.

Number of Real Zeros of a Quadratic Function

A quadratic function can have two, one, or no real zeros.

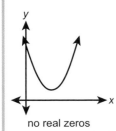

no real zeros

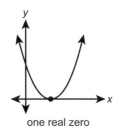

one real zero

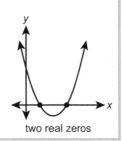

two real zeros

Example 3   Determine the number of real zeros of each quadratic function.

Ⓐ $y = x^2 + 6x + 9$

Solution $a = 1$, $b = 6$, and $c = 9$. Since $a > 0$, the parabola opens up.

Use a and b to find the x-coordinate of the vertex, and then substitute to find the y-coordinate:

$$x = -\frac{b}{2a} = -\frac{6}{2 \cdot 1} = -3$$
$$y = x^2 + 6x + 9 = (-3)^2 + 6 \cdot (-3) + 9 = 9 - 18 + 9 = 0$$

The vertex is $(-3, 0)$. The vertex is a zero of the function and because the parabola opens up, the vertex is also the lowest point on the graph. Therefore, it is the only real zero. Sketch the graph to verify this. ■

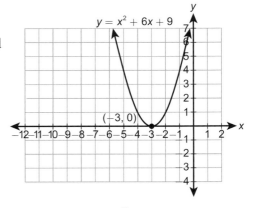

Ⓑ $y = x^2 + 2$

Solution $a = 1$, $b = 0$, and $c = 2$. Since $a > 0$, the parabola opens up.

Use a and b to find the x-coordinate of the vertex, and then substitute to find the y-coordinate:

$$x = -\frac{b}{2a} = -\frac{0}{2 \cdot 1} = 0$$
$$y = x^2 + 2 = 0^2 + 2 = 2$$

The vertex is $(0, 2)$. Since the parabola opens up, the vertex is the lowest point on the graph. Therefore, the function has no real zeros. Sketch the graph to verify this. ■

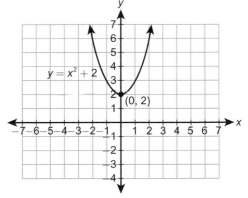

Ⓒ $y = -x^2 + 4x - 1$

Solution $a = -1$, $b = 4$, and $c = -1$. Since $a < 0$, the parabola opens down.

Use a and b to find the x-coordinate of the vertex, and then substitute to find the y-coordinate:

$$x = -\frac{b}{2a} = -\frac{4}{2 \cdot (-1)} = 2$$
$$y = -x^2 + 4x - 1 = -2^2 + 4 \cdot 2 - 1 = -4 + 8 - 1 = 3$$

The vertex is $(2, 3)$. Since the parabola opens down, the vertex is the highest point. The graph must cross the x-axis at two points; therefore, the function has two real zeros. Sketch the graph to verify this. ■

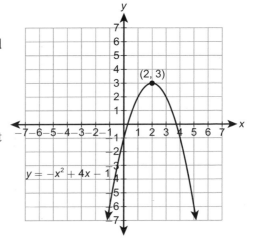

Graphing Quadratic Functions in Factored Form

Using the factored form of a quadratic function can help you graph the function.

FACTORED FORM OF A QUADRATIC FUNCTION

The **factored form of a quadratic function** is $f(x) = a(x - r_1)(x - r_2)$. The graph of $f(x) = a(x - r_1)(x - r_2)$ is a parabola with these characteristics:

- It opens up if $a > 0$; it opens down if $a < 0$.
- It has **x-intercepts** r_1 and r_2.
- It has an **axis of symmetry** with equation $x = \dfrac{r_1 + r_2}{2}$ (halfway between the *x*-intercepts).

Example 4 Use the factored form to graph each function.

A $y = x^2 - 2x - 3$

Solution Factor the trinomial: $y = x^2 - 2x - 3 = (x + 1)(x - 3)$.

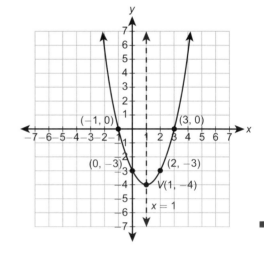

$a = 1$, so the parabola opens up.
$r_1 = -1$ and $r_2 = 3$, so the *x*-intercepts are -1 and 3.
$\dfrac{r_1 + r_2}{2} = \dfrac{-1 + 3}{2} = \dfrac{2}{2} = 1$, so the equation of the axis of symmetry is $x = 1$. Since the axis of symmetry passes through the vertex, the *x*-coordinate of the vertex must be 1. Substitute 1 for *x* in the function to find the *y*-coordinate of the vertex:

$$y = x^2 - 2x - 3 = 1^2 - 2 \cdot 1 - 3 = 1 - 2 - 3 = -4$$

So the vertex V is $(1, -4)$.

Find two more points, such as $(0, -3)$ and its reflection, $(2, -3)$. Then sketch the curve through all the points.

B $y = -0.4x^2 + 0.4x + 4.8$

Solution Factor out -0.4 and then factor the trinomial:

$y = -0.4x^2 + 0.4x + 4.8 = -0.4(x^2 - x - 12) = -0.4(x - 4)(x + 3)$
$a = -0.4$, so the parabola opens down.
$r_1 = 4$ and $r_2 = -3$, so the *x*-intercepts are 4 and -3.
$\dfrac{r_1 + r_2}{2} = \dfrac{4 + (-3)}{2} = \dfrac{1}{2} = 0.5$, so the equation of the axis of symmetry is $x = 0.5$. Since the axis of symmetry passes through the vertex, the *x*-coordinate of the vertex must be 0.5. Substitute 0.5 for *x* in the function to find the *y*-coordinate of the vertex:

$$y = -0.4(x - 4)(x + 3) = -0.4(0.5 - 4)(0.5 + 3) = 4.9$$

So the vertex V is $(0.5, 4.9)$.

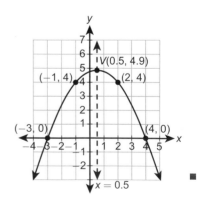

Find two more points, such as $(2, 4)$ and its reflection, $(-1, 4)$. Then sketch the curve through all the points.

Problem Set

For each function, do the following:

A. Complete the table of values.
B. Use the table of values to graph the quadratic equation.

1. $y = x^2 - 2x$

x	−2	−1	0	1	2
y					

2. $y = x^2 + 4x$

x	−4	−3	−2	−1	0
y					

3. $y = x^2 + 2$

x	−2	−1	0	1	2
y					

4. $y = -x^2 + 3$

x	−2	−1	0	1	2
y					

5. $y = x^2 + 3x - 4$

x	−2	−1	0	1	2
y					

6. $y = x^2 - 5x + 7$

x	−2	−1	0	1	2
y					

Find the *y*-intercept of each quadratic function.

7. $y = -x^2 - 3$

8. $y = 3x^2 - 4$

9. $y = x^2 + 5x - 8$

10. $y = -2x^2 + 5x$

Graph each quadratic function. For each graph, label the vertex, *x*-intercepts, and the equation of the axis of symmetry.

11. $y = -x^2 + 1$

12. $y = 2x^2$

13. $y = 7x^2 - 7$

14. $y = -3x^2 + 4x - 2$

Find the number of zeros for each quadratic function. Use a graph to check your answer.

15. $y = x^2 - 8x$

16. $y = x^2 + 2x + 1$

17. $y = 6x^2 + 8$

18. $y = x^2 - 8x + 16$

19. $y = x^2 + 6x + 8$

20. $y = -4x^2 + 5x$

Graph each function

21. $y = (x + 1)(x - 3)$

22. $y = (x + 6)(x - 1)$

23. $y = -x^2 - x + 20$

24. $y = 3x^2 + 6x - 72$

25. $y = -2x^2 + 6x + 56$

26. $y = -5x^2 - 25x - 30$

27. $y = \frac{1}{8}x^2 + \frac{1}{24}x - \frac{5}{96}$

*28. Challenge $y = -1.3x^2 + 3.9x - 5.2$

*29. Challenge $y = \frac{1}{2}x^2 - 18.4x + 4$

Solve.

30. The cost C, in dollars, of building m sewing machines at Sienna's Sewing Machines is given by the equation
$C(m) = 20m^2 - 830m + 15,000$.

A. Find the cost of building 75 sewing machines.

B. How many sewing machines should the company manufacture to minimize the cost C?

Properties of Quadratic Graphs

Just as there are different forms for the equation of a linear function, there are different forms for the equation of a quadratic function.

Quadratic Functions in Vertex Form

VERTEX FORM OF A QUADRATIC FUNCTION

The **vertex form of a quadratic function** is $f(x) = a(x - h)^2 + k$, where $a \neq 0$.

The **vertex** is (h, k). The equation of the **axis of symmetry** is $x = h$.

$f(x) = x^2$ is the **parent function** of the quadratic family. Every quadratic function $f(x) = a(x - h)^2 + k$ is a transformation of $f(x) = x^2$.

If $a > 0$, the graph opens up, extending infinitely up, left, and right. The **minimum** function value is k. There is no **maximum** function value.

If $a < 0$, the graph opens down, extending infinitely down, left, and right. The **maximum** function value is k. There is no **minimum** function value.

Example 1   Graph $f(x) = \frac{1}{2}(x - 4)^2 - 2$.

Solution $h = 4$ and $k = -2$, so the vertex is $(4, -2)$ and the line of symmetry is $x = 4$. Find two other points on the graph.

x	$\frac{1}{2}(x - 4)^2 - 2$	$f(x)$
5	$\frac{1}{2}(5 - 4)^2 - 2 = \frac{1}{2} \cdot 1 - 2$	$-1\frac{1}{2}$
6	$\frac{1}{2}(6 - 4)^2 - 2 = \frac{1}{2} \cdot 4 - 2$	0

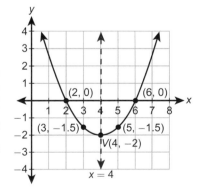

TIP

h in vertex form has the same value as $-\dfrac{b}{2a}$ in standard form. a has the same value in standard form that it has in vertex form.

Reflect the points $(5, -1.5)$ and $(6, 0)$ across the axis of symmetry to get two points on the other side: $(3, -1.5)$ and $(2, 0)$. Draw a smooth curve through all the points. ∎

Writing an Equation of a Quadratic Function, Given a Graph Showing the Vertex and Another Point

Example 2 Write an equation for each quadratic function graphed.

A

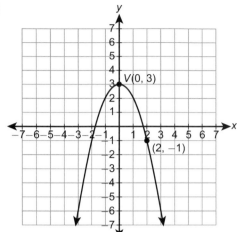

Solution The vertex $(h, k) = (0, 3)$, so $h = 0$ and $k = 3$.

$f(x) = a(x - h)^2 + k$	Vertex form
$f(x) = a(x - 0)^2 + 3$	Substitute 0 for h and 3 for k.
$f(x) = ax^2 + 3$	Simplify.
$-1 = a \cdot 2^2 + 3$	Substitute 2 for x and -1 for y.
$-1 = 4a + 3$	Simplify.
$-4 = 4a$	Solve for a.
$-1 = a$	

So the equation is $f(x) = -x^2 + 3$. ∎

B

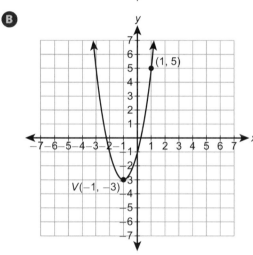

Solution The vertex $(h, k) = (-1, -3)$, so $h = -1$ and $k = -3$.

$f(x) = a(x - h)^2 + k$	Vertex form
$f(x) = a(x - (-1))^2 - 3$	Substitute -1 for h and -3 for k.
$f(x) = a(x + 1)^2 - 3$	Simplify.
$5 = a(1 + 1)^2 - 3$	Substitute 1 for x and 5 for y.
$5 = a \cdot 2^2 - 3$	Simplify.
$5 = 4a - 3$	Solve for a.
$8 = 4a$	
$2 = a$	

So the equation is $f(x) = 2(x + 1)^2 - 3$. ∎

Converting from Vertex to Standard Form

By using the FOIL method and collecting like terms, you can convert an equation given in vertex form into standard form.

Example 3 Write $y = 3(x + 4)^2 - 8$ in standard form.

Solution

$y = 3(x + 4)^2 - 8$	Original equation
$y = 3(x + 4)(x + 4) - 8$	Rewrite the exponent as multiplication.
$y = 3(x^2 + 8x + 16) - 8$	Use the FOIL method to multiply the binomials.
$y = 3x^2 + 24x + 48 - 8$	Distribute the 3.
$y = 3x^2 + 24x + 40$	Simplify. ∎

Converting from Standard to Vertex Form

Converting an equation from standard to vertex form is a bit tougher than converting the other way, but if you remember how to complete the square, you can get it done.

> **DEFINITION**
>
> **Completing the square** is the process of transforming an expression of the form $x^2 + bx$ into a perfect square trinomial by adding the term $\left(\frac{b}{2}\right)^2$ to it.

Example 4   Write each function in vertex form by completing the square.

A $f(x) = x^2 + 8x + 9$

Solution

$f(x) = x^2 + 8x + 9$

$f(x) = (x^2 + 8x) + 9$

$f(x) = (x^2 + 8x + 16 - 16) + 9$

$f(x) = (x^2 + 8x + 16) - 16 + 9$

$f(x) = (x + 4)^2 - 7$

The function in vertex form is

$f(x) = (x + 4)^2 - 7.$ ∎

B $y = -3x^2 + 12x + 5$

Solution

$y = -3x^2 + 12x + 5$

$y = -3(x^2 - 4x) + 5$

$y = -3(x^2 - 4x + 4 - 4) + 5$

$y = -3(x^2 - 4x + 4) - 3(-4) + 5$

$y = -3(x - 2)^2 + 12 + 5$

$y = -3(x - 2)^2 + 17$

The function in vertex form is

$y = -3(x - 2)^2 + 17.$ ∎

> **TIP**
>
> When you complete the square, always be sure either to add a form of zero to one side or to add the same quantity to both sides of the equation. Otherwise, the resulting equation won't be equivalent to the original equation.

Quadratic Function Graph Family: $f(x) = a(x - h)^2 + k$, where $a \neq 0$

The graph of $f(x) = a(x - h)^2 + k$, $a \neq 0$, is a parabola with vertex (h, k) and axis of symmetry $x = h$. The parent graph is $f(x) = x^2$.

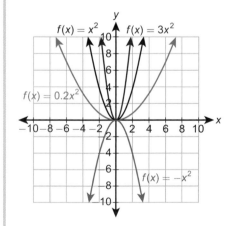

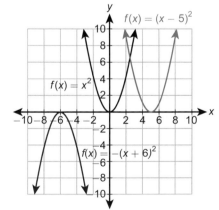

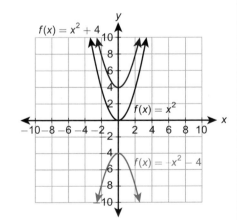

Changing a determines how wide or narrow the parabola is and whether it opens up or down.

Changing h moves the vertex left or right.

Changing k moves the vertex up or down.

Problem Set

Graph each function. Label at least three points on each graph.

1. $f(x) = (x - 4)^2$

2. $g(x) = (x - 5)^2 + 4$

3. $f(x) = 3(x - 7)^2 + 6$

4. $h(x) = 2(x - 3)^2 + 12$

5. $g(x) = -6(x - 2)^2 + 9$

6. $h(x) = \frac{1}{2}(x - 4)^2 + 1$

Write an equation for each quadratic function graphed.

7.
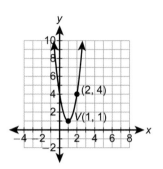

11.
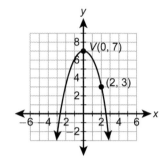

14.
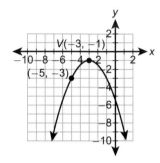

8.
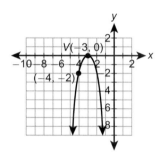

12.
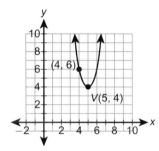

15.
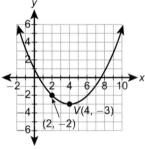

9.
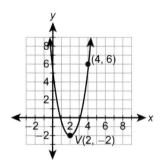

13.
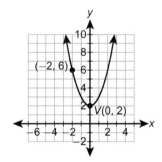

*16. **Challenge**
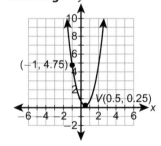

10.
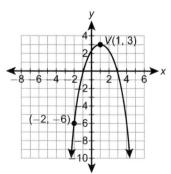

Convert each equation to standard form.

17. $y = -(x - 4.5)^2 + 6.25$

18. $y = 4(x - 2)^2 + 11$

19. $y = (3x - 2)^2$

20. $y = 6(x - 4)^2 - 5$

21. $y = \left(x - \frac{2}{3}\right)^2 - \frac{1}{3}$

22. $y = 12(x - 1)^2 + 4$

Convert each equation to vertex form.

23. $y = x^2 - 4x + 4$

24. $y = 9x^2 + 15x + \frac{25}{4}$

25. $y = x^2 - 8x + 10$

26. $y = x^2 - 5x + 16$

27. $y = 2x^2 + 24x + 25$

28. $y = 3x^2 - 9x + 18$

* 29. Challenge

$y = 4x^2 - \frac{8}{3}x - \frac{26}{9}$

Solve.

*30. Challenge A baseball player hits a baseball in the air. The height y in feet of the baseball t seconds after it is hit is given by this function: $y = -16t^2 + 96t + 14$. Find the maximum height of the baseball.

Solving Quadratic Equations

A **quadratic equation** is a second-degree polynomial equation that can be written in the standard form $0 = ax^2 + bx + c$, where $a \neq 0$.

Using a Graph to Describe Solutions of a Quadratic Equation

Recall that the zeros of a polynomial function $f(x)$ are the roots (solutions) of the equation $f(x) = 0$, and the real roots of $f(x) = 0$ are the x-intercepts of $f(x)$.

REMEMBER

You can use a graphing calculator or software to graph a quadratic function and to estimate the x-intercepts.

Example 1

A Use the graph of $f(x) = 3x^2 - 8x + 2$ to estimate the solutions of $f(x) = 0$.

Solution The x-intercepts are approximately 0.3 and 2.4. So the solutions of $0 = 3x^2 - 8x + 2$ are approximately 0.3 and 2.4.

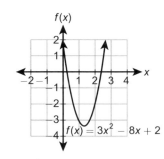

Check

$$f(x) = 3x^2 - 8x + 2$$
$$f(0.3) = 3 \cdot 0.3^2 - 8 \cdot 0.3 + 2$$
$$= 0.27 - 2.4 + 2$$
$$= -0.13$$
$$\approx 0 \checkmark$$

$$f(x) = 3x^2 - 8x + 2$$
$$f(2.4) = 3 \cdot 2.4^2 - 8 \cdot 2.4 + 2$$
$$= 17.28 - 19.2 + 2$$
$$= 0.08$$
$$\approx 0 \checkmark \blacksquare$$

B Use the graph of $y = -x^2 - 1$ to describe the solutions of $0 = -x^2 - 1$.

Solution There are no x-intercepts. So the equation $0 = -x^2 - 1$ has no real solutions. ∎

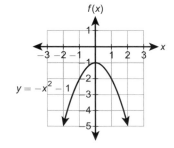

THINK ABOUT IT

The equation $0 = -x^2 - 1$ in Example 1B has two *imaginary* solutions: i and $-i$ (complex numbers $0 + i$ and $0 - i$). However, complex numbers have no representation in the real coordinate plane.

Solving a Quadratic Equation

Example 2 Solve and check each equation.

Ⓐ $2x^2 + 50 = -20x$ **Ⓑ** $0 = 6x^2 - 13x - 5$

Solutions Write each equation in standard form. Then factor and use the zero product property.

Ⓐ
$$2x^2 + 50 = -20x$$
$$2x^2 + 20x + 50 = 0$$
$$2(x^2 + 10x + 25) = 0$$
$$2(x + 5)(x + 5) = 0$$
$$(x + 5)(x + 5) = 0$$
$$x + 5 = 0 \text{ or } x + 5 = 0$$
$$x = -5 \qquad x = -5$$

The solution set is $\{-5\}$.

Check
$$2x^2 + 50 = -20x$$
$$2(-5)^2 + 50 \overset{?}{=} -20(-5)$$
$$2 \cdot 25 + 50 \overset{?}{=} -20(-5)$$
$$50 + 50 \overset{?}{=} 100$$
$$100 = 100 \checkmark \blacksquare$$

Ⓑ
$$0 = 6x^2 - 13x - 5$$
$$0 = (2x - 5)(3x + 1)$$
$$2x - 5 = 0 \text{ or } 3x + 1 = 0$$
$$2x = 5 \qquad 3x = -1$$
$$x = \frac{5}{2} \qquad x = -\frac{1}{3}$$

The solution set is $\left\{\frac{5}{2}, -\frac{1}{3}\right\}$.

Check
$$0 = 6x^2 - 13x - 5$$
$$0 \overset{?}{=} 6 \cdot \frac{5^2}{2} - 13 \cdot \frac{5}{2} - 5$$
$$0 \overset{?}{=} 6 \cdot \frac{25}{4} - 13 \cdot \frac{10}{4} - \frac{20}{4}$$
$$0 \overset{?}{=} \frac{150}{4} - \frac{130}{4} - \frac{20}{4}$$
$$0 = 0 \checkmark$$

The check for $-\frac{1}{3}$ is similar. $\blacksquare$

You can solve some quadratic equations by using the square root property.

Example 3 Solve and check: $(x + 5)^2 = 8$.

Solution The equation $(x + 5)^2 = 8$ is already in the form $x^2 = a$, with the variable expression $x + 5$ instead of the variable x.

$$(x + 5)^2 = 8$$

$x + 5 = \pm\sqrt{8}$	Square Root Property
$x = -5 \pm \sqrt{8}$	Isolate x.
$x = -5 \pm 2\sqrt{2}$	Simplify the radical.

> **REMEMBER**
>
> The square root property states that for any real number a, if $x^2 = a$, then $x = \pm\sqrt{a}$.

The solution set is $\{-5 + 2\sqrt{2}, -5 - 2\sqrt{2}\}$. The approximate solutions are $-5 + 2\sqrt{2} \approx -2.17$ and $-5 - 2\sqrt{2} \approx -7.83$.

Check You can check the approximate solutions as follows:
$(-2.17 + 5)^2 \approx 8.0089 \approx 8$, and $(-7.83 + 5)^2 \approx 8.0089 \approx 8$. $\checkmark$ $\blacksquare$

Solving a Quadratic Equation by Completing the Square

You can solve any quadratic equation by *completing the square*. To use this process, you need an expression of the form $x^2 + bx$.

HOW TO COMPLETE THE SQUARE FOR A QUADRATIC EQUATION

Starting with $x^2 + bx = c$, add $\left(\frac{b}{2}\right)^2$ to both sides to complete the square.

$x^2 + bx + \left(\frac{b}{2}\right)^2$ is a perfect square because $x^2 + bx + \left(\frac{b}{2}\right)^2 = \left(x + \frac{b}{2}\right)^2$.

Example 4 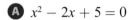 Complete the square to solve.

A $x^2 - 2x + 5 = 0$

Solution

$x^2 - 2x + 5 = 0$	
$x^2 - 2x = -5$	Subtract 5 to get the form $x^2 + bx$.
$x^2 - 2x + 1 = -5 + 1$	Add $\left(\frac{b}{2}\right)^2 = \left(\frac{-2}{2}\right)^2 = (-1)^2 = 1$ to both sides to complete the square.
$(x - 1)^2 = -4$	Rewrite $x^2 - 2x + 1$ as $(x - 1)^2$.
$x - 1 = \pm\sqrt{-4}$	Square Root Property
$x = 1 \pm \sqrt{-4}$	Solve.
$x = 1 \pm 2i$	Simplify.

The solution set is $\{1 + 2i, \ 1 - 2i\}$. ∎

B $9x = 56 - 2x^2$

Solution

$9x = 56 - 2x^2$	
$2x^2 + 9x = 56$	Add $2x^2$ to isolate the constant 56.
$x^2 + \frac{9}{2}x = 28$	Divide every term by 2 to get the form $x^2 + bx$.
$x^2 + \frac{9}{2}x + \left(\frac{9}{4}\right)^2 = 28 + \left(\frac{9}{4}\right)^2$	Add $\left(\frac{1}{2}b\right)^2 = \left(\frac{1}{2} \cdot \frac{9}{2}\right)^2 = \left(\frac{9}{4}\right)^2$ to both sides to complete the square.
$\left(x + \frac{9}{4}\right)^2 = \frac{529}{16}$	Rewrite the trinomial $x^2 + \frac{9}{2}x + \left(\frac{9}{4}\right)^2$ as $\left(x + \frac{9}{4}\right)^2$.
$x + \frac{9}{4} = \pm\sqrt{\frac{529}{16}}$	Square Root Property
$x = -\frac{9}{4} \pm \frac{23}{4}$	Subtract and simplify.

The solution set is $\left\{\frac{7}{2}, -8\right\}$. ∎

Solving a Quadratic Equation by Using the Quadratic Formula

If you use the process of completing the square to solve the general quadratic equation $ax^2 + bx + c = 0$, you get a general formula for solving any quadratic equation.

$$ax^2 + bx + c = 0$$

$$ax^2 + bx = -c$$

$$x^2 + \frac{b}{a}x = -\frac{c}{a}$$

$$x^2 + \frac{b}{a}x + \frac{b^2}{4a^2} = -\frac{c}{a} + \frac{b^2}{4a^2}$$

$$\left(x + \frac{b}{2a}\right)^2 = -\frac{4ac}{4a^2} + \frac{b^2}{4a^2}$$

$$\left(x + \frac{b}{2a}\right)^2 = \frac{b^2 - 4ac}{4a^2}$$

$$x + \frac{b}{2a} = \pm\sqrt{\frac{b^2 - 4ac}{4a^2}}$$

$$x = -\frac{b}{2a} \pm \sqrt{\frac{b^2 - 4ac}{4a^2}}$$

$$x = -\frac{b}{2a} \pm \frac{\sqrt{b^2 - 4ac}}{2a}$$

$$x = \frac{-b \pm \sqrt{b^2 - 4ac}}{2a}$$

THE QUADRATIC FORMULA

Given any quadratic equation in the standard form $ax^2 + bx + c = 0$, where $a \neq 0$, the solutions are given by the following formula:

$$x = \frac{-b \pm \sqrt{b^2 - 4ac}}{2a}$$

You've seen that a quadratic equation can have two, one, or no *real* solutions. In the quadratic formula, the expression under the radical, $b^2 - 4ac$, determines the number and nature of the solutions.

DEFINITION

For a quadratic equation in the standard form $ax^2 + bx + c = 0$, the **discriminant** is $b^2 - 4ac$.

When the discriminant is	the quadratic equation has
positive ($b^2 - 4ac > 0$)	**two real roots**
zero ($b^2 - 4ac = 0$)	**one real root**
negative ($b^2 - 4ac < 0$)	**no real roots**, but **two complex roots**

Example 5 Use the quadratic formula to solve.

(A) $3x^2 - 12x + 6 = 0$

(B) $2x^2 + 7 = -5x$

Solution Identify the coefficients and substitute into the quadratic identify formula.
$a = 3, b = -12, c = 6$

$$x = \frac{-b \pm \sqrt{b^2 - 4ac}}{2a}$$

$$x = \frac{-(-12) \pm \sqrt{(-12)^2 - 4 \cdot 3 \cdot 6}}{2 \cdot 3}$$

$$x = \frac{12 \pm \sqrt{72}}{6}$$

$$x = \frac{12 \pm 6\sqrt{2}}{6}$$

$$x = \frac{12}{6} \pm \frac{6\sqrt{2}}{6}$$

$$x = 2 \pm \sqrt{2}$$

The solution set is
$\{2 + \sqrt{2}, 2 - \sqrt{2}\}$. ■

Solution First write the equation in standard form:
$2x^2 + 5x + 7 = 0$. Then identify the coefficients and substitute into the formula.

$a = 2, b = 5, c = 7$

$$x = \frac{-b \pm \sqrt{b^2 - 4ac}}{2a}$$

$$x = \frac{-5 \pm \sqrt{5^2 - 4 \cdot 2 \cdot 7}}{2 \cdot 2}$$

$$x = \frac{-5 \pm \sqrt{-31}}{4}$$

$$x = \frac{-5 \pm i\sqrt{31}}{4}$$

The solution set is
$\left\{\dfrac{-5 + i\sqrt{31}}{4}, \dfrac{-5 - i\sqrt{31}}{4}\right\}$. ■

The approximate solutions in Example 5A above are 3.41 and 0.59.

Problem Set

Use the graph to estimate the solutions of $f(x) = 0$.
Substitute to check that your estimates are reasonable.

1.

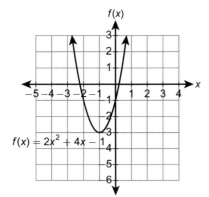

$f(x) = 2x^2 + 4x - 1$

2.

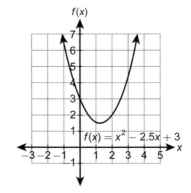

$f(x) = x^2 - 2.5x + 3$

3.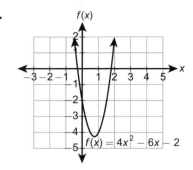

$f(x) = 4x^2 - 6x - 2$

4.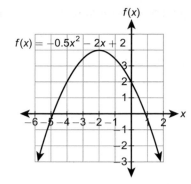

$f(x) = -0.5x^2 - 2x + 2$

Use factoring to solve.

5. $-6x + 3 = -3x^2$

6. $x^2 + 12x + 20 = -16$

7. $2x^2 - 5x - 3 = 0$

8. $10x^2 + 13x - 3 = 0$

9. $4x^2 - 20x = -24$

10. $6x^2 + 13x = 5$

Complete the square to solve.

11. $x^2 - x - 6 = 0$

12. $4x^2 + 20x + 9 = 0$

13. $2x^2 - 16x + 44 = 0$

14. $x^2 - 4x + 6 = 0$

15. $7x = 30 - x^2$

16. $3x^2 - 6x + 30 = 0$

Use the quadratic formula to solve.

17. $2x^2 - 7x + 5 = 0$

18. $3x^2 + 1 = -2x$

19. $x^2 = 5 + 4x$

20. $4x^2 = 3x - 1$

21. $-3 = 2x^2 + x$

22. $5x^2 - 6x + 2 = 0$

Use the discriminant to classify the number and types of solutions of each equation.

23. $3x^2 - x + 5 = 0$

24. $x^2 = 8x - 2$

25. $6x + 3 = -3x^2$

26. $6x^2 = 7x - 2$

*27. Challenge $(\sqrt{5}x - 1)(\sqrt{5}x + 3) = 0$

*28. Challenge $(\sqrt{7}x + 2)^2 = 0$

Quadratic Inequalities

A **quadratic inequality** involves a quadratic
expression and an inequality symbol
($<, >, \leq, \geq$, or $\neq$).

Quadratic Inequalities in One Variable

Any value of the variable that makes an inequality true is a solution for the
inequality. You can describe the solution set of an inequality in one variable
by using set notation or by graphing it on a number line.

Example 1   Determine which of $x = -4$, $x = 0$, and $x = 3$ are solutions to
$x^2 + 2x - 3 < 0$.

Solution   Substitute $x = -4$, 0, and 3 into the inequality $x^2 + 2x - 3 < 0$:

$$(-4)^2 + 2(-4) - 3 \overset{?}{<} 0 \qquad 0^2 + 2 \cdot 0 - 3 \overset{?}{<} 0 \qquad 3^2 + 2 \cdot 3 - 3 \overset{?}{<} 0$$

$$5 \not< 0 \qquad\qquad\qquad -3 < 0 \checkmark \qquad\qquad\qquad 12 \not< 0$$

Only $x = 0$ is a solution, since $x = -4$ and $x = 3$ do not satisfy the
inequality. ∎

> **TIP**
>
> There are infinitely many
> solutions to the inequality in
> Example 1. The value 0 is only
> one of them.

HOW TO GRAPH THE SOLUTION TO AN INEQUALITY IN ONE VARIABLE

Step 1   Find the real solutions of the related equation. Plot them as open
dots for a strict inequality or closed dots for a nonstrict inequality.

Step 2   These points divide the number line into intervals. Choose one test
point from each interval.

Step 3   Either all the points in an interval are solutions or none of them is.
Test each point; if it is a solution, shade the corresponding interval.

Example 2   Graph $2x^2 - 5x \geq -2$. Write the solution set using set
notation.

Solution

Step 1   The related equation, in standard form, is $2x^2 - 5x + 2 = 0$.
Its solutions will be the boundary points of the solution intervals:

$$x = \frac{-b \pm \sqrt{b^2 - 4ac}}{2a}$$

$$= \frac{-(-5) \pm \sqrt{(-5)^2 - 4 \cdot 2 \cdot 2}}{2 \cdot 2}$$

$$= \frac{5 \pm \sqrt{9}}{4} = 2, 0.5$$

Plot 2 and 0.5 with closed dots.

> **REMEMBER**
>
> Sometimes you can solve the
> related equation using factoring.
> In Example 2, however, you need
> to use the quadratic formula.

Step 2 Choose a value to represent each of the three resulting intervals. Substitute each value of x into $2x^2 - 5x \geq -2$:

$$2 \cdot 0^2 - 5 \cdot 0 \geq -2 \qquad 2 \cdot 1^2 - 5 \cdot 1 \geq -2 \qquad 2 \cdot 3^2 - 5 \cdot 3 \geq -2$$

$$0 \geq -2 \checkmark \qquad\qquad -3 \ngeq -2 \qquad\qquad 3 \geq -2 \checkmark$$

Step 3 Shade the interval containing $x = 0$. 　Do not shade the interval containing $x = 1$. 　Shade the interval containing $x = 3$.

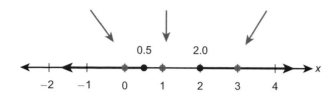

	0.5	2.0	

The solution set of $2x^2 - 5x \geq -2$ is $\{x \mid x \leq 0.5 \text{ or } x \geq 2\}$. ∎

Quadratic Inequalities in Two Variables

Some quadratic inequalities involve two variables. The solutions to these inequalities are usually graphed as regions in the Cartesian plane.

Example 3 Determine whether $(-2, 0)$ and $(5, 12)$ are solutions of $y < x^2 - 4x + 7$.

Solution Substitute each pair of x- and y-coordinates into $y < x^2 - 4x + 7$.

Test $(-2, 0)$: $0 \overset{?}{<} (-2)^2 - 4(-2) + 7$ 　　　Test $(5, 12)$: $12 \overset{?}{<} 5^2 - 4 \cdot 5 + 7$

$\qquad\qquad 0 \overset{?}{<} 4 + 8 + 7$ 　　　　　　　　　　$12 \overset{?}{<} 25 - 20 + 7$

$\qquad\qquad 0 < 19 \checkmark$ 　　　　　　　　　　　　$12 \nless 12$

This is true, so the point $(-2, 0)$ is a solution of $y < x^2 - 4x + 7$. 　　Twelve is not less than itself. So $(5, 12)$ is *not* a solution. ∎

HOW TO GRAPH THE SOLUTION TO AN INEQUALITY IN TWO VARIABLES

Step 1 Draw the related curve. Use a dashed curve for a strict inequality $(<, >)$; use a solid curve for a nonstrict inequality $(\leq, \geq)$.

Step 2 Choose a test point in each region of the plane created by the curve.

Step 3 Either all the points in a region are solutions or none of them is. Test each point; if it is a solution, shade the corresponding region.

Example 4 Graph each inequality.

Ⓐ $y > -x^2 - 4x + 5$

Solution

Step 1 The graph of the equality $y = -x^2 - 4x + 5$ is a parabola. Use any strategy to graph it, drawing a dashed curve for the strict inequality $>$.

Step 2 Choose and test a point above the parabola, such as $(2, 3)$, and a point below the parabola, such as $(0, 0)$:

Try $(2, 3)$:

$y > -x^2 - 4x + 5$

$3 \overset{?}{>} -2^2 - 4 \cdot 2 + 5$

$3 > -7$ ✓

Try $(0, 0)$:

$y > -x^2 - 4x + 5$

$0 \overset{?}{>} -0^2 - 4 \cdot 0 + 5$

$0 \not> 5$

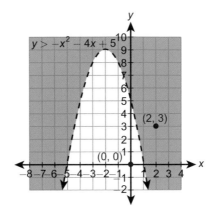

Step 3 $(2, 3)$ is a solution. Shade this region. $(0, 0)$ is not a solution. Do *not* shade this region. ∎

Ⓑ $y \geq \frac{1}{2}(x - 6)^2 + 3$

Solution

Step 1 The graph of $y = \frac{1}{2}(x - 6)^2 + 3$ is a parabola with its vertex at $(6, 3)$. Draw a solid curve, since points on the curve *are* solutions to the nonstrict inequality $\geq$.

Step 2 Test points inside and outside the parabola.

Try $(6, 5)$:

$y \geq \frac{1}{2}(x - 6)^2 + 3$

$5 \overset{?}{\geq} \frac{1}{2}(6 - 6)^2 + 3$

$5 \geq 3$ ✓

Try $(6, 2)$:

$y \geq \frac{1}{2}(x - 6)^2 + 3$

$2 \overset{?}{\geq} \frac{1}{2}(6 - 6)^2 + 3$

$2 \not\geq 3$

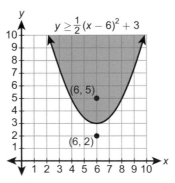

Step 3 $(6, 5)$ is a solution. Shade inside. $(6, 2)$ is not a solution. Do *not* shade outside. ∎

Graphing a Quadratic Equation to Solve an Inequality in One Variable

Example 5 Solve the inequality $x^2 + 2x - 3 < 0$.

Solution The inequality $x^2 + 2x - 3 < 0$
corresponds to x-values that make $y < 0$
for the function $y = x^2 + 2x - 3$.
Find the x-intercepts of this function,
where y is *equal* to zero:

$$x^2 + 2x - 3 = 0$$

$$(x + 3)(x - 1) = 0$$

$$x = -3 \text{ or } x = 1$$

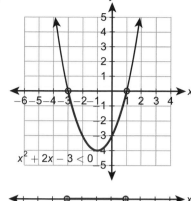

The solution set of
$x^2 + 2x - 3 < 0$ is the part of the
graph for which $y < 0$, shown in red
below the y-axis. These values are
$\{x \mid -3 < x < 1\}$, also shown on the number line. ■

Using a Quadratic Inequality to Solve a Real-World Problem

Quadratic inequalities have many applications.

Example 6 Paper is made of pulp. The strength, y, of brown wrapping
paper in pounds per square inch (psi) is related to the percentage of
hardwood, x, in the pulp by the function $y = -0.63x^2 + 11.76x - 6.67$.
What percentages of hardwood result in paper with a strength of at least
40 psi?

Solution For a strength of at least 40 psi, $y \geq 40$. So you need to solve the
inequality $-0.63x^2 + 11.76x - 6.67 \geq 40$.

Method 1 You can solve this inequality by testing intervals on a number
line. First write the inequality in standard form by subtracting 40 from both
sides: $-0.63x^2 + 11.76x - 46.67 \geq 0$. Then find the boundary points by
solving the related equation: $-0.63x^2 + 11.76x - 46.67 = 0$.

$$x = \frac{-b \pm \sqrt{b^2 - 4ac}}{2a}$$

$$= \frac{-11.76 \pm \sqrt{11.76^2 - 4 \cdot (-0.63) \cdot (-46.67)}}{2 \cdot (-0.63)}$$

$$\approx 5.72 \text{ or } 12.94$$

Plot these values with closed dots, and test values in each interval.

Test 4:

$$-0.63x^2 + 11.76x - 6.67 \geq 40$$

$$-0.63 \cdot 4^2 + 11.76 \cdot 4 - 6.67 \overset{?}{\geq} 40$$

$$30.29 \not\geq 40$$

Test 10:

$$-0.63x^2 + 11.76x - 6.67 \geq 40$$

$$-0.63 \cdot 10^2 + 11.76 \cdot 10 - 6.67 \overset{?}{\geq} 40$$

$$47.93 \geq 40 \checkmark$$

Test 14:

$$-0.63x^2 + 11.76x - 6.67 \geq 40$$

$$-0.63 \cdot 14^2 + 11.76 \cdot 14 - 6.67 \overset{?}{\geq} 40$$

$$34.49 \not\geq 40$$

Method 2 Graph $y = -0.63x^2 + 11.76x - 46.67$ with a calculator or software and find the points of intersection. The solutions to the inequality are the points where y intersects or is above the x-axis.

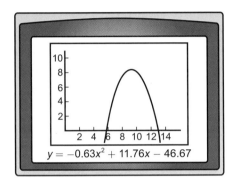

$y = -0.63x^2 + 11.76x - 46.67$

Both methods show that the solution set is approximately $\{x \mid 5.72 \leq x \leq 12.94\}$. The paper's strength is at least 40 psi for pulp that is between 5.72% and 12.94% hardwood. ∎

Problem Set

Determine whether the given values or points are solutions to the given quadratic inequality.

1. Inequality: $x^2 - 5 > 0$
   Values: $x = -2, 0, 3$

2. Inequality: $2x^2 - x - 1 < 0$
   Values: $x = -3, 0, 2$

3. Inequality: $-x^2 + 4x - 3 < 0$
   Values: $x = -1, 0, 4$

4. Inequality: $\frac{1}{3}x^2 - 2x + 1 > 0$
   Values: $x = -1, 0, 3$

5. Inequality: $x^2 - 3x + 1 > y$
   Points: $(5, 0), (-2, 4)$

6. Inequality: $y \leq x^2 - 2x + 7.5$
   Points: $(1, 10), (4, 7)$

7. Inequality: $2y < x^2 + 10x + 5$
   Points: $(-8.5, -2), (-3, 2)$

8. Inequality: $3x^2 - 7x - 9 \leq y$
   Points: $(-3, 3), (-1, 4)$

9. Inequality: $y < \frac{1}{2}x^2 + 4x - 3$
   Points: $(-2, 2), (0, -5)$

Solve the quadratic inequality. Graph the solution on a number line and write the solution in set notation.

10. $2x^2 - 4x > 0$

11. $-x^2 - 3x + 4 \leq 0$

12. $2x^2 - 16x + 32 > 0$

13. $3x^2 - 4 \leq x$

14. $4x > -1 - 2x^2$

15. $x^2 - 5 < 4x$

16. $x^2 - 4 < 0$

17. $2x^2 + x - 1 < 0$

18. $x^2 \geq 3x + 10$

For each quadratic inequality in two variables, graph the solution set on the Cartesian plane.

19. $y \leq x^2 - 3x + 2$

20. $y < x^2 + 5x + 4$

21. $y - x^2 > -12x + 32$

22. $y \geq \frac{1}{2}(x - 4)^2 + 2$

23. $y < 2(x - 1)(x - 2)$

24. $2y \leq -2x^2 - 7x + 4$

25. $y \geq -x^2 - x + 20$

26. $y \geq 3x^2 - \frac{21}{2}x + \frac{9}{2}$

27. $y \leq -2x^2 + 14x - 20$

Solve.

28. The population, in thousands, of Bronson's town Maple Woods can be modeled by the function $y = 0.45x^2 - 3x + 16$, where x is Bronson's age. For what ages was the population of his town 12,000 or fewer?

29. A ball is launched vertically upward. The height, y, of the ball in meters is related to the amount of time, x, the ball is in the air in seconds by the function $y = -9.8x^2 + 30x + 5$. For which times does the ball reach a height of at least 25 meters?

30. Kayaking Supplies' unit cost, y, of producing kayaks is related to the number of kayaks made, x, by the function $y = 0.08x^2 - 5.2x + 136$. What numbers of kayaks will result in a unit cost of more than $100?

31. Wind exerts pressure on the sides of buildings. The pressure, y, of the wind in pounds of force per square foot is related to the wind speed, x, in miles per hour by the function $y = 0.003x^2 - 0.0003x + 1.71$. What wind speeds will result in a pressure of less than 10 pounds of force per square foot?

Write a quadratic inequality or system of inequalities that corresponds to the given graph.

*32. Challenge

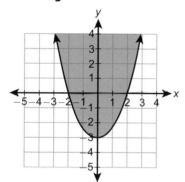

*33. Challenge

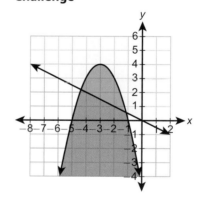

Finding a Quadratic Function from Points

It takes any two points to determine a line, but two points is not usually enough to determine a quadratic function.

There is one and only one quadratic function graph that contains three given points, as long as those points all have different first coordinates and do not all lie on a line.

Finding a Quadratic Function from Two *x*-intercepts and a Point

To find a quadratic equation from two *x*-intercepts and one point, substitute the values of the *x*-intercepts into the factored form of the equation. Then use the additional point to solve for a.

Example 1   Find the equation of the quadratic function that contains the given *x*-intercepts and point.

Ⓐ *x*-intercepts: -5 and 1, point: $(2, 7)$

Solution   The function contains $(-5, 0)$ and $(1, 0)$ because the *x*-intercepts are -5 and 1.

$y = a(x - r_1)(x - r_2)$	Quadratic equation in factored form
$y = a(x - (-5))(x - 1)$	Substitute -5 and 1 for r_1 and r_2.
$y = a(x + 5)(x - 1)$	Now only the coefficient a is unknown.
$7 = a(2 + 5)(2 - 1)$	Substitute the point $(2, 7)$ for x and y to find a.
$7 = a \cdot 7 \cdot 1$	Simplify.
$a = 1$	Solve for a.

Substitute $a = 1$ to get the function in factored form: $y = (x + 5)(x - 1)$. You could also expand this to get standard form: $y = x^2 + 4x - 5$. ∎

B x-intercepts: -6 and $\frac{1}{2}$, point: $(2, 8)$

Solution The function contains $(-6, 0)$ and $\left(\frac{1}{2}, 0\right)$ because the x-intercepts are -6 and $\frac{1}{2}$.

$y = a(x - r_1)(x - r_2)$ Quadratic equation in factored form

$y = a(x - (-6))\left(x - \frac{1}{2}\right)$ Substitute -6 and $\frac{1}{2}$ for r_1 and r_2 in the factored form.

$y = a(x + 6)\left(x - \frac{1}{2}\right)$ Now only the coefficient a is unknown.

$8 = a(2 + 6)\left(2 - \frac{1}{2}\right)$ Substitute the point $(2, 8)$ for x and y to find a.

$8 = a \cdot 8 \cdot \frac{3}{2}$

$a = \frac{2}{3}$

Substitute $a = \frac{2}{3}$ to get the function in factored form: $y = \frac{2}{3}(x + 6)\left(x - \frac{1}{2}\right)$.

You could also expand this to get standard form: $y = \frac{2}{3}x^2 + \frac{11}{3}x - 2$. ■

THINK ABOUT IT

In Examples 1 and 2, verify that the quadratic equation contains the given points.

Finding a Quadratic Function from a Vertex and a Point

To find a quadratic equation when given a vertex and one other point, substitute the ordered pair of the vertex into the vertex form of the equation. Then use the additional point to solve for a.

Example 2 Find the equation of the quadratic function that has vertex $(-2, 5)$ and contains the point $(-3, 1)$.

Solution Substitute the vertex $(-2, 5)$ for h and k in the vertex form.

$y = a(x - h)^2 + k$

$y = a(x - (-2))^2 + 5$

Only the coefficient a remains unknown.

$y = a(x + 2)^2 + 5$

Substitute $(-3, 1)$ for x and y to find a.

$1 = a(-3 + 2)^2 + 5$

$1 = a(-1)^2 + 5$

$1 = a \cdot 1 + 5$

$-4 = a$

Substitute a to get the function in vertex form: $y = -4(x + 2)^2 + 5$.

You could also expand to get standard form: $y = -4x^2 - 16x - 11$. ■

Finding a Quadratic Function from Three Points

You can find a quadratic function from three points by using a system.

Example 3 Find the equation of the quadratic function that contains $(-5, 30)$, $(-2, -3)$, and $(1, 0)$.

Solution Substitute the given points for x and y into the standard form $y = ax^2 + bx + c$ to form a system of three linear equations in a, b, and c.

Point	Substitution	Linear equation in a, b, and c
$(-5, 30)$	$30 = a(-5)^2 + b(-5) + c$	$30 = 25a - 5b + c$ (I)
$(-2, -3)$	$-3 = a(-2)^2 + b(-2) + c$	$-3 = 4a - 2b + c$ (II)
$(1, 0)$	$0 = a \cdot 1^2 + b \cdot 1 + c$	$0 = a + b + c$ (III)

In the equation $y = ax^2 + bx + c$, the letters a, b, and c are coefficients, but in Equations I, II, and III, they are variables. Eliminate a variable in the 3 by 3 system to obtain a 2 by 2 system.

Step 1 Multiply Equation II by -1, and then add the resulting equation and Equation I. This eliminates c.

$$\begin{array}{ll} 30 = 25a - 5b + c & \text{(I)} \\ +\ 3 = -4a + 2b - c & -1 \cdot \text{(II)} \\ \hline 33 = 21a - 3b & \text{(IV)} \end{array}$$

Step 2 Multiply Equation II by -1, and then add the resulting equation and Equation III. This also eliminates c.

$$\begin{array}{ll} 3 = -4a + 2b - c & -1 \cdot \text{(II)} \\ +\ 0 = \quad a + b + c & \text{(III)} \\ \hline 3 = -3a + 3b & \text{(V)} \end{array}$$

Equations IV and V form a 2 by 2 system. Solve the system.

Step 3 Add Equations IV and V to eliminate b. Then solve for a.

$$\begin{array}{ll} 33 = 21a - 3b & \text{(IV)} \\ +\ 3 = -3a + 3b & \text{(V)} \\ \hline 36 = 18a & \\ 2 = a & \end{array}$$

Step 4 Substitute 2 for a in either Equation IV or Equation V. Solve for b.

$$\begin{array}{ll} 3 = -3a + 3b & \text{(V)} \\ 3 = -3 \cdot 2 + 3b & \\ 3 = b & \end{array}$$

Step 5 Substitute 2 for a and 3 for b in any of the original three equations. Solve for c.

$$\begin{array}{ll} 0 = a + b + c & \text{(III)} \\ 0 = 2 + 3 + c & \\ -5 = c & \end{array}$$

Step 6 Substitute a, b, and c in the standard form to get the quadratic function:

$$y = ax^2 + bx + c \implies y = 2x^2 + 3x - 5 \ \blacksquare$$

TIP

A system of 3 linear equations in 3 variables is called a 3 by 3 system.

A system of 2 linear equations in 2 variables is called a 2 by 2 system.

THINK ABOUT IT

Verify that the quadratic function contains the three given points:

$y = 2x^2 + 3x - 5$

$30 = 2 \cdot (-5)^2 + 3 \cdot (-5) - 5$ ✓

$-3 = 2 \cdot (-2)^2 + 3 \cdot (-2) - 5$ ✓

$0 = 2 \cdot 1^2 + 3 \cdot 1 - 5$ ✓

Problem Set

Find the equation of the quadratic function that has the given *x*-intercepts and point.

1. *x*-intercepts: -1 and 3
point: $(2, -6)$

2. *x*-intercepts: -2 and 4
point: $(3, -15)$

3. *x*-intercepts: -3 and 1
point: $(-1, -4)$

4. *x*-intercepts: -2 and 2
point: $(1, 6)$

5. *x*-intercepts: -1 and 4
point: $(3, -4)$

6. *x*-intercepts: 1 and 3
point: $(4, 6)$

7. *x*-intercepts: 2 and 4
point: $(1, -3)$

8. *x*-intercepts: -9 and -2
point: $(-1, 3)$

9. *x*-intercepts: $\frac{3}{2}$ and 4
point: $\left(5, \frac{7}{4}\right)$

Find the equation of the quadratic function that has the given vertex and point.

10. vertex: $(1, -1)$
point: $(3, 3)$

11. vertex: $(-1, -2)$
point: $(1, 2)$

12. vertex: $(-2, 3)$
point: $(1, 21)$

13. vertex: $(2, -1)$
point: $(3, 1)$

14. vertex: $(3, 1)$
point: $(5, -3)$

15. vertex: $(-2, -1)$
point: $(2, -17)$

16. vertex: $(0, 0)$
point: $(1, 3)$

17. vertex: $(1, -1)$
point: $(0, -4)$

18. vertex: $(-1, 2)$
point: $(2, -25)$

Find the equation of the quadratic function that contains the given three points.

19. $(0, 2), (-1, 5), (2, 2)$

20. $(0, -1), (1, 1), (2, 1)$

21. $(-1, 8), (1, 2), (2, 2)$

22. $(-2, 4), (0, 2), (1, -2)$

23. $(-1, -4), (1, 0), (2, 5)$

24. $(-1, 1), (0, 2), (1, 7)$

25. $(0, -3), (1, -2), (2, 5)$

26. $(-1, -1), (0, 2), (1, 1)$

27. $(-1, 3), (0, -1), (1, 1)$

Solve.

*__28.__ **Challenge** Find the cubic function that contains points $(-1, 0), (0, 1), (1, 0),$ and $(2, 3)$.

*__29.__ **Challenge** Develop a general rule explaining how many points are needed to define a polynomial with degree *n*.

Applications: Quadratic Functions

Quadratic functions can be used to model many real-world situations.

For some problems, you can create and solve a quadratic equation; for other problems, you can create and optimize a quadratic function.

Application: Furniture Dimensions

Example 1   Television screens are described by their diagonal measurement and by their length-to-width ratio. Many widescreen televisions have a length-to-width ratio (usually called the aspect ratio) of 16 : 9. If Mr. Scott has a 40-inch widescreen television with an aspect ratio of 16 : 9, could he fit it in a piece of furniture with an opening that is 37 inches by 24 inches?

Solution   Draw a rectangular television screen. The 40-inch diagonal divides it into two congruent right triangles. Since the ratio of the sides is 16 : 9, the sides can be represented by the multiples $16x$ and $9x$.

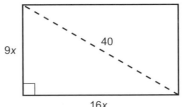

Use the Pythagorean theorem to set up a quadratic equation. Simplify the equation and solve for x.

$$a^2 + b^2 = c^2$$
$$(9x)^2 + (16x)^2 = 40^2$$
$$81x^2 + 256x^2 = 1600^2$$
$$337x^2 = 1600^2$$
$$x = \pm\sqrt{\frac{1600}{337}} \approx \pm 2.18$$

Because negative length is not helpful in this situation, -2.18 is an extraneous solution. So the television's dimensions are

$$16x \approx 16 \cdot 2.18 = 34.88$$
$$9x \approx 9 \cdot 2.18 = 19.62$$

The dimensions of the 40-inch widescreen television are approximately 35 inches by 20 inches. Mr. Scott's furniture can accommodate a 40-inch widescreen as long as the frame around the screen is no more than 1 inch wide on each side. ■

Application: Projectile Motion

The height h of a projectile after t seconds is given by the function

$$h(t) = \frac{1}{2} gt^2 + v_0 t + h_0,$$

where v_0 is the initial vertical velocity, h_0 is the initial height, and g is the downward acceleration due to gravity (on the earth, $g \approx -32 \text{ ft/s}^2 \approx -9.8 \text{ m/s}^2$).

Example 2 Kyle throws a baseball straight up from a height of 4 feet with an initial speed of 30 feet per second.

A Write an equation to model the height y of the ball after t seconds.

B Make a graph of the baseball's height as a function of time.

C What is the maximum height of the baseball?

D If Kyle doesn't catch the ball, when will the ball hit the ground?

Solution

A Use the values $g = -32$, $v_0 = 30$, and $h_0 = 4$ to write a function for the height of Kyle's baseball:

$$h(t) = -\frac{1}{2} \cdot 32 t^2 + 30t + 4 = -16t^2 + 30t + 4$$

B Make a graph using any tool, such as a table of values, software, or a calculator.

C The maximum height (the maximum value of the function) corresponds to the h-value of the vertex. You can find the vertex by using your knowledge of the properties of quadratic functions:

$$t = -\frac{b}{2a} = -\frac{30}{2 \cdot (-16)} = \frac{15}{16} = 0.9375$$

The h coordinate of the vertex is $h(0.9375) \approx 18.1$.

Therefore, the ball reaches a maximum height of about 18.1 feet.

D The ground is height $h = 0$, so the ball is on the ground when $0 = -16t^2 + 30t + 4$.

Use the graph as a guide. The graph shows two roots. The leftmost root is extraneous, since negative time has no meaning in this problem. The positive root seems to be at $t = 2$, so the positive root seems to be at $t = 2$. Check to see if $t = 2$ yields a height of 0:

$$\begin{aligned} h(2) &= -16 \cdot 2^2 + 30 \cdot 2 + 4 \\ &= -64 + 60 + 4 \\ &= 0 \end{aligned}$$

So the ball hits the ground 2 seconds after Kyle throws it. ∎

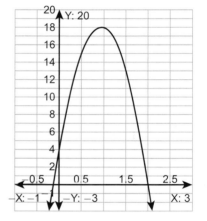

Application: Optimizing Area

Example 3   Selena bought 12 meters of fencing to make a rectangular pen for her rabbit. She will use the wall of her shed as one side of the pen and the fencing for the other three sides. What dimensions maximize the pen's area?

Solution   Sketch and label a diagram of the pen. Let x represent the length of the two sides perpendicular to the shed. Of the 12 meters of fencing, $12 - 2x$ remain for the third side. So the dimensions of the pen are x and $12 - 2x$.

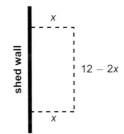

Use the area formula for a rectangle to set up a quadratic function, and simplify.

$$Area = length \cdot width$$
$$A = x \cdot (12 - 2x)$$
$$A = -2x^2 + 12x$$

Because the leading coefficient is negative, the graph of A would be a parabola that opens down; the coordinates of the vertex give the dimensions that yield the maximum area. The x-value of the vertex is

$$x = -\frac{b}{2a} = -\frac{12}{2 \cdot (-2)} = 3$$

> **REMEMBER**
> You could also find the coordinates of the vertex by completing the square.

Therefore, the pen will have maximum area when its dimensions are $x = 3$ meters and $12 - 2x = 6$ meters. This gives an area of 18 square meters. ■

Problem Set

Solve each problem by using a quadratic equation.

1. Jo can grow 5 pounds of wheat per square meter of farmland. If Jo grows 2000 pounds of wheat on a square farm, what is the length of the farm?

2. An open box is formed by cutting squares of length 4 inches out of a square piece of paper. The resulting box has a volume of 400 cubic inches. What are the dimensions of the original piece of paper?

3. Suppose a 25-foot ladder is leaning against a wall such that it reaches up the wall 17 feet farther than the distance from the base of the ladder to the wall. What is the distance from the base of the ladder to the wall?

4. A rectangular warehouse covers 20,000 square feet of ground. The warehouse is 100 feet wider than its depth. What is the width of the warehouse?

5. Suppose a sheep requires 2 square meters of space to graze. Jose has 25 sheep and decides to make his sheep pen 5 meters longer than it is wide. What is the width of the sheep pen?

6. Sarah and Nakia are racing to their homes. Sarah's home is due north and Nakia's home is due east. Nakia gives Sarah a 7-meter head start. Assuming they run at the same rate, how far will Nakia run before the distance between the two girls is 17 meters?

7. A rectangular park has dimensions of 50 km by 120 km. The park has a rectangular grass field surrounded by woods. What are the dimensions of the field if the area of the field is a quarter of the total area of the park? Assume that the width-length ratio in the field is equal to the width-length ratio in the park.

For each projectile motion problem, do the following:

A. Write a function equation to model the problem.
B. Graph the function.
C. Answer the questions.

8. Silas tosses a football up at 10 feet per second, from an initial height of 6 feet. What is the maximum height? If no one catches the ball, when will the ball hit the ground?

9. Marques drops a plate from a height of 5 feet. When will the plate hit the ground?

10. Krystal throws a rappelling rope down a 50-meter cliff at 10 meters per second. When will the rope hit the ground?

11. Santino fires a paintball 3 meters from the ground such that the initial trajectory is perfectly horizontal. Assume the paintball does not hit anything and the ground is level. When will the paintball hit the ground?

12. Khalid jumps out of an airplane at a height of 10,000 feet. If Khalid has to release his parachute at 5000 feet, at what time should he do this?

13. David throws a bucket with an initial speed of 2 meters per second into a well that is 30 meters deep. When will the bucket hit the bottom of the well?

14. Nikolai kicks a soccer ball straight up at a speed of 20 meters per second. What is the maximum height? When will the ball hit the ground?

Solve each optimization problem.

15. Brody's farm borders a river. He buys 1000 meters of fencing. What dimensions maximize the area of the farm?

16. A rectangular house is designed with two parallel interior walls. The contractor has enough material to build 800 meters of walls. What is the maximum area of the house?

17. Flags & Designs, Inc., has enough brick to build 400 meters of exterior walls for its new store. What is the maximum area of the store that the company can build?

18. Suppose the daily cost of farming x pounds of potatoes is approximated by $C(x) = 0.2x^2 - 5x + 200$. How many pounds of potatoes would minimize the costs of producing the potatoes?

19. Aleah's garden borders a wall. She buys 80 meters of fencing. What dimensions maximize the area of the garden?

20. Suppose the daily cost of producing x computers is approximated by $C(x) = 0.4x^2 - 20x + 210$. How many computers would minimize the production costs?

21. Felix sells dishwashers for $400 per machine. He averages about 12 sales a day. If Felix loses a customer for every $20 he increases the price, what is the price that maximizes his profits?

*22. **Challenge** An open box is created by cutting out squares from a piece of paper that is 10 inches by 10 inches. What are the dimensions of the cutouts that maximize the volume of the box?

*23. **Challenge** A cylinder with no top has a surface area of 6π square meters. What radius produces the largest possible volume of the cylinder?

*24. **Challenge** Suppose a missile is launched from the ground (or $(0, 0)$) and follows the path $y = 20x$ initially. At what point on the coordinate grid will the missile be closest to the point $(30, 10)$?

UNIT 9

Solving and Graphing Polynomials

You can see laminar and turbulent flow in a fountain.

When water comes out of a pipe, it usually looks very smooth. This is called laminar flow. After time, the water becomes less smooth as its flow becomes more turbulent. Engineers use polynomials to model both types of flow.

Big Ideas

▶ You can apply the rules of arithmetic to complex algebraic expressions as well as simple numeric expressions.

▶ A function is a correspondence between two sets, the domain and the range, that assigns to each member of the domain exactly one member of the range. Functions can model many events in the physical world.

▶ If you can create a mathematical model for a situation, you can use the model to solve other problems that you might not be able to solve otherwise. Algebraic equations can capture key relationships among quantities in the world.

Unit Topics

▶ Foundations for Unit 9

▶ Polynomial Long Division

▶ Synthetic Division

▶ The Polynomial Remainder Theorem

▶ Factors and Rational Roots

▶ Graphing Polynomials

▶ Factoring Polynomials Completely

▶ Applications: Polynomials

Foundations for Unit 9

Before you study factoring and graphing polynomial functions, you should know how to do the following:

▶ Perform long division with numbers.

▶ Solve a quadratic equation by factoring.

▶ Graph power functions.

Long Division

It is important to know the terms used in division.

Definitions

dividend	the number that is being divided
divisor	the number by which the dividend is being divided
quotient	the result of a division
remainder	a number that is left over after a division

In long division, the dividend is written under a division symbol.

When performing long division, you repeat the process of dividing, multiplying, and subtracting.

> **TIP**
>
> If a number divides evenly into another number, the remainder is 0.

$$\overset{\text{quotient}}{\text{divisor}\,)\overline{\text{dividend}}}$$

Example 1   Divide $23\overline{)5687}$.

Step 1   The divisor, 23, divides into 56 two times, so write 2 in the quotient. Multiply 2 by 23; write the product directly below 56. Subtract. Bring down the next number in the dividend.

Step 2   Because 23 divides into 108 four times, write 4 as the next number in the quotient. Multiply 4 by 23 and write the product below 108. Subtract. Bring down the next number in the dividend.

Step 3   Because 23 divides into 167 seven times, write 7 as the next number in the quotient. Multiply 7 by 23 and write the product below 167. Subtract. There are no more numbers to bring down. The remainder is 6.

$$
\begin{array}{r}
247 \text{ R6} \\
23\overline{)5687} \\
-46 \\
\hline
108 \\
-92 \\
\hline
167 \\
-161 \\
\hline
6
\end{array}
$$

The quotient can be written 247 R6 or $247\frac{6}{23}$.

You can check your answer to a long division problem by multiplying.

$$\text{Quotient} \cdot \text{Divisor} + \text{Remainder} = \text{Dividend}$$

Check   In Example 1, $247 \cdot 23 + 6 = 5687$, so 247 R6 is correct. ✓

Problem Set A

Divide and check.

1. $5\overline{)147}$

2. $4\overline{)180}$

3. $69\overline{)9642}$

4. $79\overline{)6241}$

5. $59\overline{)8878}$

6. $13\overline{)2197}$

Solving Quadratic Equations

You can use the zero product property to solve quadratic equations that are easily factorable.

Zero Product Property   **For any real numbers a and b, if $ab = 0$, then $a = 0$ or $b = 0$.**

Example 2   Solve each equation.

A $x^2 - 2x - 15 = 0$

$(x + 3)(x - 5) = 0$

$x + 3 = 0$ or $x - 5 = 0$

$x = -3$ $x = 5$

The solution set is $\{-3, 5\}$.

B $3x^2 + 13x + 4 = 0$

$(3x + 1)(x + 4) = 0$

$3x + 1 = 0$ or $x + 4 = 0$

$x = -\dfrac{1}{3}$ $x = -4$

The solution set is $\left\{-4, -\dfrac{1}{3}\right\}$.

Problem Set B

Solve.

7. $x^2 + 2x + 1 = 0$

8. $r^2 - 5r + 6 = 0$

9. $x^2 + 12x + 36 = 0$

10. $h^2 - 2h - 8 = 0$

11. $a^2 + 11a + 30 = 0$

12. $x^2 - 6x - 27 = 0$

13. $2x^2 - 13x + 11 = 0$

14. $5d^2 + 39d + 28 = 0$

15. $3x^2 + 9x - 120 = 0$

Graphing Power Functions

To graph a power function of the form $f(x) = ax^n + b$, plot a few ordered pairs and use what you know about the basic shape of the graph as well as the end behavior of the function.

The end behavior of a power function relies on the values of both n and a.

The End Behavior of $f(x) = ax^n + b$

	a is positive		a is negative	
n is even	As $x \to \infty, f(x) \to \infty$ As $x \to -\infty, f(x) \to \infty$	(graph)	As $x \to \infty, f(x) \to -\infty$ As $x \to -\infty, f(x) \to -\infty$	(graph)
n is odd	As $x \to \infty, f(x) \to \infty$ As $x \to -\infty, f(x) \to -\infty$	(graph)	As $x \to \infty, f(x) \to -\infty$ As $x \to -\infty, f(x) \to \infty$	(graph)

Example 3   Graph $f(x) = 2x^3 + 1$ and describe the graph's end behavior.

Make a table and plot ordered pairs.

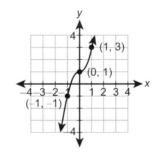

x	-1	0	1
f(x)	-1	1	3

Since $a = 2$ and $n = 3$, the values of $f(x)$ will continue to decrease as x decreases, and continue to increase as x increases.

Problem Set C

Graph and describe the graph's end behavior.

16. $f(x) = 3x^2 - 2$

17. $g(x) = -x^3 + 1$

18. $f(x) = \frac{1}{2}x^2 + 3$

19. $f(x) = -2x^2 + 2$

20. $g(x) = \frac{1}{4}x^3 + \frac{1}{2}$

21. $h(x) = -2x^3 + 5$

22. $f(x) = -x^2 - 1$

23. $h(x) = 2x^2 + 3$

24. $g(x) = -2x^3 - 1$

Polynomial Long Division

If you know how to use long division with numbers, then you can use the same strategy to divide polynomials.

You can set up a division problem with polynomials the same way you do with numbers. Place the dividend inside the division symbol and the divisor to the left of it. The quotient goes on top of the division symbol.

Numbers	Polynomials
$$\begin{array}{r} 5 \\ 15\overline{)75} \\ -75 \\ \hline 0 \end{array}$$	$$\begin{array}{r} x^2 \\ 3\overline{)3x^2} \\ -3x^2 \\ \hline 0 \end{array}$$
$75 \div 15 = 5$	$3x^2 \div 3 = x^2$

Dividing a Second-Degree Polynomial by a First-Degree Binomial

As you do when you divide numbers, repeat the process of divide, multiply, and subtract until no more divisions can be made.

Example 1   Divide.

A $(x^2 - 6x - 27) \div (x + 3)$

Solution

Step 1

$$\begin{array}{r} x \\ x + 3\overline{)x^2 - 6x - 27} \\ -(x^2 + 3x) \\ \hline -9x - 27 \end{array}$$

Divide: $\frac{x^2}{x} = x$.

Multiply: $x \cdot (x + 3) = x^2 + 3x$.

Subtract: $(x^2 - 6x) - (x^2 + 3x) = -9x$.
Bring down -27.

Step 2

$$\begin{array}{r} x - 9 \\ x + 3\overline{)x^2 - 6x - 27} \\ -(x^2 + 3x) \\ \hline -9x - 27 \\ -(-9x - 27) \\ \hline 0 \end{array}$$

Divide: $\frac{-9x}{x} = -9$.

Multiply: $-9 \cdot (x + 3) = -9x - 27$.

Subtract: $(-9x - 27) - (-9x - 27) = 0$.

So $x^2 - 6x - 27$ divided by $x + 3$ is $x - 9$. ∎

B $2x^2 + 13x - 4$ by $2x - 1$.

Solution

Step 1

$$
\begin{array}{r}
x \\
2x - 1 \overline{\smash{)}\, 2x^2 + 13x - 4} \\
-(2x^2 - x) \\
\hline
14x - 4
\end{array}
$$

Divide $\dfrac{2x^2}{2x} = x$.

Multiply: $x \cdot (2x - 1) = 2x^2 - x$.

Subtract: $(2x^2 + 13x) - (2x^2 - x) = 14x$.
Bring down -4.

Step 2

$$
\begin{array}{r}
x + 7 \\
2x - 1 \overline{\smash{)}\, 2x^2 + 13x - 4} \\
-(2x^2 - x) \\
\hline
14x - 4 \\
-(14x - 7) \\
\hline
3
\end{array}
$$

Divide: $\dfrac{14x}{2x} = 7$.

Multiply: $7 \cdot (2x - 1) = 14x - 7$.

Subtract: $(14x - 4) - (14x - 7) = 3$.

So $2x^2 + 13x - 4$ divided by $2x - 1$ is $x + 7$, with remainder 3. ■

Representing and Checking a Quotient

NAMES OF EXPRESSIONS IN A POLYNOMIAL DIVISION

Different Ways to Express Related Multiplication and Division Facts	
With Numbers	**With Polynomials**
$13 \div 5 = 2, \text{R}3$	$(2x^2 + 13x - 4) \div (2x - 1) = x + 7, \text{R}3$
$\dfrac{13}{5} = 2 + \dfrac{3}{5}$	$\dfrac{2x^2 + 13x - 4}{2x - 1} = x + 7 + \dfrac{3}{2x - 1}$

Because multiplication and division are inverse operations, you can check your answer to a division problem by multiplying.

Using Multiplication to Check a Quotient
Quotient $\cdot$ Divisor $+$ Remainder $=$ Dividend

Example 2

Ⓐ Determine if $2x + 4 + \dfrac{2}{x - 5}$ is the quotient of $(2x^2 - 6x - 18) \div (x - 5)$.

Solution

$$(2x + 4)(x - 5) + 2 \stackrel{?}{=} 2x^2 - 6x - 18 \qquad \text{Quotient} \cdot \text{Divisor} + \text{Remainder} = \text{Dividend}$$

$$2x^2 - 10x + 4x - 20 + 2 \stackrel{?}{=} 2x^2 - 6x - 18 \qquad \text{Multiply.}$$

$$2x^2 - 6x - 18 = 2x^2 - 6x - 18 \qquad \text{Simplify.}$$

So $2x + 4 + \dfrac{2}{x - 5}$ is the quotient of $(2x^2 - 6x - 18) \div (x - 5)$. ∎

Ⓑ Determine if $3x - 5$ is the quotient of $(6x^2 - 2x - 15) \div (2x + 3)$.

Solution

$$(3x - 5)(2x + 3) \stackrel{?}{=} 6x^2 - 2x - 15 \qquad \text{Quotient} \cdot \text{Divisor} = \text{Dividend}$$

$$6x^2 + 9x - 10x - 15 \stackrel{?}{=} 6x^2 - 2x - 15 \qquad \text{Multiply.}$$

$$6x^2 - x - 15 \neq 6x^2 - 2x - 15 \qquad \text{Simplify.}$$

So $3x - 5$ is not the quotient of $(6x^2 - 2x - 15) \div (2x + 3)$. ∎

Dividing a Fourth-Degree Polynomial by a First-Degree Binomial

Example 3 Divide $2x^4 - 4x + 7x^2 + 1$ by $x + 1$.

Solution Rewrite the dividend so that its terms are in order of decreasing degree, and write $0x^3$ for the missing x^3 term.

$$2x^4 - 4x + 7x^2 + 1 = 2x^4 + 0x^3 + 7x^2 - 4x + 1$$

Now divide.

$$
\begin{array}{r}
2x^3 - 2x^2 + 9x - 13 \\
x + 1 \overline{\smash{)}\, 2x^4 + 0x^3 + 7x^2 - 4x + 1} \\
-(2x^4 + 2x^3) \\
\hline
-2x^3 + 7x^2 \\
-(-2x^3 - 2x^2) \\
\hline
9x^2 - 4x \\
-(9x^2 + 9x) \\
\hline
-13x + 1 \\
-(-13x - 13) \\
\hline
14
\end{array}
$$

> **TIP**
>
> When you multiply a term in the quotient by the divisor, align the terms of the product with their like terms in the dividend. Notice that in Example 3, the product $-(2x^4 + 2x^3)$ is written so that $2x^4$ is directly below $2x^4$ and $2x^3$ is directly below $0x^3$.

The quotient is $2x^3 - 2x^2 + 9x - 13$.

The remainder is 14.

So $(2x^4 - 4x + 7x^2 + 1) \div (x + 1) = 2x^3 - 2x^2 + 9x - 13 + \dfrac{14}{x + 1}$. ∎

Determining Whether One Polynomial Is a Factor of Another Polynomial

Example 4   Use division to determine whether $a - 2$ is a factor of $a^3 - 7a + 6$.

Solution

$$
\begin{array}{r}
a^2 + 2a - 3 \\
a - 2 \overline{)\, a^3 + 0a^2 - 7a + 6} \\
\underline{-(a^3 - 2a^2)} \\
2a^2 - 7a \\
\underline{-(2a^2 - 4a)} \\
-3a + 6 \\
\underline{-(-3a + 6)} \\
0
\end{array}
$$

The remainder is 0, so $a^3 - 7a + 6 = (a - 2)(a^2 + 2a - 3)$, and $a - 2$ is a factor of $a^3 - 7a + 6$. ∎

> **THINK ABOUT IT**
>
> When the remainder is 0, both the divisor and the quotient are factors of the dividend.
>
> To check your answer, multiply $(a - 2)(a^2 + 2a - 3)$. Verify that the product is $a^3 - 7a + 6$.

Problem Set

Divide.

1. $(x^2 - 2x - 3) \div (x + 1)$

2. $(t^2 - 5t - 14) \div (t + 2)$

3. $(x^2 + 4x + 4) \div (x + 1)$

4. $(y^2 + 5y - 7) \div (y - 1)$

5. $(r^2 + 4r - 12) \div (r + 6)$

6. $(x^2 - 100) \div (2x + 10)$

7. $(3q^2 + 12q + 15) \div (3q + 3)$

8. $(2x^3 + 2x^2 + 3x + 3) \div (x + 1)$

9. $(8x^2 - 6x + 1) \div (4x - 1)$

10. $(2n^2 + 13n - 7) \div (2n + 7)$

11. $(3g^4 - 12g^3 + g - 4) \div (g - 4)$

12. $(2x^3 + 5x^2 - 4x + 5) \div (x + 3)$

13. $(h^3 - 1) \div (h - 1)$

14. $(p^4 - 4p^2 - 12) \div (p^2 + 2)$

15. $(2b^4 + 7b^2 + 5) \div (b^2 + 3)$

Use multiplication to check the quotient.

16. Determine whether $3x + 2 + \dfrac{1}{x + 1}$ is the quotient of $(3x^2 + 5x + 3) \div (x + 1)$.

17. Determine whether $9y + 5$ is the quotient of $(9y^2 + 4y - 5) \div (y + 1)$.

18. Determine whether $3c + 1$ is the quotient of $(3c^2 - 4c + 1) \div (c - 1)$.

19. Determine whether $n + 6 - \dfrac{5}{n - 5}$ is the quotient of $(n^2 + n - 35) \div (n - 5)$.

Use division to determine whether the binomial is a factor of the trinomial.

20. Determine whether $3r - 7$ is a factor of $6r^2 - 11r - 7$.

21. Determine whether $2x + 1$ is a factor of $8x^2 - 2x - 1$.

22. Determine whether $3a + 2$ is a factor of $9a^2 + 12a + 4$.

23. Determine whether $2p - 1$ is a factor of $6p^2 - p - 1$.

Solve.

*24. **Challenge** What value of k makes $x - 3$ a factor of $2x^2 - kx - 3$?

*25. **Challenge** The volume of a rectangular prism is $x^3 - 2x^2 - 5x + 6$. The length of the prism is $x + 2$ and the width is $x - 3$. Find the height of the prism.

Synthetic Division

As long as you're careful, long division always works, but it takes time; another method you can use to divide polynomials is synthetic division.

For synthetic division to work, the divisor must be a binomial in the form $x - k$, where k is a constant.

Using Synthetic Division to Divide Polynomials

Suppose you want to divide $2x^2 + 3x + 7$ by $x - 2$. The process of finding the quotient using both long division and synthetic division is shown below.

Long Division

$$
\begin{array}{r}
2x + 7 \\
x - 2\overline{)\,2x^2 + 3x + 7} \\
-(2x^2 - 4x) \\
\hline
7x + 7 \\
-(7x - 14) \\
\hline
21
\end{array}
$$

Synthetic Division

$$
\begin{array}{r|rrr}
2 & 2 & 3 & 7 \\
 & & 4 & 14 \\
\hline
 & 2 & 7 & 21
\end{array}
$$

> **THINK ABOUT IT**
>
> When you use synthetic division, notice that the coefficients of the dividend appear in the top row and the coefficients of the quotient appear with the remainder in the bottom row.

Synthetic division is considered a shorthand method for long division, but remember it only works when the divisor is in the form $x - k$.

Example 1 Divide $3x^3 + 11x^2 - 2x - 24$ by $x + 3$.

Solution The divisor is $x + 3$. To get the form $x - k$, write $x + 3$ as $x - (-3)$, so $k = -3$.

Step 1
$$
\begin{array}{r|rrrr}
-3 & 3 & 11 & -2 & -24 \\
\hline
\end{array}
$$
Put the value for k in the box and put the coefficients to the right of it.

Step 2
$$
\begin{array}{r|rrrr}
-3 & 3 & 11 & -2 & -24 \\
 & & -9 & & \\
\hline
 & 3 & & &
\end{array}
$$
Bring down the first coefficient, 3, then multiply by -3 and put the result in the next column.

Step 3
$$
\begin{array}{r|rrrr}
-3 & 3 & 11 & -2 & -24 \\
 & & -9 & -6 & \\
\hline
 & 3 & 2 & &
\end{array}
$$
Add 11 and -9, then multiply the sum, 2, by -3 and put the result in the next column.

Step 4
$$
\begin{array}{r|rrrr}
-3 & 3 & 11 & -2 & -24 \\
 & & -9 & -6 & 24 \\
\hline
 & 3 & 2 & -8 &
\end{array}
$$
Add -2 and -6, then multiply the sum, -8, by -3 and put the product in the next column.

Step 5

$$\begin{array}{r|rrrr} -3 & 3 & 11 & -2 & -24 \\ & & -9 & -6 & 24 \\ \hline & 3 & 2 & -8 & 0 \end{array}$$

Add -24 and 24. The sum, 0, is your remainder.

Step 6

$$\begin{array}{r|rrrr} -3 & 3 & 11 & -2 & -24 \\ & & -9 & -6 & 24 \\ \hline & 3 & 2 & -8 & 0 \\ & \downarrow & \downarrow & \downarrow & \downarrow \end{array}$$

$$3x^2 + 2x - 8 \quad \text{R0}$$

Now, write the quotient. Begin writing the quotient with a power of x that is one less than the greatest power of x in the dividend.

The quotient has no remainder, so
$(3x^3 + 11x^2 - 2x - 24) \div (x + 3) = 3x^2 + 2x - 8.$ ■

Example 2 Divide $x^3 - 6x^2 - x + 32$ by $x - 5$.

Solution The divisor is $x - 5$, so $k = 5$.

Step 1

$$\begin{array}{r|rrrr} 5 & 1 & -6 & -1 & 32 \\ \hline & & & & \end{array}$$

Put the value for k in the box and put the coefficients to the right of it.

Step 2

$$\begin{array}{r|rrrr} 5 & 1 & -6 & -1 & 32 \\ & & 5 & & \\ \hline & 1 & & & \end{array}$$

Bring down the first coefficient, 1, then multiply by 5 and put the result in the next column.

Step 3

$$\begin{array}{r|rrrr} 5 & 1 & -6 & -1 & 32 \\ & & 5 & -5 & \\ \hline & 1 & -1 & & \end{array}$$

Add -6 and 5, then multiply the sum, -1, by 5 and put the result in the next column.

Step 4

$$\begin{array}{r|rrrr} 5 & 1 & -6 & -1 & 32 \\ & & 5 & -5 & -30 \\ \hline & 1 & -1 & -6 & \end{array}$$

Add -1 and -5, then multiply the sum, -6, by 5 and put the product in the next column.

Step 5

$$\begin{array}{r|rrrr} 5 & 1 & -6 & -1 & 32 \\ & & 5 & -5 & -30 \\ \hline & 1 & -1 & -6 & 2 \end{array}$$

Add 32 and -30. The sum, 2, is your remainder.

Step 6

$$\begin{array}{r|rrrr} 5 & 1 & -6 & -1 & 32 \\ & & 5 & -5 & -30 \\ \hline & 1 & -1 & -6 & 2 \\ & \downarrow & \downarrow & \downarrow & \downarrow \end{array}$$

$$x^2 - x - 6 \quad \text{R2}$$

Now, write the quotient. Begin writing the quotient with a power of x that is one less than the greatest power of x in the dividend.

The quotient has remainder 2, so
$(x^3 - 6x^2 - x + 32) \div (x - 5) = x^2 - x - 6 + \dfrac{2}{x - 5}.$ ■

Example 3 Divide $2x^4 + 9x^3 - 7x + 36$ by $x + 4$.

Solution The divisor is $x + 4$. To get the form $x - k$, write $x + 4 = x - (-4)$ so $k = -4$. The dividend is missing an x^2 term, so use 0 for the coefficient.

Step 1

$$\begin{array}{r|rrrrr} -4 & 2 & 9 & 0 & -7 & 36 \\ \hline & & & & & \end{array}$$

Put the value for k in the box and put the coefficients to the right of it.

Step 2

$$\begin{array}{r|rrrrr} -4 & 2 & 9 & 0 & -7 & 36 \\ & & -8 & & & \\ \hline & 2 & & & & \end{array}$$

Bring down the first coefficient, 2, then multiply by -4 and put the result in the next column.

Step 3

$$\begin{array}{r|rrrrr} -4 & 2 & 9 & 0 & -7 & 36 \\ & & -8 & -4 & & \\ \hline & 2 & 1 & & & \end{array}$$

Add 9 and -8, then multiply the sum, 1, by -4 and put the result in the next column.

Step 4

$$\begin{array}{r|rrrrr} -4 & 2 & 9 & 0 & -7 & 36 \\ & & -8 & -4 & 16 & \\ \hline & 2 & 1 & -4 & & \end{array}$$

Add 0 and -4, then multiply the sum, -4, by -4 and put the product in the next column.

Step 5

$$\begin{array}{r|rrrrr} -4 & 2 & 9 & 0 & -7 & 36 \\ & & -8 & -4 & 16 & -36 \\ \hline & 2 & 1 & -4 & 9 & \end{array}$$

Add -7 and 16, then multiply the sum, 9, by -4 and put the product in the next column.

Step 6

$$\begin{array}{r|rrrrr} -4 & 2 & 9 & 0 & -7 & 36 \\ & & -8 & -4 & 16 & -36 \\ \hline & 2 & 1 & -4 & 9 & 0 \end{array}$$

Add 36 and -36. The sum, 0, is your remainder.

Step 7

$$\begin{array}{r|rrrrr} -4 & 2 & 9 & 0 & -7 & 36 \\ & & -8 & -4 & 16 & -36 \\ \hline & 2 & 1 & -4 & 9 & 0 \\ & \downarrow & \downarrow & \downarrow & \downarrow & \downarrow \end{array}$$

$$2x^3 + x^2 - 4x + 9 \quad \text{R0}$$

Now, write the quotient. Begin writing the quotient with a power of x that is one less than the greatest power of x in the dividend.

The quotient has no remainder, so
$(2x^4 + 9x^3 - 7x + 36) \div (x + 4) = 2x^3 + x^2 - 4x + 9.$ ∎

Dividing Polynomials Using Synthetic Division when the Given Divisor Is Not in the Form $x - k$

Example 4 Divide $4y^3 - 5y - 10$ by $2y - 3$.

Solution To use synthetic division, you must have a divisor in the form $x - k$. Rewrite the division problem by factoring 2 from the divisor and the dividend.

$$\frac{4y^3 - 5y - 10}{2y - 3} = \frac{2\left(2y^3 - \frac{5}{2}y - 5\right)}{2\left(y - \frac{3}{2}\right)} = \frac{2y^3 - \frac{5}{2}y - 5}{y - \frac{3}{2}}$$

The dividend is now $2y^3 - \frac{5}{2}y - 5$ and the divisor is $y - \frac{3}{2}$, so $k = \frac{3}{2}$. The dividend is missing a y^2 term, so use 0 for the coefficient.

Step 1

$$\begin{array}{r|rrrr} \frac{3}{2} & 2 & 0 & -\frac{5}{2} & -5 \\ & & & & \\ \hline & & & & \end{array}$$

Put the value for k in the box and put the coefficients to the right of it.

Step 2

$$\begin{array}{r|rrrr} \frac{3}{2} & 2 & 0 & -\frac{5}{2} & -5 \\ & & 3 & & \\ \hline & 2 & & & \end{array}$$

Bring down the first coefficient, 2, then multiply by $\frac{3}{2}$ and put the result in the next column.

Step 3

$$\begin{array}{r|rrrr} \frac{3}{2} & 2 & 0 & -\frac{5}{2} & -5 \\ & & 3 & \frac{9}{2} & \\ \hline & 2 & 3 & & \end{array}$$

Add 0 and 3, then multiply the sum, 3, by $\frac{3}{2}$ and put the result in the next column.

Step 4 $\frac{3}{2}\rfloor$ 2 0 $-\frac{5}{2}$ -5 Add $-\frac{5}{2}$ and $\frac{9}{2}$, then multiply the sum,

 3 $\frac{9}{2}$ 3   2, by $\frac{3}{2}$ and put the product in the next

 2 3 2   column.

Step 5 $\frac{3}{2}\rfloor$ 2 0 $-\frac{5}{2}$ -5 Add -5 and 3. The sum, -2, is your

 3 $\frac{9}{2}$ 3   remainder.

 2 3 2 -2

Step 6 $\frac{3}{2}\rfloor$ 2 0 $-\frac{5}{2}$ -5 Now, write the quotient. Begin writing

 3 $\frac{9}{2}$ 3   the quotient with a power of x that is one

 2 3 2 -2 less than the greatest power of x in the

$\downarrow\ \downarrow\ \downarrow\ \downarrow$ dividend.

$2y^2 + 3y + 2 \ \text{R}{-2}$

The quotient has a remainder of -2,

so $(4y^3 - 5y - 10) \div (2y - 3) = 2y^2 + 3y + 2 - \dfrac{2}{y - \frac{3}{2}}$, or

$2y^2 + 3y + 2 - \dfrac{4}{2y - 3}$. ∎

> **REMEMBER**
>
> To simplify a compound fraction, multiply the numerator and denominator by their least common denominator:
>
> $$\dfrac{2}{y - \frac{3}{2}} = \dfrac{2 \cdot 2}{2 \cdot \left(y - \frac{3}{2}\right)} = \dfrac{4}{2y - 3}.$$

Problem Set

Divide using synthetic division.

1. $(4a^2 + 11a + 6) \div (a + 2)$

2. $(x^2 + 9x + 25) \div (x + 5)$

3. $(2v^2 - 9v - 35) \div (v - 7)$

4. $(3y^2 - 7y - 1) \div (y - 2)$

5. $(w^2 - 4w - 45) \div (w + 5)$

6. $(5x^2 + 32x + 7) \div (x + 6)$

7. $(7x^2 - 69x + 54) \div (x - 9)$

8. $(t^2 + 6t - 20) \div (t + 9)$

9. $(12a^3 + 7a) \div (a + 4)$

10. $(2x^4 - 4x^2 + 7x + 3) \div (x + 3)$

11. $(q^4 + 6q^3 - 27q + 20) \div (q + 4)$

12. $(3x^4 - 2x^3 - 13x^2 - 16) \div (x - 2)$

13. $(2m^4 + m^3 + 6m - 9) \div (m - 1)$

14. $(4x^4 + 3x^3 + 3x^2 - 1) \div (x + 1)$

15. $(2b^2 + 10b + 2) \div (2b + 2)$

16. $(8y^2 - 18y - 12) \div (2y - 4)$

17. $(x^2 - 4x - 24) \div (2x - 8)$

18. $(9r^2 - 33r - 4) \div (3r - 4)$

19. $(5f^2 + 10f - 6) \div (5f + 2)$

20. $(6x^2 - 6x + 1) \div (3x - 1)$

21. $(9h^2 + 12h + 4) \div (3h + 6)$

22. $(9x^2 - 3x - 56) \div (3x + 7)$

23. $(6x^3 + 12x + 4) \div (3x + 6)$

24. $(20g^4 - 24g - 10) \div (4g - 4)$

25. $(15n^4 + n^3 - n^2 - 8n + 3) \div (5n - 3)$

26. $(10x^4 + 27x^3 + 13x^2 + 16x - 15) \div (2x + 5)$

Solve.

*27. **Challenge** Use synthetic division to divide $x^5 + 1$ by $x + 1$.

*28. **Challenge** The area of a triangle is given by $x^3 - 6x^2 - 16x$. Find an expression for the base of the triangle if the height is given by $x - 8$.

The Polynomial Remainder Theorem

You can use the polynomial remainder theorem to evaluate a polynomial function.

THE POLYNOMIAL REMAINDER THEOREM

If a polynomial $p(x)$ is divided by $x - a$, then the remainder is $p(a)$.

$$p(x) = q(x) \cdot (x - a) + p(a)$$

dividend = quotient $\cdot$ divisor + remainder

To prove this theorem, recall that you can check a quotient by using multiplication:

Dividend = Quotient $\cdot$ Divisor + Remainder

Let $p(x)$ represent the dividend, $q(x)$ represent the quotient, and $r(x)$ represent the remainder. If $x - a$ is the divisor, then the formula above can be written as follows:

$$p(x) = q(x) \cdot (x - a) + r(x)$$

Now substitute a for x.

$$p(a) = q(a) \cdot (a - a) + r(a) \qquad \text{Substitution}$$
$$p(a) = q(a) \cdot 0 + r(a) \qquad\qquad a - a = 0$$
$$p(a) = r(a) \qquad\qquad\qquad\quad \text{Zero Property of Multiplication}$$

Therefore, the remainder is the value of the polynomial evaluated for a.

Evaluating a Polynomial

Sometimes synthetic division is an easier and quicker method to evaluate a polynomial, especially when a calculator is not readily available.

Example 1   Given $f(x) = x^4 - 3x^3 + x^2 - 1$, find $f(-2)$.

Solution

Method 1	Method 2

Method 1

Use the remainder theorem.

Divide $x^4 - 3x^3 + x^2 - 1$ by $x + 2$.

$$\begin{array}{r|rrrrr} -2| & 1 & -3 & 1 & 0 & -1 \\ & & -2 & 10 & -22 & 44 \\ \hline & 1 & -5 & 11 & -22 & 43 \end{array}$$

The remainder is 43.

So $f(-2) = 43$. ■

Method 2

Substitute -2 for x in $f(x)$.

$$f(x) = x^4 - 3x^3 + x^2 - 1$$
$$f(-2) = (-2)^4 - 3 \cdot (-2)^3 + (-2)^2 - 1$$
$$= 16 - 3 \cdot (-8) + 4 - 1$$
$$= 16 + 24 + 4 - 1$$
$$= 43$$

Using the Remainder Theorem to Graph a Polynomial

Example 2 Graph each function by using the remainder theorem.

A $f(x) = x^2 - 4x - 1$

Solution Use synthetic division repeatedly to find and plot ordered pairs.

Organize your work in a table. List the coefficients of the dividend at the top. Perform the steps mentally and write only the numbers that appear in the bottom row. Plot each pair $(a, f(a))$.

	1	−4	−1
−1	1	−5	4
0	1	−4	−1
1	1	−3	−4
2	1	−2	−5
3	1	−1	−4
4	1	0	−1
5	1	1	4

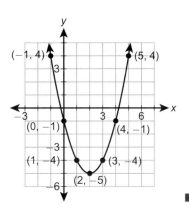

■

B $g(x) = x^3 - 5x^2 + 6x + 4$

Solution Use synthetic division repeatedly to find and plot ordered pairs.

	1	−5	6	4
−1	1	−6	12	−8
0	1	−5	6	4
1	1	−4	2	6
2	1	−3	0	4
3	1	−2	0	4
4	1	−1	2	12

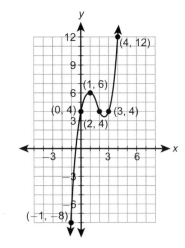

■

Application: Projectile Motion

Example 3 A baseball is hit straight up into the air with an initial velocity of 20 meters per second. The height of the baseball after t seconds is modeled by the polynomial function $h(t) = -9.8t^2 + 20t + 1$, where $h(t)$ is the height in meters (neglecting air resistance). What is the height of the baseball after 1.5 seconds?

Solution The height of the baseball in meters after t seconds is $h(t)$. So, to find the height of the baseball after 1.5 seconds, find $h(1.5)$.

Method 1

Use the remainder theorem. Divide $-9.8t^2 + 20t + 1$ by $t - 1.5$, using synthetic division.

$$
\begin{array}{r|rrr}
1.5 & -9.8 & 20 & 1 \\
 & & -14.7 & 7.95 \\
\hline
 & -9.8 & 5.3 & 8.95
\end{array}
$$

The remainder is 8.95, so $h(1.5) = 8.95$.

Method 2

Substitute 1.5 for t in $h(t)$.

$$h(t) = -9.8t^2 + 20t + 1$$
$$h(1.5) = -9.8 \cdot 1.5^2 + 20 \cdot 1.5 + 3$$
$$= -9.8 \cdot 2.25 + 20 \cdot 1.5 + 3$$
$$= 8.95$$

TIP

You can use one method to solve the problem and the other method to check your answer.

The height of the baseball after 1.5 seconds is 8.95 meters. ■

Problem Set

Use the polynomial remainder theorem to evaluate the polynomial for the given value.

1. $f(x) = 3x^3 - 2x^2 - 3x + 18; f(1)$

2. $a(r) = 8r^3 - r^2 + 4r + 6; a(2)$

3. $f(x) = 3x^2 + 2x + 3; f(-3)$

4. $h(t) = t^2 + 3t - 9; h(3)$

5. $f(x) = x^3 + x^2 - 2x - 5; f(-5)$

6. $g(v) = 2v^2 - 7v - 19; g(7)$

7. $f(x) = x^3 - 4x^2 - 12x + 15; f(6)$

8. $r(z) = 2z^4 - 9z - 3; r(3)$

9. $f(x) = 2x^4 + 3x^3 - 12x^2 - 2x + 1; f(-2)$

10. $P(y) = y^4 + 3y^3 - 7y^2 - 7y + 21; P(4)$

For each problem, do the following:
A. Use the polynomial remainder theorem to find at least four ordered pairs for each polynomial.
B. Use the points to graph the polynomial.

11. $f(x) = 2x^2 + 3x - 2$

12. $f(x) = x^2 - 4x - 1$

13. $b(n) = n^3 + 3n^2 - 4n + 1$

14. $S(y) = 4y^2 + 3y + 5$

15. $f(x) = 2x^3 - 4x^2 + 7x + 1$

16. $f(a) = -2a^3 - 3a^2 - 11x + 2$

17. $f(x) = x^3 + 2x^2 - 5x - 3$

18. $f(x) = \frac{1}{4}x^4 - 3x^2 + \frac{1}{2}x + 1$

19. $g(x) = -x^4 - x^3 - 5x + 10$

20. $f(x) = x^4 + x^3 - 9x^2 + 8$

21. $h(t) = t^3 + 8t^2 + 10t - 2$

Challenge

*22. $k(t) = 2t^4 - 8t + 3$

*23. $f(x) = 2x^4 - 10x^2 - 5x + 17$

Solve.

24. A tennis ball is thrown straight up into the air with an initial velocity of 20 feet per second. The height of the tennis ball after t seconds is modeled by the polynomial function $h(t) = -16t^2 + 20t + 5$, where $h(t)$ is the height in feet (ignoring air resistance). What is the height of the tennis ball after 0.5 seconds?

25. The temperature of a city for January can be modeled by the polynomial function $T(x) = 0.01x^3 - 0.49x^2 + 6.8x + 2$, where x is the day of the month. What is the temperature of the city on January 15?

26. The polynomial function, $f(x) = 0.3x^4 - 9x^3 + 85x^2 - 252x + 260$, models the amount of fish caught and sold by commercial fisherman in thousands of metric tons, where x is the month of the year. What is the amount of fish caught and sold for the month of June?

27. The distance (km) from an earthquake's epicenter that a seismic wave can be felt, x minutes after the earthquake occurs, can be modeled by the polynomial function $f(x) = 0.7x^4 - 17x^3 + 160x^2 - 21x + 293$. What is the distance of a seismic wave 8 minutes after the earthquake occurs?

*28. **Challenge** A soccer ball is kicked into the air with an initial upward velocity of 25 meters per second and a horizontal velocity of 15 meters per second. The height of the soccer ball after t seconds is modeled by the polynomial function $h(t) = -9.8t^2 + 25t$, where $h(t)$ is the height in meters (ignoring air resistance). The distance traveled by the soccer ball after t seconds is modeled by the function $d(t) = 15t$. What is the height of the soccer ball if it has traveled a horizontal distance of 37.5 meters?

Factors and Rational Roots

Synthetic division can help you factor polynomials.

> ## THE FACTOR THEOREM
>
> For any polynomial $p(x)$, the binomial $x - a$ is a factor of $p(x)$ if and only if $p(a) = 0$.

The remainder theorem is used to prove the factor theorem.

For the proof, use $p(x)$ for the dividend, $q(x)$ for the quotient, and $r(x)$ for the remainder. Therefore, $p(x) = q(x) \cdot (x - a) + r(x)$.

Because the theorem uses *if and only if*, there are two cases.

Case 1: Assume $p(a) = 0$. Then by the remainder theorem, $r(a) = 0$. Because the quotient does not have a remainder, $x - a$ is a factor of the dividend.

Case 2: Assume $x - a$ is a factor. Then the remainder $r(a)$ equals 0. By the remainder theorem, $r(a) = p(a)$, and $0 = p(a)$ by substitution.

Using the Factor Theorem

So what does the factor theorem mean? It means that if you evaluate a polynomial for some value of x and the result is zero, then you can use that value to factor the polynomial.

Example 1 Determine whether $x + 3$ is a factor of $f(x) = 2x^4 + 2x^3 - 11x^2 + x - 6$.

Solution Since $x + 3 = x - (-3)$, $a = -3$. So find $f(-3)$.

$$f(-3) = 2(-3)^4 + 2(-3)^3 - 11(-3)^2 + (-3) - 6$$
$$= 2 \cdot 81 + 2 \cdot (-27) - 11 \cdot 9 - 3 - 6$$
$$= 162 - 54 - 99 - 3 - 6$$
$$= 0$$

Since $f(-3) = 0$, $x + 3$ is a factor of $f(x) = 2x^4 + 2x^3 - 11x^2 + x - 6$. ∎

For any polynomial function $p(x)$, a solution of the equation $p(x) = 0$ is called a *zero* or *root* of $p(x)$. In Example 1, you could say that -3 is a zero of $p(x)$.

Example 2   Factor the polynomial $f(x) = x^3 - 19x - 30$, given that $x = 5$ is a zero.

Solution

Step 1   If $x = 5$ is a zero, then $x - 5$ is a factor. Use synthetic division to divide $x^3 - 19x - 30$ by $x - 5$.

$$
\begin{array}{r|rrrr}
5 & 1 & 0 & -19 & -30 \\
  &   & 5 & 25 & 30 \\
\hline
  & 1 & 5 & 6   & 0
\end{array}
$$

Step 2   Write the polynomial as a product of $x - 5$ and the quotient from Step 1. Then factor the quotient.

$$x^3 - 19x - 30 = (x - 5)(x^2 + 5x + 6)$$
$$= (x - 5)(x + 3)(x + 2)$$

So $f(x) = x^3 - 19x - 30 = (x - 5)(x + 3)(x + 2)$. ∎

Example 3   Find all the roots of $x^3 - 19x - 30 = 0$.

Solution   By the factor theorem, if $x - a$ is a factor of $f(x)$, then $f(a) = 0$.

Example 2 shows that $x^3 - 19x - 30 = (x - 5)(x + 3)(x + 2)$.

$(x - 5)$ is a factor of $f(x) = x^3 - 19x - 30$, so $f(5) = 0$.

$(x + 3)$ is a factor of $f(x) = x^3 - 19x - 30$, so $f(-3) = 0$.

$(x + 2)$ is a factor of $f(x) = x^3 - 19x - 30$, so $f(-2) = 0$.

Therefore 5, -3, and -2 are the roots of $x^3 - 19x - 30 = 0$. ∎

> **REMEMBER**
>
> A number that satisfies an equation is called a root, or solution, of the equation.

Finding Possible Rational Roots

It's easy to find all the roots if you are given a head start, but what if you aren't given any of the roots? How can you find all the roots on your own? The rational root theorem can give you a set of values to try.

> **THE RATIONAL ROOT THEOREM**
>
> If $\dfrac{p}{q}$ is in simplest form and is a rational root of the polynomial equation
> $a_n x^n + a_{n-1} x^{n-1} + \ldots + a_1 x + a_0 = 0$ with integer coefficients, then p
> must be a factor of a_0 and q must be a factor of a_n.

> **REMEMBER**
>
> A rational number is a real number that can be written as a quotient of two integers.

Example 4   Find the possible rational roots of each equation.

Ⓐ $2x^3 + 16x^2 + 19x + 5 = 0$

Solution   If $\dfrac{p}{q}$ is a rational root of the polynomial $2x^3 + 16x^2 + 19x + 5$, then p is a factor of the constant term, 5, and q is a factor of the leading coefficient, 2. List the factors of 5 and the factors of 2.

The factors of 5 are ± 1 and ± 5.
The factors of 2 are ± 1 and ± 2.

The possible roots are $\dfrac{p}{q}$ are $\pm\dfrac{1}{1}, \pm\dfrac{1}{2}, \pm\dfrac{5}{1}$, and $\pm\dfrac{5}{2}$.

Simplifying gives the following possible rational roots of $2x^3 + 16x^2 + 19x + 5 = 0$: $\pm 1, \pm\dfrac{1}{2}, \pm 5$, and $\pm\dfrac{5}{2}$. ∎

Ⓑ $3x^3 - 11x^2 + 20x - 9 = 0$

Solution   If $\dfrac{p}{q}$ is a rational root of the polynomial $3x^3 - 11x^2 + 20x - 9$, then p is a factor of the constant term, -9, and q is a factor of the leading coefficient, 3. List the factors of -9 and the factors of 3.

The factors of -9 are $\pm 1, \pm 3$, and ± 9.
The factors of 3 are ± 1 and ± 3.

The possible roots $\dfrac{p}{q}$ are $\pm\dfrac{1}{1}, \pm\dfrac{1}{3}, \pm\dfrac{3}{1}, \pm\dfrac{3}{3}, \pm\dfrac{9}{1}$, and $\pm\dfrac{9}{3}$.

Simplifying gives the following possible rational roots of $3x^3 - 11x^2 + 20x - 9 = 0$: $\pm 1, \pm\dfrac{1}{3}, \pm 3$, and ± 9. ∎

Using the Rational Root Theorem to Factor a Polynomial Equation

Example 5   Factor completely.

Ⓐ $x^3 - x^2 - 10x - 8 = 0$

Solution   Identify the possible rational roots: $\pm 1, \pm 2, \pm 4$, and ± 8.

Test for possible roots.

$$\begin{array}{r|rrrr}
-1 & 1 & -1 & -10 & -8 \\
   &   & -1 & 2 & 8 \\
\hline
   & 1 & -2 & -8 & 0
\end{array}$$

Because -1 is a root, $(x + 1)$ is a factor. The other factor is $x^2 - 2x - 8$, which factors into $(x - 4)(x + 2)$.

The factored form is $(x + 1)(x - 4)(x + 2) = 0$. ∎

> **TIP**
> You may need to test several roots before finding one that makes the remainder 0. Test easier numbers such as -1 and 1 before testing larger numbers and fractions.

B $x^3 - 3x^2 - 5x + 15 = 0$

Solution Identify the possible rational roots: ± 1, ± 3, ± 5, and ± 15.

Test for possible roots.

	1	−3	−5	15
1	1	−2	−7	8
−1	1	−4	−1	16
3	1	0	−5	0

TIP

Organize your work in a table. List the coefficients of the polynomial at the top. Perform the steps mentally and write only the numbers that appear in the bottom row.

Because 3 is the first possible root with a remainder of 0, $(x - 3)$ is a factor. The other factor is $x^2 - 5$. Solve $x^2 - 5 = 0$ to find the other roots.

$$x^2 - 5 = 0$$
$$x^2 = 5$$
$$x = \pm\sqrt{5}$$

The factored form is $(x - 3)(x + \sqrt{5})(x - \sqrt{5}) = 0$. ∎

C $3x^3 + x^2 - 38x + 24 = 0$

Solution The possible rational roots are $\pm\frac{1}{3}$, $\pm\frac{2}{3}$, ± 1, $\pm\frac{4}{3}$, ± 2, $\pm\frac{8}{3}$, ± 3, ± 4, ± 6, ± 8, ± 12, and ± 24.

	3	1	−38	24
1	3	4	−34	−10
−1	3	−2	−36	54
2	3	7	−24	−24
−2	3	−5	−28	80
$\frac{2}{3}$	3	3	−36	0

Testing the possible roots by synthetic division reveals that $\frac{2}{3}$ is a root. So $\left(x - \frac{2}{3}\right)$ is a factor. The other factor is $3x^2 + 3x - 36$, which factors into $3(x + 4)(x - 3)$.

The factored form is $3\left(x - \frac{2}{3}\right)(x + 4)(x - 3) = 0$, which can also be written as $(3x - 2)(x + 4)(x - 3) = 0$. ∎

Problem Set

Determine whether the given binomial expression is a factor of $f(x)$.

1. $x + 1$
$f(x) = x^3 + 5x^2 + 8x + 4$

2. $x - 2$
$f(x) = x^4 - 2x^3 + 5x^2 - 12x + 4$

3. $x + 5$
$f(x) = 5x^3 - 9x^2 + 17x - 13$

4. $x - 3$
$f(x) = x^4 + 5x^3 - x^2 - 26$

5. $x + 3$
$f(x) = x^3 + 12x^2 + 18x - 27$

6. $x + 2$
$f(x) = 2x^3 + 13x^2 - 8x - 9$

7. $x - 5$
$f(x) = x^4 - 4x^3 - 6x^2 + 4x + 5$

8. $x + 2$
$f(x) = 2x^4 + 12x^3 + 8x^2 - 5x - 10$

Factor the polynomial equation with the given zero.

9. $x^3 + 2x^2 - x - 2 = 0$; $x = -2$ is a zero

10. $x^3 - 7x^2 + 7x + 15 = 0$; $x = 5$ is a zero

11. $x^3 + 9x^2 + 11x - 21 = 0$; $x = -3$ is a zero

12. $x^4 + 2x^3 - 15x^2 + 4x + 20 = 0$; $x = 2$ is a zero

Find the roots of the polynomial equation.

13. $x^3 - x^2 - 4x + 4 = (x - 1)(x + 2)(x - 2) = 0$

14. $x^3 + 6x^2 + 9x + 4 = (x + 4)(x + 1)(x + 1) = 0$

15. $x^3 - 3x^2 - 4x + 12 = (x - 2)(x + 2)(x - 3) = 0$

16. $2x^3 + 21x^2 + 22x - 45 = (2x + 5)(x + 9)(x - 1) = 0$

Find the *possible* rational roots of the polynomial equation.

17. $6x^3 - 10x^2 + x - 11 = 0$

18. $9x^3 + 2x^2 + 2x - 21 = 0$

19. $4x^3 - 5x^2 + 7x + 28 = 0$

20. $16x^4 + 5x^2 - 7x + 4 = 0$

21. $3x^4 - 3x^3 + 7x^2 - 15 = 0$

22. $3x^4 + 2x^3 - 7x^2 + 2x + 12 = 0$

Factor completely.

23. $x^2 - 7x + 6 = 0$

24. $x^3 + x^2 - 4x - 4 = 0$

25. $x^3 + x^2 - 3x - 3 = 0$

26. $x^3 + 3x^2 - 7x - 21 = 0$

27. $5x^3 + 4x^2 - 31x + 6 = 0$

28. $7x^3 - 30x^2 - 27x + 10 = 0$

*29. **Challenge** $x^3 + 2x^2 + 9x + 18 = 0$

Solve.

*30. **Challenge** The rectangular prism shown has a volume of 6 cubic inches.

    A. Write an equation for the volume of the prism.

    B. Find the possible rational roots of the equation.

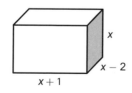

x

$x - 2$

$x + 1$

Graphing Polynomials

Because any root of $f(x) = 0$ is also an x-intercept of the graph of $f(x)$, you can determine the roots of a polynomial equation from its graph.

Using a Graph to Determine the Roots of a Polynomial Equation

Example 1

Ⓐ Find the roots of $x^2 + 4x - 21 = 0$.

Solution   The graph of $f(x) = x^2 + 4x - 21$ appears to intersect the x-axis at $(3, 0)$ and $(-7, 0)$, which means that 3 and -7 seem to be roots, both of which are consistent with the possible rational roots according to the rational root theorem.

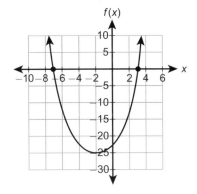

Check   Find $f(3)$ and $f(-7)$ to check your answer.

$$f(3) = 3^2 + 4 \cdot 3 - 21 \qquad f(-7) = (-7)^2 + 4 \cdot (-7) - 21$$
$$= 9 + 12 - 21 \qquad\qquad = 49 - 28 - 21$$
$$= 0 \checkmark \qquad\qquad\qquad = 0 \checkmark$$

Since $f(3) = 0$ and $f(-7) = 0$, 3 and -7 are the roots of $x^2 + 4x - 21 = 0$. ■

Ⓑ Find the roots of $x^3 - 4x^2 + x + 6 = 0$.

Solution   The graph of $f(x) = x^3 - 4x^2 + x + 6$ appears to intersect the x-axis at $(-1, 0)$, $(2, 0)$, and $(3, 0)$, which means that -1, 2, and 3 seem to be roots, all of which are consistent with the possible rational roots according to the rational root theorem.

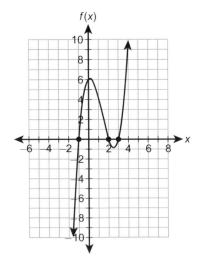

Check   You can check your answer by factoring. Use any one of the roots obtained from the graph and turn it into a factor: $x - (-1) = x + 1$. Use synthetic division to divide.

```
−1| 1  −4   1    6
        −1   5   −6
    1  −5   6    0
```

Use the quotient to write the polynomial as a product of factors:

$$x^3 - 4x^2 + x + 6 = (x + 1)(x^2 - 5x + 6)$$
$$= (x + 1)(x - 2)(x - 3) \checkmark$$

The factors show that the roots are -1, 2, and 3. ■

Graphing a Polynomial Function by Using Intercepts

You can draw the graph of a function by finding its x-intercepts and incorporating what you know about the end behavior of power functions.

Example 2   Draw the graph of $f(x) = x^4 - 3x^3 - 11x^2 + 3x + 10$.

Solution

Step 1   Use the rational root theorem to find the possible rational roots of $f(x) = 0$. The leading coefficient is 1 and the constant term is 10, so the possible rational roots are ± 1, ± 2, ± 5, and ± 10.

Step 2   Use synthetic division to test the possible roots.

$$\begin{array}{r|rrrrr} 1\!| & 1 & -3 & -11 & 3 & 10 \\ & & 1 & -2 & -13 & -10 \\ \hline & 1 & -2 & -13 & -10 & 0 \end{array}$$

Since 1 is a root, $x - 1$ is a factor. You can write the polynomial as $(x - 1)(x^3 - 2x^2 - 13x - 10)$.

Now use synthetic division to find a factor of the cubic polynomial $x^3 - 2x^2 - 13x - 10$. The leading coefficient is 1 and the constant term is -10, so the possible rational roots are ± 1, ± 2, ± 5, and ± 10.

$$\begin{array}{r|rrrr} -1\!| & 1 & -2 & -13 & -10 \\ & & -1 & 3 & 10 \\ \hline & 1 & -3 & -10 & 0 \end{array}$$

Since -1 is a root, $x + 1$ is a factor. Now you can write the polynomial as $(x - 1)(x + 1)(x^2 - 3x - 10)$.

Step 3   You could continue to use synthetic division to find the factors of the quadratic polynomial, but factoring it into two binomials is quicker. The function in factored form is $f(x) = (x - 1)(x + 1)(x - 5)(x + 2)$. The x-intercepts, then, are 1, -1, 5, and -2. Plot the x-intercepts.

Step 4   Graph the polynomial. Because the function is a polynomial with even degree and a positive leading coefficient, the graph approaches positive infinity as x approaches both negative and positive infinity. Use synthetic division to find additional points.

> **TIP**
>
> Note that there are an infinite number of polynomials with these four roots. These polynomials all have the form $f(x) = a(x - 1)(x + 1)(x - 5)(x + 2)$. When you find another point, you can determine a by substituting for x and $f(x)$ in the equation.

	1	-3	-11	3	10
-1.5	1	-4.5	-4.25	9.375	-4.0625
0	1	-3	-11	3	10
2	1	-1	-3	-23	-36
4	1	1	-7	-25	-90

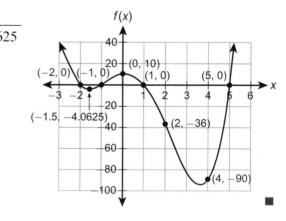

Graphing a Polynomial Function by Using Roots

Example 3   Draw the graph of $p(x) = x^3 - x^2 - 5x + 2$.

Solution

Step 1   Use the rational root theorem to find the possible rational roots of $p(x) = 0$. The leading coefficient is 1 and the constant term is 2, so the possible rational roots are ± 1 and ± 2.

Step 2   Test the possible rational roots until you find a root of the polynomial.

$$
\begin{array}{r|rrrr}
 & 1 & -1 & -5 & 2 \\
\hline
-1 & 1 & -2 & -3 & 5 \\
1 & 1 & 0 & -5 & -3 \\
-2 & 1 & -3 & 1 & 0 \\
\end{array}
$$

Since -2 is a root, $x + 2$ is a factor. You can write the polynomial as $(x + 2)(x^2 - 3x + 1)$.

Step 3   Use the quadratic formula to solve $x^2 - 3x + 1 = 0$ and find the remaining two irrational roots.

$$x = \frac{3 \pm \sqrt{(-3)^2 - 4 \cdot 1 \cdot 1}}{2 \cdot 1}$$

$$x = \frac{3 \pm \sqrt{5}}{2}$$

So the roots of the polynomial are -2, $\dfrac{3 + \sqrt{5}}{2}$, and $\dfrac{3 - \sqrt{5}}{2}$.

Step 4   Graph the polynomial. First, plot the x-intercepts, which are -2, $\dfrac{3 + \sqrt{5}}{2} \approx 2.62$, and $\dfrac{3 - \sqrt{5}}{2} \approx 0.38$.

The function is cubic, so it is S-shaped. Because the function is a polynomial with odd degree and has a positive leading coefficient, the graph approaches negative infinity as x approaches negative infinity, and the graph approaches positive infinity as x approaches positive infinity.

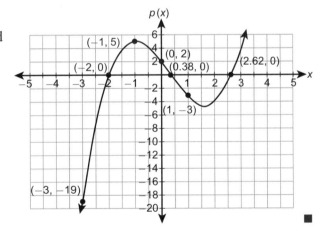

Find and plot a few additional points.

x	-3	-1	0	1
$p(x)$	-19	5	2	-3

Problem Set

Find the roots of the polynomial function.

1. $f(x) = x^2 + x - 30$

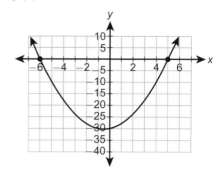

4. $g(x) = x^3 - 2x^2 - 5x + 6$

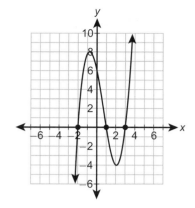

2. $f(x) = -x^2 + 4$

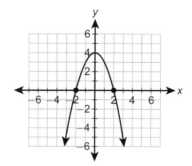

5. $h(x) = -x^3 + 9x^2 - 23x + 15$

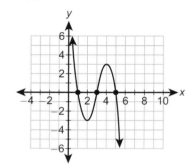

3. $g(x) = 2x^2 + 8x + 6$

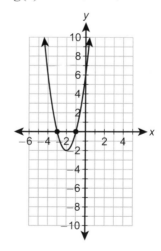

6. $p(x) = 2x^3 + 4x^2 - 10x - 12$

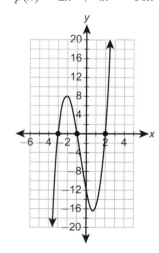

Describe the end behavior of the function.

7. $h(x) = 2x^2 - 7x + 2$

8. $f(x) = -x^4 - 2x^3 - 18x + 9$

9. $p(x) = 6x^3 + x - 12$

10. $f(x) = 5x^4 + 11x^2 + 8x - 9$

11. $f(x) = -2x^5 + 7x^3 + 7x^2 + 7x + 7$

12. $g(x) = x^5 - 3x^3 - 2x^2 + x$

13. $h(x) = -12x^8 + 17x^3 - 3x + 11$

14. $f(x) = 4x^3 + 1.2x - \sqrt{2}$

Graph the polynomial function by using its intercepts.

15. $p(x) = x^3 - 2x^2 - 11x + 12$

16. $f(x) = x^4 - 7x^2 + 10$

17. $g(x) = -x^3 - 8x^2 - 19x - 12$

18. $f(x) = x^4 - 5x^3 - 13x^2 + 77x - 60$

19. $h(x) = x^5 + x$

20. $h(x) = x^3 + 2x^2 - 16x - 32$

21. $f(x) = x^3 + 2x^2 - x - 2$

22. $g(x) = -x^3 - 2x^2 + 3x + 6$

23. $f(x) = x^4 - 4x^2 + 3$

24. $p(x) = x^4 - 5x^3 + 5x^2 + 5x - 6$

25. $f(x) = x^4 - 5x^2 + 4$

26. $h(x) = x^4 - 6x^3 + 7x^2 + 12x - 18$

27. $p(x) = -x^3 - 6x^2 - 3x + 10$

28. $f(x) = x^4 + 2x^3 - 9x^2 - 2x + 8$

29. $f(x) = -x^4 + 9x^2 - 18$

Answer the question.

*__30.__ **Challenge** Describe the degree and the leading coefficient of the function whose graph is shown below.

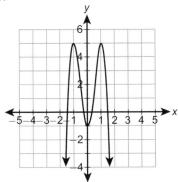

Factoring Polynomials Completely

Every polynomial of degree $n > 0$ can be written as the product of n linear factors.

Factoring a Binomial Over the Set of Complex Numbers

Example 1   Write $x^2 + 25$ as the product of two linear factors.

Solution   The equation $x^2 + 25 = 0$ is equivalent to the equation $x^2 = -25$, which has solutions $5i$ and $-5i$. Therefore, $x^2 + 25 = (x + 5i)(x - 5i)$. ∎

The polynomial in Example 1 has no real zeros, but it has two complex zeros. Some polynomials have both real zeros and complex zeros.

The Multiplicity of a Root

For a polynomial that has a linear factor appearing more than once, the idea of *multiplicity* is useful.

DEFINITION

For any polynomial $p(x)$, a root a of $p(x) = 0$ has **multiplicity** m if the factor $x - a$ occurs m times in the factorization of $p(x)$.

If a is a real root with odd multiplicity, the graph of the function crosses the x-axis at $x = a$. If a is a real root with even multiplicity, the graph of the function touches, but does not cross, the x-axis at $x = a$.

Example 2   Given that
$f(x) = x^4 - 5x^3 + x^2 + 21x - 18 = (x - 3)(x - 3)(x - 1)(x + 2)$:

A Find the multiplicity of each root of $f(x) = 0$.

Solution   The roots are 3, 3, 1, and -2. The root 3 occurs two times, so it has a multiplicity of 2. The roots 1 and -2 occur once, so each has a multiplicity of 1. ∎

B Describe the behavior of the graph at each root.

Solution   The graph of $f(x) = x^4 - 5x^3 + x^2 + 21x - 18$ shows the behavior of the function at its zeros. The graph crosses the x-axis at the roots of odd multiplicity: $x = 1$ and $x = -2$. The graph touches, but does not cross, the x-axis at the root of even multiplicity: $x = 3$. ∎

> **THINK ABOUT IT**
>
> Recall that the set of real numbers is a subset of the set of complex numbers. If a polynomial has both real zeros and complex zeros, then all of its zeros are complex. In fact, all the zeros of a polynomial are complex.

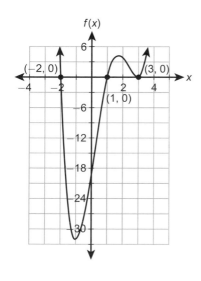

Finding the Number of Roots of a Polynomial Equation

> ### THE FUNDAMENTAL THEOREM OF ALGEBRA
>
> Every polynomial equation $p(x) = 0$ with degree n, $n > 0$, has at least one complex root.
>
> **Corollary**
> Every polynomial equation $p(x) = 0$ with degree n, $n > 0$, has n complex roots as long as any root with multiplicity m is counted m times.

Example 3 Find the number of complex roots of each equation.

A $x^5 + 3x^4 + x^2 + 1 = 0$

Solution The equation has degree 5, so there are five complex roots. ■

B $x - 3 = 0$

Solution The equation has degree 1, so there is one complex root. ■

Factoring a Polynomial Over the Set of Complex Numbers

> ### HOW TO FACTOR A POLYNOMIAL COMPLETELY OVER THE SET OF COMPLEX NUMBERS
>
> **Step 1** Use the degree of the polynomial to determine the total number of complex roots you need to find.
> **Step 2** Identify the possible rational roots.
> **Step 3** Find rational roots (using a graph, synthetic division, or other strategies) and use them to factor the polynomial.
> **Step 4** Factor the remaining polynomial.

Example 4 Factor each polynomial completely. Then sketch the graph.

A $f(x) = x^3 - 6x^2 + 10x - 8$

Solution

Step 1 The polynomial is of degree 3, so there are three complex roots.

Step 2 Use the rational root theorem to identify all possible rational roots. The leading coefficient is 1 and the constant is -8, so the possible rational roots are ± 1, ± 2, ± 4, and ± 8.

Step 3 Of the possible rational roots, only 4 is actually a root.

	1	-6	10	-8
1	1	-5	5	-3
-1	1	-7	17	-25
2	1	-4	2	-4
-2	1	-8	26	-60
4	1	-2	2	0

So $f(x) = (x - 4)(1x^2 - 2x + 2) = (x - 4)(x^2 - 2x + 2)$.

> **REMEMBER**
>
> All real numbers are complex numbers of the form $a + bi$, where $b = 0$. The real root 4 is also the complex root $4 + 0i$.

Step 4 Find the two remaining roots. Use the quadratic formula to solve $x^2 - 2x + 2 = 0$.

$$x = \frac{2 \pm \sqrt{(-2)^2 - 4 \cdot 1 \cdot 2}}{2 \cdot 1} = \frac{2 \pm \sqrt{-4}}{2}$$

$$= \frac{2 \pm 2i}{2}$$

$$= 1 \pm i$$

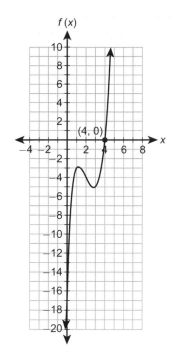

The roots $1 + i$ and $1 - i$ are complex. So the complete factorization of $f(x)$ is $f(x) = (x - 4)[x - (1 + i)][x - (1 - i)]$.

The roots of the equation $x^3 - 6x^2 + 10x - 8 = 0$ are 4, $1 + i$, and $1 - i$. In the graph of a function with both real roots and complex roots, only the real roots are x-intercepts. The graph of $f(x)$ shows that only the real root, 4, is an x-intercept. ∎

Ⓑ $f(x) = x^4 - 2x^3 - 3x^2 + 2x + 2$

Solution

Step 1 The polynomial is of degree 4, so there are four complex roots.

Step 2 By the rational root theorem, the possible rational roots are ± 1 and ± 2.

Step 3 Synthetic division shows -1 and 1 as roots.

$$
\begin{array}{r|rrrrr}
-1 & 1 & -2 & -3 & 2 & 2 \\
   &   & -1 & 3 & 0 & -2 \\
\hline
   & 1 & -3 & 0 & 2 & 0
\end{array}
\qquad
\begin{array}{r|rrrr}
1 & 1 & -3 & 0 & 2 \\
  &   & 1 & -2 & -2 \\
\hline
  & 1 & -2 & -2 & 0
\end{array}
$$

So $f(x) = (x + 1)(x - 1)(1x^2 - 2x - 2)$.

> **TIP**
>
> Use the quotient from the first synthetic division to set up the synthetic division for the next root. This will give you less work, as well as a quotient that is a quadratic.

Step 4 Find the two remaining roots. Use the quadratic formula to solve $x^2 - 2x - 2 = 0$.

$$x = \frac{2 \pm \sqrt{(-2)^2 - 4 \cdot 1(-2)}}{2 \cdot 1} = \frac{2 \pm \sqrt{12}}{2}$$

$$= \frac{2 \pm 2\sqrt{3}}{2}$$

$$= 1 \pm \sqrt{3}$$

The roots $1 + \sqrt{3}$ and $1 - \sqrt{3}$ are irrational.

The factorization of $f(x)$ is
$f(x) = (x + 1)(x - 1)[x - (1 + \sqrt{3})][x - (1 - \sqrt{3})]$.

Because all the roots are real, all four roots are x-intercepts, as shown in the graph. The irrational roots are approximately -0.73 and 2.73. ∎

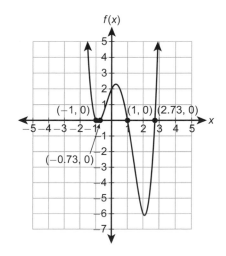

Problem Set

. . . .

Find the number of complex roots of the polynomial equation.

1. $x^6 + 5x^5 - 2x^4 - x^3 + 3x^2 - 2x + 2 = 0$

2. $x^5 - 4x^4 - 3x^3 - x^2 + 5x + 6 = 0$

3. $x^4 - 3x^2 - 11x - 8 = 0$

4. $x^7 + 5x^5 - 2x^3 - 1 = 0$

5. $2x + 2 = 0$

6. $5x^3 + 2x^2 - 12x + 7 = 0$

7. $-4x^{16} + x^8 + 7x^4 - 7x^2 + x + 4 = 0$

8. $3x^2 - 2x + 9 = 0$

Find the multiplicity of each root of $p(x) = 0$. Describe the behavior of the graph at each root.

9. $p(x) = x^4 - 2x^3 - 28x^2 - 46x - 21 = (x + 1)(x + 1)(x - 7)(x + 3)$

10. $p(x) = x^4 - 8x^2 + 16 = (x + 2)(x + 2)(x - 2)(x - 2)$

11. $p(x) = x^4 + 2x^3 - 13x^2 - 14x + 24 = (x - 1)(x + 2)(x - 3)(x + 4)$

12. $p(x) = x^4 - 12x^3 + 46x^2 - 60x + 25 = (x - 1)(x - 1)(x - 5)(x - 5)$

Find the number of real and rational roots of the polynomial equation.

13. $x^4 + x^3 - 7x^2 - x + 6 = 0$

14. $x^3 + 5x^2 - 2x - 10 = 0$

15. $x^3 - 6x^2 + 13x - 10 = 0$

16. $x^4 - 2x^3 + x^2 - 8x - 12 = 0$

Factor completely.

17. $g(x) = x^3 + 6x^2 - x - 30$

18. $f(x) = x^4 - 2x^3 - 15x^2 - 4x + 20$

19. $h(x) = 3x^3 + 26.5x^2 - 34x + 10$

20. $g(x) = x^3 - x^2 + 2$

21. $p(x) = x^4 - 2x^3 - 7x^2 + 18x - 18$

22. $h(x) = x^5 - 5x^4 + 12x^3 - 24x^2 + 32x - 16$

23. $f(x) = 3x^3 + 4x^2 - 7x + 2$

24. $f(x) = 3x^2 - x - 6$

25. $p(x) = -6x^2 + 4x + 5$

26. $f(x) = x^3 - 17.8x^2 + 83.6x - 56$

27. $g(x) = x^4 + 4x^3 + x^2 - 8x - 6$

*28. **Challenge** $f(x) = 3x^3 - 11x^2 + 116x + 40$

Applications: Polynomials

You can use polynomials to model and solve many types of real-world problems.

Application: Finance

Example 1   The daily closing price of a share of stock during one week can be modeled by $f(x) = x^3 - 9x^2 + 14x + 51$, where x is the day of the week. What was the stock's closing price on day 4?

Solution   You need to evaluate the polynomial for $x = 4$. Use synthetic division. The remainder is 27.

$$\begin{array}{r|rrrr} 4 & 1 & -9 & 14 & 51 \\ & & 4 & -20 & -24 \\ \hline & 1 & -5 & -6 & 27 \end{array}$$

REMEMBER

$f(4)$ is equal to the remainder of $f(x) \div (x - 4)$.

The stock's closing price on day 4 was $27. ∎

Application: Business

Example 2   The number of customers, in hundreds, entering a theme park on its grand-opening day is given by $f(x) = x^3 + 2x^2 - x$, where x is the number of hours since the park opened. How long does it take for a total of 1400 customers to enter the park?

Solution   Because $f(x)$ is given in hundreds, substitute 14 for $f(x)$.

$14 = x^3 + 2x^2 - x$

$0 = x^3 + 2x^2 - x - 14$ Subtract 14 from each side to get $f(x) = 0$.

To solve the equation, you need to factor the polynomial. Use the rational root theorem to find possible roots: ± 1, ± 2, ± 7, and ± 14.

$$\begin{array}{r|rrrr} & 1 & 2 & -1 & -14 \\ \hline 1 & 1 & 3 & 2 & -12 \\ 2 & 1 & 4 & 7 & 0 \end{array}$$

TIP

All numbers in the domain are positive, so there is no need to check negative roots.

Synthetic division shows that 2 is a root.

The polynomial factors into $(x - 2)(x^2 + 4x + 7)$. Use the quadratic formula to factor the quadratic expression.

$$x = \frac{-4 \pm \sqrt{4^2 - 4 \cdot 1 \cdot 7}}{2 \cdot 1}$$
$$= -2 \pm i\sqrt{3}$$

The factored form of the equation is
$0 = (x - 2)[x - (-2 + i\sqrt{3})][x - (-2 - i\sqrt{3})]$. Since 2 is the only real root, it is the only solution that makes sense for this problem.

It takes 2 hours for 1400 customers to enter the park. ∎

Application: Geometry

Area and volume of geometric figures are sometimes represented by polynomials.

Example 3

Ⓐ The area of a rectangle is $3x^3 + 32x^2 + 20x$. Find an expression for the length of the rectangle if the width is $x + 10$.

Solution Divide $3x^3 + 32x^2 + 20x$ by $x + 10$.

$$
\begin{array}{r|rrrr}
-10 & 3 & 32 & 20 & 0 \\
 & & -30 & -20 & 0 \\
\hline
 & 3 & 2 & 0 & 0
\end{array}
$$

Synthetic division shows that $(3x^3 + 32x^2 + 20x) \div (x + 10) = 3x^2 + 2x$. You can write $3x^3 + 32x^2 + 20x = (3x^2 + 2x)(x + 10)$. Because $A = lw$, the length is given by $3x^2 + 2x$. ∎

Ⓑ The length of a crate is 3 meters greater than its width, and its height is 2 meters greater than its width. If the volume is 40 cubic meters, what is the height of the box?

Solution Let x represent the width. Then $x + 3$ represents the length and $x + 2$ represents the height. Because $V = lwh$, the volume can be modeled by the equation $V = x(x + 3)(x + 2)$. Once you substitute 40 for V, you have $40 = x(x + 3)(x + 2)$.

$40 = x^3 + 5x^2 + 6x$ Multiply on the right.

$0 = x^3 + 5x^2 + 6x - 40$ Subtract 40 from both sides.

Use the factors of 40 to test for a root of the equation. Synthetic division shows that 2 is a root.

$$
\begin{array}{r|rrrr}
 & 1 & 5 & 6 & -40 \\
\hline
1 & 1 & 6 & 12 & -28 \\
2 & 1 & 7 & 20 & 0
\end{array}
$$

> **REMEMBER**
> Length must be positive, so try only positive factors of 40 when you test roots.

The equation is $0 = (x - 2)(x^2 + 7x + 20)$.

Use the quadratic formula to factor $x^2 + 7x + 20$.

$$x = \frac{-7 \pm \sqrt{7^2 - 4 \cdot 1 \cdot 20}}{2 \cdot 1}$$

$$= \frac{-7 \pm i\sqrt{31}}{2}$$

The only real solution is 2. The width is 2 meters, and the height is 2 meters greater than the width, or 4 meters. ∎

Application: Manufacturing

Example 4 Javier forms a box without a top by cutting squares of equal size from the corners of a piece of cardboard measuring 10 centimeters by 8 centimeters. After removing the squares, he folds up the sides. Write and graph the function that gives the volume of the box, where x is the side length of a square Javier removes. Use the graph to estimate the greatest possible volume.

Solution A diagram of the cardboard piece is shown at the right. Once Javier folds up the sides the height will be x, the length will be $10 - 2x$, and the width will be $8 - 2x$. This makes the volume function $V(x) = x(10 - 2x)(8 - 2x)$.

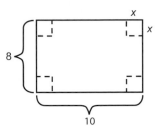

Multiply the right side to get $V(x) = 4x^3 - 36x^2 + 80x$. To graph the function, use synthetic division to evaluate the polynomial for different values of x. Because the side of a square must be greater than 0, choose only positive values of x. Use these ordered pairs—and what you know about the end behavior of a cubic equation with a positive leading coefficient—to complete the graph.

	4	−36	80	0
1	4	−32	48	48
1.5	4	−30	35	52.5
2	4	−28	24	48
3	4	−24	8	24
4	4	−20	0	0
4.5	4	−18	−1	−4.5
5	4	−16	0	0
6	4	−12	8	48

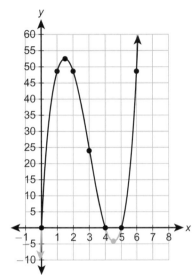

The side length of a removed square must be less than 4 centimeters because the width is only 8 centimeters. Therefore, the domain for this situation is restricted to values between 0 and 4. In this region, the greatest volume occurs when x is about 1.5. When $x = 1.5$, $V(x) = 52.5$.

The greatest possible volume is about 52.5 cubic centimeters. ∎

THINK ABOUT IT

When $x = 0$, $V(x) = 0$ because this means no squares are being removed, and no box can be made. A flat sheet of cardboard has no volume.

Problem Set

Solve.

1. Over the course of a day, the price of a share of stock can be modeled by $P(x) = -x^3 + 14x^2 - 8x + 5$, where x is the number of hours after 9:30 a.m., when the Stock Exchange opens. What was the stock's price at noon?

2. The number of birds living in a tree over the course of a year is given by $B(x) = x^3 + 6x^2 + 9x + 4$, where x is the number of months. How long does it take for there to be 54 birds living in the tree?

3. The width, in meters, of a rectangular garden is $x + 5$. If the area of the garden is $x^3 + 4x^2 + 25x + 150$, what is the length?

4. The volume of a crate in meters is $V(x) = x^3 + 14x^2 + 63x + 90$. The length is given by $x + 5$, while the width is $x + 3$. Find the value of x for the crate to have a volume 2900 m³.

5. The width of a cooler is 12 centimeters shorter than its length, and its height is 6 centimeters shorter than its length. If the volume is 5184 cubic centimeters, what is the length of the cooler?

6. The flight path of a bird can be modeled by $f(x) = -x^4 + 6x^3 + 50$, where x is number of minutes after the bird takes off and $f(x)$ is the vertical distance (in meters) between the bird and the ground. What is the height of the bird after 4 minutes?

7. The number of bees living in a hive can be modeled by $b(x) = x^3 + 7x^2 + 14x + 8$, where x is the number of weeks. Once the population reaches 560, some of the bees leave to start a new hive. In about how many weeks will the bees start a new hive?

8. The graph represents the volume of a feeding trough, where x is the area of the plastic used. If the maximum amount of material available is 20 square meters, what is the domain?

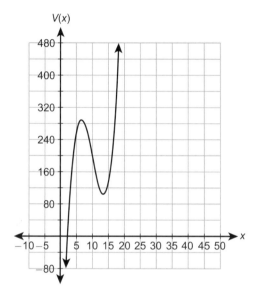

9. A kingfisher is a type of bird that often dives under water to catch its prey. The height, in meters, of a particular kingfisher above the water can be modeled by $h(x) = x^3 - 3x^2 - x + 3$, where x is the number of seconds after the bird starts to dive. How much time does the bird spend under the water ($h(x) < 0$)?

10. The rise and fall of the worth of DanBo, Inc., in dollars, on the stock market over a week can be modeled by $W(x) = x^4 - 9x^3 + 23x^2 - 15x$, where x is the day. Draw the graph of the model.

11. The value of a house can rise and fall with the real-estate market. The value of a particular house over the course of a decade can be modeled by $f(x) = x^4 - 8x^3 + 19x^2 - 12x$, where x is the year and $f(x)$ is the difference between the value in that year and the original purchase value, in hundreds of dollars. In which years did the house have the same value as it did when it was purchased?

12. The slope of a cliff can be modeled by $S(x) = x^3 - 7x^2 - 2x - 4$, where x is the horizontal distance from the edge in feet. What is the slope of the cliff 2 feet from the edge?

13. Would it be wise to purchase a stock whose predicted value on day x can be modeled by $v(x) = -2x^4 + 5x^3 + 8x^2 + 9x$? Explain your answer.

14. The shape of a crevice is given by $f(x) = x^4 - 16x^3 + 94x^2 - 240x + 225$, where x is the horizontal distance from the edge in meters. Draw the graph of the model for the first 8 meters.

15. A box without a top is formed when squares of equal size are cut from the corners of a piece of cardboard measuring 12 inches by 15 inches. After the squares are removed, the sides are folded up. Write and graph the function that gives the volume of the box, where x is the side length of a removed square.

16. The area of a driveway is $A(x) = 3x^3 - x^2 + 12x - 4$. The width of the driveway is $3x - 1$. Find the length.

17. The graph represents the volume of a cabinet, where x is the area of wood used. What is the minimum value of x for which the model can be accurate?

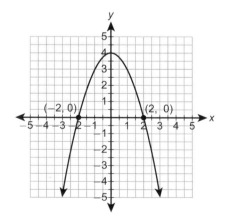

18. Would it be wise to purchase a stock whose predicted value on day x can be modeled by $v(x) = x^4 - 4x^2 - 3x$? Explain your answer.

19. The depth, in meters, of a submarine over the course of a day can be modeled by $d(h) = -h^4 + 8h^3 - 22h^2 + 24h - 9$, where h is the hour of the day. At what times does the submarine surface ($d(h) = 0$)?

20. The volume of a dumpster in cubic meters is $V(x) = 2x^3 + 22x^2 + 70x + 50$. The length is $x + 5$, and the width is $2x + 2$. Find the value of x for the dumpster to have a volume of 1200 m³.

21. Gina forms a box without a top by cutting squares of equal size from the corners of a piece of paper measuring 8 cm by 8 cm. When she removes the squares, she folds up the sides. Write and graph the function that gives the volume of the box, where x is the side length of a removed square.

22. The slope of a rock-climbing wall can be modeled by $f(x) = x^4 - 8x^3 + 20x^2 - 16x + 4$, where x is the horizontal distance from the floor in meters. What is the slope of the wall 3 meters from the floor?

23. The area of a room is $f(x) = 2x^3 - 5x^2 + 40x - 100$. The width of the room is $2x - 5$. Find the length.

24. The height of a wave is $f(x) = x^4 - 14x^3 + 61x^2 - 84x + 36$, where x is the distance in kilometers from the shore and $f(x)$ is the wave's height in meters. Draw the graph of the model for the first 6 kilometers.

UNIT 10　Exponentials and Logarithms

Bacteria like *Staph aureus* are very common.

In the right environment, the rate of growth of the number of bacteria in a petri dish may continuously increase. You can describe this kind of growth with an exponential function.

Big Ideas

▶ A function is a correspondence between two sets, the domain and the range, that assigns to each member of the domain exactly one member of the range. Functions can model many events in the physical world.

▶ In a family of functions, once you know the graph of the parent function, you can use transformations to graph related functions.

▶ If you can create a mathematical model for a situation, you can use the model to solve other problems that you might not be able to solve otherwise.

Unit Topics

▶ Foundations for Unit 10

▶ Exponential Expressions and Equations

▶ Graphing Exponential Functions

▶ Applications: Growth and Decay

▶ Logarithms

▶ Using Logs to Solve Exponential Equations

▶ Solving Logarithmic Equations

▶ Graphing Logarithmic Functions

▶ Applications: Logarithms

Foundations for Unit 10

Before you learn about exponential and logarithmic expressions, equations, and functions, take time to ensure you know how to do the following:

▶ Use exponential properties to simplify exponential expressions.

▶ Simplify products of powers and powers of products.

▶ Simplify quotients of powers and powers of quotients.

Zero and Negative Exponent Properties

ZERO AND NEGATIVE EXPONENTS

Let a be a nonzero real number and let m be any integer.

Property	Statement
Zero Exponent	$a^0 = 1$
Negative Exponent	$a^{-m} = \dfrac{1}{a^m}$

Example 1   Evaluate each expression.

A $0^0 = $ undefined   **B** $(-3.71)^0 = 1$ **C** $-\pi^0 = -1$

Example 2   Simplify each expression. Use positive exponents only.

A $6^{-2} = \dfrac{1}{6^2} = \dfrac{1}{36}$ **B** $xy^{-2} = \dfrac{x}{y^2}$ **C** $\left(\dfrac{2}{3}\right)^{-3} = \left(\dfrac{3}{2}\right)^3 = \dfrac{3^3}{2^3} = \dfrac{27}{8}$

Problem Set A

Simplify each expression. Use positive exponents only.

1. 7^0

2. y^0

3. 2^{-4}

4. $\left(\dfrac{2}{5}\right)^{-4}$

5. ab^0

6. $(xy)^0 z^{-3}$

Using Product Properties of Exponents

Use the product properties of exponents when you multiply powers with the same base or raise a product to a power.

PRODUCT PROPERTIES OF EXPONENTS

Let a and b be real numbers. Let m and n be integers.

Property	Statement
Product of Powers	$a^m \cdot a^n = a^{m+n}$
Power of a Product	$(ab)^m = a^m b^m$

Example 3 Simplify each expression. Use positive exponents only.

A $3x^2 \cdot 4x^6 = 12x^{2+6} = 12x^8$

B $(2rs)^4 = 2^4 r^4 s^4 = 16r^4 s^4$

C $\left(\frac{1}{2}\right)^{-2} \cdot \left(\frac{1}{2}\right)^{-2} \cdot \left(\frac{1}{2}\right)^{3} = \left(\frac{1}{2}\right)^{-2+(-2)+3} = \left(\frac{1}{2}\right)^{-1} = 2$

Problem Set B

Simplify each expression. Use positive exponents only.

7. $x^4(2x)^3$

8. $3^{-9} \cdot 3^{12}$

9. $(xyz)^6$

10. $\left(\frac{3}{5}\right)^{-4} \cdot \left(\frac{3}{5}\right)^{7}$

11. $(pq)^0 \cdot (pq)^2 \cdot (pq)^{-3}$

12. $2^{-4} \cdot 2^5 \cdot 2^{-3}$

13. $(3a^2 b)^5$

14. $\left(\frac{1}{4}\right)^{-9} \cdot \left(\frac{1}{4}\right)^{8}$

Using Quotient Properties of Exponents

Use the quotient properties of exponents to divide powers with the same base or raise a quotient to a power.

QUOTIENT PROPERTIES OF EXPONENTS

Let a and b be nonzero real numbers. Let m and n be integers.

Property	Statement
Quotient of Powers	$\dfrac{a^m}{a^n} = a^{m-n}$
Power of a Quotient	$\left(\dfrac{a}{b}\right)^m = \dfrac{a^m}{b^m}$

Example 4 Simplify each expression. Use positive exponents only.

A $\dfrac{6^{12}}{6^9} = 6^{12-9} = 6^3 = 216$

B $\left(\dfrac{3}{4}\right)^4 = \dfrac{3^4}{4^4} = \dfrac{81}{256}$

C $\dfrac{(2xy)^3}{(3xy)^4} = \dfrac{2^3x^3y^3}{3^4x^4y^4} = \dfrac{8}{81}x^{3-4}y^{3-4} = \dfrac{8}{81}x^{-1}y^{-1} = \dfrac{8}{81xy}$

Problem Set C

Simplify each expression. Use positive exponents only.

15. $\dfrac{7^{15}}{7^{12}}$

16. $\left(\dfrac{8}{9}\right)^2$

17. $\dfrac{a^8}{a^{-2}}$

18. $\dfrac{x^2y^3}{x^2y^4}$

19. $\dfrac{(4ab)^2}{(2ab)^4}$

20. $\dfrac{12x^2y^6}{8x^4y^5}$

21. $\dfrac{(3pq)^{-5}}{(pq)^3}$

22. $\left(\dfrac{3}{4}\right)^3 \cdot \left(\dfrac{2}{3}\right)^4$

Using the Power of a Power Property of Exponents

To raise a power to another power, simply multiply the exponents.

POWER OF A POWER PROPERTY OF EXPONENTS

Let a be a real number. Let m and n be integers.
$$(a^m)^n = a^{mn}$$

Example 5 Simplify each expression. Use positive exponents only.

A $\left(2^2\right)^3 = 2^{2 \cdot 3} = 2^6 = 64$

B $\left(a^{-3}b^2\right)^{-2} = a^{(-3)(-2)}b^{(2)(-2)} = a^6b^{-4} = \dfrac{a^6}{b^4}$

C $\left(\dfrac{3x^3}{5y^2}\right)^2 = \dfrac{(3x^3)^2}{(5y^2)^2} = \dfrac{3^2(x^3)^2}{5^2(y^2)^2} = \dfrac{9 \cdot x^{3 \cdot 2}}{25 \cdot y^{2 \cdot 2}} = \dfrac{9x^6}{25y^4}$

Problem Set D

Simplify each expression. Use positive exponents only.

23. $\left(3^3\right)^2$

24. $\left(f^4g^{-3}\right)^5$

25. $\left(12x^{-2}y^6z^4\right)^2$

26. $\left(\dfrac{2a^4}{3b^5}\right)^3$

27. $\dfrac{\left(4z^3\right)^0}{(2yz)^5}$

28. $\left(s^2t\right)^3\left(st^2\right)^{-2}$

Exponential Expressions and Equations

Any root of a number can be written as a fractional power of the number.

Rational Exponents and Radical Form

> ### PROPERTY OF RATIONAL EXPONENTS
>
> For any positive integers n and m, where $n \neq 0$, and any $b \in \mathbb{R}$,
>
> $$b^{\frac{m}{n}} = \left(\sqrt[n]{b}\right)^m = \sqrt[n]{b^m},$$
>
> except when $b < 0$ and n is even.

> **REMEMBER**
>
> A rational exponent is an exponent that can be written as a fraction.

Example 1 Express each of the following in radical form.

A $10^{\frac{5}{4}}$ **B** $(-3)^{\frac{2}{3}}$ **C** $\left(2^{\frac{1}{6}}\right)^3$

Solution

$10^{\frac{5}{4}} = \left(\sqrt[4]{10}\right)^5$

$\quad = \sqrt[4]{10^5}$ ∎

Solution

$(-3)^{\frac{2}{3}} = \sqrt[3]{(-3)^2}$

$\quad = \sqrt[3]{9}$ ∎

Solution

$\left(2^{\frac{1}{6}}\right)^3 = 2^{\frac{1}{6} \cdot 3}$

$\quad = 2^{\frac{1}{2}}$

$\quad = \sqrt{2}$ ∎

> **THINK ABOUT IT**
>
> If there were no parentheses in Example 1B, the result would be different: $-3^{\frac{2}{3}} = -\sqrt[3]{3^2} = -\sqrt[3]{9}$.

Example 2 Express each of the following in rational exponent form.

A $\sqrt[4]{6^3}$ **B** $\sqrt[5]{(-2)^3}$ **C** $\left(\sqrt[3]{7^4}\right)^{\frac{1}{2}}$

Solution

$\sqrt[4]{6^3} = 6^{\frac{3}{4}}$ ∎

Solution

$\sqrt[5]{(-2)^3} = (-2)^{\frac{3}{5}}$ ∎

Solution

$\left(\sqrt[3]{7^4}\right)^{\frac{1}{2}} = \left(7^{\frac{4}{3}}\right)^{\frac{1}{2}}$

$\quad = 7^{\frac{4}{3} \cdot \frac{1}{2}}$

$\quad = 7^{\frac{2}{3}}$ ∎

Using Properties of Exponents to Simplify Expressions

The properties of exponents can be used to simplify expressions containing rational exponents.

Example 3 Simplify. Assume all variables are positive.

Ⓐ $4^{\frac{1}{2}} \cdot 4^{\frac{3}{2}}$

Solution Here are two strategies you can use to simplify this expression.

Method 1 Combine exponents first.

$$4^{\frac{1}{2}} \cdot 4^{\frac{3}{2}} = 4^{\left(\frac{1}{2} + \frac{3}{2}\right)}$$

$$= 4^{\frac{4}{2}}$$

$$= 4^2$$

$$= 16 \ \blacksquare$$

Method 2 Simplify each factor first.

$$4^{\frac{1}{2}} \cdot 4^{\frac{3}{2}} = \sqrt{4} \cdot \left(\sqrt{4}\right)^3$$

$$= 2 \cdot 2^3$$

$$= 2 \cdot 8$$

$$= 16 \ \blacksquare$$

THINK ABOUT IT

When you solve problems with fractional exponents, values are usually easier to work with if you find the root before raising to the power: $4^{\frac{3}{2}} = \left(\sqrt{4}\right)^3 = 2^3 = 8$ has smaller values than $4^{\frac{3}{2}} = \sqrt{4^3} = \sqrt{64} = 8$.

Ⓑ $\dfrac{8}{8^{\frac{1}{3}}}$

Solution

$$\frac{8}{8^{\frac{1}{3}}} = 8^{1 - \frac{1}{3}} \qquad \text{Quotient of Powers Property}$$

$$= 8^{\frac{2}{3}} \qquad \text{Subtract: } \frac{3}{3} - \frac{1}{3} = \frac{2}{3}.$$

$$= \left(\sqrt[3]{8}\right)^2 \qquad \text{Property of Rational Exponents}$$

$$= 2^2 \qquad \text{The cube root of 8 is 2.}$$

$$= 4 \qquad \text{Simplify.} \ \blacksquare$$

Ⓒ $\left(16^{\frac{1}{2}} a^2 b^{-2}\right)^{\frac{1}{2}}$

Solution

$$\left(16^{\frac{1}{2}} a^2 b^{-2}\right)^{\frac{1}{2}} = (4 a^2 b^{-2})^{\frac{1}{2}} \qquad 16^{\frac{1}{2}} = \sqrt{16} = 4$$

$$= 4^{\frac{1}{2}} a^{2 \cdot \frac{1}{2}} b^{-2 \cdot \frac{1}{2}} \qquad \text{Power of a Power Property}$$

$$= 4^{\frac{1}{2}} a b^{-1} \qquad \text{Simplify.}$$

$$= \frac{\sqrt{4} \cdot a}{b} \qquad \text{Property of Rational Exponents}$$

$$= \frac{2a}{b} \qquad \text{Simplify.} \ \blacksquare$$

Ⓓ $\left(\dfrac{4x^{2r} y^{4r} z^{8r}}{25 z^{2r}}\right)^{\frac{1}{2}}$

Solution

$$\left(\frac{4x^{2r} y^{4r} z^{8r}}{25 z^{2r}}\right)^{\frac{1}{2}} = \frac{\left(4x^{2r} y^{4r} z^{8r}\right)^{\frac{1}{2}}}{(25 z^{2r})^{\frac{1}{2}}} \qquad \text{Power of a Quotient Property}$$

$$= \frac{4^{\frac{1}{2}} x^{\frac{2r}{2}} y^{\frac{4r}{2}} z^{\frac{8r}{2}}}{25^{\frac{1}{2}} z^{\frac{2r}{2}}} \qquad \text{Power of a Product Property}$$

$$= \frac{\sqrt{4} \cdot x^r y^{2r} z^{4r}}{\sqrt{25} \cdot z^r} \qquad \text{Property of Rational Exponents}$$

$$= \frac{2x^r y^{2r} z^{4r - r}}{5} \qquad \text{Quotient of Powers Property}$$

$$= \frac{2x^r y^{2r} z^{3r}}{5} \qquad \text{Simplify.} \ \blacksquare$$

THINK ABOUT IT

If x, y, or z in Example 3D is less than zero and n is even, the property of rational exponents is not valid. If $x = -3$, for example, $(x^2)^{\frac{1}{2}} = \sqrt{(-3)^2} = 3 \neq x$.

Using Rational Exponents to Express Radical Expressions in Simplified Radical Form

Example 4   Express each of the following in simplified radical form with the smallest index possible.

Ⓐ $\sqrt[10]{50^5}$

Solution

$$\sqrt[10]{50^5} = 50^{\frac{5}{10}} \qquad\qquad \text{Rewrite in rational exponent form.}$$
$$= 50^{\frac{1}{2}} \qquad\qquad \text{Simplify.}$$
$$= (25 \cdot 2)^{\frac{1}{2}} \qquad\qquad \text{Factor.}$$
$$= 25^{\frac{1}{2}} \cdot 2^{\frac{1}{2}} \qquad\qquad \text{Power of a Product Property}$$
$$= \sqrt{25} \cdot \sqrt{2} \qquad\qquad \text{Property of Rational Exponents}$$
$$= 5\sqrt{2} \qquad\qquad \text{Simplify.} \ \blacksquare$$

Ⓑ $\sqrt[8]{a^2 b^4}$

Solution

$$\sqrt[8]{a^2 b^4} = \left(a^{\frac{2}{8}} b^{\frac{4}{8}}\right) \qquad\qquad \text{Rewrite in rational exponent form.}$$
$$= \left(a^{\frac{1}{4}} b^{\frac{2}{4}}\right) \qquad\qquad \text{Simplify.}$$
$$= (ab^2)^{\frac{1}{4}} \qquad\qquad \text{Product Property of Exponents}$$
$$= \sqrt[4]{ab^2} \qquad\qquad \text{Property of Rational Exponents} \ \blacksquare$$

Ⓒ $\left(\sqrt[12]{16x^8 y^4}\right)$

Solution

$$\left(\sqrt[12]{16x^8 y^4}\right) = \left(\sqrt[12]{2^4 x^8 y^4}\right) \qquad\qquad 16 = 2^4$$
$$= (2^4 x^8 y^4)^{\frac{1}{12}} \qquad\qquad \text{Rewrite in rational exponent form.}$$
$$= (2^4)^{\frac{1}{12}} (x^8)^{\frac{1}{12}} (y^4)^{\frac{1}{12}} \qquad\qquad \text{Product Property of Exponents}$$
$$= \left(2^{4 \cdot \frac{1}{12}}\right)\left(x^{8 \cdot \frac{1}{12}}\right)\left(y^{4 \cdot \frac{1}{12}}\right) \qquad\qquad \text{Power of a Power Property}$$
$$= \left(2^{\frac{1}{3}}\right)\left(x^{\frac{2}{3}}\right)\left(y^{\frac{1}{3}}\right) \qquad\qquad \text{Simplify.}$$
$$= (2x^2 y)^{\frac{1}{3}} \qquad\qquad \text{Product Property of Exponents}$$
$$= \sqrt[3]{2x^2 y} \qquad\qquad \text{Property of Rational Exponents} \ \blacksquare$$

Solving Exponential Equations

An **exponential equation** is an equation with variable expressions as exponents.

PROPERTY OF EQUALITY FOR EXPONENTIAL EQUATIONS

If a is a positive number other than 1, then
$$a^x = a^y \text{ if and only if } x = y.$$

The property of equality for exponential equations can be used to solve some types of exponential equations.

Example 5   Solve, then check.

A $4^x = 8$

Solution

$4^x = 8$

$(2^2)^x = 2^3$ Rewrite each term so that the bases are the same.

$2^{2x} = 2^3$ Power of a Power Property

$2x = 3$ Property of Equality for Exponential Equations

$x = \dfrac{3}{2}$ Division Property of Equality

Check

$4^x \overset{?}{=} 8$

$4^{\frac{3}{2}} \overset{?}{=} 8$

$\sqrt{4^3} \overset{?}{=} 8$

$\sqrt{64} \overset{?}{=} 8$

$8 = 8$ ✓ ■

B $5^y = 5^{2y+4}$

Solution

$5^y = 5^{2y+4}$

$y = 2y + 4$ Property of Equality for Exponential Equations

$y = -4$ Solve for y.

Check

$5^{-4} \overset{?}{=} 5^{2(-4)+4}$

$5^{-4} \overset{?}{=} 5^{-8+4}$

$5^{-4} = 5^{-4}$ ✓ ■

C $8^{x^2} = 64$

Solution

$8^{x^2} = 64$

$8^{x^2} = 8^2$ Rewrite each term so that the bases are the same.

$x^2 = 2$ Property of Equality for Exponential Equations

$x = \pm\sqrt{2}$ Solve for x.

> **TIP**
> Always check for extraneous solutions when you solve exponential equations.

Check

Substitute $\sqrt{2}$ for x:

$8^{x^2} \overset{?}{=} 64$

$8^{(\sqrt{2})^2} \overset{?}{=} 64$

$8^2 \overset{?}{=} 64$

$64 = 64$ ✓

Substitute $-\sqrt{2}$ for x:

$8^{x^2} \overset{?}{=} 64$

$8^{(-\sqrt{2})^2} \overset{?}{=} 64$

$8^2 \overset{?}{=} 64$

$64 = 64$ ✓

So the solution set is $\{\pm\sqrt{2}\}$. ■

> **REMEMBER**
> Carefully follow the order of operations:
> $(-\sqrt{2})^2 = (-\sqrt{2})(-\sqrt{2})$
> $= \sqrt{2} \cdot \sqrt{2}$
> $= 2$

Problem Set

Express each of the following in simplified radical form.

1. $8^{\frac{3}{4}}$

2. $(-2)^{\frac{4}{5}}$

3. $\left(3^{\frac{1}{4}}\right)^5$

4. $\left(y^4\right)^{\frac{1}{6}}$

Express each of the following in rational exponent form.

5. $\sqrt[5]{10^3}$

6. $\sqrt[3]{(-3)^4}$

7. $\left(\sqrt[4]{8^3}\right)^{\frac{1}{3}}$

8. $\sqrt[4]{81x^4}$

Simplify by using properties of exponents.

9. $7^{\frac{1}{3}} \cdot 7^{\frac{4}{3}}$

10. $25^{\frac{1}{2}} \cdot 25^{\frac{3}{2}}$

11. $\dfrac{10}{10^{\frac{3}{5}}}$

12. $\dfrac{x^{\frac{6}{5}}}{x^{\frac{1}{5}}}$

13. $\left(64^{\frac{1}{2}}x^4y^{-2}\right)^{\frac{1}{4}}$

14. $(3^6 \cdot 5^6)^{-\frac{1}{6}}$

15. $\left(\dfrac{27x^{3t} \cdot y^{9t} \cdot z^{12t}}{64y^{3t}}\right)^{\frac{1}{3}}$

16. $\dfrac{16pq^{\frac{1}{3}}}{8p^{\frac{3}{4}}r^{-6}}$

Simplify the radical expressions. Use the smallest index possible.

17. $\sqrt[12]{80^3}$

18. $\sqrt[3]{64n^9}$

19. $\sqrt[4]{16x^2y^6z^{12}}$

20. $\sqrt[6]{a^3b^6}$

21. $\sqrt[3]{27x^7z^{15}}$

22. $\sqrt[8]{64f^6 \cdot g^4 \cdot h^2}$

Solve and check.

23. $36^x = 216$

24. $9^{4n} = 81$

25. $8^{d-1} = 2^{d+1}$

26. $27^{1-x} = \left(\dfrac{1}{9}\right)^{2-x}$

27. $36^{y^2} = \sqrt{6}$

28. $25^{x^2} = 125$

*29. Challenge $5x^{\frac{1}{4}} = 20$

*30. Challenge $(3a-1)^{-\frac{2}{3}} = \dfrac{1}{4}$

Graphing Exponential Functions

An **exponential function** has an equation of the form $f(x) = ab^{x-h} + k$, where $a \neq 0$, $b > 0$, and $b \neq 1$.

The function $f(x) = b^x$ is the parent function for the family of exponential functions.

Exponential Functions of the Form: $f(x) = b^x$

When $b > 1$, the function $f(x) = b^x$ is called an **exponential growth function**.

General shape:

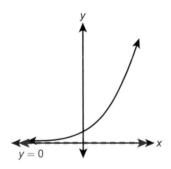

When $0 < b < 1$, the function $f(x) = b^x$ is called an **exponential decay function**.

General shape:

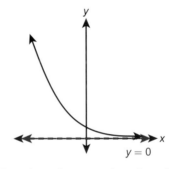

End behavior: As x increases in value, $f(x)$ increases in value. As x decreases in value, $f(x)$ decreases in value, approaching the x-axis.

End behavior: As x decreases in value, $f(x)$ increases in value. As x increases in value, $f(x)$ decreases in value, approaching the x-axis.

The following properties are common to both types of exponential functions:

Asymptote: Since the graph gets close to the axis, but never meets or crosses it, the line $y = 0$ (the x-axis) is the asymptote of the graph.

Domain: the set of all real numbers

Range: all real numbers greater than 0

y-intercept: 1

Using a Table of Values to Graph an Exponential Function

Example 1   Use a table of values to graph.

Ⓐ $f(x) = 2^x$

Solution   In the function $f(x) = 2^x$, $b = 2$. Since $b > 1$, this is an exponential growth function.

Step 1   Make a table of values. Use both positive and negative values of x. Since this is an exponential growth function of the form $f(x) = b^x$, you know that the y-intercept is 1 and that the point $(1, 2)$ lies on the graph.

x	−3	−2	−1	0	1	2	3
f(x)	$\frac{1}{8}$	$\frac{1}{4}$	$\frac{1}{2}$	1	2	4	8

Step 2   Plot the points from the table. Then connect the points in a smooth curve. Use the general shape of an exponential growth function as a guide. Since 2^x is always a positive number, the range of the function is $f(x) > 0$. The graph of the function gets close to the x-axis, but does not meet or cross it, so the line $y = 0$ is an asymptote of the function.

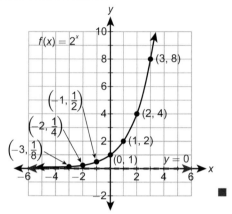

Ⓑ $f(x) = (0.5)^x$

Solution   In the function $f(x) = (0.5)^x$, $b = 0.5$. Since $0 < b < 1$, this is an exponential decay function.

Step 1   Make a table of values. Since this is an exponential decay function of the form $f(x) = b^x$, you know that the y-intercept is 1 and that the point $(1, 0.5)$ lies on the graph.

x	−3	−2	−1	0	1	2	3
f(x)	8	4	2	1	0.5	0.25	0.125

Step 2   Plot the points from the table. Then connect the points in a smooth curve. Use the general shape of an exponential decay function as a guide. Since $(0.5)^x$ is always a positive number, the range of the function is $f(x) > 0$. The x-axis is an asymptote of the function.

Notice that the graph of $f(x) = (0.5)^x$ is a reflection across the y-axis of the graph of $f(x) = 2^x$.

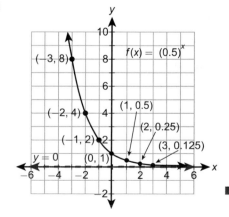

Exponential Functions Graph Family: $f(x) = a \cdot b^{x-h} + k$

Functions of the form $f(x) = a \cdot b^{x-h} + k$ are in the family of exponential functions whose parent function is $f(x) = b^x$. The graph of $f(x) = a \cdot b^{x-h} + k$ intersects the y-axis at $(0,\ a \cdot b^{-h} + k)$ and has asymptote $y = k$. The domain of the function is the set of real numbers, and the range, for $b > 0$, is the set of all real numbers greater than k.

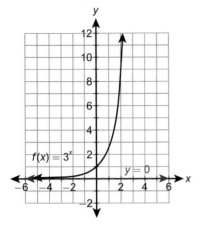

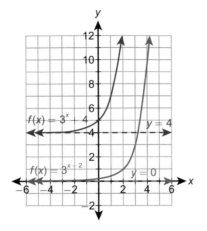

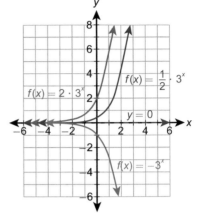

| Graph of $f(x) = b^x$, where $b > 0$. | A change in the parameter h shifts the graph left or right h units. A change in the parameter k shifts the graph up or down k units. | If $a < 0$, reflect the graph across the x-axis.

If $|a| > 1$, stretch vertically by a factor of $|a|$. If $0 < |a| < 1$, shrink vertically by a factor of $|a|$. |

Graphing a Function in the Family $f(x) = a \cdot b^{x-h} + k$

Example 2 Graph $f(x) = 3 \cdot 2^{x-1} + 3$. Then find its asymptote, domain, and range.

Solution

Method 1 Make a table of values. To sketch the graph, use the ordered pairs and the knowledge that the function is an exponential growth function.

REMEMBER

The values *a*, *h*, and *k* all have the same effect on the graph that they do in transforming the parent function $p(x) = x^2$ into the function $f(x) = a(x - h)^2 + k$.

x	$3 \cdot 2^{x-1} + 3$	$f(x)$
-2	$3 \cdot 2^{(-2-1)} + 3 = 3 \cdot 2^{-3} + 3 = 3 \cdot \frac{1}{8} + 3$	$3\frac{3}{8}$
-1	$3 \cdot 2^{(-1-1)} + 3 = 3 \cdot 2^{-2} + 3 = 3 \cdot \frac{1}{4} + 3$	$3\frac{3}{4}$
0	$3 \cdot 2^{(0-1)} + 3 = 3 \cdot 2^{-1} + 3 = 3 \cdot \frac{1}{2} + 3$	$4\frac{1}{2}$
1	$3 \cdot 2^{(1-1)} + 3 = 3 \cdot 2^0 + 3 = 3 \cdot 1 + 3$	6
2	$3 \cdot 2^{(2-1)} + 3 = 3 \cdot 2^1 + 3 = 3 \cdot 2 + 3$	9

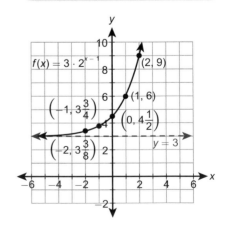

Method 2 Transform the graph of the parent function.

In the function $f(x) = 3 \cdot 2^{x-1} + 3$, $a = 3$, $b = 2$, $h = 1$, and $k = 3$.

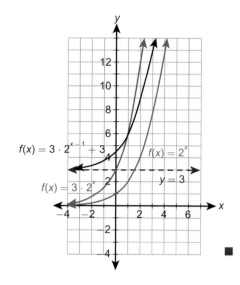

The green graph is $f(x) = 2^x$. Since $a > 0$, the function $f(x) = 3 \cdot 2^{x-1} + 3$ does not get reflected across the x-axis. Since $|a| > 1$, the parent function is stretched vertically by a factor of 3. The blue graph is the graph of the function $f(x) = 3 \cdot 2^x$. The graph of $f(x) = 3 \cdot 2^x$ is then translated horizontally by 1 unit (h) and vertically by 3 units (k). The black line shows the graph of $\mathbf{f(x) = 3 \cdot 2^{x-1} + 3}$.

Domain: the set of real numbers

Range: the set of real numbers greater than 3

Asymptote: $y = 3$

Using the Graph of a Function to Find an Equation for the Function

Example 3 Find the equation of the function shown in the graph, given the parent function $f(x) = \left(\dfrac{1}{2}\right)^x$.

Solution The graph intersects the y-axis at the point $(0, -8)$ and has asymptote $y = -5$, so $k = -5$. Find the unknown parameter a by substituting the point $(0, -8)$.

$$f(x) = a \cdot \left(\frac{1}{2}\right)^x - 5$$

$$-8 = a \cdot \left(\frac{1}{2}\right)^0 - 5$$

$$-8 = a \cdot 1 - 5$$

$$-3 = a$$

Check

$$f(x) = -3 \cdot \frac{1}{2}^x - 5$$

$$-6\frac{1}{2} \overset{?}{=} -3 \cdot \frac{1}{2}^1 - 5$$

$$-6\frac{1}{2} = -\frac{13}{2} \checkmark$$

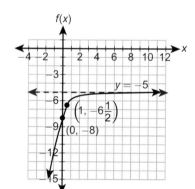

So $f(x) = -3\left(\dfrac{1}{2}\right)^x - 5$ is an accurate equation for the function. ∎

Problem Set

Use a table of values to graph each exponential function.

1. $f(x) = 3^x$

2. $g(x) = 4^x$

3. $f(x) = \left(\frac{1}{3}\right)^x$

4. $p(t) = 0.5^{t-1}$

5. $b(x) = 2 \cdot 2^x$

6. $f(t) = 3^{t+4}$

7. $g(x) = 0.3^x$

8. $r(t) = 11 \cdot 2.9^t$

9. $h(x) = 5^x - 1$

Graph each function. Then find its domain and range, and the equation of its asymptote.

10. $f(x) = 2 \cdot 3^{x+2} - 1$

11. $f(x) = -4^{x+1} + 2$

12. $f(x) = 4 \cdot 2^{x+3} - 3$

13. $f(x) = 2 \cdot \left(\frac{1}{10}\right)^{x-1} + 4$

14. $f(x) = 0.5 \cdot (0.2)^{x+4} - 5$

15. $f(x) = 0.7 \cdot (0.1)^{x-2} + 6$

Describe the effect each parameter has on the graph, given that the parent function is $f(x) = 4^x$.

16. $f(x) = 4^x + 7$

17. $f(x) = 3 \cdot 4^x$

18. $f(x) = -4^{x-2}$

19. $f(x) = 2 \cdot 4^{x-3} + 9$

20. $f(x) = \frac{1}{2} \cdot 4^{x+5} - 7$

21. $f(x) = 5 \cdot 4^{x-6} - 10$

Find an equation of the function shown in the graph, given the parent function.

22. $f(x) = 2^x$

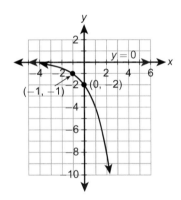

24. $f(x) = 3^x$

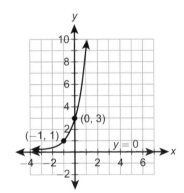

23. $f(x) = 2^x$

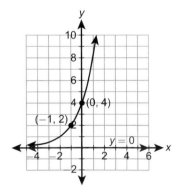

25. $f(x) = 0.5^x$

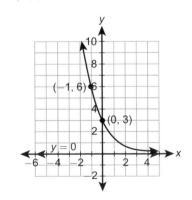

26. $f(x) = \left(\frac{1}{2}\right)^x$

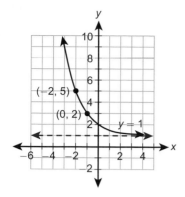

27. $f(x) = 3^x$

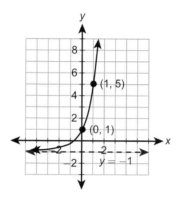

28. $f(x) = \left(\frac{1}{4}\right)^x$

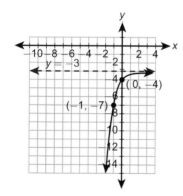

29. $f(x) = (0.2)^x$

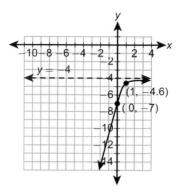

*__30.__ **Challenge** $f(x) = \left(\frac{1}{6}\right)^x$

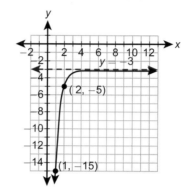

31. $f(x) = \left(\frac{1}{3}\right)^x$

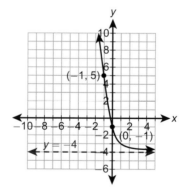

Applications: Growth and Decay

Exponential equations can be used to solve many real-world problems.

Money in a bank and populations of people or bacteria often grow, while radioactive substances gradually lose their radioactivity. Exponential formulas can help you solve many problems involving growth or decay.

Solving Growth Problems

> **EXPONENTIAL GROWTH FORMULA**
>
> If a quantity is growing exponentially from initial amount b for time t and with growth rate r, then the total amount y is
>
> $$y = b(1 + r)^t.$$

Example 1   Suki starts a bacterial culture in her Biology class. She records her observations for the first several hours. How many bacteria should Suki expect to see after 5 hours, 10 hours, 15 hours, and 24 hours?

Hour	0	1	2
Bacteria (in thousands)	10	20	40

Solution   The initial amount is 10,000 bacteria, so $b = 10$. The bacteria are expected to grow at a rate of 100% each hour, so $r = 1$. Use the exponential growth formula, $y = b(1 + r)^t$.

$y = b(1 + r)^t$

$y = 10(1 + 1)^t$

$y = 10 \cdot 2^t$

Hour	0	1	2	5	10	15	24
Bacteria (in thousands)	10	20	40	320	10,240	327,680	167,772,160

> **THINK ABOUT IT**
>
> At some point in time the bacteria will stop growing because of the limited amount of food in a petri dish.

Example 2   In 2000, the population of a country was 10,234,678. The population is expected to grow at a rate of 0.8% each year.

A Predict the population of the country in 2015.

B In what year will the population first exceed 12 million?

THINK ABOUT IT

Populations can also decrease at a constant rate. In such a case, you would use an exponential decay function.

Solution

A The initial population is 10,234,678, so $b = 10,234,678$. The growth rate is 0.8%, so $r = 0.008$. The time period is years, and the difference between 2015 and 2000 is 15 years, so $t = 15$. Use the exponential growth formula.

$y = b(1 + r)^t$

$y = 10,234,678(1 + 0.008)^{15}$

$y = 10,234,678(1.008)^{15}$

$y = 10,234,678(1.26958651)$

$y \approx 11,534,059$

If the growth rate of 0.8% remains constant, the population in 2015 will be approximately 11,534,059.

B Since the population is predicted to be 11,534,059 in 2015, you can predict that it will exceed 12 million sometime after 2015. Plug in some values of t that are greater than 15 to test if the population becomes greater than 12 million. It seems reasonable to begin by testing $t = 20$.

$y = 10,234,678(1 + 0.008)^{20}$

$y = 10,234,678(1.008)^{20}$

$y = 10,234,678(1.172764043)$

$y \approx 12,002,862$

The population is just over 12 million in 2020. Testing $t = 19$, you can show that the population is 11,907,601, which is under 12 million, in 2019. So the population first exceeds 12 million in 2020. ∎

Solving Decay Problems

EXPONENTIAL DECAY FORMULA

If a quantity is decaying exponentially from initial amount b for time t and with decay rate r, then the amount y remaining is

$$y = b(1 - r)^t.$$

Example 3   The sales of a popular doll decreased between the years 2000 to 2005, as shown in the table. If the decrease in sales continues at this rate, what will the sales be for 2010 and 2020?

Year	2000	2001	2002	2003	2004	2005
Sales	1,496,330	1,421,515	1,350,440	1,283,001	1,218,769	1,158,037

Solution

Step 1 Determine the decay rate. Divide the sales for each year by the sales for the previous year. The sales have declined at a constant rate of approximately 5% every year, so $r = .05$.

Step 2 Use the exponential decay formula to determine the equation. The initial population is 1,496,330, so $b = 1,496,330$. From Step 1, $r = 0.05$.

$$y = b(1 - r)^t$$

$$y = 1,496,330(1 - 0.05)^t$$

$$y = 1,496,330(0.95)^t$$

Step 3 Substitute 10 (for 2010) and 20 (for 2020) for t.

$$y = 1,496,330(0.95)^t \qquad y = 1,496,330(0.95)^t$$

$$y = 1,496,330(0.95)^{10} \qquad y = 1,496,330(0.95)^{20}$$

$$y \approx 895,908 \qquad y \approx 536,413$$

The sales for 2010 will fall to about \$895,908, and the sales in 2020 will fall to about \$536,413. ∎

THINK ABOUT IT

If the sales were increasing at a constant rate, you would use the exponential growth formula: $y = b(1 + r)^t$.

Radioactive Decay

Every substance that is radioactive loses particles or energy from the nucleus of its atoms. As a result, radioactive elements change from one kind of atom to another over time. This process of a radioactive substance changing from one kind of atom to another is called *radioactive decay*.

DEFINITION

The **half-life** of a radioactive substance is the length of time it takes for one half of the substance to decay.

HALF-LIFE FORMULA

The amount y of a radioactive substance after t time periods, where b is the initial amount and h is the half-life, is

$$y = b\left(\frac{1}{2}\right)^{\frac{t}{h}}.$$

Example 4 Carbon-14 has a half-life of 5730 years. Archaeologists find bone material from what seems to be a human leg. One of the archaeologists thinks the leg is 10,000 years old. What percentage of normal carbon-14 levels should she expect to find in the leg?

Solution   The half-life is 5730, so $h = 5730$. The time is 10,000 years, so $t = 10,000$. We don't know the original amount, so just use 1 for b. The answer for y will give us a value we can treat as a percentage.

After 10,000 years, the archaeologist should expect about 29.83% of normal carbon-14 levels. ∎

$$y = \left(\frac{1}{2}\right)^{\frac{t}{h}}$$

$$y = \left(\frac{1}{2}\right)^{\frac{10{,}000}{5730}}$$

$$y = \left(\frac{1}{2}\right)^{1.7452}$$

$$y = 0.2983$$

Compound Interest

Using compound interest is one good way to earn money. It is interest that is earned on both the principle and on any interest that has already been earned.

COMPOUND INTEREST FORMULA

The total amount A of an investment with initial principal P, earning compound interest at an annual interest rate r and compounded n times per year for t years, is given by the following formula

$$A = P\left(1 + \frac{r}{n}\right)^{nt}.$$

THINK ABOUT IT

Exponential equations and expressions can describe many real-world phenomena.

Example 5   Find the total amount after 2 years of an investment of $1500 in an account paying 4% interest, compounded for each of the given time periods.

A annually

B quarterly

Solution   The initial amount invested is $1500, so $P = 1500$. The interest rate is 4%, so $r = 0.04$. You are finding the balance after 2 years, so $t = 2$.

When the interest is compounded annually, $n = 1$.

$$A = P\left(1 + \frac{r}{n}\right)^{nt}$$

$$A = 1500\left(1 + \frac{0.04}{1}\right)^{1 \cdot 2}$$

$$A = 1500(1.04)^2$$

$$A = 1500 \cdot 1.0816$$

$$A = 1622.40$$

The total amount after 2 years is $1622.40. ∎

A quarterly event happens four times a year, so $n = 4$.

$$A = P\left(1 + \frac{r}{n}\right)^{nt}$$

$$A = 1500\left(1 + \frac{0.04}{4}\right)^{4 \cdot 2}$$

$$A = 1500(1.01)^8$$

$$A = 1500 \cdot 1.082856706$$

$$A \approx 1624.29$$

The total amount after 2 years is $1624.29. ∎

Problem Set

. . . .

Solve each growth problem.

1. In 2004, the population of a country was 15,500,321. The population is expected to grow at a rate of 0.6% each year. Predict the population of the country in 2012.

2. A colony of ants has 50,000 members. Sione thinks the colony will grow at a rate of 3.1% each hour. How many ants should he expect there to be in the colony after 10 hours?

3. Juan starts a bacteria culture and records the number of bacteria in the petri dish for the first couple of hours. How many bacteria can he expect to find after 17 hours?

Hours	0	1	2
Bacteria (in thousands)	160	320	640

4. A population of insects grows exponentially, as indicated in the table. If the increase in population continues at the same rate, at the end of what hour will the insect population first exceed 100,000?

At End of Hour	Insect Population
1	51,500
2	53,045
3	54,636
4	56,275
5	57,963

5. Shae starts a bacteria culture by swabbing the door handle in her lab. She records the number of bacteria for the first several hours. How many bacteria should she expect to find after 10 hours?

Hours	0	1	2
Bacteria (in thousands)	9.8	19.6	39.2

6. In 2002, the number of people infected with a virus was 12,987. Malakai estimates that the number of infected people will grow at a rate of 1.5% each year. What does he expect the number of infected people will be in 2010?

7. In 2002, the population of a county was 12,567. The population is expected to grow at a rate of 0.2% each year. Predict the population of the county in 2020.

*8. **Challenge** The table shows the number of U.S. citizens that developed a certain type of disease from 1990 to 2008. If the rate of developing the disease grows exponentially and continues to occur at the same rate, in what year will the number of cases first exceed 500,000?

Year	Number of Cases
1990	140,000
1991	142,800
1992	145,656
1993	148,569
1994	151,540

Solve each decay problem.

9. Filipe bought a classic car in the year 2000. He believes that the value of the car depreciates exponentially at a rate of 4% each year. If the car was originally valued at $70,000, what should Filipe expect the value of the car to be in 2012?

10. The sales of large homes decreased between the years 2005 and 2009, as indicated in the table. If the decrease in sales continues at this rate, what will the large-home sales be in 2015?

Year	Large-Home Sales
2005	1,920,000
2006	1,843,200
2007	1,769,472
2008	1,698,693
2009	1,630,745

11. Zhang thinks that the value of a baseball card can be modeled by exponential decay and that the value will decrease at a rate of 0.2% each year. If the card was originally valued at $250 in 2000, what should Zhang expect the value of the card to be in 2011?

12. Archaeologists find a bone fragment of an animal that they expect became extinct over 20,000 years ago. What is the maximum percentage of normal carbon-14 levels that the archaeologists should find in the bone if they are right?

13. In 2000, the population of a country was 25,300,987. The population is expected to decrease at a rate of 2% each year. Predict the population of the country in 2008.

14. Jesslyn hypothesizes that the value of antique furniture can be modeled by exponential decay and that the value of a particular piece will decrease at a rate of 0.15% each year. If the furniture was originally valued at $15,000 in 1990, what should Jesslyn expect the value of the furniture to be in 2010?

Solve each compound interest problem.

17. Find the total amount after 10 years of a compound interest investment of $20,000 at 5.5% interest, compounded annually.

18. Find the total amount after 25 years of a compound interest investment of $70,000 at 4% interest, compounded twice a year.

19. Find the total amount after 15 years of a compound interest investment of $40,000 at 4.2% interest, compounded monthly.

20. Find the total amount after 5 years of a compound interest investment of $50,000 at 3.5% interest, compounded quarterly.

21. Find the total amount after 5 years of a compound interest investment of $10,000 at 3% interest, compounded monthly.

15. Uranium-238 has a half-life of about 4.47 billion years. A geologist believes that a rock she found on the floor of the ocean is 0.1 billion years old. What percentage of normal uranium-238 levels should she expect to find in the rock?

*16. **Challenge** The sales of SUVs decreased between the years 2004 and 2009, as indicated in the table. If the decrease in sales continues at this rate, in what year will the sale of SUVs be 80,000?

Year	SUV Sales
2004	1,500,000
2005	1,425,000
2006	1,353,750
2007	1,286,062
2008	1,221,759

22. Find the total amount after 30 years of a compound interest investment of $100,000 at 5% interest, compounded annually.

*23. **Challenge** The total amount of $5663.54 was earned on an investment of $5000, compounded quarterly for 5 years. What interest rate did the account pay?

*24. **Challenge** Determine the principal for an account paying 3% interest, compounded annually for 5 years and with the total amount of $3477.82.

Logarithms

Just as taking a square root is the opposite of squaring a number, the opposite of raising a base to a variable power is called taking a logarithm.

A **logarithm** is the exponent to which a base would have to be raised to result in a given value. Using logarithms, you would write $2^x = 10$ as $x = \log_2 10$.

<table>
<tr><td>

DEFINITION

The **logarithm** of a with base b, **$\log_b a$**, where $b > 0$, $b \neq 1$, and $a > 0$, is defined as follows:

$$\log_b a = x \text{ if and only if } b^x = a.$$

</td><td>

NOTATION

The expression $\log_b a$ is read as "log base b of a."

</td></tr>
</table>

Converting Between Logarithmic and Exponential Forms

The definition of a logarithm can be used to convert between exponential and logarithmic forms.

Exponential Form   **Logarithmic Form**

$$2^4 = 16 \qquad\qquad \log_2 16 = 4$$

Example 1   The table below shows equivalent equations written in both exponential and logarithmic forms.

Exponential Form	$5^2 = 25$	$4^{-3} = \dfrac{1}{64}$	$81^{\frac{1}{2}} = 9$	$10^0 = 1$
Logarithmic Form	$\log_5 25 = 2$	$\log_4 \dfrac{1}{64} = -3$	$\log_{81} 9 = \dfrac{1}{2}$	$\log_{10} 1 = 0$

Logarithmic Properties

Many properties of logarithms are similar to properties of exponents.

PROPERTIES OF LOGARITHMS

Let $b > 0$, $b \neq 1$, $m > 0$, $n > 0$, and p be any real number.

Property	Statement
Product Property	$\log_b (mn) = \log_b m + \log_b n$
Quotient Property	$\log_b \left(\dfrac{m}{n}\right) = \log_b m - \log_b n$
Power Properties	$\log_b m^p = p \log_b m$ and $\log_b (\sqrt[n]{m}) = \dfrac{\log_b m}{n}$

Example 2

A Write $\log_3 8 + \log_3 4$ as a single logarithm.

Solution

$$\log_3 8 + \log_3 4 = \log_3 (8 \cdot 4) \qquad \text{Product Property of Logarithms}$$
$$= \log_3 32 \qquad \text{Simplify.} \ \blacksquare$$

B Simplify $\log_4 10 - \log_4 5 + 3 \log_4 2$.

Solution

$$\log_4 10 - \log_4 5 + 3 \log_4 2 = \log_4 \left(\frac{10}{5}\right) + 3 \log_4 2 \qquad \text{Quotient Property of Logarithms}$$
$$= \log_4 2 + 3 \log_4 2 \qquad \text{Simplify.}$$
$$= \log_4 2 + \log_4 2^3 \qquad \text{Power Property of Logarithms}$$
$$= \log_4 2 + \log_4 8 \qquad \text{Simplify.}$$
$$= \log_4 (2 \cdot 8) \qquad \text{Product Property of Logarithms}$$
$$= \log_4 16 \qquad \text{Simplify.}$$
$$= 2 \ \blacksquare$$

> **TIP**
>
> Remember that a logarithm is an exponent. To evaluate $\log_4 16$, ask, "To what power do I raise 4 in order to get a result of 16?"

C Write $\log_7 (3x^9)$ in expanded form.

Solution

$$\log_7 (3x^9) = \log_7 3 + \log_7 x^9 \qquad \text{Product Property of Logarithms}$$
$$= \log_7 3 + 9 \log_7 x \qquad \text{Power Property of Logarithms} \ \blacksquare$$

D Given that $\log_2 5 \approx 2.3219$ and $\log_2 3 \approx 1.5850$, use logarithm properties to estimate $\log_2 \frac{3}{10}$.

Solution

$$\log_2 \frac{3}{10} = \log_2 3 - \log_2 10 \qquad \text{Quotient Property of Logarithms}$$

$$= \log_2 3 - \log_2 (2 \cdot 5) \qquad \text{Factor 10.}$$

$$= \log_2 3 - (\log_2 2 + \log_2 5) \qquad \text{Product Property of Logarithms}$$

$$\approx 1.5850 - (1 + 2.3219) \qquad \text{Substitute.}$$

$$\approx 1.5850 - 3.3219 \qquad \text{Simplify.}$$

$$\approx -1.7369 \qquad \text{Simplify. } \blacksquare$$

THINK ABOUT IT

$\log_b b = 1$ since $b^1 = b$.

Using a Calculator to Find Common and Natural Logarithms

Logarithms with special bases have names.

DEFINITIONS

A **common logarithm** is a logarithm with base 10. Common logarithms, such as $\log_{10} x$, are usually written without the base, as $\log x$.
A **natural logarithm** is a logarithm with base e. Natural logarithms, such as $\log_e x$, are often written using the notation $\ln x$.

REMEMBER

Like π, the number e is an irrational number.

$$e \approx 2.718...$$

Calculators are programmed to calculate common and natural logarithms.

Example 3 Use a calculator to evaluate each logarithm to four decimal places.

THINK ABOUT IT

Pietro Mengoli and Nicholas Mercator called the natural logarithm *logarithmus naturalis*.

A $\log 8$

Solution

On a graphing calculator, press **LOG**, type **8)**, and press **ENTER**.
$\log 8 \approx 0.9031$ $\blacksquare$

B $\ln 53$

Solution

On a graphing calculator, press **LN**, type **53)**, and press **ENTER**.
$\ln 53 \approx 3.9703$ $\blacksquare$

TIP

The **LOG** key on a calculator is usually a common logarithm with base 10.
The **LN** key on a calculator is a natural logarithm with base e.

```
log (8)
    .903089987
```

```
ln (53)
    3.970291914
```

Changing Bases of Logarithms

The change of base property can be applied to evaluate a logarithm when the base is neither 10 nor e.

$$x = \log_b a$$

$$b^x = a \qquad \text{Rewrite in exponential form.}$$

$$\log_n b^x = \log_n a \qquad \text{Take the logarithm with base } n \text{ of both sides.}$$

$$x \log_n b = \log_n a \qquad \text{Power Property of Logarithms}$$

$$x = \frac{\log_n a}{\log_n b} \qquad \text{Division Property of Equality}$$

$$\log_b a = \frac{\log_n a}{\log_n b} \qquad \text{Substitute for } x.$$

This result gives you the logarithmic change of base property.

LOGARITHMIC CHANGE OF BASE PROPERTY

For positive real numbers a, b, and n, where $n \neq 1$, $b \neq 1$, and $a > 0$,

$$\log_b a = \frac{\log_n a}{\log_n b}.$$

Example 4   Evaluate $\log_5 20$ to four decimal places.

Solution   Use the change of base property. Then enter the expression in a calculator.

Changing the base to 10 or e gives the same result:

Base 10:

$$\log_5 20 = \frac{\log 20}{\log 5}$$
$$\approx 1.8614$$

Base e:

$$\log_5 20 = \frac{\ln 20}{\ln 5}$$
$$\approx 1.8614 \ \blacksquare$$

Problem Set

· ·

Convert each expression to logarithmic form.

1. $6^3 = 216$

2. $3^{-3} = \frac{1}{27}$

3. $8^{\frac{1}{3}} = 2$

4. $49^{\frac{1}{2}} = 7$

Convert each expression to exponential form.

5. $\log_4 64 = 3$

6. $\log_5 \frac{1}{25} = -2$

7. $\log_{16} 16 = 1$

8. $\log_{\frac{1}{3}} 3 = 27$

Write as a single logarithm.

9. $\log_4 3 + \log_4 5$

10. $\log_6 6 + \log_6 4$

11. $\log_8 16 - \log_8 4$

12. $\log_5 21 - \log_5 7$

13. $\log_3 15 - \log_3 3 + \log_3 4$

14. $\log_7 16 - \log_7 4 + \log_7 3$

Write in expanded form.

15. $\log_9 (4x^5)$

16. $\log_2 (7x^3)$

17. $\log_5 \left(\frac{1}{2}x^8\right)$

Estimate each expression, given that $\log_3 2 = 0.6309$, $\log_3 5 = 1.4650$, and $\log_3 6 = 1.6309$.

18. $\log_3 \frac{2}{5}$

19. $\log_3 3$

20. $\log_3 30$

Evaluate each logarithm to four decimal places.

21. $\log 14$

22. $\log 19$

23. $\log 2$

24. $\ln 10$

25. $\ln 17$

26. $\ln 8$

27. $\log_7 17$

28. $\log_3 6$

29. $\log_9 30$

Solve.

*30. Challenge Simplify $\ln \dfrac{2^y + \ln x^y}{y}$.

*31. Challenge Evaluate $\log_3 \left(\dfrac{27}{9}\right)^2$.

Using Logs to Solve Exponential Equations

You can solve an exponential equation such as $2^x = 8$ simply by rewriting it as $2^x = 2^3$, so $x = 3$. However, to solve an exponential equation such as $2^x = 10$, you have to use a logarithm.

Just as you use addition, multiplication, or square roots to transform and solve equations, you can use logarithms to transform and solve equations.

Using Logarithms to Solve Exponential Equations

> **PROPERTY OF EQUALITY FOR LOGARITHMIC EQUATIONS**
>
> If a, x, and y are positive numbers and $a \neq 1$, then
> $$\log_a x = \log_a y \text{ if and only if } x = y.$$

Example 1 Solve. Round your answer to four decimal places.

A $2^x = 10$

Solution

$$2^x = 10$$

$\log 2^x = \log 10$	Take the common (base 10) logarithm of both sides.
$x \log 2 = \log 10$	Power Property of Logarithms
$x \log 2 = 1$	$\log_{10} 10 = 1$ because $10^1 = 10$.
$x = \dfrac{1}{\log 2}$	Divide both sides by $\log 2$.
$x \approx 3.3219$	Use a calculator to approximate the expression.

Check for reasonableness: Because $2^3 = 8$ and $2^4 = 16$, it is reasonable that $2^{3.3219} \approx 10$. You may use a calculator to verify the result. ■

> **TIP**
>
> It is customary to round the value of a logarithmic expression to four decimal places.

$5^{2n} = 101$

Solution

$$5^{2n} = 101$$

$\log 5^{2n} = \log 101$ Take the common logarithm of both sides.

$2n \log 5 = \log 101$ Power Property of Logarithms

$n = \dfrac{\log 101}{2 \log 5}$ Divide both sides by 2 log 5.

$n \approx 1.4338$ Use a calculator to approximate the expression. ∎

TIP

Always solve the equation thoroughly before approximating the value of the variable. The equation $n = \dfrac{\log 101}{2 \log 5}$ gives the exact value of n; $n \approx 1.4338$ gives an approximation.

When an exponential equation contains the number e, it can be easier to take the natural logarithm of both sides to solve the equation.

Example 2   Solve each equation by using logarithms. Round your answer to four decimal places.

Ⓐ $e^{3a} = 9$

Solution

$$e^{3a} = 9$$

$\ln e^{3a} = \ln 9$ Take the natural logarithm of both sides.

$3a \ln e = \ln 9$ Power Property of Logarithms

$3a = \ln 9$ $\ln e = 1$ because $e^1 = e$.

$a = \dfrac{\ln 9}{3}$ Divide both sides by 3.

$a \approx 0.7324$ Use a calculator to approximate the expression.

TIP

The equations in Example 1 could also have been solved using the natural logarithm.

For an equation with a variable in the exponent, you can choose to use either the natural or the common logarithm.

Check   To verify the result, substitute the approximate value in the original equation. Use a calculator to evaluate the left side of the equation.

$$e^{3a} = 9$$

$$e^{3 \cdot 0.7324} \stackrel{?}{\approx} 9$$

$$8.9998 \approx 9 \checkmark$$

The solution $a \approx 0.7324$ is correct. ∎

 $7^x = e^{x+1}$

Solution

Method Using LN	**Method Using LOG**

$$7^x = e^{x+1}$$

$$\ln 7^x = \ln e^{x+1}$$

$$x \ln 7 = (x + 1) \ln e$$

$$x \ln 7 = (x + 1) \cdot 1$$

$$x \ln 7 = x + 1$$

$$x \ln 7 - x = 1$$

$$x((\ln 7) - 1) = 1$$

$$x = \frac{1}{(\ln 7) - 1}$$

$$x \approx 1.0572$$

$$7^x = e^{x+1}$$

$$\log 7^x = \log e^{x+1}$$

$$x \log 7 = (x + 1) \log e$$

$$x \log 7 = x \cdot \log e + 1 \cdot \log e$$

$$x \log 7 - x \log e = \log e$$

$$x(\log 7 - \log e) = \log e$$

$$x = \frac{\log e}{\log 7 - \log e}$$

$$x \approx 1.0572$$

Check To verify the result, substitute the approximate value in the original equation. Use a calculator to evaluate each side of the equation.

$$7^x = e^{x+1}$$

$$7^{1.0572} \overset{?}{\approx} e^{1.0572+1}$$

$$7.8242 \approx 7.8240 \checkmark$$

The calculator gives the same value, if rounded to three decimal places, for each expression. ■

Interpreting a Calculator Error Message

Example 3 Solve $10^x + 2 = -6$.

Solution

$10^x + 2 = -6$	
$10^x = -8$	Subtract 2 from both sides.
$\log 10^x = \log(-8)$	Take the common logarithm of both sides.
$x \log 10 = \log(-8)$	Power Property of Logarithms
$x = \log(-8)$	$\log 10 = 1$
$x = Error\ Message$	

> **THINK ABOUT IT**
>
> The statement $10^x = -8$ indicates that the original equation has no real solution. It is not possible for any power of 10 to be negative.

The calculator gives an error message indicating that computing $\log(-8)$ is not possible. The reason is that it is not possible to take the logarithm of a negative number. In this case, there is no real solution to the equation. ■

Problem Set

Solve. Find each exact answer and use a calculator to approximate answers that involve logarithms to four decimal places.

1. $3^x = 10$

2. $4^c = 100$

3. $5^x = 1000$

4. $10^x = \dfrac{1}{100}$

5. $7^h = 22$

6. $10^x + 13 = 10$

7. $7^{2p} = 50$

8. $4^{3x} = 20$

9. $6^{4x} = 110$

10. $9^{2x} = 27$

11. $3^{5z} + 1 = 220$

12. $19^{2x} + 4 = 2$

13. $e^{2y} = 1$

14. $e^{4x} = 5$

15. $e^{3x} = 4$

16. $3e^{2x-2} = 12$

17. $2e^{5x+1} = 100$

18. $9e^{4r} + 32 = 25$

19. $6^x = e^{x+2}$

20. $4^t = e^{t-1}$

21. $20^x = e^{x+3}$

22. $2^{2x} = e^{3x+5}$

23. $9^{3b} = e^{1-4b}$

24. $3^{4x+1} = e^{9x+5}$

25. $4^{3x} = e^{2x-2}$

26. $3^{-n} = e^{n+4}$

27. $5^{-3x} = e^{2-5x}$

28. $7^{-x} = e^{-4x+1}$

*29. **Challenge** $e^{6y^2-13y} - e^5 = 0$

*30. **Challenge** $8 = 4^{2e^x - 1}$

Solving Logarithmic Equations

You can use logarithmic and exponential properties to solve logarithmic equations.

You can use the properties of equality for exponential and logarithmic equations to solve some types of logarithmic equations.

REMEMBER

The property of equality for exponential equations states the following:

If a is a positive number other than 1, then $a^x = a^y$ if and only if $x = y$.

Solving Logarithmic Equations by Rewriting in Exponential Form

If you can write an equation in the form $\log_b a = c$, then you can use the definition of logarithms to write the equivalent exponential equation. This strategy can be helpful for some problems.

Example 1   Solve and check.

Ⓐ $\log_4 64 = x$

Solution

$\log_4 64 = x$

$4^x = 64$	Definition of a logarithm
$4^x = 4^3$	Rewrite 64 as 4^3.
$x = 3$	Property of Equality for Exponential Equations

Check

$\log_4 64 \overset{?}{=} 3$

$4^3 \overset{?}{=} 64$

$64 = 64 \checkmark$

The solution $x = 3$ is correct. ■

Ⓑ $\log_7 (x + 1) = 2$

Solution

$\log_7 (x + 1) = 2$

$7^2 = x + 1$	Definition of a logarithm
$49 - 1 = x$	Subtraction Property of Equality
$x = 48$	Subtract.

Check

$\log_7 (48 + 1) \overset{?}{=} 2$

$\log_7 49 \overset{?}{=} 2$

$7^2 \overset{?}{=} 49$

$49 = 49 \checkmark$

The solution $x = 48$ is correct. ■

C $\log_2 (x + 2) + \log_2 (x - 5) = 3$

Solution

$$\log_2 (x + 2) + \log_2 (x - 5) = 3$$

$\log_2 (x + 2)(x - 5) = 3$	Product Property of Logarithms
$(x + 2)(x - 5) = 2^3$	Definition of a logarithm
$x^2 - 3x - 10 = 8$	Simplify.
$x^2 - 3x - 18 = 0$	Subtraction Property of Equality
$(x - 6)(x + 3) = 0$	Factor the trinomial.
$x = 6 \quad \text{or} \quad x = -3$	Use the zero product property to solve for x.

Check

Substitute 6 for x:

$$\log_2 (6 + 2) + \log_2 (6 - 5) \stackrel{?}{=} 3$$

$$\log_2 8 + \log_2 1 \stackrel{?}{=} 3$$

$$\log_2 8 \cdot 1 \stackrel{?}{=} 3$$

$$\log_2 8 = 3 \checkmark$$

The only solution is $x = 6$. ∎

Substitute -3 for x:

$$\log_2 (-3 + 2) + \log_2 (-3 - 5) \stackrel{?}{=} 3$$

$$\log_2 (-1) + \log_2 (-8) \stackrel{?}{=} 3$$

$\log_2 (-1)$ and $\log_2 (-8)$ are undefined, so -3 is an extraneous solution.

> **TIP**
>
> **Always check for extraneous solutions when you solve logarithmic equations.**

Solving Logarithmic Equations by Using the Logarithmic Property of Equality

If you can transform an equation into the form $\log_b a = \log_b c$, then you can use the logarithmic property of equality to write it as $a = c$.

Example 2 Solve and check.

A $\log_5 (x + 6) - \log_5 x = \log_5 4$

Solution

$$\log_5 (x + 6) - \log_5 x = \log_5 4$$

$$\log_5 \left(\frac{x + 6}{x} \right) = \log_5 4$$

$$\frac{x + 6}{x} = 4$$

$$x + 6 = 4x$$

$$6 = 3x$$

$$x = 2$$

Check

$$\log_5 (2 + 6) - \log_5 2 \stackrel{?}{=} \log_5 4$$

$$\log_5 8 - \log_5 2 \stackrel{?}{=} \log_5 4$$

$$\log_5 \left(\frac{8}{2} \right) \stackrel{?}{=} \log_5 4$$

$$\log_5 4 = \log_5 4 \checkmark$$

B $2 \log_{10} r = \frac{1}{2} \log_{10} 64$

Solution   ┈┈► **Check**

$2 \log_{10} r = \frac{1}{2} \log_{10} 64$ Substitute $\sqrt{8}$ for r: Substitute $-\sqrt{8}$ for r:

$\log_{10} r^2 = \log_{10} 64^{\frac{1}{2}}$ $2 \log_{10} \sqrt{8} \overset{?}{=} \frac{1}{2} \log_{10} 64$ $2 \log_{10} \left(-\sqrt{8}\right) \overset{?}{=} \frac{1}{2} \log_{10} 64$

$\log_{10} r^2 = \log_{10} 8$ $\log_{10} \left(\sqrt{8}\right)^2 \overset{?}{=} \log_{10} 64^{\frac{1}{2}}$ $\log_{10} \left(-\sqrt{8}\right)$ is undefined, so $-\sqrt{8}$

$r^2 = 8$ $\log_{10} 8 = \log_{10} 8 \checkmark$ is an extraneous solution.

$r = \pm\sqrt{8}$ The only solution is $x = \sqrt{8} = 2\sqrt{2}$. ∎

Problem Set

Write each equation in exponential form and then solve. Check for extraneous solutions.

1. $\log_3 81 = x$

2. $\log_2 32 = x$

3. $\log_6 6 = a$

4. $\log_{15} 1 = n$

5. $\log_{\frac{1}{5}} 625 = x$

6. $\log_7 \frac{1}{49} = y$

7. $\log_2 (x + 4) = 5$

8. $\log_8 (t + 6) = 3$

9. $\log_6 (2x + 8) = 4$

10. $\log_3 (2g - 5) = 5$

Solve. Check for extraneous solutions.

11. $\log_{81} (r - 5) + \log_{81} (r + 3) = \frac{1}{2}$

12. $2 \log_8 (4 - x) = 2$

13. $\log_8 \left(\frac{5 - v}{16v}\right) = -2$

14. $2 \log_4 (k + 5) = 3$

15. $\log_{81} (x + 2) - \log_{81} \left(\frac{x}{3}\right) = \frac{1}{2}$

16. $\log_2 (c - 12) + \log_2 (2c) = 7$

17. $\log_4 x + \log_4 (x + 6) = 2$

18. $\log_4 (9z + 5) - \log_4 (2z + 2) = 1$

19. $\log_6 4 + \log_6 6x = 3$

20. $\log_{\frac{1}{3}} (7x - 2) - \log_{\frac{1}{3}} (x - 6) = -3$

21. $\log_6 (2y + 3) = \log_6 (7y)$

22. $\log_2 (2h - 11) = \log_2 (h + 3)$

23. $\log_7 2q + \log_7 q = \log_7 32$

24. $\log_5 (5x - 1) - \log_5 (x + 1) = \log_5 4$

25. $2 \log_9 b = \frac{1}{4} \log_9 81$

26. $2 \log_8 (2x - 5) = \frac{1}{3} \log_8 729$

27. $\frac{1}{3} \log_{10} x = 2 \log_{10} 2$

28. $\log_9 (n - 5) + \log_9 (n + 2) = \frac{3}{5} \log_9 32$

*29. Challenge $\log_{625} 125 = w$

*30. Challenge

$\frac{1}{2} \log_3 5x - \frac{1}{2} \log_3 (8x - 15) = \log_3 \frac{4}{5}$

Graphing Logarithmic Functions

A **logarithmic function** is an equation of the form $f(x) = \log_b (x - h) + k$, where $x - h > 0$, $b > 0$, and $b \neq 1$.

Since $f(g(x)) = f(b^x) = \log_b b^x = x$ and $g(f(x)) = g(\log_b x) = b^{\log_b x} = x$, the logarithmic function $f(x) = \log_b x$ and the exponential function $g(x) = b^x$ are inverses of each other.

Graphing Logarithmic Functions

The function $f(x) = \log_b x$ is the parent function for logarithmic functions.

Logarithmic Functions of the Form: $f(x) = \log_b x$

$f(x) = \log_b x$, when $b > 1$.

End behavior:
As x increases in value, $f(x)$ slowly increases in value. As x decreases in value, $f(x)$ decreases in value.

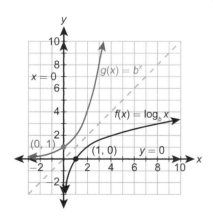

$f(x) = \log_b x$, when $0 < b < 1$.

End behavior:
As x increases in value, $f(x)$ decreases in value. As x decreases in value, $f(x)$ increases in value.

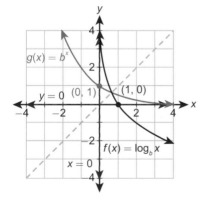

The following properties are common to both types of logarithmic functions:

General shape: $f(x) = \log_b x$ is the inverse of $g(x) = b^x$. Notice that the graph of $f(x) = \log_b x$ is the reflection of $g(x) = b^x$ across the line $y = x$.

Asymptote: As x decreases in value, the function nears the y-axis but never meets or crosses it, so the line $x = 0$ (the y-axis) is an asymptote of the graph.

Domain: all real numbers greater than 0

Range: the set of all real numbers

x-intercept: 1

Example 1   Graph each of the following.

Ⓐ $f(x) = \log_2 x$

Solution   In the function $f(x) = \log_2 x$, $b = 2$.

Step 1   Make a table of values. Include a few positive and negative values, as well as zero. The x-intercept is 1, and the point (2, 1) lies on the graph.

x	$\frac{1}{8}$	$\frac{1}{4}$	$\frac{1}{2}$	1	2	4	8
f(x)	−3	−2	−1	0	1	2	3

THINK ABOUT IT

$f(x) = \log_2 x$ is the inverse of $g(x) = 2^x$, so you know that $f(g(x)) = \log_2 2^x = x$ and $g(f(x)) = 2^{\log_2 x} = x$.

Step 2   Plot the points from the table. Then connect the points in a smooth curve. As a guide, use the general shape of the parent function when $b > 1$.

Notice that the graph gets closer to the y-axis as the values of x get smaller. So the line $x = 0$ is an asymptote of the function $f(x) = \log_2 x$.

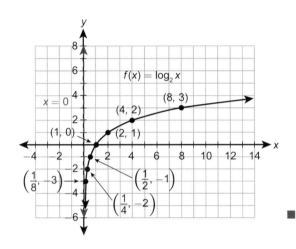

THINK ABOUT IT

Since $f(x) = \log_2 x$ is the inverse of $g(x) = 2^x$, if $\left(\frac{1}{8}, -3\right)$ is a point on the graph of $f(x) = \log_2 x$, then $\left(-3, \frac{1}{8}\right)$ lies on the graph of $g(x) = 2^x$. In general, if (x, y) is a point on $f(x) = \log_2 x$, then (y, x) is a point on $g(x) = 2^x$.

Ⓑ $f(x) = \log_{\frac{1}{2}} x$

Solution   In the function $f(x) = \log_{\frac{1}{2}} x$, $b = \frac{1}{2}$.

Step 1   Make a table of values. The x-intercept is 1, and the point $\left(\frac{1}{2}, 1\right)$ lies on the graph.

x	8	4	2	1	$\frac{1}{2}$	$\frac{1}{4}$	$\frac{1}{8}$
f(x)	−3	−2	−1	0	1	2	3

Step 2   Plot the points from the table. Then connect the points in a smooth curve. As a guide, use the general shape of the parent function when $0 < b < 1$.

Notice that the graph gets closer to the y-axis as the values of x get smaller. So the line $x = 0$ is an asymptote of the function $f(x) = \log_{\frac{1}{2}} x$.

The graph of $f(x) = \log_{\frac{1}{2}} x$ is a reflection across the x-axis of the graph of $g(x) = \log_2 x$.

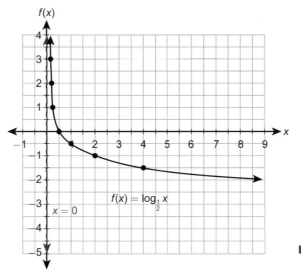

You can use the change of base formula to write any logarithmic function using common or natural logarithms. This makes it easier to check your graphs on a graphing calculator. For example, to graph $f(x) = \log_2 x$, graph $y = \dfrac{\log x}{\log 2}$.

Graphing a Function in the Family $f(x) = \log_b (x - h) + k$

Logarithmic Functions Graph Family: $f(x) = \log_b (x - h) + k$

Functions of the form $f(x) = \log_b (x - h) + k$ are in the family of logarithmic functions whose parent function is $g(x) = \log_b x$.

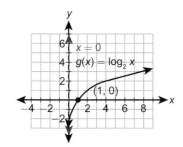

Parent function

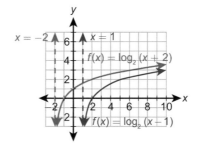

If $h < 0$, the graph of the parent function is translated to the left. If $h > 0$, it is translated to the right.

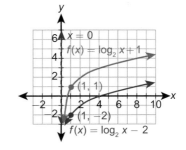

If $k < 0$, the graph of the parent function is translated down. If $k > 0$, it is translated up.

The graph of $f(x) = \log_b (x - h) + k$ has asymptote $x = h$. The domain of the function is the set of real numbers greater than h, and the range is the set of all real numbers.

Example 2 Graph $f(x) = \log_2 (x + 1) - 3$. Then find its domain, its range, and the equation of its asymptote.

Solution **Method 1** Make a table of values.

x	$\log_2 (x + 1) - 3$	$f(x)$
$-\dfrac{7}{8}$	$\log_2\left(-\dfrac{7}{8} + 1\right) - 3 = \log_2 \dfrac{1}{8} - 3 = -3 - 3$	-6
$-\dfrac{1}{2}$	$\log_2\left(-\dfrac{1}{2} + 1\right) - 3 = \log_2 \dfrac{1}{2} - 3 = -1 - 3$	-4
0	$\log_2 (0 + 1) - 3 = \log_2 1 - 3 = 0 - 3$	-3
1	$\log_2 (1 + 1) - 3 = \log_2 2 - 3 = 1 - 3$	-2
7	$\log_2 (7 + 1) - 3 = \log_2 8 - 3 = 3 - 3$	0

To sketch the graph, use the ordered pairs and the knowledge that the function is a logarithmic function.

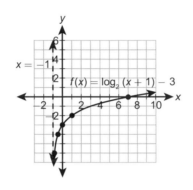

Method 2 Transform the graph of the parent function. In the function $f(x) = \log_2 (x + 1) - 3$, $b = 2$, $h = -1$, and $k = -3$.

$g(x) = \log_2 x$ is shown in red on the graph. The graph of $f(x) = \log_2 (x + 1) - 3$ gets translated down by 3 units and left by 1 unit.

The domain of the function $f(x) = \log_2 (x + 1) - 3$ is the set of real numbers greater than -1. The range is the set of all real numbers. The asymptote is the line $x = -1$.

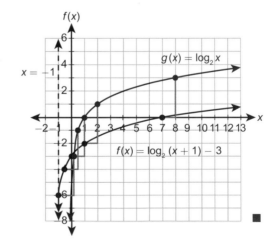

Using the Graph of a Function to Find the Equation for the Function

Example 3 What is the equation of the function shown in the graph?

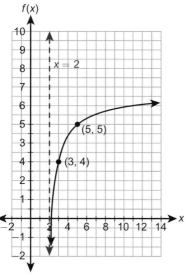

Solution The asymptote is at $x = 2$, so you know the graph has been translated two units to the right. This means that $h = 2$.

$$f(x) = \log_b (x - 2) + k$$

Now, substitute the ordered pair (3, 4).

$$4 = \log_b (3 - 2) + k$$
$$4 = \log_b 1 + k$$

But the log of 1 is always zero, so you know that k has to be 4:

$$f(x) = \log_b (x - 2) + 4$$

Now, substitute the other ordered pair to find the value for b.

$$5 = \log_b (5 - 2) + 4$$
$$1 = \log_b 3$$
$$b^1 = 3$$
$$b = 3$$

So, the equation is $f(x) = \log_3 (x - 2) + 4$. ∎

> **THINK ABOUT IT**
>
> Changing the parameter b results in different end behavior. When $b > 1$, $f(x)$ increases/decreases more slowly as b increases. When $b < 1$, $f(x)$ increases/decreases more quickly as b increases.

Problem Set

Graph each logarithmic function.

1. $f(x) = \log_3 x$

2. $f(x) = \log_4 x$

3. $f(x) = \log_{\frac{1}{10}} x$

4. $f(x) = \log_{\frac{1}{5}} x$

5. $f(x) = -\log_{\frac{1}{3}} x$

6. $f(x) = \log_5 x + 2$

Graph each function. Then find its domain, its range, and the equation of its asymptote.

7. $f(x) = 2 \log_2 (x - 1) + 4$

8. $f(x) = -\log_3 (x + 2) - 1$

9. $f(x) = 3 \log_4 (x + 4) + 2$

10. $f(x) = \frac{1}{2} \log_5 (x - 3) - 5$

11. $f(x) = -4 \log_{\frac{1}{2}} (x + 3) + 1$

12. $f(x) = -\frac{1}{3} \log_{\frac{1}{5}} (x - 5) - 4$

Describe the effect each parameter has on the graph, given that the parent function is $f(x) = \log_2 x$.

13. $f(x) = \log_2 (x + 9)$

14. $f(x) = \log_2 (x - 4) + 10$

15. $f(x) = -\log_2 (x + 5) - 3$

16. $f(x) = \frac{1}{2} \log_2 (x - 3) - 7$

17. $f(x) = 3 \log_2 (x + 11) + 8$

18. $f(x) = -3 \log_2 (x) - \frac{1}{2}$

Find the equation of the function shown in the graph. The parent function is given.

19. $f(x) = \log_4 x$

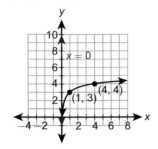

23. $f(x) = \log_6 x$

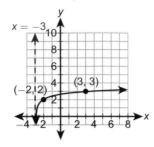

20. $f(x) = \log_5 x$

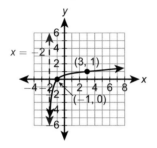

24. $f(x) = -\log_2 (x - 2)$

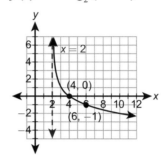

21. $f(x) = \log_{\frac{1}{3}} x$

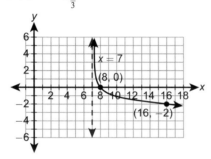

*25. Challenge $f(x) = \log_{\frac{1}{2}} x$

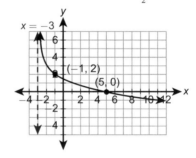

22. $f(x) = \log_3 (x + 1)$

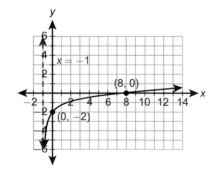

*26. Challenge $f(x) = \log_b x$

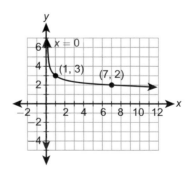

Applications: Logarithms

Logarithmic functions have applications in many scientific fields.

Chemistry Application: pH

The pH of a substance indicates its acidity. Substances that are more acidic have a lower pH than substances that are less acidic. The logarithmic function $f(x) = -\log_{10} x$ models the pH of different substances. Specifically, the function $pH = -\log_{10} [H^+]$ measures the pH of a substance, where $[H^+]$ is the hydrogen-ion concentration of the substance, measured in moles per liter.

Example 1   The pH of a brand of apple juice is 3.5. What is the $[H^+]$ for the apple juice?

Solution   Use the logarithmic function $pH = -\log_{10} [H^+]$. The pH level of the juice is 3.5.

$$pH = -\log_{10} [H^+]$$

$3.5 = -\log_{10} [H^+]$ Substitute 3.5 for pH.

$-3.5 = \log_{10} [H^+]$ Multiply both sides by -1.

$[H^+] = 10^{-3.5}$ Definition of a logarithm

There are exactly $10^{-3.5}$ moles of hydrogen ions in a liter of apple juice whose pH level is 3.5. By using a calculator and rounding the result to four decimal places, you can determine that $[H^+]$ is approximately 0.0003 mole per liter. ■

THINK ABOUT IT

Pure water has a pH level of 7.0, which is considered neutral on the pH scale. You can use pH paper to test whether a substance is acidic (below 7.0 on the pH scale), alkaline (above 7.0), or neutral.

TIP

The value in the calculator window may read 3.16227766E−4, which means $3.16227766 \times 10^{-4}$.

Biology Application: Exponential Growth

Under the right conditions, the bacteria grow exponentially according to this formula: $N_t = N_0 e^{ct}$, where N_0 is the initial number of bacteria (at time $t = 0$), t is the number of days, and N_t is the number of bacteria after t days. The constant c is the growth factor for a particular type of bacteria in a given environment.

Example 2   At the beginning of an experiment, a culture has 400 bacteria. Three days later, the culture has 2000 bacteria.

Ⓐ Calculate the growth factor.

Ⓑ Predict the number of bacteria 8 days after the beginning of the experiment.

THINK ABOUT IT

This formula is the same as the one used in Applications: Growth and Decay, but written differently:

$$N_t = N_0 (e^c)^t$$
$$y = b(1 - r)^t$$

Solution

A First, find the value of c by substituting the given data:

$N_0 = 400$, $t = 3$, $N_t = 2000$.

$$N_t = N_0 e^{ct}$$

$$2000 = 400 \cdot e^{3c}$$

$$\frac{2000}{400} = e^{3c} \qquad \text{Divide both sides by 400.}$$

$$5 = e^{3c}$$

$$\ln 5 = \ln e^{3c} \qquad \text{Take the natural logarithm of both sides.}$$

$$\ln 5 = 3c \qquad \text{Power Property of Logarithms}$$

$$\frac{\ln 5}{3} = c \qquad \text{Divide both sides by 3.}$$

The growth factor of the function is $\dfrac{\ln 5}{3}$.

B Substitute the value for c to predict the number after 8 days:

$$N_t = N_0 e^{ct}$$

$$N_t = 400 \cdot e^{8 \cdot \frac{\ln 5}{3}}$$

$$N_t \approx 29{,}240 \qquad \text{Use a calculator and round your answer.}$$

The prediction is that there will be about 29,240 bacteria 8 days after the beginning of the experiment. ■

> **TIP**
>
> Substitute the exact value $\left(\dfrac{\ln 5}{3} = c\right)$ in the formula. Round only at the *end* of the calculation.

Physics Application: Decibels

The decibel scale measures the relative intensity R of a sound to the human ear. The *threshold of hearing* I_0 is the intensity of the faintest sound that can be heard by the human ear. Other sound intensities I are often measured by comparing them to the threshold of hearing. The logarithmic function $R = 10 \log_{10} \dfrac{I}{I_0}$ can be used to find the relative intensity of a sound in decibels.

Example 3   The sound intensity of a vacuum cleaner is about 10^8 times greater than the threshold of hearing. What is the relative intensity of a vacuum cleaner, measured in decibels?

Solution   Use the logarithmic function $R = 10 \log_{10} \dfrac{I}{I_0}$. Since the sound of the vacuum cleaner is 10^8 times greater than the threshold of hearing, $I = 10^8 \cdot I_0$. Substitute $10^8 \cdot I_0$ in the equation for I:

$$R = 10 \log_{10} \frac{I}{I_0}$$

$$R = 10 \log_{10} \frac{10^8 \cdot I_0}{I_0} \qquad \text{Substitute } 10^8 \cdot I_0 \text{ for } I.$$

$$R = 10 \log_{10} 10^8 \qquad \text{Simplify by using exponential form.}$$

$$R = 10 \cdot 8$$

$$R = 80$$

The relative intensity of a vacuum cleaner is about 80 decibels. ■

Seismology Application: Richter Scale

The Richter scale is not linear, which means that an earthquake of magnitude 8 does *not* release twice as much energy as one of magnitude 4.

Example 4   An earthquake in the region of the Dominican Republic measured 3.2 on the Richter scale, while an earthquake near New Zealand measured 6.4. Compare the amount of energy released by these two earthquakes.

Solution   Use $M = \frac{2}{3} \log_{10} \frac{E}{10^{11.8}}$ to calculate the amount of energy released by each earthquake.

Dominican Republic earthquake:

$$3.2 = \frac{2}{3} \log_{10} \frac{E}{10^{11.8}}$$

$$4.8 = \log_{10} \frac{E}{10^{11.8}}$$

$$10^{4.8} = \frac{E}{10^{11.8}}$$

$$10^{4.8} \cdot 10^{11.8} = E$$

$$10^{16.6} = E$$

$$3.9810 \times 10^{16} \approx E$$

New Zealand earthquake:

$$6.4 = \frac{2}{3} \log_{10} \frac{E}{10^{11.8}}$$

$$9.6 = \log_{10} \frac{E}{10^{11.8}}$$

$$10^{9.6} = \frac{E}{10^{11.8}}$$

$$10^{9.6} \cdot 10^{11.8} = E$$

$$10^{21.4} = E$$

$$2.5119 \times 10^{21} \approx E$$

To compare the stronger quake to the weaker one, write the fraction:

$$\frac{2.5119 \times 10^{21}}{3.9810 \times 10^{16}} = \frac{2.5119 \times 10^{5}}{3.9810} \approx 6.31 \times 10^{4}$$

The 6.4 quake released roughly 63,100 times the energy of the 3.2 quake. ∎

THINK ABOUT IT

An earthquake with magnitude between 3.5 and 5.4 on the Richter scale is felt, but rarely causes major damage. One of magnitude 7 or more is major and can cause serious damage.

Nuclear Application: Calculating Half-Life

The function $f(t) = b \cdot \left(\frac{1}{2}\right)^{\frac{t}{h}}$ gives the amount remaining, in milligrams, of a radioactive sample of b milligrams that has a half-life h after a period of time t.

Example 5   A sample of 50 mg of technetium-99m is given to a patient during a medical test. If the radioactive substance decays to 2.8 mg after 25 hours, find the half-life of this substance.

Solution

$$f(t) = b \cdot \frac{1}{2}^{\frac{t}{h}}$$

$$2.8 = 50 \cdot \left(\frac{1}{2}\right)^{\frac{25}{h}} \qquad \text{Substitute the given values.}$$

$$0.056 = \left(\frac{1}{2}\right)^{\frac{25}{h}} \qquad \text{Divide both sides by 50.}$$

$$\log 0.056 = \log \left(\frac{1}{2}\right)^{\frac{25}{h}} \qquad \text{Take the common logarithm of both sides.}$$

$$\log 0.056 = \frac{25}{h} \log \frac{1}{2} \qquad \text{Power Property of Logarithms}$$

$$h = 25 \cdot \frac{\log \frac{1}{2}}{\log 0.056} \qquad \text{Multiply both sides by } \frac{h}{\log 0.056}.$$

REMEMBER

The *half-life* of a radioactive substance is the time it takes for half of the substance to decay.

TIP

The units for h and t must be the same.

Use a calculator to find an approximate value of h, the half-life of this substance. Then check the result.

Calculate

$$h = 25 \cdot \frac{\log \frac{1}{2}}{\log 0.056}$$

$$h \approx 6$$

Recall that h and t have the same units—in this case, hours.

Check

$$2.8 = 50\left(\frac{1}{2}\right)^{\frac{25}{h}}$$

$$2.8 \stackrel{?}{\approx} 50\left(\frac{1}{2}\right)^{\frac{25}{6}}$$

$$2.8 \approx 2.7841 \checkmark$$

The half-life of technetium-99m is approximately 6 hours. ■

Example 6 Carbon-14 has a half life of 5730 years. Archaeologists find a wooden bowl that has 40% of the normal carbon-14 levels. When you replace b in the half-life formula with 1, the formula $f(t) = \left(\frac{1}{2}\right)^{\frac{t}{h}}$ gives the percentage left after t years, where h is the half-life. What is the approximate age of the bowl?

Solution

$$f(t) = \left(\frac{1}{2}\right)^{\frac{t}{h}}$$

$$0.4 = \left(\frac{1}{2}\right)^{\frac{t}{5730}} \qquad \text{Substitute the given values.}$$

$$\log 0.4 = \log \left(\frac{1}{2}\right)^{\frac{t}{5730}} \qquad \text{Take the common logarithm of both sides.}$$

$$\log 0.4 = \frac{t}{5730} \log \frac{1}{2} \qquad \text{Power Property of Logarithms}$$

$$\frac{5730}{\log \frac{1}{2}} \cdot \log 0.4 = t \qquad \text{Multiply both sides by } \frac{5730}{\log \frac{1}{2}}.$$

Use a calculator to find an approximate value of t, the age of the bowl. Then check the result.

Calculate

$$t = \frac{5730}{\log \frac{1}{2}} \cdot \log 0.4$$

$$t \approx 7575$$

Check

$$0.4 = \left(\frac{1}{2}\right)^{\frac{t}{5730}}$$

$$0.4 \stackrel{?}{\approx} \left(\frac{1}{2}\right)^{\frac{7575}{5730}}$$

$$0.4 \approx 0.39999 \checkmark$$

The age of the wooden bowl is approximately 7575 years. ■

Problem Set

Solve.

1. The pH level of distilled white vinegar is 2.4. What is the [H^+] for the solution?

2. At the beginning of an experiment, a culture has 1000 bacteria. Four days later, the culture has increased to 3000 bacteria. Predict the number of bacteria 10 days after the beginning of the experiment.

3. About 25 mg of tritium is spilled into the surrounding soil of a nuclear facility. About 7.87 mg is found to be present in the same area after 20 years. Find the half-life of this substance.

4. The sound intensity of thunder is 10^{12} times greater than the threshold of hearing. What is the relative intensity of thunder, measured in decibels?

5. The pH level of ammonia is 11. What is the [H^+] for the solution?

6. An earthquake measured 7 on the Richter scale. What was the amount of energy released by the earthquake?

7. At 2 p.m., a culture has 400 bacteria. At 5 p.m., the culture has grown to 1000 bacteria. Predict the number of bacteria that will be present at 10 p.m.

8. The pH level of milk is 6.6. What is the [H^+] for the solution?

9. A bone fragment contains 60% of the carbon-14 scientists assume was present initially. Approximately how old is it?

10. An earthquake measured 6.9 on the Richter scale. What was the amount of energy released by the earthquake?

11. On Day 1, a culture has 200 bacteria. On Day 3, the culture has increased to 800 bacteria. Predict the number of bacteria that will be present on Day 9.

12. The sound intensity of heavy traffic is 10^9 times greater than the threshold of hearing. What is the relative intensity of heavy traffic, measured in decibels?

13. The sound intensity of a quiet conversation is 10^3 times greater than the threshold of hearing. What is the relative intensity of a quiet conversation, measured in decibels?

14. At the beginning of an experiment, a culture has 50 bacteria. Five days later, the culture has increased to 120 bacteria. Predict the number of bacteria 6 days after the beginning of the experiment.

15. The pH level of lemon juice is 2.2. What is the [H^+] for the solution?

16. An earthquake measured 9.1 on the Richter scale. What was the amount of energy released by the earthquake?

17. The decibel level of a train entering a station is 110. How many times greater is the sound intensity of the train than the threshold of hearing?

18. About 20 mg of americium-241 is initially present in contaminated water. The radioactive sample decays to 18.55 mg after 50 years. Find the half-life of this substance.

19. At the beginning of a pesticide experiment, a colony has 300 insects. Two days later, the colony has shrunk to 180 insects. Predict the number of insects 5 days after the beginning of the experiment.

20. An earthquake in California measured 4.5 on the Richter scale, while an earthquake in China measured 7.2. Compare the amount of energy released by these two earthquakes.

21. The decibel level of a child's toy is 40. How many times greater is the sound intensity of the toy than the threshold of hearing?

22. About 60 mg of fluorine in a sample of tap water decays to 9.06 mg after 30 seconds. Find the half-life of this substance.

*23. **Challenge** Radium-226 has a half-life of 1620 years. If a groundwater sample containing the substance has 30% of its original level, what is the time of decay?

*24. **Challenge** An earthquake in Japan measured 5.7 on the Richter scale. Scientists predict a future earthquake in Russia will release 30 times the energy of the 5.7 earthquake. Determine the magnitude of the future quake.

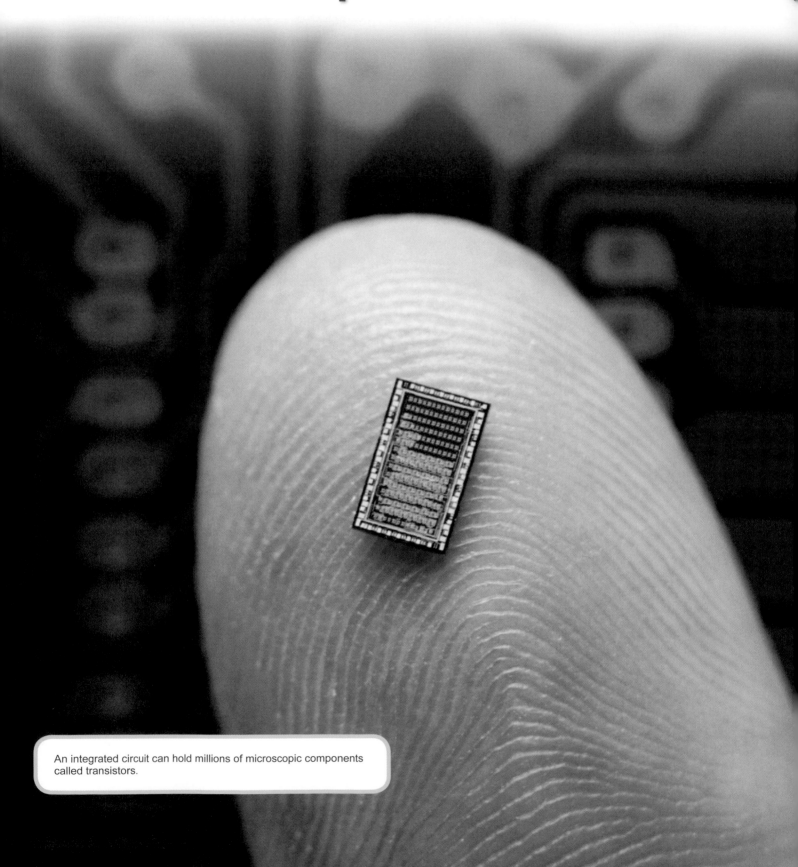

UNIT 11   Sequences and Series

An integrated circuit can hold millions of microscopic components called transistors.

How many transistors can fit in a chip on the tip of your finger? Moore's law predicts that the number doubles every two years. Sequences like the one Gordon Moore predicted can help solve many real-world problems.

Big Ideas

▶ A number is anything that obeys the laws of arithmetic; all numbers obey the laws of arithmetic. You can use the laws of arithmetic to create and write rules for sequences and series.

▶ If you use a mathematical model to represent a certain situation, you can use the model to solve other problems that you might not be able to solve otherwise.

▶ A function is a correspondence between two sets, the domain and the range, that assigns to each member of the domain exactly one member of the range. Many functions can be described by algebraic expressions.

Unit Topics

▶ Foundations for Unit 11

▶ Sequences and Patterns

▶ Arithmetic Sequences

▶ Geometric Sequences

▶ Applications: Sequences

▶ Series and Sigma Notation

▶ Arithmetic Series

▶ Geometric Series

▶ Applications: Series

▶ Technology: Sequences and Series

Foundations for Unit 11

Before you learn about sequences and series, make sure you know how to do the following:

▶ Identify the next term in a number pattern.

▶ Identify the domain and range for a function when given a table or graph.

▶ Calculate function values for given domain values.

Identifying the Next Term in a Number Pattern

Example 1 Find the next term in each number pattern.

Ⓐ 6, 9, 12, 15, 18, …

The difference between each pair of consecutive numbers is 3.
So, because $18 + 3 = 21$, the next number in the pattern is 21.

Ⓑ 8192, 2048, 512, 128, 32, …

Each number is the previous number divided by 4.
So, because $32 \div 4 = 8$, the next number in the pattern is 8.

Ⓒ 1, 4, 9, 16, 25, …

Each number is a square: $1 = 1^2, 4 = 2^2, 9 = 3^2, 16 = 4^2, 25 = 5^2$.
So the next number in the pattern is 36, or 6^2.

Ⓓ 33, 25, 18, 12, 7, …

The differences between successive numbers are 8, 7, 6, and 5.
Therefore, the next number in the pattern is 4 less than the previous number.
So, because $7 - 4 = 3$, the next number in the pattern is 3.

Problem Set A

· ·

Find the next term in each number pattern.

1. 3, 8, 13, 18, 23, …

2. 56, 42, 30, 20, 12, …

3. 1, 8, 27, 64, 125, …

4. 256, 128, 64, 32, 16, …

5. $\dfrac{7}{8}, \dfrac{6}{7}, \dfrac{5}{6}, \dfrac{4}{5}, \dfrac{3}{4}$, …

6. $\dfrac{3}{6}, \dfrac{5}{7}, \dfrac{7}{8}, \dfrac{9}{9}$, …

7. $\dfrac{2}{1}, \dfrac{3}{4}, \dfrac{4}{9}, \dfrac{5}{16}$, …

8. 0.5, 2.0, 4.5, 8.0, 12.5, …

9. 1, 1, 2, 3, 5, 8, 13, …

Identifying the Domain and Range for a Function

Definitions

relation	any set of ordered pairs
function	a relation that assigns to each member of the domain exactly one member of the range
domain	the set of allowable inputs
range	the set of possible outputs

Example 2 Identify the domain and range for each function.

 A

n	1	2	3	4	5
f(n)	4	6	8	10	12

Domain = {1, 2, 3, 4, 5}
Range = {4, 6, 8, 10, 12}

 B

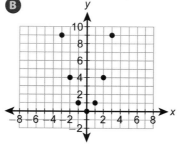

Domain = {−3, −2, −1, 0, 1, 2, 3}
Range = {0, 1, 4, 9}

THINK ABOUT IT

Continuous functions are functions with a connected graph.

Discrete functions are functions with a graph that is disconnected. The function in Example 2B is discrete.

Problem Set B

Identify the domain and range for each function.

10.

n	1	2	3	4	5
f(n)	27	21	15	9	3

11.

x	1	2	3	4
g(x)	2	2	2	2

12.

x	−3	−1	1	3	5	7
h(x)	5	7	5	7	5	7

13.

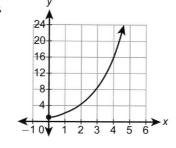

14.

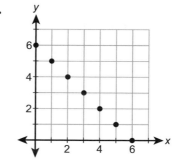

Calculating Function Values for Given Domain Values

When you evaluate $f(x)$, which is read "f of x," substitute the input value to find the corresponding output value.

Example 3 Calculate the function output for the input values 2 and 3.

Ⓐ $f(n) = 5 + 2n$ **Ⓑ** $f(x) = x^x$

Substitute 2 and 3 for x.   Substitute 2 and 3 for x.

$f(2) = 5 + 2 \cdot 2 = 5 + 4 = 9$ $f(2) = 2^2 = 4$

$f(3) = 5 + 2 \cdot 3 = 5 + 6 = 11$ $f(3) = 3^3 = 27$

Problem Set C

For each function, calculate the function output for the input values 1, 2, and 3.

15. $f(n) = 3 - 2n$ **18.** $f(x) = 30 - x^3$ **21.** $h(a) = a^{\frac{1}{3}}$

16. $f(b) = 5^b$ **19.** $h(t) = \log t$ **22.** $g(c) = c!$

17. $g(x) = x^3$ **20.** $f(r) = -3r - 11$ **23.** $f(n) = \dfrac{5!}{n!(5-n)!}$

Sequences and Patterns

A *sequence* can be thought of as a list of numbers that follow a particular pattern.

Each number of the sequence is called a *term*. Subscripts are used to describe each term's position in the list.

$$a_1, a_2, a_3, \ldots, a_n, \ldots$$

For instance, in the sequence

$$3, 6, 9, 12, \ldots,$$

$a_1 = 3$ because the first term is 3, $a_2 = 6$ because the second term is 6, and so on. The term a_n represents the nth term of the sequence.

Identifying Terms of a Sequence

A sequence can also be thought of as a function.

> **DEFINITIONS**
>
> A **sequence** is a function whose domain is the set of natural numbers. The range of the sequence is the set of **terms**, or the values of the function.

> **REMEMBER**
>
> The natural numbers are the counting numbers: 1, 2, 3, 4, ...

Example 1   Use the table of sequence values to determine the following.

n	1	2	3	4	5	6	7
a_n	2	6	18	54	162	486	1458

A What is the 3rd term of the sequence?

B Which term in the sequence is 486?

Solution

A The 3rd term of the sequence is found when $n = 3$. So $a_3 = 18$.

B a_n is 486 when $n = 6$. So 486 is the 6th term of the sequence. ∎

> **THINK ABOUT IT**
>
> You could write the nth element of the sequence as $a(n)$ instead of a_n, but you'll usually see the n written as a subscript.

Recursive Rules

> **DEFINITION**
>
> A **recursive rule** is a rule for generating terms of a sequence that depends on one or more previous terms of the sequence.

Example 2

A List the first four terms of the sequence: $a_1 = 8$, and $a_n = a_{n-1} + 6$ for $n \geq 2$.

Solution   The first term is 8. Use this term and the recursive rule to generate the next three terms.

$$a_1 = 8$$
$$a_2 = a_{2-1} + 6 = a_1 + 6 = 8 + 6 = 14$$
$$a_3 = a_{3-1} + 6 = a_2 + 6 = 14 + 6 = 20$$
$$a_4 = a_{4-1} + 6 = a_3 + 6 = 20 + 6 = 26$$

So the first four terms are 8, 14, 20, and 26. ■

> **THINK ABOUT IT**
>
> Because a_{n-1} represents the term just before a_n, each term in Example 2A can be found by adding 6 to the previous term.

B List the first four terms of the sequence: $b_1 = -2$, and $b_n = (b_{n-1})^2$ for $n \geq 2$.

Solution   The first term is -2.

$$b_1 = -2$$
$$b_2 = (b_{2-1})^2 = (b_1)^2 = (-2)^2 = 4$$
$$b_3 = (b_{3-1})^2 = (b_2)^2 = 4^2 = 16$$
$$b_4 = (b_{4-1})^2 = (b_3)^2 = 16^2 = 256$$

So the first four terms are -2, 4, 16, and 256. ■

C List the first six terms of the Fibonacci sequence: $f_1 = 1$, $f_2 = 1$, and $f_n = f_{n-2} + f_{n-1}$ for $n \geq 3$.

Solution   Use the rule when n is 3 or greater:

$$f_1 = 1$$
$$f_2 = 1$$
$$f_3 = f_{3-2} + f_{3-1} = f_1 + f_2 = 1 + 1 = 2$$
$$f_4 = f_{4-2} + f_{4-1} = f_2 + f_3 = 1 + 2 = 3$$
$$f_5 = f_{5-2} + f_{5-1} = f_3 + f_4 = 2 + 3 = 5$$
$$f_6 = f_{6-2} + f_{6-1} = f_4 + f_5 = 3 + 5 = 8$$

So the first six terms of the Fibonacci sequence are 1, 1, 2, 3, 5, and 8. ■

> **THINK ABOUT IT**
>
> The nth term of the Fibonacci sequence is the sum of the previous two terms.

Iterative Rules

Unlike a recursive rule, an *iterative* rule allows you to determine the *n*th term of a sequence, given the value of *n*.

> **DEFINITION**
>
> An **iterative rule** is a rule that can be used to find the *n*th term of a sequence without calculating previous terms of the sequence.

To find a term using an iterative rule, evaluate the rule for the given domain value.

Example 3

A Determine the 4th term of the sequence: $a_n = -n^3$.

Solution Substitute 4 for *n*: $a_4 = -4^3 = -(4)^3 = -64$. ∎

B Determine the 3rd, 8th, and 91st terms of the sequence: $a_n = -5n - 1$.

Solution Substitute 3, 8, and 91 for *n*:

$$a_3 = -5 \cdot 3 - 1 = -15 - 1 = -16$$

$$a_8 = -5 \cdot 8 - 1 = -40 - 1 = -41$$

$$a_{91} = -5 \cdot 91 - 1 = -455 - 1 = -456$$

So the 3rd, 8th, and 91st terms are -16, -41, and -456. ∎

Problem Set

Use the table of sequence values to answer the questions.

1.

n	1	2	3	4	5	6
k_n	3.4	4.0	4.6	5.2	5.8	6.4

A. What is the 4th term?

B. Which term of the sequence is 3.4?

2.

n	1	2	3	4	5	6
r_n	48	12	3	0.75	0.1875	0.046875

A. What is the 5th term?

B. Which term of the sequence is 12?

3.

n	5	6	7	8	9	10
a_n	$\dfrac{3}{16}$	$\dfrac{3}{32}$	$\dfrac{3}{64}$	$\dfrac{3}{128}$	$\dfrac{3}{256}$	$\dfrac{3}{512}$

A. What is the 5th term?

B. Which term of the sequence is $\dfrac{3}{512}$?

4.

n	3	4	5	6	7	8
h_n	11	7	3	-1	-5	-9

A. What is the 7th term?

B. Which term of the sequence is 3?

5.

n	10	11	12	13	14	15
b_n	87	96	105	114	123	132

A. What is the 12th term?

B. Which term of the sequence is 114?

6.

n	2	3	4	5	6	7
p_n	3.9	11.7	35.1	105.3	315.9	947.7

A. What is the 6th term?

B. Which term of the sequence is 947.7?

Use the recursive rule to find the first five terms of the sequence.

7. $a_1 = 3$, and $a_n = 2\left(a_{n-1}\right)^2$

8. $a_1 = \dfrac{2}{3}$, and $a_n = 5a_{n-1}$

9. $a_1 = 6$, and $a_n = a_{n-1} + 3$

10. $a_1 = 52$, and $a_n = a_{n-1} - 8.1$

11. $a_1 = 1.27$, and $a_n = 3a_{n-1}$

12. $a_1 = 1$, and $a_n = \left(a_{n-1}\right)^3$

13. $a_1 = 126$, and $a_n = \dfrac{a_{n-1}}{3}$

14. $a_1 = 5$, and $a_n = 2a_{n-1} + \dfrac{1}{2}$

15. $a_1 = 400$, and $a_n = \sqrt{a_{n-1}}$

16. $a_1 = 4$, and $a_n = \dfrac{1}{a_{n-1}} - 1$

Use the iterative rule to find the given term or terms of the sequence.

17. Determine the 11th term of the sequence: $a_n = n + 4$.

18. Determine the 7th term of the sequence: $a_n = -3n$.

19. List the first four terms of the sequence: $a_n = n^4$.

20. Determine the 16th term of the sequence: $a_n = -2(n - 1)$.

21. Determine the 9th term of the sequence: $a_n = 6n^2$.

22. Determine the 20th term of the sequence: $a_n = \dfrac{n + 6}{4}$.

23. Determine the 10th term of the sequence: $a_n = 5n - 2$.

24. Find the 24th term of the sequence: $a_n = -n + \sqrt{n}$.

25. Find the 6th term of the sequence: $a_n = 2n^2 - 3$.

26. Find the 84th term of the sequence: $a_n = \dfrac{7}{n} + 4$.

27. List the first two terms of the sequence: $a_n = 6(n - 1) - \dfrac{1}{n}$.

28. Find the 3rd term of the sequence: $a_n = -12n + \sqrt{n + 1}$.

Solve.

*29. **Challenge** An auditorium with six sections has 30 seats in the front section, 36 seats in the second section, 42 seats in the third section, and so on in an increasing pattern.

A. Write a recursive rule for the situation.

B. Write an iterative rule for the situation.

C. How many seats are in all six sections altogether?

*30. **Challenge** For the sequence: $\dfrac{1}{4}, \dfrac{3}{4}, \dfrac{9}{4}, \dfrac{27}{4}, \ldots$

A. Write a recursive rule.

B. Write an iterative rule.

Arithmetic Sequences

Sequences with a constant difference between consecutive terms have interesting properties and come up in many situations.

Common Differences

DEFINITION

A sequence is an **arithmetic sequence** if the difference between consecutive terms is a constant:
$$d = a_n - a_{n-1}$$
The constant d is called the **common difference** of the sequence.

TIP

If the differences between consecutive terms in a sequence are not equal, the sequence is not arithmetic.

To find the common difference of a given sequence, select any term of the sequence and subtract it from the next consecutive term.

Example 1   For each arithmetic sequence, find the common difference.

Ⓐ 14, 11, 8, 5, 2, …

Ⓑ $-9, -7.5, -6, -4.5, -3, \ldots$

Solution   Find the difference between c_3 and c_2:

$$d = 8 - 11 = -3$$

The common difference is -3. ■

Solution   Find the difference between h_2 and h_1:

$$d = -7.5 - (-9) = -7.5 + 9 = 1.5$$

The common difference is 1.5. ■

Writing and Using Recursive Rules for Arithmetic Sequences

RECURSIVE RULE FOR AN ARITHMETIC SEQUENCE

The formula for the common difference $d = a_n - a_{n-1}$ can be rearranged to obtain the following recursive rule for arithmetic sequences:

any term (after first) ← $a_n = a_{n-1} + d$ → common difference

previous term

When you define an arithmetic sequence recursively, you also need to provide the value for a_1.

Example 2 For the sequence $12, -3, -18, -33, -48, ...$:

A Find a recursive rule.

B Use the recursive rule to find the next two terms in the sequence.

Solution

A Begin by finding the common difference: $d = -3 - 12 = -15$. Substitute -15 for d in the equation $m_n = m_{n-1} + d$. So the recursive rule is $m_n = m_{n-1} - 15$.

The sequence starts with 12, so $m_1 = 12$.

B Find the next two terms, m_6 and m_7, as follows:

$$m_6 = m_{6-1} - 15 \qquad\qquad m_7 = m_{7-1} - 15$$
$$= m_5 - 15 \qquad\qquad\qquad = m_6 - 15$$
$$= -48 - 15 = -63 \qquad\quad = -63 - 15 = -78$$

The next two terms of the sequence are -63 and -78. ∎

THINK ABOUT IT

Note that an infinite number of sequences can be defined by the recursive rule $a_n = a_{n-1} - 15$ such as

$-5, -20, -35, -50, ...,$ and

$47, 32, 17, 2, ...,$

but only one has $a_1 = 12$.

Writing and Using Iterative Rules for Arithmetic Sequences

Using the recursive rule, you can see an iterative rule for jumping straight to the nth term in an arithmetic sequence.

$$a_1 = a_1 + 0d$$
$$a_2 = a_1 + d = a_1 + 1d$$
$$a_3 = a_2 + d = (a_1 + d) + d = a_1 + 2d$$
$$a_4 = a_3 + d = (a_1 + 2d) + d = a_1 + 3d$$

... and so on. Notice that each multiple of d is always 1 less than n.

ITERATIVE RULE FOR AN ARITHMETIC SEQUENCE

The iterative rule for the nth term of an arithmetic sequence with first term a_1 and common difference d is
$$a_n = a_1 + (n - 1)d.$$

This rule makes it possible to find any term of an arithmetic sequence if you know the first term and the common difference.

Example 3 For the sequence $16, 20, 24, 28, 32, ...$:

A Find an iterative rule.

B Use the iterative rule to find the 82nd term in the sequence.

Solution

A The first term is $f_1 = 16$, and the common difference is $d = 20 - 16 = 4$. Substitute 16 for f_1 and 4 for d in the rule $f_n - f_1 + (n - 1)d$, and then simplify:

$$f_n = 16 + (n - 1)4$$
$$= 16 + 4n - 4$$
$$= 12 + 4n$$

So the iterative rule is $f_n = 12 + 4n$.

B To find the 82nd term, substitute 82 for n in the rule:

$$f_{82} = 12 + 4 \cdot 82 = 340$$

The 82nd term of the sequence is 340. ∎

Graphing Arithmetic Sequences

Example 4 Graph each arithmetic sequence in the coordinate plane.

A $a_n = -5 + 4(n - 1)$

Solution The domain is the set of positive integers. Make a table of some points and plot those points to get a partial graph.

n	$a_n = -5 + 4(n - 1)$	a_n
1	$a_1 = -5 + 4(1 - 1) = -5 + 4 \cdot 0 = -5 + 0$	-5
2	$a_2 = -5 + 4(2 - 1) = -5 + 4 \cdot 1 = -5 + 4$	-1
3	$a_3 = -5 + 4(3 - 1) = -5 + 4 \cdot 2 = -5 + 8$	3
4	$a_4 = -5 + 4(4 - 1) = -5 + 4 \cdot 3 = -5 + 12$	7
5	$a_5 = -5 + 4(5 - 1) = -5 + 4 \cdot 4 = -5 + 16$	11

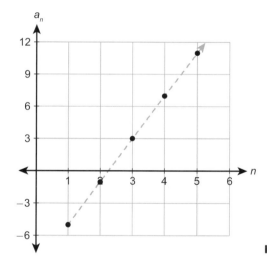

∎

B $q_n = 12 + (-2)(n - 1)$

Solution

n	$q_n = 12 + (-2)(n - 1)$	q_n
1	$q_1 = 12 + (-2)(1 - 1) = 12 + (-2)(0) = 12 + 0$	12
2	$q_2 = 12 + (-2)(2 - 1) = 12 + (-2)(1) = 12 - 2$	10
3	$q_3 = 12 + (-2)(3 - 1) = 12 + (-2)(2) = 12 - 4$	8
4	$q_4 = 12 + (-2)(4 - 1) = 12 + (-2)(3) = 12 - 6$	6
5	$q_5 = 12 + (-2)(5 - 1) = 12 + (-2)(4) = 12 - 8$	4

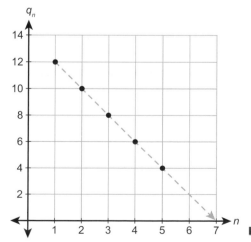

∎

Problem Set

. . . .

Use the iterative rule to find the 9th term of the sequence.

1. $a_n = 2 + n$

2. $b_n = 18 - 2n$

3. $p_n = 21 + 5n$

4. $a_n = -10 + 5n$

Find the common difference.

5. $1, 3, 5, 7, 9, \ldots$

6. $-25, -21, -17, -13, \ldots$

7. $15, 28, 41, 54, 67, \ldots$

8. $144, 132, 120, 108, 96, \ldots$

9. $-3.7, -10.5, -17.3, -24.1, -30.9, \ldots$

10. $\dfrac{1}{6}, \dfrac{2}{3}, \dfrac{7}{6}, \dfrac{5}{3}, \dfrac{13}{6}, \ldots$

For each sequence, do the following:

A. Write an iterative rule.
B. Write a recursive rule.
C. Find the next two terms of the sequence.

11. $2, 4, 6, 8, 10, \ldots$

12. $-1, -4, -7, -10, -13, \ldots$

13. $6, 8, 10, 12, 14, \ldots$

14. $-26, -31, -36, -41, -46, \ldots$

15. $20, 16, 12, 8, 4, \ldots$

16. $33, 9, -15, -39, -63, \ldots$

17. $10.5, 14, 17.5, 21, 24.5, \ldots$

18. $-\dfrac{3}{4}, -1, -\dfrac{5}{4}, -\dfrac{3}{2}, -\dfrac{7}{4}, \ldots$

19. $95.1, 87.9, 80.7, 73.5, 66.3, \ldots$

20. $\dfrac{8}{3}, 4, \dfrac{16}{3}, \dfrac{20}{3}, 8, \ldots$

Graph the arithmetic sequence in the coordinate plane.

21. $2, 3, 4, 5, 6, \ldots$

22. $12, 8, 4, 0, -4, \ldots$

23. $1, 1.5, 2, 2.5, 3, 3.5, 4, \ldots$

24. $\dfrac{1}{2}, 4, \dfrac{15}{2}, 11, \dfrac{29}{2}, \ldots$

25. $3, -7, -17, -27, \ldots$

26. $0, 0.125, 0.25, 0.375, 0.5, \ldots$

Solve.

*27. **Challenge** José saves spare change in a jar. Each day he adds the same amount in order to save up for a DVD that costs \$22.50. The amount José has in the jar follows the recursive rule $t_n = t_{n-1} + 0.50$. If he starts with \$5.00, in how many days will he be able to buy the DVD?

*28. **Challenge** Sabra has \$135 saved for lunch money. Each day, she takes out \$2.40 to buy lunch. Write the iterative rule for this situation. In how many days will she run out of lunch money?

Geometric Sequences

Sequences for which consecutive terms have a constant ratio come up in many situations and have interesting properties.

Common Ratios

> ### DEFINITION
>
> A sequence is a **geometric sequence** if the ratio between consecutive terms is a constant:
>
> $$r = \frac{a_n}{a_{n-1}}.$$
>
> The constant r is called the **common ratio** of the sequence.

Example 1 For each geometric sequence, find the common ratio.

A $76, 38, 19, 9.5, 4.75, \ldots$ **B** $-3, 9, -27, 81, -243, \ldots$

Solution To find the common ratio, select any term of the sequence except the first term. Then divide it by the previous term.

A If you select 38,
then $r = \frac{38}{76} = \frac{1}{2}$.
So the common ratio is $\frac{1}{2}$. ∎

B If you select -27,
then $r = \frac{-27}{9} = -3$.
So the common ratio is -3. ∎

> ### THINK ABOUT IT
>
> **If the common ratio is negative, then the terms of the sequence alternate between positive and negative values.**

Recursive Rules for Geometric Sequences

> ### RECURSIVE RULE FOR A GEOMETRIC SEQUENCE
>
> The formula for the common ratio $r = \dfrac{a_n}{a_{n-1}}$ can be rearranged to obtain the following recursive rule for geometric sequences:
>
> any term (after first) ← $a_n = r \cdot a_{n-1}$ → previous term
>
> common ratio

> ### THINK ABOUT IT
>
> **In the sequence 5, 15, 45, 135, 405, …,**
>
> $$a_1 = \text{given}$$
> $$a_2 = 3a_1$$
> $$a_3 = 3a_2$$
> $$a_4 = 3a_3$$
> **and so on ….**

When you define a geometric sequence recursively, you also need to provide the value for a_1.

Example 2 For the sequence 8, −16, 32, −64, 128, …:

Ⓐ Find a recursive rule.

Ⓑ Use the recursive rule to find the next two terms in the sequence.

Solution

Ⓐ Begin by finding the common ratio: $r = \dfrac{g_2}{g_1} = \dfrac{-16}{8} = -2$.

Substitute −2 for r in the equation $g_n = r \cdot g_{n-1}$.

The recursive rule is $g_n = -2 \cdot g_{n-1}$.

The sequence starts with 8, so $g_1 = 8$.

Ⓑ The next two terms are g_6 and g_7.

$$g_6 = -2 \cdot g_{6-1} \qquad\qquad\qquad g_7 = -2 \cdot g_{7-1}$$
$$= -2 \cdot g_5 \qquad\qquad\qquad\quad = -2 \cdot g_6$$
$$= -2 \cdot 128 = -256 \qquad\qquad = -2 \cdot (-256) = 512$$

So the next two terms of the sequence are −256 and 512. ∎

> **THINK ABOUT IT**
>
> Note that an infinite number of sequences can be defined by the recursive rule $a_n = -2 \cdot a_{n-1}$ such as
>
> −3, 6, −12, 24, …, and
> $\dfrac{1}{16}, -\dfrac{1}{8}, \dfrac{1}{4}, -\dfrac{1}{2}, \ldots$,
> but only 16, one has $a_1 = 8$.

Writing and Using Iterative Rules for Geometric Sequences

Using the recursive rule, you can see an iterative rule for jumping straight to the nth term in a geometric sequence.

$$a_1 = a_1 \cdot r^0$$
$$a_2 = a_1 \cdot r = a_1 \cdot r^1$$
$$a_3 = a_2 \cdot r = (a_1 \cdot r^1) \cdot r = a_1 \cdot r^2$$
$$a_4 = a_3 \cdot r = (a_1 \cdot r^2) \cdot r = a_1 \cdot r^3$$

… and so on. Notice that each power of r is always 1 less than n.

> **ITERATIVE RULE FOR A GEOMETRIC SEQUENCE**
>
> The iterative rule for the nth term of a geometric sequence with first term a_1 and common ratio r is
> $$a_n = a_1 \cdot r^{n-1}.$$

This rule makes it possible to find any term of a geometric sequence, given the first term and the common ratio.

Example 3 For the sequence $\dfrac{1}{64}, \dfrac{1}{16}, \dfrac{1}{4}, 1, 4, \ldots$:

Ⓐ Find an iterative rule.

Ⓑ Use the iterative rule to find the 10th term in the sequence.

Solution

Ⓐ Find the constant ratio, $r = c_2 \div c_1 = \dfrac{1}{16} \div \dfrac{1}{64} = \dfrac{1}{16} \cdot 64 = 4$.

Substitute $\dfrac{1}{64}$ for c_1 and 4 for r in the equation, $c_n = c_1 \cdot r^{n-1}$,

to obtain the iterative rule: $c_n = \dfrac{1}{64} \cdot 4^{n-1}$.

B To find the 10th term, substitute 10 for n:

$$c_{10} = \frac{1}{64} \cdot 4^{10-1}$$

$$= \frac{1}{64} \cdot 4^9$$

$$= 4096 \ \blacksquare$$

Graphing Geometric Sequences

Example 4 Graph each geometric sequence in the coordinate plane.

A $b_n = 1 \cdot 3^{n-1}$

Solution The domain is the set of positive integers. Make a table of some points and plot those points to get a partial graph.

n	$b_n = 1 \cdot 3^{n-1}$	b_n
1	$b_1 = 1 \cdot 3^{1-1} = 1 \cdot 3^0 = 1 \cdot 1$	1
2	$b_2 = 1 \cdot 3^{2-1} = 1 \cdot 3^1 = 1 \cdot 3$	3
3	$b_3 = 1 \cdot 3^{3-1} = 1 \cdot 3^2 = 1 \cdot 9$	9
4	$b_4 = 1 \cdot 3^{4-1} = 1 \cdot 3^3 = 1 \cdot 27$	27
5	$b_5 = 1 \cdot 3^{5-1} = 1 \cdot 3^4 = 1 \cdot 81$	81

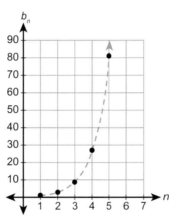

B $k_n = 32 \cdot \left(\frac{1}{2}\right)^{n-1}$

Solution

n	$k_n = 32 \cdot \left(\frac{1}{2}\right)^{n-1}$	k_n
1	$k_1 = 32 \cdot \left(\frac{1}{2}\right)^{1-1} = 32 \cdot \left(\frac{1}{2}\right)^0 = 32 \cdot 1$	32
2	$k_2 = 32 \cdot \left(\frac{1}{2}\right)^{2-1} = 32 \cdot \left(\frac{1}{2}\right)^1 = 32 \cdot \frac{1}{2}$	16
3	$k_3 = 32 \cdot \left(\frac{1}{2}\right)^{3-1} = 32 \cdot \left(\frac{1}{2}\right)^2 = 32 \cdot \frac{1}{4}$	8
4	$k_4 = 32 \cdot \left(\frac{1}{2}\right)^{4-1} = 32 \cdot \left(\frac{1}{2}\right)^3 = 32 \cdot \frac{1}{8}$	4
5	$k_5 = 32 \cdot \left(\frac{1}{2}\right)^{5-1} = 32 \cdot \left(\frac{1}{2}\right)^4 = 32 \cdot \frac{1}{16}$	2

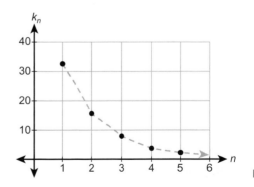

Problem Set

Use the iterative rule to find the 5th term of the sequence.

1. $c_n = -2 \cdot 2^{n-1}$

2. $f_n = 4 \cdot 3^{n-1}$

3. $a_n = -\dfrac{1}{36} \cdot 6^{n-1}$

4. $h_n = 5\left(\dfrac{1}{2}\right)^{n-1}$

5. $z_n = 2 \cdot 1^{n-1}$

6. $a_n = 0.7 \cdot 2^{n-1}$

Find the common ratio.

7. $1, 7, 49, 343, 2401, \ldots$

8. $-5, -15, -45, -135, \ldots$

9. $16, -4, 1, -\dfrac{1}{4}, \dfrac{1}{16}, \ldots$

10. $7, 29.4, 123.48, 518.616, \ldots$

11. $9, 13.5, 20.25, 30.375, \ldots$

12. $-3, 24, -192, 1536, \ldots$

13. $700, 350, 175, 87.5, \ldots$

14. $\dfrac{1}{625}, \dfrac{1}{125}, \dfrac{1}{25}, \dfrac{1}{5}, \ldots$

For each sequence, do the following:

A. Write an iterative rule.
B. Write a recursive rule.
C. Find the next two terms of the sequence.

15. $3, 6, 12, 24, 48, \ldots$

16. $-\dfrac{1}{64}, -\dfrac{1}{8}, -1, -8, \ldots$

17. $216, -36, 6, -1, \ldots$

18. $-36, -432, -5184, -62{,}208, \ldots$

19. $5, 1.5, 0.45, 0.135, \ldots$

20. $4.5, -22.5, 112.5, -562.5, \ldots$

21. $22, 88, 352, 1408, \ldots$

22. $420, 84, 16.8, 3.36, \ldots$

23. $-9, 3, -1, \dfrac{1}{3}, \ldots$

24. $2, 34, 578, 9826, \ldots$

Graph each geometric sequence in the coordinate plane.

25. $-3, -1, -\dfrac{1}{3}, -\dfrac{1}{9}, -\dfrac{1}{27}, \ldots$

26. $1, -4, 16, -64, \ldots$

27. $1, 3, 9, 27, \ldots$

28. $4, 2, 1, \dfrac{1}{2}, \dfrac{1}{4}, \ldots$

29. $-25, 5, -1, \dfrac{1}{5}, -\dfrac{1}{25}, \ldots$

30. $5, 10, 20, 40, 80, \ldots$

Solve.

***31.** **Challenge** Deshawn deposits $100 into a bank account that earns compound interest at 2% annually. Use this information to write an iterative rule for the amount in his bank account. *Hint*: The constant ratio is 1.02.

***32.** **Challenge** Yin deposits $100 into a bank account that earns compound interest at 1.5% annually. How much money will she have in 10 years?

Applications: Sequences

You can use sequences to solve problems that involve number patterns.

A sequence may be arithmetic, geometric, or neither. For example, the sequence 1, -2, 3, -4, 5, ... is neither arithmetic nor geometric, but you can examine the pattern and predict that the 6th term is -6.

Determining Whether a Sequence Is Arithmetic, Geometric, or Neither

Example 1 Decide whether each sequence is arithmetic, geometric, or neither.

Ⓐ $-\dfrac{3}{2}, \ -\dfrac{3}{8}, \ -\dfrac{3}{32}, \ -\dfrac{3}{128}, \ ...$

Solution

Is it arithmetic?
Test for a common difference by subtracting:

$$b_2 - b_1 = -\frac{3}{8} - \left(-\frac{3}{2}\right) = \frac{9}{8} \qquad b_3 - b_2 = -\frac{3}{32} - \left(-\frac{3}{8}\right) = \frac{9}{32}$$

There is no common difference, so it is not arithmetic.

Is it geometric?
Test for a common ratio by dividing:

$$b_2 \div b_1 = -\frac{3}{8} \div \left(-\frac{3}{2}\right) = -\frac{3}{8} \cdot \left(-\frac{2}{3}\right) = \frac{1}{4}$$

$$b_3 \div b_2 = -\frac{3}{32} \div \left(-\frac{3}{8}\right) = -\frac{3}{32} \cdot \left(-\frac{8}{3}\right) = \frac{1}{4}$$

$$b_4 \div b_3 = -\frac{3}{128} \div \left(-\frac{3}{32}\right) = -\frac{3}{128} \cdot \left(-\frac{32}{3}\right) = \frac{1}{4}$$

The common ratio is $\dfrac{1}{4}$. The sequence is geometric. ∎

Ⓑ 13, -8, -29, -50, ...

Solution

Is it arithmetic?
Test for a common difference by subtracting:

$z_2 - z_1 = -8 - 13 = -21$

$z_3 - z_2 = -29 - (-8) = -21$

$z_4 - z_3 = -50 - (-29) = -21$

The sequence is arithmetic. ∎

> **REMEMBER**
>
> In an arithmetic sequence, the *difference* between consecutive terms is the common difference.
>
> In a geometric sequence, the *ratio* between consecutive terms is the common ratio.

C 6, 7, 9, 12, ...

Solution

Is it arithmetic?

Test for a common difference by subtracting:

$$t_2 - t_1 = 7 - 6 = 1 \qquad\qquad t_3 - t_2 = 9 - 7 = 2$$

There is no common difference, so it is not arithmetic.

Is it geometric?

Test for a common ratio by dividing:

$$t_2 \div t_1 = 7 \div 6 \approx 1.167 \qquad\qquad t_3 \div t_2 = 9 \div 7 \approx 1.286$$

There is no common ratio, so it is not geometric.

The sequence is neither arithmetic nor geometric. ■

Example 2   Decide whether each sequence is arithmetic, geometric, or neither. Find the common difference or the common ratio, if there is one. Use the sequence to answer the question.

A   A display of soup cans in the grocery store is stacked so that the top layer has 1 can, the next layer is 2 by 2 and has 4 cans, the next layer is 3 by 3 and has 9 cans, and the next layer is 4 by 4 with 16 cans. How many cans are in the layer below that?

Solution   Write the sequence of numbers: 1, 4, 9, 16, ...

Is it arithmetic?

Test for a common difference by subtracting: $4 - 1 = 3; 9 - 4 = 5$. There is no common difference.

Is it geometric?

Test for a common ratio by dividing: $\frac{4}{1} = 4; \frac{9}{4} = 2.25$.

There is no common ratio.

This sequence is neither arithmetic nor geometric.

Use the pattern to find the next number in the sequence: $1^2 = 1; 2^2 = 4$; $3^2 = 9; 4^2 = 16$. The next layer will have 5^2 or 25 cans. ■

B   Suppose you find 1 penny on Monday, 2 pennies on Tuesday, 4 pennies on Wednesday, 8 pennies on Thursday, and 16 pennies on Friday. If this pattern continues, how many pennies will you find on Saturday?

Solution   Write the sequence of numbers: 1, 2, 4, 8, 16, ...

Is it arithmetic?

Test for a common difference: $2 - 1 = 1; 4 - 2 = 2$. There is no common difference.

Is it geometric?

Test for a common ratio: $\frac{2}{1} = 2; \frac{4}{2} = 2; \frac{8}{4} = 2; \frac{16}{8} = 2$.

The common ratio is 2. This sequence is geometric.

Use the common ratio to find the next number in the sequence: $16 \cdot 2 = 32$. The next number in the pattern is 32. You will find 32 pennies on Saturday. ■

> **TIP**
>
> To show that the test for a common difference or a common ratio *fails*, you only need to use two calculations. If the results are not the same, the test fails. However, to show that a common difference or a common ratio *exists*, you must test all the given numbers in the sequence.

C Makena adds $15 every month to her savings jar. Every month, she counts how much money there is in the jar. What will her savings be after 6 months?

Solution   Write the sequence of numbers: $15, $30, $45, $60, $75, ….

Is it arithmetic?
Test for a common difference: $30 - 15 = 15$; $45 - 30 = 15$; $60 - 45 = 15$; $75 - 60 = 15$.
The common difference is $15. This is an arithmetic sequence.

Use the common difference to find the next number in the sequence:
$75 + 15 = 90$. After 6 months, she will have $90. ■

Application: Money

Example 3   Suppose someone offers to pay you 1 penny on the first day, 2 pennies the second day, and so on, doubling the number of pennies each day. (This is the same pattern as in Example 2B.) What is the first day on which your pay would be at least $10?

Solution   Begin by changing $10 to pennies. So the question is, on which day would you be paid 1000 pennies?

Step 1   Write what you know, and what you are looking for, in terms of the sequence rules.

You know the common ratio: $r = 2$. You know the first term: $a_1 = 1$.
You know the value of the nth term: $a_n = 1000$.

You will be paid $10 on day n. What you don't know is the value of n.

Step 2   Use the iterative rule, $a_n = a_1 \cdot r^{n-1}$, with the values you know.

$$a_n = a_1 \cdot r^{n-1}$$
$$1000 = 1 \cdot 2^{n-1} \qquad \text{Substitute.}$$
$$10^3 = 2^{n-1} \qquad \text{Simplify.}$$
$$\log 10^3 = \log 2^{n-1} \qquad \text{Take the common logarithm of both sides.}$$
$$3 = (n-1)\log 2 \qquad \text{Definition and Power Property of Logarithms}$$
$$\frac{3}{\log 2} = n - 1 \qquad \text{Divide both sides by } \log 2.$$
$$\frac{3}{\log 2} + 1 = n \qquad \text{Add 1 to both sides.}$$
$$9.97 \approx n \qquad \text{Use a calculator to approximate the value.}$$

Step 3   Check for reasonableness: On day 10, $a_{10} = 1 \cdot 2^{10-1}$, so $a_{10} = 512$ pennies, and on day 11, $a_{11} = 1 \cdot 2^{11-1}$, so $a_{11} = 1024$ pennies. On day 11, you will be paid more than $10. ■

THINK ABOUT IT

What do the three dots following a list of numbers mean?

1, 2, 4, 8, 16, …

The dots show that the sequence continues in the same pattern without end.

REMEMBER

When you know one term of an arithmetic or geometric sequence, you use a recursive rule to find the next term:

For an arithmetic sequence:
$a_n = a_{n-1} + d$.

For a geometric sequence:
$a_n = r \cdot a_{n-1}$.

In both of these rules, a_n is any term after the first, called the nth term. The previous term is a_{n-1}. The common difference is d and the common ratio is r.

Application: Population Growth

Example 4   A small town had a population of 968 in 2000. By the next year, the population had grown to 1007. In 2002, there were 1047 people, and the next year there were 1089.

A What kind of sequence is this?

B If this pattern continues, what will be the population after 15 years?

Solution

A Write the sequence of numbers: 968, 1007, 1047, 1089, ...

Step 1   Test for a common difference by subtracting: $1007 - 968 = 39$; $1047 - 1007 = 40$; $1089 - 1047 = 42$.
There is no common difference.

Step 2   Test for a common ratio by dividing:

$\frac{1007}{968} \approx 1.04$; $\frac{1047}{1007} \approx 1.04$; $\frac{1089}{1047} \approx 1.04$.

There is a common ratio. This sequence is geometric.
Each year the population increases by about 4%.

B Use the iterative rule, $a_n = a_1 \cdot r^{n-1}$, with the values you know.

$a_n = a_1 \cdot r^{n-1}$
$a_{15} = 968 \cdot 1.04^{15-1}$ Substitute.
$a_{15} = 968 \cdot 1.04^{14}$ Simplify.
$a_{15} \approx 1676$ Use a calculator to approximate the value.

After 15 years, the population will be about 1676. ■

Application: Finance

Example 5   The balance on a car loan is $7600. The car owner makes a payment of $200 every month.

A Write a sequence showing the balance for the first 5 months.
What kind of sequence is this?

B When will the balance be less than $600?

Solution

A The sequence is $7600, $7400, $7200, $7000, ... There is a common difference of $-$200, so this is an arithmetic sequence.

B Find the number of the term that is equal to $600.

$c_n = c_1 + (n - 1) \cdot d$
$600 = 7600 + (n - 1) \cdot (-200)$ Substitute.
$600 = 7600 - 200n + 200$ Distribute -200.
$-7200 = -200n$ Simplify.
$36 = n$ Divide both sides by -200.

Notice that the first term, c_1, is $7600, and the balance after 1 payment is c_2, or $7400. So c_{36} is the balance after 35 payments, and $c_{36} = 600$. This means the balance will be less than $600 after 36 payments. ■

Application: Physics

Example 6   A ball is dropped from a height of 100 inches. The ball bounces, each time reaching a lower and lower height. The height of each bounce is 80% of the height of the previous bounce.

A What height, rounded to the nearest inch, will the ball reach after bouncing 4 times?

B How many bounces will it take for the ball to reach a height of less than 1 inch?

Solution

A In this situation, the first height in this geometric sequence is 100 inches. So $f_1 = 100$. The second height will be 80% of 100 inches, and so forth. This means that the height, after bouncing 4 times, is the fifth height in the sequence, f_5.

Step 1   Write what you know, and what you are looking for, in sequence notation.

The common ratio is 80%, or 0.8, so $r = 0.8$, and you know $f_1 = 100$.

You are looking for the value of the fifth term, f_5.

Step 2   Find f_n when $n = 5$.

$$f_n = f_1 \cdot r^{n-1}$$

$f_5 = 100 \cdot 0.8^{5-1}$	Substitute.
$f_5 = 100 \cdot 0.8^4$	Simplify.
$f_5 = 40.96$	Use a calculator to evaluate.

After bouncing 4 times, the ball will reach a height of almost 41 inches.

B Now you need to solve for n when the height f_n is 1 inch.

$f_n = f_1 \cdot r^{n-1}$	
$1 = 100 \cdot 0.8^{n-1}$	Substitute.
$10^{-2} = 0.8^{n-1}$	Divide both sides by 100. Simplify.
$\log 10^{-2} = \log 0.8^{n-1}$	Take the common logarithm of both sides.
$-2 = (n-1) \cdot \log 0.8$	Definition and Power Property of Logarithms
$\dfrac{-2}{\log 0.8} + 1 = n$	Divide each side by $\log 0.8$. Add 1 to each side.
$21.6377 \approx n$	Use a calculator to approximate the value.

Since we can only assign meanings to whole number values of n (it does not make sense to talk about a portion of a bounce), we should check the value of the function at $n = 21$ and $n = 22$ in order to answer the question. When $n = 21$, $f_{21} = 100 \cdot 0.8^{21-1} \approx 0.92$ and when $n = 22$, $f_{22} = 100 \cdot 0.8^{22-1} \approx 1.15$. So, the ball reaches a height of less than 1 inch on its 22nd bounce. ■

Actually, if you try this with a real ball, the ball would probably not bounce as many as 22 times. It would lose energy and stop bouncing before that.

<aside>
THINK ABOUT IT

Because the height of each successive bounce is 80% of a positive number, the ball's bounce, in theory, will never reach a zero height. In practice, however, the ball loses energy and does eventually stop bouncing.
</aside>

<aside>
THINK ABOUT IT

To be sure of the pattern in a sequence, you may need to know more than just three terms. For example, the pattern in 1, 2, 4, ... could be to *double* the previous number, or it could be to *square* the previous number. You can't tell until you know the fourth term.
</aside>

Problem Set

For each problem, do the following:

A. **Decide whether each sequence is arithmetic, geometric, or neither.**
B. **Find the common difference or the common ratio, if there is one.**
C. **Write the next term in the sequence.**

1. $170, 110, 50, -10, \ldots$

2. $1, -3, 9, -27, \ldots$

3. $\frac{1}{2}, 1, 2, 4, \ldots$

4. $19, 29, 39, 49, \ldots$

5. $1, 2, 1, 2, 1, \ldots$

6. $4, 5, 7, 10, 14, \ldots$

Decide whether each sequence is arithmetic or geometric, and then solve.

7. Mr. Brown's salary is $32,000 and increases by $300 each year. Write a sequence showing the salary for the first 5 years. When will he make over $34,700?

8. A city has a population of 23,000 in 2005, 27,600 in 2006, 33,120 in 2007, and 39,744 in 2008. If this pattern continues, what will the population be in 2012?

9. Kori adds 4 pictures to her new scrapbook each day. How many pictures will be in her book in 10 days?

10. A limbo pole is set 4.5 feet from the ground. After each challenge, the pole is lowered a half foot. After which challenge will the pole hit the ground?

11. Dai'Anna decides to start a savings account. She deposits 1 penny on the first day, 3 pennies on the second day, and so on, tripling the number of pennies each day. How much money will she deposit into the account on the 9th day?

12. A ball is dropped from a height of 50 meters. Each time the ball bounces, its height is 70% of the previous height. How many bounces will it take for the ball to reach a height close to 4 meters?

13. Kuki loses 2.5 kilograms per week on his diet. Before the diet, Kuki weighed 90 kilograms. Write a sequence showing his weight for the first 6 weeks.

14. Archie constructs a bull's-eye by using 4 concentric circles. The radius of each circle is four times greater than the radius of the closest inner circle. If the radius of the innermost circle is 3 centimeters, write a sequence showing the radius of each circle. How many circles would have to be added to make a radius greater than 3000 centimeters?

15. The balance on an interest-free loan for a commercial property is $120,000. The property owner makes a payment of $2250 each month. Write a sequence showing the balance for the first 5 months. When will the balance be less than $100,000?

16. A water tank contains 5000 liters of water. By the end of each day, 70% of the water remains. When will there be less than 1000 liters in the tank?

17. Tamika cuts fabric for a school project. She begins by cutting 8 meters from a large bolt. The next piece she cuts is half the length of the previous piece. How much does she cut off on the 6th cut?

18. Olympic athletes train every day. One runner has shaved 1% off of his time for the mile run every month for the last 3 months. If this pattern continues and his initial time was 300 seconds, what will his time be in the 6th month?

19. The population of Hampton decreases each year by 0.1%. If the population was 9000 in 2001, what will Hampton's population be in 2005?

20. Hugh is saving for a CD player. He has $10 in his bank account and saves $1.50 per week. Write a sequence showing the amount in his account for the first 4 weeks. When will he be able to buy a $50 player?

21. An outdoor storage bin contains 10,000 kilograms of road salt. Each day, a quarter of the salt is removed. How much salt is in the bin at the end of the 19th day?

22. Home Decor Supplies is testing the durability of new paint. The manager places a painted object in a room of 10°F. Each day, the manager increases the temperature of the room by 10%. When will the temperature reach 80°F?

*23. **Challenge** Ali makes a starting salary of $35,000 and is guaranteed to earn a raise of $400 each year he works for the company. Miko makes a starting salary of $36,800 and is promised a raise of $250 each year. In what year will their salaries be equal?

*24. **Challenge** Corrie drops a ball from a height of 1000 meters. After the 12th bounce, the ball reaches a height of 282.4 meters. How high does the ball bounce as compared to the height of the previous bounce? Express this as a percentage to the nearest tenth.

Series and Sigma Notation

The sum of the first four terms of the sequence
1, 3, 5, 7, … is represented by the sum $1 + 3 + 5 + 7$.

The expression $1 + 3 + 5 + 7$ is called a *series*.

> **DEFINITION**
>
> A **series** is the sum of consecutive terms of a sequence.

The notation S_n represents the sum of the first n terms of a series:

$$\textbf{Sequence: } 2, 5, 8, 11, 14, \ldots$$
$$\textbf{Corresponding Series: } 2 + 5 + 8 + 11 + 14 + \ldots$$
$$S_1 = 2$$
$$S_2 = 2 + 5 = 7$$
$$S_3 = 2 + 5 + 8 = 15$$
$$S_4 = 2 + 5 + 8 + 11 = 26$$
$$S_5 = 2 + 5 + 8 + 11 + 14 = 40$$
$$\ldots \text{ and so on.}$$

> **THINK ABOUT IT**
>
> The sum of the first n terms of a series is called the **nth partial sum.**

When a series has many terms, it can be convenient to use *sigma notation*, also known as *summation notation*. Sigma notation uses the Greek capital letter sigma: $\sum$.

Finding a Sum in Sigma Notation

> **DEFINITION**
>
> The sum S_n of the first n terms of a sequence can be represented as follows:
>
> $$S_n = \sum_{i=1}^{n} a_i = a_1 + a_2 + a_3 + \ldots + a_n.$$
>
> S_n is equivalent to $\sum_{i=1}^{n} a_1$, which is read as "the sum from 1 to n of a_i."
> In this notation, i is called the **index**, n is called the **upper limit**, and 1 is the **lower limit**.

> **TIP**
>
> The lower limit of a series in sigma notation is not always equal to 1. The lower limit can be any whole number less than or equal to n.

To find the sum of a series given in sigma notation, begin by writing it in *expanded* form. You can then find the sum by adding the terms of the series.

Example 1 Write the series in expanded form. Then simplify and find the sum.

(A) $\displaystyle\sum_{i=1}^{4} 6i$

Solution

$$\sum_{i=1}^{4} 6i = 6 \cdot 1 + 6 \cdot 2 + 6 \cdot 3 + 6 \cdot 4 \qquad \text{Expanded form}$$

$$= 6 + 12 + 18 + 24 \qquad \text{Simplify.}$$

$$= 60 \ \blacksquare$$

(B) $\displaystyle\sum_{k=1}^{6} k^2$

Solution

$$\sum_{k=1}^{6} k^2 = 1^2 + 2^2 + 3^2 + 4^2 + 5^2 + 6^2 \qquad \text{Expanded form}$$

$$= 1 + 4 + 9 + 16 + 25 + 36 \qquad \text{Simplify.}$$

$$= 91 \ \blacksquare$$

(C) $\displaystyle\sum_{n=2}^{6} (2n - 1)$

Solution

$$\sum_{n=2}^{6} (2n - 1) = \underbrace{(2 \cdot 2 - 1) + (2 \cdot 3 - 1) + (2 \cdot 4 - 1) + (2 \cdot 5 - 1) + (2 \cdot 6 - 1)}_{\text{Expanded form}}$$

$$= (4 - 1) + (6 - 1) + (8 - 1) + (10 - 1) + (12 - 1)$$

$$= 3 + 5 + 7 + 9 + 11$$

$$= 35 \ \blacksquare$$

Using Sigma Notation to Describe a Series

Example 2 Write each series using sigma notation.

(A) $4 + 9 + 14 + 19 + 24 + 29 + 34$

Solution This series is arithmetic, with a first term of 4 and a common difference of 5. So the iterative rule for the related sequence is $a_i = 5i - 1$. There are $n = 7$ terms in the series.

So the answer is $\displaystyle\sum_{i=1}^{7} (5i - 1)$. You can check your answer by writing it in expanded form. $\blacksquare$

> **REMEMBER**
>
> The iterative rule for an arithmetic sequence is $a_n = a_1 + (n - 1)d$, and the iterative rule for a geometric sequence is $a_n = a_1 \cdot r^{n-1}$.

B $1 + \frac{1}{2} + \frac{1}{4} + \frac{1}{8}$

Solution This series is geometric, with a first term of 1 and a common ratio of $\frac{1}{2}$. So the iterative rule for the related sequence is $a_i = \left(\frac{1}{2}\right)^{n-1}$.

There are $n = 4$ terms in the series.

So the answer is $\sum_{i=1}^{4} \left(\frac{1}{2}\right)^{i-1}$. You can check your answer by writing it in expanded form. ■

Problem Set

Write each series in expanded form and find the sum.

1. $\sum_{n=1}^{8} n$

2. $\sum_{m=1}^{6} 2m$

3. $\sum_{i=1}^{5} 3+i$

4. $\sum_{i=1}^{6} (2i+3)$

5. $\sum_{k=1}^{4} (3k-1)$

6. $\sum_{p=1}^{5} (2p)^2$

7. $\sum_{n=1}^{5} (-2n+4)$

8. $\sum_{k=1}^{4} (4k+1)$

9. $\sum_{f=4}^{11} -2f$

10. $\sum_{m=3}^{5} -(3m)^2$

11. $\sum_{i=10}^{17} \left(\frac{1}{2}i + \frac{5}{2}\right)$

12. $\sum_{n=17}^{20} 5n$

13. $\sum_{c=2}^{9} (-7c-2)$

14. $\sum_{b=1}^{5} (4b)^2$

15. $\sum_{k=6}^{12} \frac{1}{2}k$

Write each series using sigma notation.

16. $5 + 7 + 9 + 11 + 13 + 15 + 17 + 19 + 21$

17. $1 + 2 + 4 + 8 + 16 + 32 + 64$

18. $4, 2, 0, -2, -4, -6$

19. $4 + 1 + \frac{1}{4} + \frac{1}{16} + \frac{1}{64} + \frac{1}{256}$

20. $-5 - 20 - 80 - 320$

21. $4 + 4.5 + 5 + 5.5 + 6 + 6.5 + 7$

22. $2 + 6 + 18 + 54 + 162$

23. $-64 + (-16) + (-4) + (-1) + \left(-\frac{1}{4}\right)$

24. $3 + 10 + 17 + 24 + 31 + 38$

25. $5 + 25 + 125 + 625 + 3125$

26. $\frac{1}{36} + \frac{1}{6} + 1 + 6 + 36 + 216$

27. $9 + 6 + 3 + 0 + (-3)$

28. $1 + 6 + 11 + 16 + 21 + 26 + 31 + 36$

29. $49 - 7 + 1 - \frac{1}{7} + \frac{1}{49}$

Solve.

*30. **Challenge** For a contest, people need to identify how many marbles are in an opaque jar on the last day of the county fair. Each day for one week, 3 more marbles are added to the jar than were added the day before. The number of marbles in the jar is defined by $\sum_{i=1}^{7} (3i + 7)$, where i is the day.

    A. Write the series in expanded form and find the sum.

    B. How many marbles are in the jar at the end of the week?

*31. **Challenge** Raoul saves pennies in a jug. Each day he saves 10 more pennies than the day before. For the first 10 days, he saves $10 + 20 + 30 + 40 + 50 + 60 + 70 + 80 + 90 + 100$.

    A. Write the series in sigma notation and find the sum.

    B. How much money did he save in 10 days?

Arithmetic Series

How quickly can you add the numbers from 1 to 100 in your head?

It is said that in elementary school, the famous mathematician Carl Friedrich Gauss added the integers from 1 to 100 in seconds by recognizing that the sum was 50 pairs of numbers, each of which added to 101.

Arithmetic Series

DEFINITION

An **arithmetic series** is a series that results from adding the terms of an arithmetic sequence.

REMEMBER

A series is the sum of consecutive terms of a sequence.

For example, if you start with the arithmetic sequence

$$5, 8, 11, 14, \ldots,$$

then you can define the corresponding series:

$$5 + 8 + 11 + 14 + \ldots.$$

Because the sequence goes on forever, the sum also goes on forever. In general, if a_n represents the terms of an arithmetic sequence, then the sum of all the terms of the sequence is

$$S = a_1 + a_2 + a_3 + a_4 + \ldots.$$

When you are interested in the sum of the first n terms of the arithmetic sequence, you can write the nth partial sum of the series as follows:

$$S_n = a_1 + a_2 + a_3 + a_4 + \ldots + a_{n-2} + a_{n-1} + a_n.$$

Finding the Sum of the First n Terms of an Arithmetic Series

A general formula for the sum, S_n, of the first n terms of an arithmetic series can be seen with the help of an example.

sums of pairs
$20 + 23 = 43$
$17 + 26 = 43$
$14 + 29 = 43$
$11 + 32 = 43$
$8 + 35 = 43$
$5 + 38 = 43$

$$5 + 8 + 11 + 14 + 17 + 20 + 23 + 26 + 29 + 32 + 35 + 38$$

You can see that each of these six pairs sums to 43. This is the type of pattern that Gauss recognized and used to calculate the sum so quickly.

ARITHMETIC SERIES FORMULA

The sum of the first n terms of an arithmetic series with first term a_1 and nth term a_n is given by

$$S_n = \frac{n}{2}(a_1 + a_n).$$

Example 1

A Find the sum of the first 100 positive even integers.

Solution There are $n = 100$ terms. Also, $a_1 = 2$ and $a_n = 200$.

$$S_{100} = \frac{100}{2}(2 + 200)$$

$$= 50 \cdot 202 = 10{,}100$$

So the sum of the first 100 positive even integers is 10,100. ∎

B Find the sum: $\displaystyle\sum_{i=1}^{17}(2i + 5)$.

Solution There are $n = 17$ terms. Find a_1 and a_n.

$$a_1 = 2 \cdot 1 + 5 = 7$$

$$a_{17} = 2 \cdot 17 + 5 = 39$$

Now find S_{17}:

$$S_{17} = \frac{17}{2}(7 + 39)$$

$$= 8.5 \cdot 46 = 391$$

So $\displaystyle\sum_{i=1}^{17}(2i + 5) = 391$. ∎

> **TIP**
>
> To find the sum of the first n terms of an arithmetic series by using the formula
>
> $$S_n = \frac{n}{2}(a_1 + a_n),$$
>
> you need to know the number of terms, n, the first term, a_1, and the last term, a_n.

An Alternate Formula for the Sum of the First n Terms of an Arithmetic Series

If you substitute $a_1 + (n - 1)d$ for a_n in the formula $S_n = \frac{n}{2}(a_1 + a_n)$, you get an alternate formula for the sum of the first n terms of an arithmetic series.

$$S_n = \frac{n}{2}(a_1 + a_n) = \frac{n}{2}(a_1 + a_1 + (n - 1)d) = \frac{n}{2}(2a_1 + (n - 1)d)$$

ALTERNATE ARITHMETIC SERIES FORMULA

The sum of the first n terms of an arithmetic series with first term a_1 and common difference d is given by

$$S_n = \frac{n}{2}(2a_1 + (n - 1)d).$$

Example 2

A Find the sum of the first 20 terms: $-35 + (-30) + (-25) + (-20) + \dots$.

Solution The first term is $b_1 = -35$, and the constant difference is $d = 5$.
So the sum of the first 20 terms can be found as shown:

$$S_n = \frac{n}{2}(2b_1 + (n-1)d)$$
$$= \frac{20}{2}[2(-35) + (20-1)5]$$
$$= 10(-70 + 19 \cdot 5)$$
$$= 10 \cdot 25$$
$$= 250$$

So the sum of the first 20 terms is 250. ■

B Find the sum of the first 14 terms of the arithmetic series where
$c_1 = 32{,}000$ and common difference $d = 1500$.

Solution There are $n = 14$ terms in the series. The first term is $c_1 = 32{,}000$,
and the constant difference is $d = 1500$. So the sum of the first 14 terms is

$$S_n = \frac{n}{2}(2c_1 + (n-1)d)$$
$$= \frac{14}{2}[2 \cdot 32{,}000 + (14-1)1500]$$
$$= 7(64{,}000 + 19{,}500)$$
$$= 7 \cdot 83{,}500$$
$$= 584{,}500$$

So the sum of the first 14 terms is 584,500. ■

Graphing the Partial Sums of an Arithmetic Series

Example 3 Graph the first five partial sums of the arithmetic series.

$$1 + 2 + 3 + 4 + 5 + 6 + 7 + \dots$$

Solution Make a table of the five partial sums and then plot the points.

n	S_n
1	1
2	$1 + 2 = 3$
3	$1 + 2 + 3 = 6$
4	$1 + 2 + 3 + 4 = 10$
5	$1 + 2 + 3 + 4 + 5 = 15$

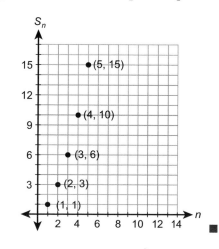

Problem Set

Find the indicated partial sum of the arithmetic series.

1. first 50 positive integers

2. first 20 positive integers that are multiples of 3

3. first 10 positive integers that are multiples of 5

4. $\displaystyle\sum_{i=1}^{42}(-3i+7)$

5. $\displaystyle\sum_{i=1}^{30}(5i-6)$

6. $\displaystyle\sum_{i=1}^{9}(9i-21)$

7. S_9 for $116+91+66+41+\dots$

8. S_{12} for $2+3.5+5+6.5+8+\dots$

9. S_{20} for $-9+(-17)+(-25)+(-33)+\dots$

10. S_{13} for $84.2+64.6+45+25.4+\dots$

11. S_7 for $-2+2+6+10+14+\dots$

12. S_{23} for $\dfrac{1}{2}+\dfrac{5}{4}+2+\dfrac{11}{4}+\dfrac{7}{2}+\dots$

13. S_{10} where $a_1=150$ and $d=-15$

14. S_9 where $a_1=15$ and $d=12$

15. S_{11} where $a_1=-7$ and $d=2$

16. S_{16} where $a_1=4$ and $d=-3$

17. S_{15} where $a_1=12$ and $d=6$

18. S_{22} where $a_1=-1$ and $d=-5$

19. S_7 where $a_1=5$ and $d=-4$

20. S_9 where $a_1=9$ and $d=4$

21. S_8 where $a_1=-19$ and $d=7$

22. S_{12} where $a_1=3200$ and $d=-250$

Graph the first 5 partial sums of the arithmetic series.

23. $2+3+4+5+6+\dots$

24. $4+2+0+(-2)+(-4)+\dots$

25. $1+3+5+7+9+11+\dots$

26. $-1+3+7+11+15+\dots$

27. $7+5+3+1+(-1)+\dots$

28. $-3+(-2)+(-1)+0+1+2+\dots$

Solve.

*29. **Challenge** Making Earth Greener, a nonprofit organization, is having a lottery to raise money. Each day there is no winner, the organization adds an amount of money i to the prize. If i increases by $5 each day, and the initial prize on Day 1 is $10, write the sum in sigma notation for the prize money at the end of 7 days. Then evaluate the sum.

*30. **Challenge** Chloe decides to start a savings account at her local bank. At the end of each week she deposits money in the account. The amount of money Chloe deposits increases by $2 each week, and her balance at the end of the first week is $102. Write the sum in sigma notation for the amount of money in Chloe's account at the end of 12 weeks. Then evaluate the sum.

Geometric Series

The sum of the terms of an arithmetic sequence is an arithmetic series. Likewise, you can sum the terms of a geometric sequence to get a geometric series.

DEFINITION

A **geometric series** is a series that results from adding the terms of a geometric sequence.

For example, if you start with the geometric sequence

$$2, -6, 18, -54, 162, \ldots,$$

then you can define the corresponding series:

$$2 + (-6) + 18 + (-54) + 162 + \ldots.$$

Finding the Sum of the First *n* Terms of a Geometric Series

A general formula for the sum, S_n, of the first n terms of a geometric series can be seen with the help of an example.

Consider a geometric series where $a_1 = 1$ and $r = 2$. Now consider the 8th partial sum: $S_8 = 1 + 2 + 4 + 8 + 16 + 32 + 64 + 128$. Multiply both sides by 2, then subtract:

REMEMBER

The iterative rule for a geometric sequence is $a_n = a_1 \cdot r^{n-1}$.

$$
\begin{aligned}
S_8 &= 1 + 2 + 4 + 8 + 16 + 32 + 64 + 128 \\
-2S_8 &= - (2 + 4 + 8 + 16 + 32 + 64 + 128 + 256) \\
\hline
(1-2)S_8 &= 1 + 0 + 0 + 0 + 0 + 0 + 0 + 0 - 256 \\
S_8 &= \frac{1 - 256}{(1 - 2)}
\end{aligned}
$$

In the numerator, notice that $1 = a_1$ and that $256 = a_9$. In the denominator, $2 = r$.

You can find the general rule for the sum of the first n terms of a geometric series as follows:

$$S_n = a_1 + a_1 r + a_1 r^2 + \ldots + a_1 r^{n-2} + a_1 r^{n-1}$$

$$-rS_n = - \quad (a_1 r + a_1 r^2 + \ldots + a_1 r^{n-2} + a_1 r^{n-1} + a_1 r^n)$$

$$S_n - rS_n = a_1 - a_1 r^n$$

$$S_n(1 - r) = a_1 - a_1 r^n$$

$$S_n = \frac{a_1 - a_1 r^n}{1 - r}$$

$$S_n = \frac{a_1(1 - r^n)}{1 - r} \text{ , where } r \neq 1.$$

GEOMETRIC SERIES FORMULA

The sum of the first n terms of a geometric series with first term a_1 and common ratio r is

$$S_n = \frac{a_1(1 - r^n)}{1 - r},$$

where $r \neq 1$.

THINK ABOUT IT

Dividing by zero is undefined, which is why $r \neq 1$ in the formula for the sum of the first n terms of a geometric series.

Example 1 Find the indicated sum of the geometric series.

Ⓐ S_7 for the series $400 + 200 + 100 + 50 + \ldots$

Solution Notice that $n = 7$, $a_1 = 400$, and $r = \frac{1}{2}$. So

$$S_7 = \frac{400\left(1 - \left(\frac{1}{2}\right)^7\right)}{1 - \frac{1}{2}} = \frac{400\left(1 - \frac{1}{128}\right)}{\frac{1}{2}} = \frac{400 \cdot \frac{127}{128}}{\frac{1}{2}} = 793\frac{3}{4}.$$

So the sum is $793\frac{3}{4}$. ■

Ⓑ $\displaystyle\sum_{i=2}^{7} 3^i$

Solution Here, $a_1 = 9$, $n = 6$ and $r = 3$.

$$S_6 = \frac{9(1 - 3^6)}{1 - 3} = \frac{9(1 - 729)}{-2} = \frac{-6552}{-2} = 3276$$

So the sum is 3276. ■

An Alternate Formula for the Sum of the First n Terms of a Geometric Series

You can see that, in order to use the formula for a geometric series, you need to know the first term, the common ratio, and the number of terms being summed.

With a little work, you can also derive a formula for the nth partial sum of a geometric series when you know the first term, the common ratio, and the value of the nth term.

Multiply both sides of the iterative rule for a geometric sequence by r:

$$a_n = a_1 r^{n-1}$$
$$a_n \cdot r = a_1 r^{n-1} \cdot r$$
$$a_n r = a_1 r^{n-1+1}$$
$$a_n r = a_1 r^n$$

Replacing $a_1 r^n$ with $a_n r$ in the formula $S_n = \dfrac{a_1 - a_1 r^n}{1-r}$ yields the following formula:

ALTERNATE GEOMETRIC SERIES FORMULA

The sum of the first n terms of a geometric series is given by

$$S_n = \frac{a_1 - a_n r}{1-r},$$

where $r \neq 1$.

TIP

This formula does not require you to know n.

Example 2 Find the sum of each geometric series.

Ⓐ $3 - 6 + 12 - 24 + \ldots + 192$

Solution Notice that $a_1 = 3$, $r = -2$, and $a_n = 192$. Use the formula that does not require knowing n.

$$S_n = \frac{a_1 - a_n r}{1-r}$$

$$= \frac{3 - 192 \cdot (-2)}{1 - (-2)}$$

$$= \frac{3 + 384}{3}$$

$$= \frac{387}{3}$$

$$= 129$$

So the sum of the series is 129. ∎

Ⓑ $2 + 1 + 0.5 + 0.25 + 0.125 + \ldots + 0.015625$

Solution Here, $a_1 = 2$, $r = 0.5$, and $a_n = 0.015625$. Use the formula that does not require knowing n.

$$S_n = \frac{a_1 - a_n r}{1-r}$$

$$= \frac{2 - 0.015625 \cdot 0.5}{1 - 0.5}$$

$$= \frac{2 - 0.0078125}{0.5}$$

$$= \frac{1.9921875}{0.5}$$

$$= 3.984375$$

So the sum of the series is 3.984375. ∎

Graphing the Partial Sums of a Geometric Series

Example 3 Graph the first 6 partial sums of each geometric series.

Ⓐ $1 + \dfrac{1}{2} + \dfrac{1}{4} + \dfrac{1}{8} + \dfrac{1}{16} + \dfrac{1}{32} + \cdots$

Solution   Make a table of the first 6 partial sums, and then plot the points.

n	S_n
1	1
2	$1 + \dfrac{1}{2} = 1.5$
3	$1 + \dfrac{1}{2} + \dfrac{1}{4} = 1.75$
4	$1 + \dfrac{1}{2} + \dfrac{1}{4} + \dfrac{1}{8} \approx 1.88$
5	$1 + \dfrac{1}{2} + \dfrac{1}{4} + \dfrac{1}{8} + \dfrac{1}{16} \approx 1.94$
6	$1 + \dfrac{1}{2} + \dfrac{1}{4} + \dfrac{1}{8} + \dfrac{1}{16} + \dfrac{1}{32} \approx 1.97$

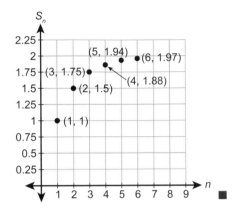

Ⓑ $(-0.8) + 1.6 + (-3.2) + 6.4 + (-12.8) + 25.6 + \cdots$

Solution   Make a table of the first 6 partial sums, and then plot the points.

n	S_n
1	-0.8
2	$-0.8 + 1.6 = 0.8$
3	$-0.8 + 1.6 + (-3.2) = -2.4$
4	$-0.8 + 1.6 + (-3.2) + 6.4 = 4$
5	$-0.8 + 1.6 + (-3.2) + 6.4 + (-12.8) = -8.8$
6	$-0.8 + 1.6 + (-3.2) + 6.4 + (-12.8) + 25.6 = 16.8$

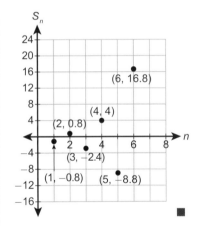

Problem Set

Find the indicated partial sum of the geometric series.

1. first 8 terms: $20 + 40 + 80 + 160 + \ldots$

2. first 7 terms: $250 + 50 + 10 + 2 + \ldots$

3. first 6 terms: $\frac{1}{3} + 1 + 3 + 9 + \ldots$

4. first 9 terms: $-3 + 27 - 243 + 2187 + \ldots$

5. first 10 terms: $-2 - 1 - \frac{1}{2} - \frac{1}{4} + \ldots$

6. S_8 for $1.5 + 13.5 + 121.5 + 1093.5 + \ldots$

7. S_{10} for $-192 + 48 - 12 + 3 + \ldots$

8. S_8 for $1 - \frac{1}{6} + \frac{1}{36} - \frac{2}{216} + \ldots$

9. S_{12} for $0.01024 + 0.0512 + 0.256 + 1.28 + \ldots$

10. S_7 for $-22 - 44 - 88 - 176 - 352 - \ldots$

11. S_9 for $1000 - 400 + 160 - 64 + \ldots$

12. $\displaystyle\sum_{i=2}^{10} 5^i$

13. $\displaystyle\sum_{i=1}^{6} 4^i$

14. $\displaystyle\sum_{i=3}^{10} \left(\frac{1}{10}\right)^i$

15. $2 + 6 + 18 + 54 + \ldots + 486$

16. $-2 + 8 - 32 + 128 + \ldots + 2048$

17. $-16 + 4 - 1 + \frac{1}{4} - \ldots + \frac{1}{1024}$

18. $\frac{1}{343} + \frac{1}{49} + \frac{1}{7} + 1 + \ldots + 2401$

19. $1 + 6 + 36 + 216 + \ldots + 46{,}656$

20. $-25 - 5 - 1 - 0.2 - \ldots - 0.0016$

21. $-5 + 4 - 3.2 + 2.56 - \ldots + 1.6384$

22. $-80 - 4 - 0.2 - 0.01 - \ldots - 0.000025$

*23. **Challenge** $-100 + 25 - 6.25 + 1.5625 - \ldots + 0.09765625$

*24. **Challenge** $50 + 0.1 + 0.0002 + 0.0000004 + \ldots + 3.2 \cdot 10^{-15}$

Graph the first 6 partial sums of the geometric series.

25. $1 + \frac{1}{3} + \frac{1}{9} + \frac{1}{27} + \frac{1}{81} + \frac{1}{243}$

26. $-0.003 + 0.015 - 0.075 + 0.375 - 1.875 + 9.375$

27. $-16 + 2 - \frac{1}{4} + \frac{1}{32} - \frac{1}{256} + \frac{1}{2048}$

28. $0.6 + 1.8 + 5.4 + 16.2 + 48.6 + 145.8$

29. $36 + 6 + 1 + \frac{1}{6} + \frac{1}{36} + \frac{1}{216} + \frac{1}{1296}$

30. $-40 + 4 - 0.4 + 0.04 - 0.004 + 0.0004$

Answer.

31. Explain what happens to the graph of a geometric series for the common ratio described.

    A. $|r| > 1$

    B. $|r| < 1$

32. Determine whether the series will approach one value. Explain why or why not.

    A. $10 - 5 + 2.5 - 1.25 + \ldots$

    B. $-\frac{1}{4096} - \frac{1}{512} - \frac{1}{64} - \frac{1}{8} + \ldots$

Applications: Series

Series have many applications in everyday life.

Determining Whether a Series Is Arithmetic, Geometric, or Neither

Before you use series to solve problems, you should know how to tell whether a series is arithmetic, geometric, or neither.

A *geometric* series is a series for which the terms are the elements of a geometric sequence.

An *arithmetic* series is a series for which the terms are the elements of an arithmetic sequence.

Example 1　Determine whether each series is arithmetic, geometric, or neither.

Ⓐ　$4 + 12 + 36 + 108 + \ldots$

Solution　Test to see if it is arithmetic.

$$a_2 - a_1 = 12 - 4 = 8$$
$$a_3 - a_2 = 36 - 12 = 24$$

The differences are not the same, so test to see if it is geometric.

$$\frac{a_2}{a_1} = \frac{12}{4} = 3$$
$$\frac{a_3}{a_2} = \frac{36}{12} = 3$$
$$\frac{a_4}{a_3} = \frac{108}{36} = 3$$

The ratios are the same, so the series is geometric.　■

Ⓒ　$480 + 360 + 240 + 120 + \ldots$

Solution　Test to see if it is arithmetic.

$$a_2 - a_1 = 360 - 480 = -120$$
$$a_3 - a_2 = 240 - 360 = -120$$
$$a_4 - a_3 = 120 - 240 = -120$$

The differences are the same, so the series is arithmetic.　■

Ⓑ　$1 + 2 + 6 + 24 + \ldots$

Solution　Test to see if it is arithmetic.

$$a_2 - a_1 = 2 - 1 = 1$$
$$a_3 - a_2 = 6 - 2 = 4$$

The differences are not the same, so test to see if it is geometric.

$$\frac{a_2}{a_1} = \frac{2}{1} = 2$$
$$\frac{a_3}{a_2} = \frac{6}{2} = 3$$

The ratios are not the same, so the series is neither arithmetic nor geometric.　■

Ⓓ　$-8 + 4 - 2 + 1 + \ldots$

Solution　Test to see if it is arithmetic.

$$a_2 - a_1 = 4 - (-8) = 12$$
$$a_3 - a_2 = -2 - 4 = -6$$

The differences are not the same, so test to see if it is geometric.

$$\frac{a_2}{a_1} = \frac{4}{-8} = -\frac{1}{2}$$
$$\frac{a_3}{a_2} = \frac{-2}{4} = -\frac{1}{2}$$
$$\frac{a_4}{a_3} = \frac{1}{-2} = -\frac{1}{2}$$

The ratios are the same, so the series is geometric.　■

Application: Money

Example 2 Brian and Kayla try different methods of saving money. Determine the total amount of money each will have after 10 days. Who will end up saving more money?

A Brian saves $0.51 on Day 1, $0.52 on Day 2, $0.53 on Day 3, ….

B Kayla saves $0.01 on Day 1, $0.02 on Day 2, $0.04 on Day 3, ….

Solution

A The total amount of money Brian saves after 10 days, given $0.51 on Day 1, $0.52 on Day 2, $0.53 on Day 3, …, is an arithmetic series $51 + 52 + 53 + 54 + \ldots$, where $n = 10$, $a_1 = 51$, and $d = 1$.

$$S_n = \frac{n}{2}(2a_1 + (n-1)d)$$

$$S_{10} = \frac{10}{2}(2 \cdot 51 + (10-1) \cdot 1)$$

$$S_{10} = 5(102 + 9 \cdot 1)$$

$$S_{10} = 5(102 + 9)$$

$$S_{10} = 5 \cdot 111$$

$$S_{10} = 555$$

The total amount of money Brian saves after 10 days is $5.55.

B The total amount of money Kayla saves after 10 days, given $0.01 on Day 1, $0.02 on Day 2, $0.04 on Day 3, …, is a geometric series $1 + 2 + 4 + 8 + \ldots$, where $n = 10$, $a_1 = 1$, and $r = 2$.

$$S_n = \frac{a_1(1 - r^n)}{1 - r}$$

$$S_{10} = \frac{1(1 - 2^{10})}{1 - 2}$$

$$S_{10} = \frac{1 \cdot (-1023)}{-1}$$

$$S_{10} = 1023$$

The total amount of money Kayla saves after 10 days is $10.23. Kayla saves more money with her method than Brian saves with his. ■

Application: Seating Capacity

Example 3 Suppose an auditorium has 30 rows of seats. There are 30 seats in the first row, 32 in the second row, 34 in the third row, and so on. How many seats are in all 30 rows?

Solution The total number of seats in the 30 rows form an arithmetic series with $n = 30$, $a_1 = 30$, and $d = 2$.

Step 1 Find the 30th term.

$$a_n = a_1 + (n-1)d$$

$$a_{30} = 30 + (30-1) \cdot 2$$

$$a_{30} = 30 + 29 \cdot 2$$

$$a_{30} = 30 + 58$$

$$a_{30} = 88$$

Step 2 Find the sum of the series.

$$S_n = \frac{n}{2}(a_1 + a_n)$$

$$S_{30} = \frac{30}{2}(30 + 88)$$

$$S_{30} = 15 \cdot 118$$

$$S_{30} = 1770$$

There are 1770 seats in the auditorium. ■

Application: Bouncing Distance

Example 4 Silas drops a ball from a height of 25 feet. Each time it drops h feet, it rebounds to a height of $0.8h$ feet. How much vertical distance does the ball travel from the time he drops it until it reaches the peak after its 6th bounce?

Solution The ball travels 25 feet on the first drop. On each bounce after that, it goes up to its peak, and then back down the same distance, so it travels $2 \cdot 25 \cdot 0.8^k$ feet for $k = 1$ to 5. The ball then goes up after the 6th bounce: $25 \cdot 0.8^6 = 6.5536$.

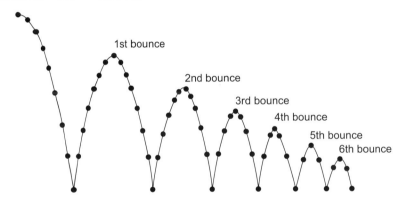

The five bounces, up and down, form the geometric series
$2 \cdot 25 \cdot 0.8^1 + 2 \cdot 25 \cdot 0.8^2 + 2 \cdot 25 \cdot 0.8^3 + 2 \cdot 25 \cdot 0.8^4 + 2 \cdot 25 \cdot 0.8^5$,
where $n = 5$, $a_1 = 2 \cdot 25 \cdot 0.8^1 = 40$, and $r = 0.8$.

Substitute the values of n, a_1, and r into the formula, $S_n = \dfrac{a_1(1 - r^n)}{1 - r}$.

$$S_5 = \frac{40(1 - 0.8^5)}{1 - 0.8}$$

$$S_5 = \frac{40(0.67232)}{0.2}$$

$$S_5 = \frac{26.8928}{0.2}$$

$$S_5 = 134.464$$

The total vertical distance the ball travels is
$25 + 134.464 + 6.5536 = 166.0176$. The ball travels a vertical distance of about 166 feet. ■

Application: Salary with Raises

Example 5 Maya starts working for Titanium Works Company with a salary of $30,000. If she gets a 5% raise at the end of each year, what will Maya's total earnings be after 30 years on the job?

Solution The salaries form a geometric sequence with $a_1 = 30,000$ and $r = 1.05$.

Year	Raise from Previous Year	Salary
1		30,000
2	$30,000 \cdot 0.05 = 1500$	$30,000 \cdot 1.05^1 = 31,500$
3	$31,500 \cdot 0.05 = 1575$	$30,000 \cdot 1.05^2 = 33,075$
4	$33,075 \cdot 0.05 = 1653.75$	$30,000 \cdot 1.05^3 = 34,728.75$

To find Maya's total earnings, find the sum of the first 30 terms ($n = 30$) of the geometric series:

$$S_n = \frac{a_1(1 - r^n)}{1 - r}$$

$$S_{30} = \frac{30,000(1 - 1.05^{30})}{1 - 1.05}$$

$$S_{30} \approx \frac{30,000(-3.32194)}{-0.05}$$

$$S_{30} \approx \frac{-99,658.27125}{-0.05}$$

$$S_{30} \approx 1,993,164.425$$

Maya's total earnings for 30 years will be about $1,993,164. ∎

Problem Set

Determine whether each series is arithmetic, geometric, or neither.

1. $2 + 6 + 18 + 54 + \ldots$

2. $6 + 9 + 12 + 15 + \ldots$

3. $-0.5 - 0.2 - 0.08 - 0.32 + \ldots$

4. $1 + 6 + 10 + 15 + \ldots$

5. $52 + 45 + 38 + 31 + \ldots$

6. $\frac{1}{2} + \frac{1}{6} + \frac{1}{24} + \frac{1}{120} + \ldots$

Determine whether each series is arithmetic or geometric, and then solve.

7. Gio stacks soup cans in the shape of a pyramid. He has put 1 can in the top row, 2 cans in the second row, 3 cans in the third row, and so on. If there are 15 rows, what is the total number of soup cans?

8. Mrs. Yang cuts fabric for men's clothes. She cuts 10 yards from a bolt. The second piece she cuts is 8 yards, and the third piece is 6 yards. What are the total yards cut?

9. Leticia drops a ball from a height of 50 feet. Each time it drops h feet, it rebounds $0.5h$ feet. How far does the ball travel from the time she drops it until it reaches the peak of its 9th bounce?

10. Elia's initial salary is $40,000. If she gets a 3% cost-of-living increase each year for the next 29 years, what would her total earnings be after 30 years?

11. Frederic earns $45,000 per year. A cost-of-living increase of $400 is added to his salary each year. What is the total he earns after 20 years?

12. Shankar doubles his calorie intake each week during intensive training. If he ate 1500 calories during the first week, how many total calories will he consume in 4 weeks?

13. The *Denominator Gazette* increases its circulation by 4% each year. If it began with 200 readers, what is the total number of readers it serves after 10 years?

14. Sheena jumps on a pogo stick. Her first jump is 0.3 meters. The height of each of her jumps after that increases at the rate of $1\frac{1}{4}h$, where h is the height of the previous jump. What is Sheena's total jumping distance after 4 complete jumps?

15. Alonzo has $100 in a savings account. He deposits $50 plus the previous balance into the account each month. When will the balance of his account be greater than $2000?

16. The stock for Radical Investments increases its dividends by 20% each year. If the first dividends were worth $10, what is the total value after 20 years?

17. St. Paul's Church has 25 rows of seats. The first row has 20 seats, the second row has 24, the third row has 28, and so on. How many seats are in rows 1 through 8 altogether?

18. Each day, the population of an insect colony is 3 times the previous day's population. If the colony began with 50 bugs, what will be the total number of bugs after 7 days?

19. In the first week of starting her own home business, Theresa works 10 hours. Each week she will increase her work hours by 3 hours. In what week will she reach a 60-hour work week?

20. Alberto increases the duration of his workout by 5 minutes each day. If he works out for 20 minutes the first day, how many total minutes will he have exercised on days 2 through 30?

21. A sponge toy expands in water. Its initial length is 2 inches and each minute it expands, the new length is $1\frac{1}{5}$ inches times its previous length. What is the sum of the lengths after 5 minutes?

22. Gerald opens a savings account. The first year he deposits $5000. Each year he deposits 60% of the previous year's deposit amount. How much money will he have after 10 years?

23. Anjali is creating a mosaic with small tiles. On her first day, she places 50 tiles. Each day she places 30 more tiles in the mosaic. If the mosaic will contain 2000 tiles, when will Anjali's mosaic be finished?

24. Mr. Mukherjee gives his wife 2 gifts on their 1st anniversary, 5 gifts on their 2nd anniversary, and 8 gifts on their 3rd anniversary. If this pattern continues, what will be the total number of anniversary gifts Mrs. Mukherjee has received after their 25th anniversary?

25. Kyle has 6 hours to complete his chores. Which plan will enable him to accomplish the most work?
    A. He will complete 1 job in the first hour and complete 3 more jobs each hour.
    B. He will complete $\frac{1}{2}$ of a job in one hour and double his work each hour.

26. Which would give Sarah more money after 12 days? How much more will she end up with?
    A. $1 on Day 1, $3 on Day 2, $5 on Day 3, and so on
    B. $1 on Day 1, $3 on Day 2, $9 on Day 3, and so on

27. Mrs. Tsai assigns her class an increasing number of pages to read over 6 weeks. She allows her students to choose between 2 patterns. Identify the pattern that will result in the fewest number of pages being read by the end of 6 weeks and by how many.
    A. Start with 4 pages and increase it by a factor of 1.5 each week.
    B. Start with 10 pages and increase it by 2 pages every week.

28. Which would give you the most money after 8 days? How much more will you end up with?

A. $0.50 on Day 1, $1 on Day 2, $2 on Day 3, and so on

B. $0.25 on Day 1, $0.50 on Day 2, $0.75 on Day 3, and so on

*29. **Challenge** Two stores on the same block selling similar items are discounting an increasing number of items. Child Play puts 7 items on sale during the first week and adds 5 more items every week for 18 weeks. Cool Kids puts up 1 item for sale during the first week and increases the number of sale items by a factor of 2 each week.

A. Which store puts up 300 items for sale first?

B. In what week does the number of sale items at Cool Kids exceed the number of sale items at Child Play?

*30. **Challenge** A farmer is planning his crops for now and in future years.

Plan A. Start with 5 acres and increase the planting area by 2.5 acres per year.

Plan B. Start with 3 acres and double the planting area each year.

He has only 15 acres to plant and must plant more than 40 acres in 5 years to receive a maximum profit. Which plan will meet the farmer's needs? Why?

Technology: Sequences and Series

You can compute the terms of an arithmetic or geometric sequence by using a graphing calculator or a spreadsheet.

A spreadsheet is a handy way to organize data. Each entry in a spreadsheet is called a *cell*. Each cell has a column (a letter) and a row (a number), so **B3** is the cell that is in the second column and the third row.

In many spreadsheet applications, starting a cell entry with an equals sign indicates that you are entering a formula and not a value. When you are entering a formula, use

- parentheses to indicate the order in which calculations should be performed
- cell names such as B3 to refer to other cells
- * for multiplication and / for division

Computing the Terms of an Arithmetic Sequence

If you can write an iterative formula for a sequence, you can let a spreadsheet do the calculations for you. Put the term numbers (n) in Column A and the sequence terms (a_n) in Column B.

Example 1   Find the first seven terms of the arithmetic sequence $a_n = 3(n - 1) - 5$.

Solution

Step 1   Enter the numbers 1 to 7 in Column A. Then in cell B1, enter the formula **=3*(A1−1)−5**, where A1 represents n.

Formula: =3*(A1-1)-5		
	A	B	C
		B1	
1	1	=3*(A1-1)-5	
2	2		
3	3		
4	4		
5	5		
6	6		
7	7		
8			
9			
10			

Step 2   Fill in cells B2 to B7.

Formula:	=3*(A7-1)-5		
	A	B	C
1	1	-5	
2	2	-2	
3	3	1	
4	4	4	
5	5	7	
6	6	10	
7	7	13	
8			
9			
10			

The first seven terms are $-5, -2, 1, 4, 7, 10$, and 13. ∎

Computing Partial Sums of an Arithmetic Series

If you put the term numbers (n) in Column A and the sequence terms (a_n) in Column B, then you can use Column C for the partial sums of the series. For each value in Column C, add the corresponding term in Column B to the previous term from Column C (which is the previous partial sum).

Example 2   Find the first five partial sums of the series $a_n = -2(n - 1) + 11$.

Solution

Step 1   Enter the numbers 1 to 5 in Column A. Then, in cell B1, enter the formula for the sequence $=-2*(A1-1)+11$. Fill in cells B2 to B5.

Formula:	=-2*(A5-1)+11		
	A	B	C
1	1	11	
2	2	9	
3	3	7	
4	4	5	
5	5	3	
6			
7			
8			
9			
10			

Step 2   Enter **=B1** in cell C1. Enter **=B2+C1** in cell C2. Then fill down.

TIP

To find the partial sums of a different series, change the formula in cell B1 and fill down the rest of the column. The numbers in Column C will automatically update.

Formula: =B2+C1

	A	B	C
1	1	11	11
2	2	9	20
3	3	7	27
4	4	5	32
5	5	3	35
6			
7			
8			
9			
10			

The first five partial sums are 11, 20, 27, 32, and 35. ∎

Computing the Terms of a Geometric Sequence

You can also compute the values of a geometric sequence using a recursive formula. The advantage to this approach is that you can quickly change your a_1 and r. You can also compute the values of an arithmetic sequence given its recursive rule by entering r instead of d in cell C1 and its value in D1.

Example 3   Find the first six terms of the geometric sequence:
$a_n = -2 \cdot a_{n-1}; a_1 = 3$

Solution

Step 1   Enter the label **a(1)** in cell A1 and its value, **3**, in B1. Then, enter the label **r** in C1 and its value, **−2**, in D1. In the second row, enter the label **n** in Column A and the label **a(n)** in Column B. Type in numbers 1 to 6 starting with cell A3 in Column A.

Formula:

	A	B	C	D
1	a(1)	3	r	-2
2	n	a(n)		
3	1			
4	2			
5	3			
6	4			
7	5			
8	6			
9				
10				

Step 2 Enter **=B1** in cell B3. Enter **=B3*D1** in cell B4. Then fill down.

Formula: =B7*D1

	A	B	C	D
1	a(1)	3	r	-2
2	n	a(n)		
3	1	3		
4	2	-6		
5	3	12		
6	4	-24		
7	5	48		
8	6	-96		
9				
10				

The first six terms are 3, −6, 12, −24, 48, and −96. ■

Computing the Partial Sums of a Geometric Series

Example 4 Find the first nine partial sums of the sequence

$$a_n = \frac{1}{2} \cdot (-3)^{n-1}.$$

Solution

Step 1 Enter the numbers 1 to 9 in Column A. Then, in cell B1, enter the formula for the sequence **=(1/2)*(−3)^(A1−1)**. Fill in cells B2 to B9.

Formula: =(1/2)*(-3)^(A9-1)

	A	B	C
1	1	0.5	
2	2	-1.5	
3	3	4.5	
4	4	-13.5	
5	5	40.5	
6	6	-121.5	
7	7	364.5	
8	8	-1093.5	
9	9	3280.5	
10			

Step 2 Enter $=\mathbf{B1}$ in cell C1. Enter $=\mathbf{B2}+\mathbf{C1}$ in cell C2. Then fill down.

Formula: =B2+C1		
	A	**B**	**C**
1	1	0.5	0.5
2	2	-1.5	-1
3	3	4.5	3.5
4	4	-13.5	-10
5	5	40.5	30.5
6	6	-121.5	-91
7	7	364.5	273.5
8	8	-1093.5	-820
9	9	3280.5	2460.5
10			

The first nine partial sums are $0.5, -1, 3.5, -10, 30.5, -91, 273.5, -820,$ and 2460.5. ∎

Problem Set

$\cdots\cdots\cdots\cdots\cdots\cdots\cdots\cdots\cdots\cdots\cdots\cdots\cdots\cdots\cdots\cdots\cdots\cdots\cdots\cdots\cdots\cdots$

Compute the first seven terms of each arithmetic sequence.

1. $a_n = 2(n - 1) - 4$

2. $a_n = 4(n - 1) + 2$

3. $a_n = -6(n - 1) + 8$

4. $a_n = 10(n - 1) - 20$

5. $a_n = -5(n - 1) + 0.25$

6. $a_n = 6(n - 1) + \frac{1}{7}$

7. $a_n = 0.75(n - 1) + 3$

8. $a_n = -\frac{1}{4}(n - 1) - 1$

Compute the first seven terms of each geometric sequence.

9. $a_n = 3 \cdot 4^{n-1}$

10. $a_n = -2 \cdot 10^{n-1}$

11. $a_n = -3 \cdot 9^{n-1}$

12. $a_n = 2 \cdot (-8)^{n-1}$

13. $a_n = 0.55 \cdot 7^{n-1}$

14. $a_n = -6 \cdot \left(\frac{1}{5}\right)^{n-1}$

15. $a_n = \frac{1}{9} \cdot (-3)^{n-1}$

16. $a_n = -11 \cdot 3^{n-1}$

Compute the first five partial sums of each arithmetic series.

17. $a_n = 3(n - 1) + 10$

18. $a_n = -8(n - 1) - 12$

19. $a_n = 4(n - 1) - 5$

20. $a_n = -2(n - 1) - 2$

21. $a_n = -7(n - 1) + 0.6$

22. $a_n = \frac{1}{15}(n - 1) - \frac{2}{5}$

23. $a_n = 0.67(n - 1) + 0.88$

***24.** **Challenge** $a_{12} = -91$ and $d = -8$

Compute the first six partial sums of each geometric series.

25. $a_n = -18 \cdot (-4)^{n-1}$

26. $a_n = -9 \cdot (-2)^{n-1}$

27. $a_n = \dfrac{3}{4} \cdot 5^{n-1}$

28. $a_n = -\dfrac{2}{3} \cdot \left(-\dfrac{3}{8}\right)^{n-1}$

29. $a_n = 0.9 \cdot (-6.6)^{n-1}$

30. $a_n = -0.345 \cdot (-0.234)^{n-1}$

31. $a_n = -\dfrac{9}{13} \cdot \left(-\dfrac{5}{8}\right)^{n-1}$

*32. Challenge $a_5 = 5$ and $r = \dfrac{1}{2}$

UNIT 12   Counting and Probability

You can use probability to determine your chances of hitting a target.

What are the chances that you will hit the bull's-eye? What about the chance of hitting it two or three times in a row? Probability can help you figure out your chances of reaching a particular result in various situations.

Big Ideas

. . . .

► A number is any entity that obeys the laws of arithmetic; all numbers obey the laws of arithmetic. The laws of arithmetic can be used to simplify expressions.

► A set is a well-defined collection of numbers or objects. Sets and operations defined on sets provide a clear way to communicate about collections of numbers or objects.

► If you can create a mathematical model for a situation, you can use the model to make predictions and solve problems that you might not be able to solve or predict otherwise.

Unit Topics

. . . .

► Foundations for Unit 12

► Counting Principles

► Permutations and Factorials

► Combinations

► Basic Probability

► Probability With and Without Replacement

► Independent and Dependent Events

► Mutually Exclusive Events

► Binomial Probability

► Making Predictions

Foundations for Unit 12

Before you learn more about counting and probability, take time to make sure you know how to do the following:

▶ Convert between decimal, fraction, and percent representations.

▶ Calculate a power of a fraction or decimal.

▶ Expand a power of a binomial.

Converting Between Decimals, Percents, and Fractions

Any number that can be written as a decimal, fraction, or percent can be converted from one form to another.

Fraction	Decimal	Percent
$\frac{1}{5}$	0.2	20%

Example 1 Convert each decimal to a percent and to a fraction.

A $0.04 = 0.04 = 4\%$

$0.04 = \frac{4}{100} = \frac{1}{25}$

B $0.125 = 0.125 = 12.5\%$

$0.125 = \frac{125}{1000} = \frac{1}{8}$

Example 2 Convert each percent to a decimal and to a fraction.

A $100\% = 100.\% = 1$

$100\% = \frac{100}{100} = 1$

B $15.7\% = 15.7\% = 0.157$

$15.7\% = \frac{15.7}{100} = \frac{157}{1000}$

Example 3 Convert the fraction to a decimal by using division. Then convert the decimal to a percent.

A $\frac{3}{8} = 3 \div 8 = 0.125 = 12.5\%$

B $\frac{5}{16} = 5 \div 16 = 0.3125 = 31.25\%$

Problem Set A

Convert each decimal to a percent and to a fraction.

1. 0.03

2. 0.45

3. 0.7

4. 0.335

5. 0.6

6. 0.008

Convert each percent to a decimal and to a fraction.

7. 6%

8. 80%

9. 0.5%

10. 1%

11. 99%

12. 62.5%

Convert each fraction to a decimal and to a percent.

13. $\frac{7}{8}$

14. $\frac{9}{10}$

15. $\frac{39}{100}$

16. $\frac{27}{1000}$

17. $\frac{3}{50}$

18. $\frac{1}{10,000}$

Calculating a Power of a Fraction or Decimal

A whole number power of a fraction or decimal that has an absolute value between 0 and 1 is a number that has an absolute value less than the original fraction or decimal.

A whole number power of a fraction or decimal that has absolute value greater than 1 has absolute value that is greater than the original number.

Example 4 Calculate each power.

Ⓐ $\left(\frac{5}{8}\right)^2 = \frac{5^2}{8^2} = \frac{25}{64}$

Ⓑ $\left(-\frac{1}{3}\right)^5 = \frac{(-1)^5}{3^5} = -\frac{1}{243}$

Ⓒ $(-0.9)^4 = 0.6561$

Ⓓ $(0.65)^3 = 0.274625$

Ⓔ $\left(\frac{7}{4}\right)^6 = \frac{7^6}{4^6} = \frac{117,649}{4096}$

Ⓕ $(8.3)^2 = 68.89$

Problem Set B

Calculate each power.

19. $\left(\frac{3}{16}\right)^2$

20. $\left(\frac{3}{4}\right)^4$

21. $\left(\frac{1}{10}\right)^3$

22. $(0.08)^3$

23. $(0.75)^2$

24. $(0.25)^4$

Expanding a Power of a Binomial

You can expand a power of a binomial by using the FOIL method and the distributive property.

Example 5 Expand and simplify each binomial.

Ⓐ $(x + y)^2$

$(x + y)(x + y)$

$x^2 + xy + xy + y^2$

$x^2 + 2xy + y^2$

Ⓑ $(2a - 3b)^2$

$(2a - 3b)(2a - 3b)$

$4a^2 - 6ab - 6ab + 9b^2$

$4a^2 - 12ab + 9b^2$

Ⓒ $(m + 2n)^3$

$(m + 2n)(m + 2n)(m + 2n)$

$(m^2 + 2mn + 2mn + 4n^2)(m + 2n)$

$m^3 + 2m^2n + 2m^2n + 4mn^2 + 2m^2n + 4mn^2 + 4mn^2 + 8n^3$

$m^3 + 6m^2n + 12mn^2 + 8n^3$

Problem Set C

Expand and simplify.

25. $(a + b)^2$

26. $(3p + 2q)^2$

27. $(m - 2n)^2$

28. $(2x + y)^3$

29. $(a - 0.2b)^3$

30. $(p + q)^4$

Expanding a Power of a Binomial for Specific Values

Example 6   Expand each binomial.

Ⓐ $(p + q)^3$ for $p = \frac{1}{4}$ and $q = \frac{3}{4}$

$(p + q)^3 = p^3 + 3p^2q + 3pq^2 + q^3$

$= \left(\frac{1}{4}\right)^3 + 3\left(\frac{1}{4}\right)^2\left(\frac{3}{4}\right) + 3\left(\frac{1}{4}\right)\left(\frac{3}{4}\right)^2 + \left(\frac{3}{4}\right)^3$

$= \frac{1}{64} + \frac{9}{64} + \frac{27}{64} + \frac{27}{64}$

$= 1$

> **THINK ABOUT IT**
>
> If $p + q = 1$, then $(p + q)^n = 1^n = 1$. For parts A and B, check to see that the sum of the terms in the expansion is 1.

Ⓑ $(p + q)^4$ for $p = 0.4$ and $q = 0.6$

$(p + q)^4 = p^4 + 4p^3q + 6p^2q^2 + 4pq^3 + q^4$

$= (0.4)^4 + 4(0.4)^3\,(0.6) + 6(0.4)^2\,(0.6)^2 + 4(0.4)(0.6)^3 + (0.6)^4$

$= 0.0256 + 0.1536 + 0.3456 + 0.3456 + 0.1296$

$= 1$

Problem Set D

Expand the power of each binomial.

31. $(a + b)^2$ for $a = 2$ and $b = 3$

32. $(p + q)^3$ for $p = -1$ and $q = 7$

33. $(a + b)^4$ for $a = 0.1$ and $b = 0.4$

34. $(p + q)^3$ for $p = \frac{2}{3}$ and $q = \frac{1}{3}$

35. $(p + q)^4$ for $p = 0.7$ and $q = 0.3$

36. What is the 4th term in the expansion $(p + q)^{10}$?

Counting Principles

You already know how to count. But when you study probability, you need to learn how to count in a way that is more complicated than the way you would count the number of apples on a table.

> **DEFINITIONS**
>
> In the study of counting and probability, an **experiment** is any process that results in one or more results, called **outcomes**.

Tree diagrams, the addition principle, and the multiplication principle can be used to count possible outcomes.

Using a Tree Diagram

When an experiment can be broken down into stages, you can use a tree diagram to represent the possible outcomes of each stage.

Example 1 A director who is casting the lead roles in *Romeo and Juliet* will select from 2 boys (Ben and Julio) and 3 girls (Clara, Yvonne, and Zenit). How many ways can the director select a boy for Romeo and a girl for Juliet?

Solution This situation involves two actions: *select a boy* and *select a girl*. A tree diagram shows all possible outcomes.

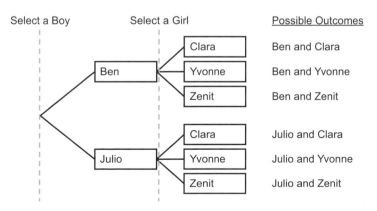

There are 6 ways of selecting a boy and a girl for Romeo and Juliet. ■

> **TIP**
>
> In discussions of counting and probability, different words are sometimes used for *experiment*. Some of these words are *action*, *process*, *procedure*, *study*, *observation*, and *survey*.

Applying the Addition and Multiplication Principles

When you use a tree diagram, you list outcomes and then count them. The following methods of counting outcomes do not require listing the outcomes.

> **COUNTING PRINCIPLES**
>
> The **addition counting principle** states that if there are m ways of doing one thing and n ways of doing another thing, then there are $m + n$ ways of doing one thing *or* the other.
>
> The **multiplication counting principle** states that if a task can be broken into two stages and there are m ways of doing the first stage and n ways of doing the second stage, then there are $m \cdot n$ ways of doing one thing *and* the other.

> **TIP**
>
> The addition counting principle and the multiplication counting principle can be extended to three or more things.

Example 2   Use counting principles to solve.

A A breakfast special includes an entree (pancakes, waffles, French toast, omelet, or country scramble), a meat (sausage or bacon), and a beverage (coffee, tea, juice, or soda). How many different breakfast specials are possible?

Solution   Choosing a breakfast special requires three actions: *picking an entree*, *picking a meat*, and *picking a beverage*. Use the multiplication principle. There are 5 entrees, 2 meats, and 4 beverages.

$5 \cdot 2 \cdot 4 = 40$

There are 40 possible breakfast specials. ■

B Jasmine has accumulated 5000 bonus points with her credit card. She can redeem them by either choosing 1 of 10 gifts or making a donation to 1 of 7 charities. How many ways can Jasmine redeem her bonus points?

Solution   This situation requires one action—*redeeming bonus points*—with two different types of outcomes—*choosing a gift* or *donating to a charity*. Use the addition principle. There are 10 gifts and 7 charities.

$10 + 7 = 17$

There are 17 ways Jasmine can redeem her bonus points. ■

C How many ways can 4 runners finish in first, second, third, and fourth place in a race?

Solution   There are four actions: *finishing first*, *finishing second*, *finishing third*, and *finishing fourth*. There are 4 runners, so there are 4 possible outcomes for first place. After someone comes in first place, there are only 3 possible outcomes for second place, and so on. Use the multiplication principle.

$$\underset{\text{first}}{4} \cdot \underset{\text{second}}{3} \cdot \underset{\text{third}}{2} \cdot \underset{\text{fourth}}{1} = 24$$

There are 24 ways 4 runners can finish the race. ■

> **TIP**
>
> You can think of the possible outcomes in Example 2C as results of *observations*. That is, someone observes who finishes in each place. In counting and probability theory, observations are *experiments* because they have outcomes.

Evaluating Factorials

The product $4 \cdot 3 \cdot 2 \cdot 1$ can be written as 4! (read as "four factorial").

DEFINITION

The **factorial** of a positive integer n, written $n!$, is the product of all the positive integers less than or equal to n.

$$n! = n \cdot (n-1) \cdot (n-2) \cdot \ldots \cdot 1$$

Zero factorial is a special case, defined as $0! = 1$.

Example 3 Evaluate each expression.

A 7!

B 3!5!

C $\dfrac{8!}{6!}$

Solution

A $7! = 7 \cdot 6 \cdot 5 \cdot 4 \cdot 3 \cdot 2 \cdot 1$

$= 5040$ ∎

Solution

B $3!5! = (3 \cdot 2 \cdot 1)(5 \cdot 4 \cdot 3 \cdot 2 \cdot 1)$

$= 6 \cdot 120$

$= 720$ ∎

Solution

C $\dfrac{8!}{6!} = \dfrac{8 \cdot 7 \cdot \cancel{6} \cdot \cancel{5} \cdot \cancel{4} \cdot \cancel{3} \cdot \cancel{2} \cdot \cancel{1}}{\cancel{6} \cdot \cancel{5} \cdot \cancel{4} \cdot \cancel{3} \cdot \cancel{2} \cdot \cancel{1}}$

$= 8 \cdot 7$

$= 56$ ∎

Problem Set

Evaluate each expression.

1. $4!$

2. $2!5!$

3. $\dfrac{10!}{3!}$

4. $0!$

5. $\dfrac{2 \cdot 8!}{12!}$

6. $7!2!6!$

7. $\dfrac{100!}{99!}$

8. $-1(4! - 3!)$

Use the tree diagram to answer each question.

Select Meat	Select Cheese	Possible Outcomes

Ham → American, Swiss, Provolone

Turkey → American, Swiss, Provolone

Veggie → American, Swiss, Provolone

9. How many possible sandwiches are there?

10. How many ways could Jaheim have Swiss cheese on his sandwich?

11. How many ways could Lorena have a turkey sandwich?

Solve each problem by drawing a tree diagram.

12. Samantha can choose to have milk, juice, or tea with her chocolate cake. How many different combinations are possible?

13. Jon can wear either dress shoes or sneakers with gray, black, or white socks. How many different footwear combinations are there?

14. A restaurant menu offers a choice of 3 kinds of steak (sirloin, flank, and filet mignon) and 2 sides (salad and soup). How many ways can a customer have a steak dinner?

15. Mario is looking to remodel his bedroom. He can select from 3 colors of paint (blue, yellow, and green), 2 types of curtains (french pleat and tab top), and 2 types of floors (hardwood and carpet). How many ways can Mario remodel the room?

Determine whether each situation requires the addition or multiplication counting principle. Solve.

16. In how many ways can 5 family members be arranged in a row for a family portrait?

17. Carrie can choose from one of the following options to raise her grade: redo an assignment, earn extra credit, or complete a project. How many ways can she raise her grade?

18. What is the total number of batting orders possible for a little-league baseball team of 9 players?

19. Tanya can select 1 of 10 dresses, 1 of 4 pairs of shoes, and 1 of 20 nail colors. How many ways can she select her look?

20. Mr. Rich is buying a car. He can select 1 of 2 interior fabrics, 1 of 2 transmissions, 1 of 7 colors, and 1 of 2 stereo systems. How many ways can Mr. Rich select his car options?

21. If 4 green lights, 3 red lights, 2 blue lights, and 3 yellow lights make up a light string, how many different light patterns are possible?

Use the addition or multiplication counting principle to solve each problem.

22. Gloves are made of either cotton or leather and come in 3 sizes and 4 colors. How many pairs are required for a complete assortment?

23. Sheila won a writing contest, so she gets to choose from 1 of 3 trips, 1 of 5 cars, or 1 of 4 appliances. How many ways can she choose her prize?

24. At an arcade, Matilda has earned 100 points. She can select from 10 toys or 20 types of candy, or she can save the points for another time. How many ways can Matilda use her points?

25. Sonny earned a degree in finance. Of the 20 local positions, 15 out-of-state positions, and 4 international positions he is interested in, he must pick 1 job to apply for. How many ways can he apply for a job?

26. A quiz consists of 10 true-or-false questions. In how many ways could the quiz be completed?

27. Mikey wants to become involved in community activities. He can join 1 of 12 clubs, try out for 1 of 5 sport teams, or try out for 1 of 2 music programs. How many ways can Mikey become involved?

*28. Challenge A license plate consists of 3 letters followed by 3 numbers, where letters and numbers can be used more than once. How many different license plates are possible?

*29. Challenge A zip code consists of 5 digits, where each digit can appear more than once. How many zip codes exist?

Permutations and Factorials

Sometimes you need to find the number of ways a set of objects can be arranged in order. Each possible arrangement is called a *permutation*.

Counting Permutations

Example 1 Ishmael has a soccer trophy, a bowling trophy, and a curling trophy. In how many ways can he arrange the trophies on his trophy shelf, which has three places for trophies?

Solution

There are 3 trophies to choose from, so there are 3 ways that Ishmael can select a trophy for the first spot. Once the first trophy is placed, Ishmael has 2 trophies left to choose from, so he can fill the second spot in 2 ways. Now he has 1 trophy left, so he has only 1 way to fill the last spot.

To get the total number of ways that Ishmael can arrange the trophies, multiply all the numbers of ways: $3 \cdot 2 \cdot 1 = 6$ ways. ∎

In this example, each possible arrangement of the same 3 trophies counted as a distinct outcome. The 6 ways describe the total number of permutations.

DEFINITION

A **permutation** of a set of distinct objects is an arrangement of those objects in which order matters.

Using the Multiplication Principle to Count Permutations

You can use the multiplication principle to count permutations.

Example 2   A television singing competition features 12 singers.

(A) In how many ways can all 12 singers finish the competition?

(B) The first-place singer receives a $1,000,000 recording contract, and the second-place singer receives a $250,000 recording contract. In how many ways can the two recording contracts be awarded?

Solution   Both situations involve permutations because in each case, you need to consider arrangements of singers in which order matters.

(A) There are 12 positions in each possible arrangement: *first place*, *second place*, and so on, ending with *twelfth place*. Any of the 12 singers could finish in first place. Then, any of the remaining 11 singers could finish in second place, and so on. Using the multiplication principle, the number of permutations is a factorial.

$$12! = 12 \cdot 11 \cdot 10 \cdot 9 \cdot 8 \cdot 7 \cdot 6 \cdot 5 \cdot 4 \cdot 3 \cdot 2 \cdot 1 = 479,001,600$$

There are 479,001,600 ways the 12 singers can finish the competition.

(B) In this case, there are only 2 positions in each possible arrangement: *first place* and *second place*. Any of the 12 singers could finish in first place, and any of the remaining 11 singers could finish in second place.

$$12 \cdot 11 = 132$$

There are 132 ways the two recording contracts can be awarded. ■

Finding the Number of Permutations of *n* Objects Taken *r* at a Time

In Example 2B, you found the number of ways to arrange 2 singers, choosing from 12 singers. That is called "the number of permutations of 12 objects taken 2 at a time."

PERMUTATIONS OF *n* OBJECTS TAKEN *r* AT A TIME

Given a set of *n* distinct objects, the number of permutations of *r* of those objects (where $r \leq n$) is the following:

$$_nP_r = \frac{n!}{(n-r)!}$$

> **NOTATION**
>
> An alternate notation for $_nP_r$ is $P(n, r)$.

Example 3   Evaluate each permutation expression.

(A) $_{12}P_2$

Solution   Write the factorials in expanded form and divide out common factors.

$$_{12}P_2 = \frac{12!}{(12-2)!} = \frac{12!}{10!}$$

$$= \frac{12 \cdot 11 \cdot \cancel{10} \cdot \cancel{9} \cdot \cancel{8} \cdot \cancel{7} \cdot \cancel{6} \cdot \cancel{5} \cdot \cancel{4} \cdot \cancel{3} \cdot \cancel{2} \cdot \cancel{1}}{\cancel{10} \cdot \cancel{9} \cdot \cancel{8} \cdot \cancel{7} \cdot \cancel{6} \cdot \cancel{5} \cdot \cancel{4} \cdot \cancel{3} \cdot \cancel{2} \cdot \cancel{1}} = 132$$

The number of permutations of 12 objects taken 2 at a time is 132. ■

> **THINK ABOUT IT**
>
> The answer in Example 3A verifies the answer in Example 2B.

B $_{13}P_4$

Solution

$$_{13}P_4 = \frac{13!}{(13-4)!} = \frac{13!}{9!}$$

$$= \frac{13 \cdot 12 \cdot 11 \cdot 10 \cdot \cancel{9} \cdot \cancel{8} \cdot \cancel{7} \cdot \cancel{6} \cdot \cancel{5} \cdot \cancel{4} \cdot \cancel{3} \cdot \cancel{2} \cdot \cancel{1}}{\cancel{9} \cdot \cancel{8} \cdot \cancel{7} \cdot \cancel{6} \cdot \cancel{5} \cdot \cancel{4} \cdot \cancel{3} \cdot \cancel{2} \cdot \cancel{1}} = 17{,}160$$

The number of permutations of 13 objects taken 4 at a time is 17,160. ■

C $_5P_5$

Solution

$$_5P_5 = \frac{5!}{(5-5)!} = \frac{5!}{0!} = \frac{120}{1} = 120$$

The number of permutations of 5 objects taken 5 at a time is 120. ■

> **THINK ABOUT IT**
>
> $_nP_n = n!$ for all integers $n \geq 0$.

Solving a Problem Involving Permutations

Example 4   Trevor's band wants to compile a 3-track demo CD to send to record companies. The band has decided to choose from 8 songs. How many different ways could they compile 3 songs for the demo CD?

Solution   Because songs are put on a CD in a certain order, each possible way to arrange 3 songs is a permutation. Find the number of permutations of 8 songs taken 3 at a time.

$$_8P_3 = \frac{8!}{(8-3)!} = \frac{8!}{5!} = \frac{8 \cdot 7 \cdot 6 \cdot \cancel{5} \cdot \cancel{4} \cdot \cancel{3} \cdot \cancel{2} \cdot \cancel{1}}{\cancel{5} \cdot \cancel{4} \cdot \cancel{3} \cdot \cancel{2} \cdot \cancel{1}} = 336$$

Trevor's band could compile the 3-track demo CD in 336 ways. ■

Finding the Number of Permutations of *n* Objects of Which *p* Are Alike and *q* Are Alike

When finding permutations where some letters or objects are alike, you need to account for the identical objects by dividing out the permutations of those identical objects.

> **PERMUTATIONS OF *n* OBJECTS OF WHICH *p* ARE ALIKE AND *q* ARE ALIKE**
>
> Given a set of *n* objects of which *p* are alike and *q* are alike, the number of permutations of those objects (where $p \leq n$ and $q \leq n$) is the following:
>
> $$\frac{_nP_n}{p!\,q!}$$

Example 5 Find the number of permutations of the letters *boo*.

Solution If all the letters *boo* were different, they could be arranged in $_3P_3 = 6$ ways as follows:

> *boo*   *boo*   *obo*   *obo*   *oob*   *oob*

But because the two *o*'s are identical, you need to divide out the 2! ways the two *o*'s can be arranged: $\dfrac{_3P_3}{2!} = \dfrac{3!}{2!} = \dfrac{6}{2} = 3$. The permutations are *boo*, *obo*, and *oob*. ∎

Finding the Number of Permutations of *n* Objects Arranged in a Circle

Arranging objects in a circle changes the number of permutations of the objects. For example, the numbers 1, 2, and 3 can be arranged in a line in 3! ways as follows:

123   231   312   132   321   213

In a circle, though, 123, 231, and 312 are equivalent because the circle can be rotated. For the same reason, 132, 321, and 213 are also equivalent.

So the number of arrangements of 1, 2, and 3 in a circle is $(3 - 1)! = 2$. The two ways are shown below:

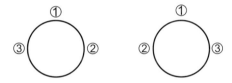

PERMUTATIONS OF *n* OBJECTS ARRANGED IN A CIRCLE
The number of ways to arrange *n* distinct objects around a circle is $(n - 1)!$

THINK ABOUT IT

A circle cannot be picked up out of the plane and turned over, so you can assume that it is fixed (except for the possibility of rotation).

Example 6 Find the number of ways a hostess can seat 12 people around a round table.

Solution The position in which the first guest is seated is not important because all the chairs appear the same until somebody is seated in one of them. Once that person is seated, there are $(12 - 1)! = 11! = 39{,}916{,}800$ ways to seat the remaining people. ∎

Problem Set

Evaluate each permutation expression.

1. $_6P_3$

2. $_2P_1$

3. $_{10}P_2$

4. $_9P_8$

5. $_8P_8$

6. $_{100}P_3$

7. $6 \cdot {_4P_4}$

8. $_7P_0$

9. $\dfrac{_5P_2}{2!3!}$

10. $\dfrac{_9P_4}{_9P_5}$

Write and evaluate a permutation expression for each problem.

11. Five students are selected to fill 5 openings on the academic quiz team. In how many ways could the students fill the openings?

12. How many different displays of 5 products can be formed from 15 products if the products are arranged in a row?

13. How many ways can 4 people finish a marathon?

14. How many ways can 10 elementary students fill their class's 6 job positions?

15. How many distinct 4-letter words can be formed from the letters *JUMP* if a word consists of any combination of the given letters?

16. A dinner party has 6 guests. In how many ways can the guests be seated in 6 chairs around the table?

Solve.

17. Seven swimmers compete in a race. How many possible ways can they fill the top 3 spots for the fastest times?

18. Find the number of permutations of the letters *BANANA*.

19. How many ways could Santa line up his 9 reindeer if Rudolph must always be in front?

20. How many distinct 5-letter words can be formed from the letters *DIGIT* if a word consists of any combination of the given letters?

21. Find the number of ways you can arrange 6 beads of different colors on a bracelet.

22. At a class meeting, 4 girls and 4 boys attend. If they sit at a round table, in how many ways can the group be seated so that no one is seated next to a person of the same gender?

*23. **Challenge** A group of 5 children forms a row. The group includes 1 set of identical twins who are dressed alike. How many visually distinct arrangements are possible?

*24. **Challenge** A 10-member cheerleading squad forms a pyramid. Four members are in the bottom row, 3 are in the next row, 2 are in the next row, and 1 student is on top. How many different pyramids are possible if the cheerleaders cannot change rows?

Combinations

For permutations, order matters. For combinations, order does *not* matter.

> **DEFINITION**
>
> A **combination** is a selection of objects in which order does *not* matter.

Comparing Permutations and Combinations

Example 1 Consider these four people: Ana (A), Brody (B), Cecilia (C), and DeAndre (D).

A If the 4 people compete in a race, in how many ways can first-place and second-place medals be awarded to 2 people?

B If the 4 people organize a school dance, in how many ways can 2 people be selected for the refreshments committee?

Solution

A Because order matters, each way of awarding the medals is a permutation. The number of permutations is $_4P_2 = \dfrac{4!}{(4-2)!} = \dfrac{4!}{2!} = 12$. Specifically, the 12 permutations for first and second place are as follows:

AB	AC	AD	BC	BD	CD
BA	CA	DA	CB	DB	DC

The 2 medals can be awarded in 12 ways.

B In this case, order does not matter. For example, the committee of Ana and Brody is equivalent to the committee of Brody and Ana. Because order does not matter, each way of selecting 2 people is a combination.

Equivalent Committees

AB	AC	AD	BC	BD	CD
BA	CA	DA	CB	DB	DC

There are 6 ways to select members of the 2-person committee. ■

Finding Combinations of *n* Objects Taken *r* at a Time

The number of ways to select 2 people out of 4 people when order does not matter is called "the number of combinations of 4 objects taken 2 at a time."

Given a set of *n* distinct objects, the number of combinations of *r* of those objects (where $r \leq n$) is written $_nC_r$ and is evaluated as follows:

$$_nC_r = \frac{n!}{(n - r)!\, r!}$$

Verify that the formula works for Example 1B:

$$_4C_2 = \frac{4!}{(4 - 2)!\, 2!} = \frac{4!}{2!\, 2!} = \frac{4 \cdot 3 \cdot \cancel{2 \cdot 1}}{(2 \cdot 1)(\cancel{2 \cdot 1})} = \frac{12}{2} = 6.$$

Example 2   Evaluate each combination expression.

A $_6C_4$

Solution

$$_6C_4 = \frac{6!}{(6 - 4)!\, 4!} = \frac{6!}{2!\, 4!} = \frac{6 \cdot 5 \cdot \cancel{4 \cdot 3 \cdot 2 \cdot 1}}{(2 \cdot 1)(\cancel{4 \cdot 3 \cdot 2 \cdot 1})} = \frac{30}{2} = 15$$

The number of combinations of 6 objects taken 4 at a time is 15. (There are 15 ways to choose 4 objects from 6 objects when order does not matter.) ■

B $_{28}C_1$

Solution

$$_{28}C_1 = \frac{28!}{(28 - 1)!\, 1!} = \frac{28!}{27!\, 1!} = \frac{28 \cdot \cancel{27!}}{\cancel{27!} \cdot 1} = 28$$

The number of combinations of 28 objects taken 1 at a time is 28. (There are 28 ways to choose 1 object from 28 objects when order does not matter.) ■

C $_{35}C_{35}$

Solution

$$_{35}C_{35} = \frac{35!}{(35 - 35)!\, 35!} = \frac{35!}{0!\, 35!} = \frac{\cancel{35!}}{1 \cdot \cancel{35!}} = 1$$

The number of combinations of 35 objects taken 35 at a time is 1. (There is only 1 way to choose all 35 objects when order does not matter.) ■

Determining Whether a Problem Is a Combination or Permutation

Example 3   Determine whether each situation would be better represented by a permutation or a combination.

A The coach of a track team is selecting runners for the 4 × 4 relay race. If there are 20 runners on the team, how many ways can the coach form a lineup for the race?

Solution   In a 4 × 4 relay race, the runners race one at a time in a specific order. Since the order matters, this situation is better represented by a permutation. ■

B The owner of a construction company is promoting two of his employees to be managers of a new job site. If he has 126 employees, how many ways can he choose 2 people to be managers?

Solution The order of the selection does not matter because each position has the same rank and there is only one job site. Since the order does not matter, this situation is better represented by a combination. ■

Solving a Problem Involving Combinations

Example 4 Solve.

A Zaire is planting a garden. How many ways can she plant 4 vegetables if she has 7 to choose from?

Solution Order does not matter, so each selection is a combination. Find the number of combinations of 7 vegetables taken 4 at a time.

$$_7C_4 = \frac{7!}{(7-4)!\,4!} = \frac{7!}{3!\,4!} = \frac{7 \cdot 6 \cdot 5 \cdot \cancel{4!}}{(3 \cdot 2 \cdot 1)(\cancel{4!})} = 35$$

Zaire can select 4 vegetables from 7 vegetables in 35 ways. ■

B A national conference is holding a raffle in which a person buys a ticket and selects 6 different integers from 1 to 49. The player wins the raffle if all 6 numbers match the official winning numbers, without regard to order. How many ways can a player select 6 different integers, choosing from 49 different integers?

Solution Order does not matter, so each selection is a combination. Find the number of combinations of 49 integers taken 6 at a time.

$$_{49}C_6 = \frac{49!}{(49-6)!\,6!} = \frac{49!}{43!\,6!} = \frac{49 \cdot 48 \cdot 47 \cdot 46 \cdot 45 \cdot 44 \cdot \cancel{43!}}{(\cancel{43!})(6 \cdot 5 \cdot 4 \cdot 3 \cdot 2 \cdot 1)} = 13{,}983{,}816$$

A person can select 6 integers from 49 integers in almost 14 million ways. ■

Solving a Problem Involving Combinations and the Multiplication Principle

Example 5 A standard deck of playing cards contains 52 cards. The cards are divided into 4 suits (hearts, diamonds, spades, and clubs), and each suit has 13 ranks (ace, 2, 3, ..., 9, 10, jack, queen, king).

A How many 5-card hands are possible that contain 5 cards of the same suit?

B How many 5-card hands are possible that contain 4 cards of the same rank?

Solution These situations involve combinations because the order in which the cards are dealt does not matter.

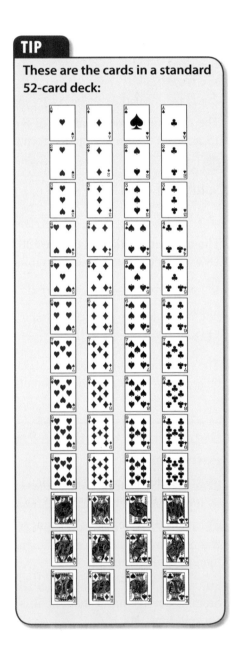

TIP

These are the cards in a standard 52-card deck:

A There are 4 suits. In each suit, the number of ways to get 5 cards of that suit is the number of combinations of 13 cards taken 5 at a time. Use the multiplication principle.

$$4 \cdot {}_{13}C_5 = 4 \cdot 1287 = 5148$$

There are 5148 different possible 5-card hands that contain 5 cards of the same suit. ∎

B There are 13 ranks. In each rank, when you get four of one rank, you also get a fifth card. The number of ways to get four of any rank is the same as the number of ways to get a fifth card from the 48 remaining cards. That is the number of combinations of 48 cards taken 1 at a time. Use the multiplication principle.

$$13 \cdot {}_{48}C_1 = 13 \cdot 48 = 624$$

There are 624 different possible 5-card hands that contain 4 of one rank. ∎

Using the Binomial Theorem to Expand a Power of a Binomial

An important algebraic application of combinations is the expansion of a binomial expression raised to a nonnegative integer power.

BINOMIAL THEOREM

Given a binomial of the form $(x + y)$ and an integer $n \geq 0$, the expansion of $(x + y)^n$ is the following:

$$(x + y)^n = \sum_{r=0}^{n} {}_nC_r\, x^{n-r} y^r$$

$$= {}_nC_0\, x^n y^0 + {}_nC_1\, x^{n-1} y^1 + {}_nC_2\, x^{n-2} y^2 + \ldots + {}_nC_n\, x^0 y^n$$

TIP

In mathematics, the Greek capital letter sigma, Σ, means summation.

In a binomial expansion, the resulting binomial coefficients correspond to the numbers in row n of Pascal's triangle:

row 0	1	
row 1	1 1	$x + y$
row 2	1 2 1	$x^2 + 2xy + y^2$
row 3	1 3 3 1	$x^3 + 3x^2y + 3xy^2 + y^3$
row 4	1 4 6 4 1	$x^4 + 4x^3y + 6x^2y^2 + 4xy^3 + y^4$
	$\cdots$	$\cdots$

TIP

To create your own Pascal's triangle, start with 1 at the top and imagine 0 on either side of it. Next, for every pair of numbers, put their sum between them in the row below. For instance, in row 4, you can see that 4 is $1 + 3$ and 6 is $3 + 3$.

Always imagine 0 at the far left and right ends of the triangle.

The triangle can be used to calculate combinations in general. For ${}_nC_r$, n is the row of the triangle and r is the $(r + 1)$th element in that row.

Example 6 Use Pascal's triangle to find each combination.

A ${}_4C_2$

Solution The 4th row of the triangle is 1 4 6 4 1. The 3rd element in the row is 6. So ${}_4C_2 = 6$. ∎

B $_7C_5$

Solution Expand the triangle to determine the 7th row.

$$1$$
$$1 \quad 1$$
$$1 \quad 2 \quad 1$$
$$1 \quad 3 \quad 3 \quad 1$$
$$1 \quad 4 \quad 6 \quad 4 \quad 1$$
$$1 \quad 5 \quad 10 \quad 10 \quad 5 \quad 1$$
$$1 \quad 6 \quad 15 \quad 20 \quad 15 \quad 6 \quad 1$$
$$1 \quad 7 \quad 21 \quad 35 \quad 35 \quad 21 \quad 7 \quad 1$$

The 6th element in the row is 21. So $_7C_5 = 21$. ∎

Example 7 Use the binomial theorem to expand each expression.

A $(2x + 3y)^2$

Solution Substitute 2 for n in the expansion of $(x + y)^n$.

$$(2x + 3y)^2 = ((2x) + (3y))^2$$
$$= \sum_{r=0}^{2} {}_2C_r(2x)^{2-r}(3y)^r$$
$$= {}_2C_0(2x)^{2-0}(3y)^0 + {}_2C_1(2x)^{2-1}(3y)^1 + {}_2C_2(1x)^{2-2}(3y)^2$$
$$= 1 \cdot 4x^2 \cdot 1 + 2 \cdot 2x \cdot 3y^1 + 1 \cdot 1 \cdot 9y^2$$
$$= 4x^2 + 12xy + 9y^2 \quad ∎$$

> **TIP**
>
> In this expression, $n = 2$, and row 2 of Pascal's triangle consists of 1 2 1.

B $(x - 5)^3$

Solution Rewrite the difference as a sum and expand it by using -5 for y.

$$(x - 5)^3 = (x + (-5))^3$$
$$= \sum_{r=0}^{3} {}_3C_r x^{3-r}(-5)^r$$
$$= {}_3C_0 x^{3-0}(-5)^0 + {}_3C_1 x^{3-1}(-5)^1 + {}_3C_2 x^{3-2}(-5)^2 + {}_3C_3 x^{3-3}(-5)^3$$
$$= 1 \cdot x^3 \cdot 1 + 3 \cdot x^2 \cdot (-5) + 3 \cdot x^1 \cdot 25 + 1 \cdot x^0 \cdot (-125)$$
$$= x^3 - 15x^2 + 75x - 125 \quad ∎$$

> **TIP**
>
> In this expression, $n = 3$, and row 3 in Pascal's triangle consists of 1 3 3 1.

Finding a Specific Term of a Binomial Expansion

Example 8 Find the 5th term in the expansion of $(3x - 4)^{10}$.

Solution Note that in the expansion in the binomial theorem, $r = 0$ in the 1st term, $r = 1$ in the 2nd term, and so on. The value of r is always 1 less than the number of the term. So in the 5th term, $r = 4$.

Every term in the expansion of $(3x - 4)^{10}$ has the form $_{10}C_r(3x)^{10-r}(-4)^r$. So the value of the 5th term is

$$_{10}C_4(3x)^{10-4}(-4)^4 = {}_{10}C_4(3x)^6(-4)^4 = 210 \cdot (729x^6) \cdot 256 = 39{,}191{,}040x^6. \quad ∎$$

Problem Set

Evaluate the combination expression.

1. $_8C_4$

2. $_{12}C_6$

3. $_{14}C_{14}$

4. $_{10}C_8$

5. $_9C_6$

6. $_7C_1$

Determine whether the situation would be better represented by a permutation or a combination. Explain your answer.

7. There are 64 basketball teams in a tournament. How many ways can first, second, and third place be awarded?

8. There are 15 people on a baseball team. How many ways can the coach arrange a batting lineup of 9 people?

9. There are 14 people trying out for a scholarship. How many ways could the selection committee award first prize, second prize, and third prize?

10. Reese is selecting astronauts for a mission. If there are 22 astronauts requesting a mission, how many ways could she select three people?

11. The student body takes a poll to select the new school colors. Of the 8 colors to choose from, how many ways could Felix select 2?

12. There are 10 books about a particular subject in the library. Suki can check out only 3 books at a time on this subject. How many different ways can she pick the books?

Write and evaluate the combination expression for the situation.

13. Gunner wants to buy 12 DVDs, but he can buy only 2. How many ways can he buy 2 DVDs?

14. A school has 9 girls' sports teams. How many different ways can Alina play 3 sports?

15. Tomas volunteers 10 days in September to help the hungry. How many ways can he choose what days to volunteer?

16. Sasha wants to send 3 letters. She has 14 different stamps. How many ways can she stamp the letters?

Use Pascal's triangle to find each combination.

17. $_7C_3$

18. $_5C_0$

19. $_8C_8$

20. $_{13}C_7$

Use the binomial theorem to expand each expression.

21. $(3x - 4y)^2$

22. $(x + 2y)^2$

23. $(5x + 4y)^3$

24. $(2x - 2y)^3$

Use the binomial theorem to find the 6th term of the binomial expansion.

25. $(x + y)^{10}$

26. $(3x - 3)^8$

27. $(x - 1)^9$

28. $(3x + 2y)^7$

Write and evaluate the combination expression for the situation.

29. A store has 12 different styles of shirts. Nehemiah wants to buy at least 2 but no more than 4 shirts. How many different choices of shirts are possible?

30. Sixteen people try out for the basketball team. The coach must accept at least 8 but no more than 10 players. How many different teams are possible?

31. Gwen's Language Arts class reading list consists of 8 book titles. She must write a report on 2 books. She can write up to 2 more reports for extra credit. How many different combinations of books could Gwen read?

32. A class of 14 is working on a group project. Each group must have at least 3 but no more than 6 students. How many different combinations of teams are possible?

*33. **Challenge** A football league is made up of 32 teams. There are 2 conferences with 16 teams in each. Only 6 teams from each conference can make it to the playoffs. How many combinations of teams can qualify in the playoffs?

*34. **Challenge** A fashion designer needs 4 pairs of pants that are the same color. A designer's store has 10 styles of pants in 8 different colors. How many combinations are possible?

Basic Probability

An experiment is any process that results in one or more outcomes.

Now that you've learned how to count outcomes, you'll use **probability** to describe how likely it is that particular outcomes will occur.

DEFINITION

A **sample space** is the set of all possible outcomes of an experiment.

Determining a Sample Space

Example 1   Determine the sample space S for each experiment.

A Flip a coin.

Solution   There are 2 possible outcomes when you flip a coin: heads or tails. You can state the sample space in set notation. Use S to denote the sample space, and enclose the possible outcomes in braces.

$$S = \{\text{heads, tails}\} \quad \blacksquare$$

B Roll a standard 6-faced die.

Solution   There are 6 possible outcomes when you roll a standard 6-faced die. As an alternative to set notation, you can create a tree diagram to represent the sample space for this experiment. Notice that each branch represents a possible outcome.

Set notation: $S = \{1, 2, 3, 4, 5, 6\}$

Tree diagram:

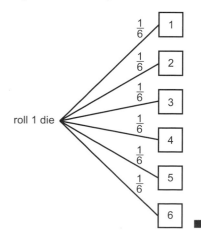

C Roll two standard 6-faced dice.

Solution On the basis of the multiplication principle, there are $6 \cdot 6 = 36$ outcomes in the sample space. Each outcome is an ordered pair. The table shows all 36 outcomes in the sample space.

Note that (1, 2) and (2, 1) are different outcomes. (Imagine that one die is red and the other die is blue. Then it is easy to see that (1, 2) and (2, 1) are different outcomes.)

Sample Space S					
1, 1	1, 2	1, 3	1, 4	1, 5	1, 6
2, 1	2, 2	2, 3	2, 4	2, 5	2, 6
3, 1	3, 2	3, 3	3, 4	3, 5	3, 6
4, 1	4, 2	4, 3	4, 4	4, 5	4, 6
5, 1	5, 2	5, 3	5, 4	5, 5	5, 6
6, 1	6, 2	6, 3	6, 4	6, 5	6, 6

Probability

DEFINITIONS

An **event** is any particular subset of a sample space.

A **simple event** is a single outcome of an experiment (a single element of a sample space).

A **compound event** is an event that consists of two or more simple events.

The **probability** of an event is a measure of the likelihood that the event will occur; probability is always a number between 0 and 1 (inclusive) that can be written as a fraction, a decimal, or a percent.

PROBABILITY OF AN EVENT *E*

Assuming all outcomes are equally likely, the probability of event *E* is

$$P(E) = \frac{\text{number of outcomes in event } E}{\text{total number of outcomes in sample space } S} = \frac{n(E)}{n(S)}.$$

From the probability formula, you can derive two important results:

$P(E) = 0$ if and only if it is impossible for event E to occur.
$P(E) = 1$ if and only if it is certain that event E will occur.

Example 2 Use the sample spaces in Example 1 to find the probability of each event.

A Roll 3 with a die.

Solution The sample space has 6 outcomes, and one outcome is 3.

$$P(3) = \frac{n(3)}{n(S)} = \frac{1}{6} \approx 0.17, \text{ or about } 17\%$$

Example 2A is a *simple event* because it is a single outcome of the sample space. Examples 2B and 2C are *compound events* because each consists of two or more outcomes.

B Roll at least 1 with a die.

Solution   When you roll a die, every outcome is at least 1. This is a certain event.

$$P(\text{at least } 1) = \frac{n(\text{at least } 1)}{n(S)} = \frac{6}{6} = 1 = 100\% \ \blacksquare$$

C Roll a sum of 10 with two dice.

Solution   The sample space has 36 outcomes, and 3 outcomes have a sum of 10: $(6, 4)$, $(5, 5)$, and $(4, 6)$.

$$P(\text{sum of } 10) = \frac{n(\text{sum of } 10)}{n(S)} = \frac{3}{36} = \frac{1}{12} \approx 0.08, \text{ or about } 8\% \ \blacksquare$$

Determining Probabilities Involving Permutations

Example 3   A set of encyclopedias contains 10 books. If the 10 books are randomly placed on a shelf, what is the probability that they are arranged in alphabetical order?

Solution   The number of ways that the encyclopedias could be arranged is $_{10}P_{10}$, the number of permutations of 10 different objects taken 10 at a time. Only 1 arrangement is in alphabetical order.

$$P(\text{books in order}) = \frac{n(\text{books in order})}{n(S)} = \frac{1}{_{10}P_{10}} = \frac{1}{10!} = \frac{1}{3,628,800} \ \blacksquare$$

Determining Probabilities Involving Combinations

Example 4   Given a standard deck of playing cards, what is the probability of getting a 5-card hand that contains 5 face cards (jacks, queens, or kings)?

Solution   A hand of cards is a combination because order does not matter. The number of ways to get 5 cards from 52 cards is $_{52}C_5$, the number of combinations of 52 objects taken 5 at a time. There are 12 face cards in all (3 in each of 4 suits), so the number of ways to get 5 face cards is $_{12}C_5$.

$$P(5 \text{ face cards}) = \frac{n(5 \text{ face cards})}{n(S)} = \frac{_{12}C_5}{_{52}C_5} = \frac{792}{2,598,960} \approx 0.0003 \ \blacksquare$$

Problem Set

Determine the sample space S for each experiment.

   1.   Choose a suit from a standard deck of cards.

   2.   Choose a number between 10 and 20, inclusive.

   3.   Roll a 5-sided die.

   4.   Choose a letter from the alphabet.

   5.   Choose an hour from an analog clock.

   6.   Choose a month of the year.

   7.   Choose a season of the year.

   8.   Choose a day of the week.

   9.   Choose a color from a traffic light.

   10.   Choose a continent.

   11.   Choose a vowel from the alphabet (exclude y).

   12.   Choose a number between 5 and 20, inclusive.

Find the probability of each event.

13. Roll 5 with a die.

14. Choose a 10 from a deck of cards.

15. Choose a spade from a deck of cards.

16. Roll an even number with a die.

17. Roll a prime number with a die.

18. Choose a face card (jack, queen, or king) from a deck of cards.

19. Choose a vowel from the alphabet (exclude *y*).

20. Guess a random person's birthday correctly (exclude leap year).

21. If 4 people compete in a race, what is the probability that they finish in the order of their birthdays, oldest to youngest?

22. Anja is rearranging the items in her cupboard. If she randomly lines up 15 spices in a row, what is the probability they are arranged in alphabetical order from either direction?

23. A toddler is randomly arranging 4 different letter magnets in a row—*P, R, C,* and *O*. What is the probability that her arrangement forms the word *CROP*?

24. Yessina is creating a mix CD. She has 24 songs to choose from, but only 15 tracks can be burned onto the CD. If she randomly arranges the songs, what is the probability that they are arranged in order by track length (shortest to longest)?

25. Keith is randomly placing 5 sets of DVDs of the same TV series on a shelf. What is the probability that they are arranged in order by season?

26. Luis is shuffling a standard deck of playing cards. What is the probability that none of the first 5 cards he pulls out is a face card?

27. Rachelle randomly pulls out 2 cards from a standard deck. What is the probability of getting a pair of aces?

28. The teacher allows Mindy to pull out 2 marbles from the marble bag. The bag contains 8 red marbles, 3 white marbles, 4 green marbles, and 5 blue marbles. Find the probability that both of Mindy's marbles are blue.

*29. **Challenge** Drew and a friend are playing the game rock–paper–scissors. If Drew chooses scissors, what are his friend's chances of winning the game?

*30. **Challenge** Given a standard deck of playing cards, what is the probability of getting 3 of a kind and 2 of a kind in the same 5-card hand?

Probability With and Without Replacement

The probability of an event depends on the sample space, but how does probability change when the sample space changes?

Finding Probability With Replacement

Example 1   A bag contains 4 black marbles and 2 red marbles. Felipe draws a marble from the bag. Felipe then replaces the marble and Peyton draws a marble. What is the probability that Felipe and Peyton both draw red marbles?

Solution   Because the marble drawn the first time is *replaced* before the second draw, the two sample spaces are exactly the same. In other words, the first drawing does *not* affect the second drawing.

Step 1   There are 2 red marbles, so $n(E) = 2$. There are 6 marbles in the bag, so $n(S) = 6$.

$$P(E) = \frac{n(E)}{n(S)} = \frac{2}{6}$$

The probability that Felipe draws a red marble is $\frac{1}{3}$.

Step 2   There are still 2 red marbles, so $n(E) = 2$. There are still 6 marbles in the bag, so $n(S) = 6$.

$$P(E) = \frac{n(E)}{n(S)} = \frac{2}{6}$$

The probability that Peyton draws a red marble on the second draw is also $\frac{1}{3}$.

You can use a tree diagram to find the probability that both events happen: $P(\text{red and red})$. Each branch shows a possible outcome, along with the probability of that outcome.

> **REMEMBER**
>
> The probability of event E is $P(E)$. The number of successful outcomes in which E occurs is $n(E)$. The total number of outcomes possible in sample space S is $n(S)$.

To compute the probability of drawing 2 red marbles with replacement, follow the path on the tree diagram that represents this event and multiply the probabilities.

The probability that both marbles are red $P(\text{red and red})$ is $\frac{4}{36} = \frac{1}{9}$. ■

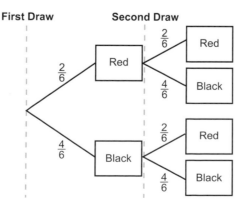

Finding Probability Without Replacement

What happens to these probabilities if Felipe does *not* replace his marble in the bag? Probability that involves more than one step when the result of the previous outcome is *not* replaced is called *probability without replacement*.

Example 2 A bag contains 4 black marbles and 2 red marbles. Felipe randomly draws a marble and does not replace it. Assume that Felipe does not look at the results of his random draw. Then Peyton randomly draws a marble from the same bag. What is the probability that both marbles drawn are red?

Solution The probability that Felipe draws a red marble is the same as before: P(Felipe draws red) is $\frac{1}{3}$. But then the situation changes.

The number of marbles in the bag after Felipe's draw is not the same as the number before his draw. Now there are only 5 total marbles. Given that Felipe drew a red marble, there is only 1 red marble left. The probability that Peyton will also draw a red marble is $\frac{1}{5}$, so P(Peyton draws red) is $\frac{1}{5}$.

Draw a tree diagram to represent possibilities of drawing 2 red marbles in this situation. Notice that the probabilities involved in the second draw have denominators of 5 because Felipe previously drew a marble without replacement.

NOTATION

$P(B$ **after** $A)$ **means the probability when event** B *follows* **event** A **and has been affected by event** A**.**

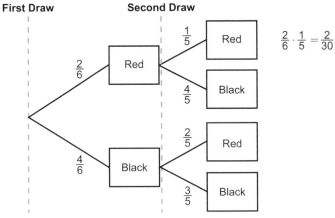

Compute the probability of drawing a red marble after a red marble is drawn without replacement by multiplying the probabilities on the appropriate branches.

The probability that both marbles are red P(red after red) is $\frac{2}{30} = \frac{1}{15}$. ∎

TIP

From now on, when a problem says "without replacement," assume that it means that the result of the first step is *not* known.

Using the Multiplication Rule

When you compute probabilities with and without replacement, applying one of the following multiplication rules is a quicker method than using the tree diagram:

MULTIPLICATION RULES FOR PROBABILITY

If event B occurs after event A and there is replacement,
$$P(A \text{ and } B) = P(A) \cdot P(B).$$
If event B occurs after event A and there is *no* replacement,
$$P(A \text{ and } B) = P(A) \cdot P(B \text{ after } A).$$

Example 3 Joanie and Chachi are friends. Each has a box that contains 3 raisin cookies and 5 lemon cookies.

Ⓐ Without looking, Joanie takes a cookie from her box. This first cookie is lemon, so she puts it back, mixes up the cookies, and picks another cookie. The second cookie is lemon as well! What is the probability of Joanie's 2-lemon-cookie outcome (which was with replacement)?

Solution The first lemon cookie is replaced, so the probability of drawing the second cookie is not affected by the first drawing. Use the multiplication rule for the situation when A does *not* affect B:

$$P(\text{lemon}) \cdot P(\text{lemon}) = \frac{5}{8} \cdot \frac{5}{8} = \frac{25}{64} \blacksquare$$

Ⓑ Chachi chooses a cookie from his box. It's a lemon cookie. He likes lemon cookies, so he eats it and then takes another cookie from the box. The second cookie is lemon as well. What is the probability of Chachi's 2-lemon-cookie outcome (which was without replacement)?

Solution The first cookie is not replaced. The probability of drawing another lemon cookie, given that the first cookie drawn was lemon, is $\frac{4}{7}$. Use the multiplication rule for the situation when A *does* affect B:

$$P(\text{lemon}) \cdot P(\text{lemon after lemon}) = \frac{5}{8} \cdot \frac{4}{7} = \frac{20}{56} = \frac{5}{14} \blacksquare$$

Problem Set

For each problem, do the following:

A. **Draw a tree diagram to represent the sample space.**
B. **Use the tree diagram to compute the probability of the indicated event.**

1. A box contains 10 red balls, 8 blue balls, and 4 green balls. A blindfolded magician pulls 1 ball from the box and then pulls another ball after replacing the first. What is the probability that the magician pulled 2 blue balls?

2. What is the probability of randomly selecting a king and then a jack from a standard deck of 52 cards if the first card is not replaced before the second is drawn?

3. Julia's drawer contains 17 tubes of lipstick: 5 are red, 9 are pink, and 3 are mauve. Julia randomly picks 1 tube, puts it back, and then picks another without looking. Find the probability she chose 2 tubes of red lipstick.

4. A jar contains 8 yellow marbles, 5 white marbles, and 3 blue marbles. If Jonah draws 2 marbles at random without replacement, what is the probability that both marbles are blue?

Use the multiplication rules to compute the probability of each event.

5. Otto selects cards from a standard deck of 52 cards. If he randomly chooses 1 card, puts it back in the deck, and then selects another card without looking, what is the probability that he selected 2 queens?

6. The numbers 1 through 10 are written on slips of paper and put into a bag. If you choose 2 slips without replacement, what is the probability of pulling a 5 on the first pick and a 6 on the second pick?

7. A child has 5 stuffed cats, 8 stuffed dogs, and 7 stuffed pigs in her toy box. The child closes her eyes and randomly chooses 1 stuffed animal, puts it back, and then chooses another. What is the probability that the child chose 2 pigs?

8. A map shows 10 cities. If you randomly select 1 city and then another, what is the probability that you chose the same city each time?

9. A class consists of 12 boys and 14 girls. A teacher randomly pulls names from a hat. If the teacher chooses 1 name and then another without replacement, what is the probability that 2 boys are selected?

10. A box contains 7 rings, 9 necklaces, and 4 pins. If Anya selects 1 piece at random without replacement and then another, what is the probability that she selected 2 rings?

11. A box of candy has 8 caramels and 12 nougats. If Jose randomly takes 1 piece and then another piece without replacement, what is the probability that Jose drew 1 caramel and then 1 nougat?

12. A dealer randomly deals 4 cards from a standard deck of 52, face down, 1 at a time without replacement. What is the probability that the dealer dealt 4 queens?

13. A box contains 6 bags of potato chips, 6 bags of nachos, and 8 bags of corn chips. If Hugh randomly selects 1 bag, replaces it and then selects another bag without looking, what is the probability that Hugh chose 1 bag of nachos and then 1 bag of corn chips?

14. A store cart contains 30 marked-down DVDs: 20 are dramas, 6 are comedies, and 4 are adventures. If you randomly choose 1 DVD and then another, what is the probability that you selected 2 dramas?

15. A box contains 8 red pencils, 10 blue pencils, 7 green pencils, and 2 silver pencils. June randomly chooses 1 pencil, returns it to the box, and then selects another pencil without looking. What is the probability that June chose 1 green pencil and then 1 red pencil?

16. A hardware store bin contains 5 brass knobs, 6 silver knobs, and 8 pewter knobs. If Jamal selects a piece at random without replacement and then selects another piece, what is the probability that Jamal chose a brass knob and then a silver knob?

17. There are 18 family-contestant and 27 single-person-contestant entry forms in a box. One winner is selected, and the entry form is returned to the box. A second winner is chosen. What is the probability that a family won the first prize and a single person won the second prize?

18. A child selects from a prize box of 6 black action figures, 8 green action figures, 3 red action figures, and 8 blue action figures. The child randomly chooses 1 prize, puts it back, and then chooses another prize. What is the probability that the child chose a black action figure and then a blue action figure?

19. While blindfolded, Su Mi bobs for apples in a tub that contains 9 red and 15 yellow apples. If Su Mi randomly selects 1 apple on her first try and without replacing it, selects another apple on her second attempt, what is the probability that both apples are red?

20. A store clerk is clearing a shelf of soup cans. If the shelf contains 10 cans of tomato soup and 6 cans of chicken noodle, what is the probability that the clerk randomly selects 1 can of tomato soup without replacement and then another can of tomato?

21. A bag of hard candy contains 5 lemon, 10 cherry, 15 orange, and 8 pineapple pieces. Without looking, a child randomly selects 1 piece and returns it, selects another piece, returns it, and then selects a third piece. What is the probability that the child selected 3 cherry pieces?

22. A baseball player sprains his ankle in a game. The coach has 4 girls and 8 boys on the bench. The coach randomly chooses 1 substitute in the fourth inning. In the fifth inning, without looking, the coach randomly chooses another substitute. What is the probability that the coach chose a boy both times?

*23. **Challenge** A bag contains 4 quarters, 7 nickels, and 3 dimes. Sue randomly picks 1 coin from the bag without replacement. Sue picks another coin, which she returns to the bag. She picks a third coin, which she keeps. What is the probability that she will select a quarter, nickel, and dime—in that order?

*24. **Challenge** Joaquin randomly draws 5 cards from a standard deck of 52 cards without looking. He draws each card 1 at a time and replaces it before drawing the next card. What is the probability that Joaquin drew a 2 of clubs, 3 of spades, 4 of hearts or diamonds, 5 of diamonds, and a 6 of any suit, in that order?

Independent and Dependent Events

A *compound event* consists of two or more events.

Some compound events are made up of *independent* events; some compound events are made up of *dependent* events.

Determining Whether Events Are Independent or Dependent and Finding Probabilities

DEFINITIONS

Two events are **independent** if and only if knowing one outcome *has no effect* on the probability of the other event.

Two events are **dependent** if and only if knowing one outcome *has an effect* on the probability of the other event.

To find the probability of two events, independent or dependent, you multiply probabilities.

PROBABILITY OF DEPENDENT AND INDEPENDENT EVENTS

If events A and B are independent, then:

$$P(A \text{ and } B) = P(A) \cdot P(B).$$

If events A and B are dependent, then:

$$P(A \text{ and } B) = P(A) \cdot P(B \mid A).$$

where $P(B \mid A)$ is the **conditional probability** of event B or the probability of B, given that A has already occurred.

TIP

These properties extend to three or more events.

Example 1 A bag contains 10 marbles: 6 red, 3 black, and 1 white. A marble is chosen from the bag at random, and then another marble is chosen from the bag at random. Determine whether each compound event consists of independent events or dependent events, and find each indicated probability.

Ⓐ choosing 2 red marbles, with replacement

Ⓑ choosing 1 red marble and then 1 white marble, with replacement

Ⓒ choosing 2 white marbles, with replacement

Ⓓ choosing 2 red marbles, without replacement

Ⓔ choosing 1 red marble and then 1 white marble, without replacement

Ⓕ choosing 2 white marbles, without replacement

Solution Each of the pairs of events in parts A, B, and C is independent because the outcome of the first pick *does not affect* the probability of any particular outcome on the second pick. There are 10 marbles in the bag for each pick. Use the formula $P(A \text{ and } B) = P(A) \cdot P(B)$.

Ⓐ $P(\text{red and red}) = P(\text{red}) \cdot P(\text{red}) = \dfrac{6}{10} \cdot \dfrac{6}{10} = \dfrac{36}{100} = \dfrac{9}{25} = 0.36$

Ⓑ $P(\text{red and white}) = P(\text{red}) \cdot P(\text{white}) = \dfrac{6}{10} \cdot \dfrac{1}{10} = \dfrac{6}{100} = \dfrac{3}{50} = 0.06$

Ⓒ $P(\text{white and white}) = P(\text{white}) \cdot P(\text{white}) = \dfrac{1}{10} \cdot \dfrac{1}{10} = \dfrac{1}{100} = 0.01$

Each of the pairs of events in parts D, E, and F is dependent because the outcome of the first pick *does affect* the probability of any particular outcome on the second pick. There are only 9 marbles in the bag for the second pick. Use the formula $P(A \text{ and } B) = P(A) \cdot P(B \mid A)$.

Ⓓ $P(\text{red after red}) = P(\text{red}) \cdot P(\text{red} \mid \text{red}) = \dfrac{6}{10} \cdot \dfrac{5}{9} = \dfrac{30}{90} = \dfrac{1}{3} \approx 0.33$

Ⓔ $P(\text{red after white}) = P(\text{red}) \cdot P(\text{white} \mid \text{red}) = \dfrac{6}{10} \cdot \dfrac{1}{9} = \dfrac{6}{90} = \dfrac{1}{5} \approx 0.07$

Ⓕ $P(\text{white after white}) = P(\text{white}) \cdot P(\text{white} \mid \text{white}) = \dfrac{1}{10} \cdot \dfrac{0}{9} = 0$

It is impossible to get white on the second pick because, without replacement, there is no white marble in the bag for the second pick. ■

TIP

With replacement means the object is replaced before the next object is chosen. In general, events are independent when there is replacement.

Without replacement means the object is not replaced before the next object is chosen. In general, events are dependent when there is no replacement.

REMEMBER

$P(\text{red} \mid \text{red})$ means the probability of getting red on the second pick, given that red was the outcome on the first pick. In Example 1D, after red is picked first, there are 9 marbles left, and 5 of them red.

Determining Probability of Several Independent Events

Example 2 On a television game show, a contestant has a chance to win a car by rolling 5 dice. Each die has 3 faces with pictures of cars and 3 faces with amounts of money ($500, $1000, and $1500). The contestant wins the car if she rolls a car on each of the 5 dice. What is the probability, expressed as a percent, that the contestant wins the car with one roll of the 5 dice?

Solution The probability of getting a car on any one die is $P(\text{car}) = \dfrac{3}{6} = \dfrac{1}{2}$.

The outcome on each die is an event, and all outcomes are independent.

$P(\text{car and car and car and car and car}) = \dfrac{1}{2} \cdot \dfrac{1}{2} \cdot \dfrac{1}{2} \cdot \dfrac{1}{2} \cdot \dfrac{1}{2} = \dfrac{1}{32} = 0.03125$

The probability that the contestant wins the car with one roll of the 5 dice is 3.125%. ■

Determining the Probability of Several Dependent Events

Example 3 On a game show, there are 5 identical cases—1 contains a grand prize of $1 million and 4 are empty. A contestant wins $1 million if he can eliminate the 4 empty cases, one by one. What is the probability, expressed as a percent, of eliminating the 4 empty cases, one by one?

Solution Eliminating the 4 empty cases is a series of dependent events. On the first pick, there are 4 empty cases out of 5. Assuming the contestant picks an empty case, then 3 of the 4 remaining cases are empty, and so on.

$$P(\text{4 empty cases}) = \frac{4}{5} \cdot \frac{3}{4} \cdot \frac{2}{3} \cdot \frac{1}{2} = \frac{24}{120} = \frac{1}{5} = 0.2$$

The probability of eliminating the 4 empty cases, one by one, is 20%. ∎

> **THINK ABOUT IT**
>
> The probability of eliminating the 4 empty cases, one by one, is the same as the probability of picking the grand prize on the first pick: $\frac{1}{5}$.

Problem Set

Determine whether the events are dependent or independent.

1. flipping a coin multiple times

2. rolling a die multiple times

3. picking cards from a deck without replacement

4. picking marbles out of a bag with replacement

5. picking pennies from a jar of change with replacement

6. picking pennies from a jar of change without replacement

A hat is filled with 10 slips of paper, numbered 1 to 10. Davian and 9 other people take turns picking the numbers from the hat. Determine whether the events are dependent or independent.

7. picking numbers less than 10, with replacement

8. picking numbers greater than 5, without replacement

9. picking consecutive numbers, without replacement

10. picking even numbers, with replacement

11. picking odd numbers, without replacement

12. picking prime numbers, without replacement

Find the probability of each event. Assume replacement, where applicable.

13. picking 2 white marbles out of a bag of 3 red, 2 black, 2 white, and 4 yellow marbles

14. spinning 3 or higher on a spinner with numbers 1 to 6

15. flipping a coin and getting 3 heads in a row

16. picking 3 hearts in a row from a deck of cards

17. rolling a multiple of 3 four times in a row with a 6-sided die

18. picking a face card (jack, queen, or king) 2 times in a row from a deck of cards

19. rolling a 2 two times in a row with a 6-sided die

20. flipping a coin and getting 3 tails in a row

21. rolling a 5 three times in a row with a 6-sided die

Kory is picking cards from a standard deck without replacement. Find the probability of each event. Express your answer as a percent, rounded to 6 decimal places.

22. picking 4 tens in a row

23. picking 5 cards of the same suit

24. picking 5 clubs

25. picking a heart, then a club, then a spade

26. picking 5 cards that are in sequence, but not necessarily the same suit.

27. picking 5 face cards (jack, queen, or king)

28. picking three cards greater than 5 (6 through ace)

Answer each question.

*29. **Challenge** Ramone has 5 difficult questions left to answer on a multiple choice test. Each question has 3 choices. For the first 2 of these questions, he eliminated 1 of the 3 choices. Find the probability that he will answer the first 2 questions, as well as at least 2 of the 3 remaining questions correctly.

*30. **Challenge** In a board game, does rolling doubles (rolling the same value on each die) with two 6-sided dice involve dependent or independent events? Explain your answer.

Mutually Exclusive Events

Some compound events consist of *mutually exclusive* events.

Identifying Mutually Exclusive Events

> **DEFINITION**
>
> Two events are **mutually exclusive** if and only if one event's occurrence guarantees that the other event does not occur.

Example 1   For each compound event described, determine whether the events that make up the compound event are mutually exclusive.

A getting an ace or a king with one draw of a single card from a standard deck of cards

Solution   Yes, these are mutually exclusive events. If you get an ace, you cannot get a king. If you get a king, you cannot get an ace. The occurrence of one event guarantees that the other event does not occur. ■

B getting a prime number or an even number with one roll of a die

Solution   No, these are not mutually exclusive events. If you roll a 2, you have both a prime number and an even number at the same time. ■

C getting heads with one flip of a coin or 6 on the roll of a die

Solution   No, these are not mutually exclusive events. It is possible to get heads on the coin flip and 6 on the roll of the die. ■

An event is a set of outcomes. A compound event can be defined as a union ($\cup$) or intersection ($\cap$) of events. Two events A and B are mutually exclusive if and only if $A \cap B = \{\ \}$.

> **THINK ABOUT IT**
>
> If two events are mutually exclusive, they cannot be independent, because if one of the events occurs, the probability of the other event is affected (it is 0).

Here are diagrams for Example 1, along with explanations in terms of sets.

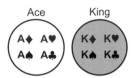

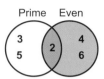

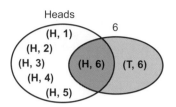

Drawing an ace or a king describes mutually exclusive events because the intersection is empty. (Sets are *disjoint* if their intersection is empty.)

Rolling a prime number or an even number does not describe mutually exclusive events because the outcome 2 is in the intersection.

Flipping heads or rolling a 6 does not describe mutually exclusive events because the outcome (H, 6) is in the intersection.

Note: The experiment in Example 1C is *flip a coin and roll a die*. The sample space for this experiment is {(H, 1), (H, 2), (H, 3), (H, 4), (H, 5), (H, 6), (T, 1), (T, 2), (T, 3), (T, 4), (T, 5), (T, 6)}. The event flip heads or roll 6 is this subset of the sample space: {(H, 1), (H, 2), (H, 3), (H, 4), (H, 5), (H, 6), (T, 6)}.

Finding Probability of the Union of Two Events

The word *or* is often used to describe a union of events. The following formulas can be used to find probabilities of unions of events.

PROBABILITY OF THE UNION OF TWO EVENTS

For any events A and B,
$$P(A \text{ or } B) = P(A) + P(B) - P(A \text{ and } B).$$
Events A and B are **mutually exclusive** if and only if
$$P(A \text{ or } B) = P(A) + P(B).$$

> **TIP**
>
> These properties extend to three or more events.

You can use the first formula whether or not the events are mutually exclusive. The formula for *mutually exclusive* events A and B is a special case of the formula for *any* events A and B, because if A and B are mutually exclusive, then $P(A \text{ and } B) = 0$.

Example 2   Find the probability of each compound event.

Ⓐ getting doubles or a sum of 6 with one roll of two dice

Solution   These are not mutually exclusive events because (3, 3) is both doubles and a sum of 6. Use the formula
$$P(A \text{ or } B) = P(A) + P(B) - P(A \text{ and } B).$$

$P(\text{sum of 6 or doubles}) = P(\text{sum of 6}) + P(\text{doubles}) - P(\text{sum of 6 and doubles})$

$$= \frac{5}{36} + \frac{6}{36} - \frac{1}{36} = \frac{10}{36} = \frac{5}{18} \blacksquare$$

Ⓑ getting a face card or a 10 with one draw from a standard deck of cards

Solution   A 10 is not a face card, so these events are mutually exclusive.

$$P(\text{face card or 10}) = P(\text{face card}) + P(10) = \frac{12}{52} + \frac{4}{52} = \frac{16}{52} = \frac{4}{13} \blacksquare$$

> **THINK ABOUT IT**
>
> The 5 outcomes that have a sum of 6 are (1, 5), (2, 4), (3, 3), (4, 2), and (5, 1). So $P(\text{sum of 6}) = \frac{5}{36}$. Meanwhile, six outcomes are doubles, so $P(\text{doubles}) = \frac{6}{36}$. But the sum $\frac{5}{36} + \frac{6}{36}$ includes the outcome (3, 3) twice. To get the correct probability, subtract $\frac{1}{36}$ so that (3, 3) is counted only once.

Finding Probability Involving Mutually Exclusive Events and Combinations

Example 3 Given a standard 52-card deck, what is the probability of drawing 5 cards (without replacement) that include at least 3 aces?

Solution Getting at least 3 aces is equivalent to this compound event: getting exactly 3 aces or getting exactly 4 aces (these are two mutually exclusive events). There are $_{52}C_5$ ways to get 5 cards from the 52 cards in the deck. There are $_4C_3$ ways to get 3 aces from 4 aces, and $_{48}C_2$ ways to get 2 cards from the remaining 48 cards in the deck.

So there are $\dfrac{_4C_3 \cdot {}_{48}C_2}{_{52}C_5} = \dfrac{4512}{2,598,960}$ ways to get exactly 3 aces. By similar reasoning, there are $\dfrac{_4C_4 \cdot {}_{48}C_1}{_{52}C_5} = \dfrac{48}{2,598,960}$ ways to get exactly 4 aces.

So P(at least 3 aces) $= P$(exactly 3 aces or exactly 4 aces)

$$= P(\text{exactly 3 aces}) + P(\text{exactly 4 aces})$$

$$= \frac{4512}{2,598,960} + \frac{48}{2,598,960}$$

$$\approx 0.002 \ \blacksquare$$

> **THINK ABOUT IT**
>
> If $\dfrac{_4C_3 \cdot {}_{48}C_2}{_{52}C_5}$ is written as
>
> $$\dfrac{\binom{4}{3} \cdot \binom{48}{2}}{\binom{52}{5}},$$
>
> you can see that the top numbers in the numerator add to get the top number in the denominator and the bottom numbers in the numerator add to get the bottom number in the denominator.

Problem Set

Determine whether the events that make up the compound event are mutually exclusive. If not, explain why.

1. getting a 6 or a 2 with one roll of a die

2. drawing a red card or a spade from a standard deck of cards by selecting one card

3. drawing a diamond or a 10 from a standard deck of cards

4. getting a composite number or an odd number with one roll of a die

A bag is filled with red marbles, blue marbles, yellow marbles, black marbles, red jacks, blue jacks, yellow jacks, and white jacks. Determine whether the events that make up each compound event are mutually exclusive. If not, explain why.

5. getting a red object or getting a marble

6. getting a marble or getting a jack

7. getting a marble or getting a white object

8. getting a marble or getting a blue object

9. getting a red marble or getting a blue marble

10. getting a jack or getting a yellow object

11. getting a jack or getting a black object

12. getting a red marble or getting a red jack

13. getting a black object or getting a white jack

14. getting a black object or getting a marble

Find the probability of the compound event.

15. getting a diamond or getting a 3 from a standard deck of cards

16. getting a 10 or getting an ace from a standard deck of cards

17. getting a heart or getting a black card from a standard deck of cards

18. getting a sum of 12 or 2 with one roll of two dice

19. getting doubles or getting a sum of 10 with one roll of two dice

20. getting a sum of 5 or 8 with one roll of two dice

Silvia is offered one car at random from a car dealership. The lot has 15 red cars, 9 blue cars, 32 black cars, 7 red trucks, 3 blue trucks, 17 silver trucks, 3 red vans, 4 blue vans, and 10 green vans. Find the probability of the compound event.

21. getting a red vehicle or a car

22. getting a van or a red vehicle

23. getting a green vehicle or a truck

24. getting a black vehicle or a car

25. getting a red vehicle or a blue vehicle

26. getting a red truck or a silver vehicle

27. getting a truck or a van

28. getting a green van or a blue van

Answer each question.

29. Explain how you know whether two events are mutually exclusive.

*30. **Challenge** With a standard deck of cards, what is the probability of drawing an even number, a jack, or a red card?

Binomial Probability

The **complement** of an event *A* is the set of all outcomes in the sample space that are not in *A*.

For example, given the event "roll 2 with a die," the complement is "do not roll 2 with a die," or "roll 1, 3, 4, 5, or 6 with a die."

> **PROBABILITY OF COMPLEMENTARY EVENTS**
>
> If events *A* and *B* are complementary, then
> $$P(A) = 1 - P(B).$$

Identifying Binomial Experiments

For a *binomial experiment,* the sample space is separated into two complementary events; these events are usually labeled *success* and *failure*.

> **DEFINITION**
>
> A **binomial experiment** is a probability experiment that meets the following conditions:
> - There are a fixed number of independent trials.
> - Each outcome for each trial is labeled either *success* or *failure,* where success and failure are complementary events.
> - The probability *p* of success is the same for each trial. The probability of failure for each trial is $1 - p$.

Example 1   Determine whether each experiment can be called a binomial experiment.

Ⓐ Roll a die three times. Each time, record whether you get a 2.

Solution   Yes, this is a binomial experiment. The number of trials is fixed at three. The trials are independent because no outcome affects the probability of the outcome on any other trial. Each outcome is either success (2) or failure (not 2). The probability of rolling a 2 is the same for each trial. ■

Ⓑ Flip a coin until you get heads.

Solution   No, this is not a binomial experiment. Because you flip the coin until you get heads, the number of trials is not fixed. ■

C Draw 5 cards from a deck without replacement. Each time, record whether you get an ace.

Solution   No, this is not a binomial experiment. The trials are not independent because the number of cards is different on each draw, causing the probability of success to change with each trial. ∎

Finding a Binomial Probability

The tree diagram shows rolling a die 3 times and recording **Yes** if a 6 is rolled or **No** if a 6 is not rolled.

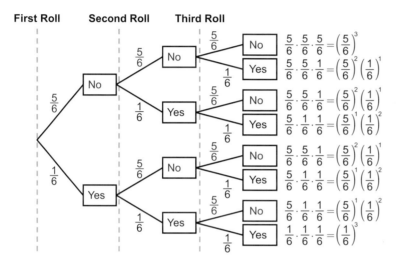

The sum of the probabilities of getting different numbers of 6s in 3 rolls is
$P(\text{zero 6s}) + P(\text{one 6}) + P(\text{two 6s}) + P(\text{three 6s})$

$$1 \cdot \left(\frac{5}{6}\right)^3 + 3 \cdot \left(\frac{5}{6}\right)^2\left(\frac{1}{6}\right)^1 + 3 \cdot \left(\frac{5}{6}\right)^1\left(\frac{1}{6}\right)^2 + 1 \cdot \left(\frac{1}{6}\right)^3 = \sum_{r=0}^{3} {}_3C_r\left(\frac{5}{6}\right)^{n-r}\left(\frac{1}{6}\right)^r$$

The sum of the probabilities of getting different numbers of 6s in 4 rolls is
$P(\text{zero 6s}) + P(\text{one 6}) + P(\text{two 6s}) + P(\text{three 6s}) + P(\text{four 6s})$

$$1 \cdot \left(\frac{5}{6}\right)^4 + 4 \cdot \left(\frac{5}{6}\right)^3\left(\frac{1}{6}\right)^1 + 6 \cdot \left(\frac{5}{6}\right)^2\left(\frac{1}{6}\right)^2 + 4 \cdot \left(\frac{5}{6}\right)^1\left(\frac{1}{6}\right)^3 + 1 \cdot \left(\frac{1}{6}\right)^4 = \sum_{r=0}^{4} {}_4C_r\left(\frac{5}{6}\right)^{n-r}\left(\frac{1}{6}\right)^r$$

The binomial theorem states that $(x+y)^n = \sum_{r=0}^{n} {}_nC_r\, x^{n-r}y^r$.

Substituting $1-p$ for x and p for y, you have

$$((1-p)+p)^n = \sum_{r=0}^{n} {}_nC_r(1-p)^{n-r}p^r.$$

So the probability of r successes in n trials is a term of a binomial expansion.

For a binomial experiment with n trials, the probability of exactly r successes is

$$P(\text{exactly } r \text{ successes}) = {}_nC_r\, p^r\, (1-p)^{n-r},$$

where p is the probability of success in each trial.

Example 2 What is the probability of rolling five dice and getting exactly three 2s?

Solution If you imagine that each die is rolled individually, this is a binomial experiment with five trials: $n = 5$. You want three 2s, so $r = 3$.

The probability of success on any one roll is $p = P(2) = \frac{1}{6}$.

$$P(\text{exactly } r \text{ successes}) = {}_nC_r\, p^r\, (1-p)^{n-r}$$

$$
\begin{aligned}
P(\text{exactly three 2s}) &= {}_5C_3 \left(\frac{1}{6}\right)^3 \left(1 - \frac{1}{6}\right)^{5-3} \\
&= 10 \cdot \frac{1}{216} \cdot \left(\frac{5}{6}\right)^2 \\
&= 10 \cdot \frac{1}{216} \cdot \frac{25}{36} \\
&\approx 0.032 \quad \blacksquare
\end{aligned}
$$

Recall that you can use Pascal's triangle to determine the value of a binomial coefficient. In this expression, $n = 5$, row 5 of Pascal's triangle matches the binomial coefficients ${}_5C_0, {}_5C_1, {}_5C_2, {}_5C_3, {}_5C_4$, and ${}_5C_5$. So ${}_5C_3 =$ the 4th term in row 5 $= 10$.

```
row 0            1
row 1           1  1
row 2          1  2  1
row 3         1  3  3  1
row 4        1  4  6  4  1
row 5      1  5 10 10  5  1
                 . . .
```

Example 3 According to the U.S. Census Bureau, 64% of citizens aged 18 or over voted in the 2004 presidential election. Vashonne surveys 10 citizens who were 18 or over in 2004.

(A) What is the probability that exactly 6 of them voted in the presidential election?

Solution This is a binomial experiment with $n = 10$ and $r = 6$. Because 64% of citizens voted, the probability of success is $p = 0.64$.

$$
\begin{aligned}
P(\text{exactly 6 voted}) &= {}_{10}C_6(0.64)^6(1 - 0.64)^{10-6} \\
&= 210(0.64)^6(0.36)^4 \\
&\approx 0.242 \quad \blacksquare
\end{aligned}
$$

B What is the probability that at least 1 of them voted?

Solution You could find the probability of the union of these 10 mutually exclusive events: *exactly 1 voted* or *exactly 2 voted* or *exactly 3 voted* or ... *exactly 10 voted*. But a quicker method is to find the probability of the complementary event and then subtract it from 1. The complement of *at least 1 voted* is *exactly 0 voted*.

$$P(\text{at least 1 voted}) = 1 - P(\text{exactly 0 voted})$$
$$= 1 - {}_{10}C_0(0.64)^0(0.36)^{10}$$
$$\approx 1 - 0.00004$$
$$\approx 0.99996 \quad \blacksquare$$

Problem Set

Determine whether the events are complementary.

1. **A.** rolling a 2 with a die

    B. rolling a 6 with a die

2. **A.** rolling an even number with a die

    B. rolling an odd number with a die

3. **A.** landing on heads

    B. landing on tails

4. **A.** landing on tails

    B. not landing on heads

5. **A.** choosing a black card from a deck of cards

    B. choosing a red card (with replacement)

6. **A.** choosing a spade from a deck of cards

    B. choosing a club (with replacement)

7. **A.** choosing a black card from a deck of cards

    B. choosing a red card (without replacement)

8. **A.** choosing a nickel from a jar of change

    B. choosing a dime from a jar of change (with replacement)

Determine whether each experiment is a binomial experiment. If not, explain why.

9. Flip a coin 3 times. Each time, record whether you get heads.

10. Roll a die until you get 1.

11. Draw 5 cards from a deck with replacement. Each time, record whether you get a diamond.

12. Roll a die 3 times. Each time, record whether you get an even number.

13. Draw 5 cards from a deck without replacement. Each time, record whether you get a face card.

14. Draw cards from a deck until you get a red card.

15. Flip a coin until you get tails.

16. Roll a die 4 times. Each time, record whether you get a composite number.

Find the binomial probability.

17. rolling five dice and getting exactly four even numbers

18. rolling four dice and getting exactly two 5s

19. rolling six dice and getting exactly three 1s

20. drawing 5 cards (with replacement) and getting exactly 2 aces

21. drawing 3 cards (with replacement) and getting exactly 1 red card

22. drawing 4 cards (with replacement) and getting exactly 2 hearts

23. Assume that about 40% of employees at Pay Less Insurance prefer working shorter shifts with less promotion potential than working longer shifts with a higher chance of promotion. On the basis of this information, if Rahul surveys 10 employees, what is the probability that exactly half will say they prefer a shorter shift with less promotion potential?

24. In the Better Pet Care clinic, assume that an average of 14 out of 23 pets come to the clinic for minor health needs. If on one day the clinic attended to 18 pets, what is the probability that 12 or more had only minor problems, based on the average rate of pets with minor needs?

Assume that 23% of new models of cars sold last year were black. Based on this information, Omarion surveys 8 car owners who purchased new models last year.

25. What is the probability that exactly 2 of them bought black cars?

26. What is the probability that exactly 4 of them did not buy black cars?

27. If Omarion surveys 200 people, how many would he expect to have bought black cars?

28. If Omarion surveys 200 people, how many would he expect not to have bought black cars?

Solve.

*29. **Challenge** A bag is full of 25 marbles and 25 jacks. Five marbles and 5 jacks are red, 10 marbles and 10 jacks are blue, and the rest of the marbles and jacks are green.

   A. Are picking a green object and picking a marble complementary events? Explain.

   B. Dasia picks 5 objects without replacement, noting each time she picks a blue jack. Is this a binomial event? Explain.

Making Predictions

A certain type of probability that is calculated as a ratio of lengths, areas, or volumes is called *geometric probability*.

Finding Geometric Probability by Using Area

> ### GEOMETRIC PROBABILITY
>
> Suppose figure *A* is contained entirely within figure *B* and the ratio of the area of figure *A* to the area of figure *B* is *p*. If a point is chosen at random within figure *B*, then the probability that the point lies within figure *A* is *p*.

> **TIP**
>
> This property also applies for length and volume.

Example 1 This target consists of four concentric circles with radii 2 inches, 4 inches, 6 inches, and 8 inches. Assuming that a dart hits the target at a random point, find the probability of each event.

A The dart hits the bull's-eye labeled S.

B The dart hits the ring labeled Q.

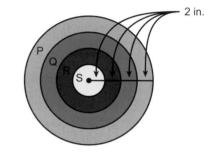

2 in.

Solution Find the ratio of the area of circle S to the area of the entire target.

A $P(\text{bull's-eye S}) = \dfrac{\text{area of circle S}}{\text{area of entire target}} = \dfrac{\pi \cdot 2^2}{\pi \cdot 8^2} = \dfrac{4\pi}{64\pi} = \dfrac{1}{16}$

The area of ring Q is the difference between the areas of the two circles that form the ring (the outer and inner circles).

B $P(\text{ring Q}) = \dfrac{\text{area of ring Q}}{\text{area of entire target}}$

$= \dfrac{\pi \cdot 6^2 - \pi \cdot 4^2}{\pi \cdot 8^2} = \dfrac{36\pi - 16\pi}{64\pi} = \dfrac{20\pi}{64\pi} = \dfrac{5}{16}$ ∎

Use Geometric Probability to Make a Prediction

Example 2 Use the conditions in Example 1. Suppose a dart hits the target 50 times, each time at a random point. Based on geometric probability, what is the most likely number of times the dart will hit the following?

A the bull's-eye labeled S **B** the ring labeled Q

Solution   Multiply the number of times hit by the geometric probability.

A $\frac{1}{16} \times 50 = \frac{1}{16} \times \frac{50}{1} = \frac{50}{16} = 3.125$

The most likely number of times the dart will hit bull's-eye S is 3.

B $\frac{5}{16} \times 50 = \frac{5}{16} \times \frac{50}{1} = \frac{250}{16} = 15.625$

The most likely number of times the dart will hit ring Q is 16. ∎

Finding Geometric Probability by Using Length

Example 3   A stick of candy falls on the floor and breaks into two pieces. What is the probability that one piece is at least twice as long as the other?

Solution   Think of the candy as a line segment with length 1 unit. One piece is at least twice as long as the other if the candy breaks at any point in either the $\left(0, \frac{1}{3}\right)$ interval or the $\left(\frac{2}{3}, 1\right)$ interval. The combined length of the two intervals is $\frac{1}{3} + \frac{1}{3} = \frac{2}{3}$, so the probability that one piece is at least twice as long as the other is the ratio $\dfrac{\frac{2}{3}}{1}$, or $\frac{2}{3}$. ∎

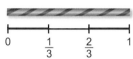

Favorable breaking points

Using Experimental Probability to Make a Prediction

Probability is often defined as a measure of the likelihood that an event will occur, based on the assumption that all outcomes in a sample space are equally likely. That type of probability is called *theoretical probability*. Geometric probability is theoretical probability; it is based on the assumption that all points in a figure are equally likely to be selected (or hit) if a point is selected at random.

In some cases, there is no way to determine how likely the possible outcomes are. In other cases, you might want to simply observe and record actual outcomes to collect data. In such cases, you can calculate *experimental probability*.

EXPERIMENTAL PROBABILITY OF EVENT *E*

When *n* independent trials of an experiment have been performed, the experimental probability of event *E* is

$$P(E) = \frac{\text{number of times event } E \text{ has occurred}}{n}.$$

Example 4 The graph shows data about Barry Bonds's career hits for the San Francisco Giants as of June 16, 2007. Based on the data, predict the most likely number of home runs in his next 100 hits.

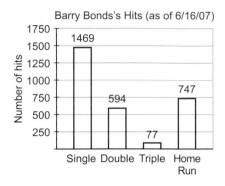

Barry Bonds's Hits (as of 6/16/07)

Solution In this real-world situation, the experiment is "Barry Bonds gets a hit," and the event to consider is "the hit is a home run."

The experiment had $1469 + 594 + 77 + 747 = 2887$ independent trials. Of those trials, a home run occurred 747 times.

So, based on the data, $P(\text{a hit is a home run}) = \dfrac{747}{2887} \approx 0.259$. Multiply the specified number of hits by the experimental probability: $0.259 \cdot 100 = 25.9$.

A good prediction for the number of home runs in his next 100 hits is 26. ■

It is important to keep in mind that what actually happens can be different (sometimes very different) from a prediction. For example, consider the experiment of rolling a die 12 times. Based on theoretical probability, the most likely number of times any particular outcome would occur is $\dfrac{1}{6} \times 12 = 2$. But if you actually roll a die 12 times, you might get the results shown in the first bar graph. And if you actually roll a die 1000 times (or simulate 1000 rolls), you might get the results shown in the second bar graph. Notice that with more rolls, we expect the number of occurrences of each outcome to get closer to what the theoretical probability would suggest.

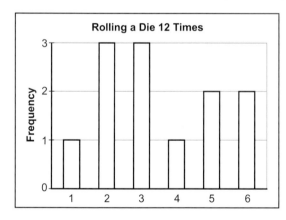

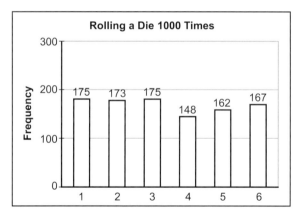

The bar graphs illustrate the following concept in probability theory, which is related to a property called the *law of large numbers*.

Identifying Appropriate Use of the Law of Large Numbers

LAW OF LARGE NUMBERS

As the number of independent trials in an experiment increases, it becomes more likely that the experimental probability of an event gets closer to the theoretical probability of that event.

Example 5 Determine whether the law of large numbers is appropriately used.

(A) Pat predicts getting a 3 about 100 times if he rolls a fair die 600 times.

Solution Yes, this is an appropriate use of the law of large numbers. Six hundred rolls is a fairly large number of independent trials, so it is reasonable to predict $\frac{1}{6} \times 600 = 100$ occurrences of the outcome 3. ∎

(B) India rolls a fair die 59 times and gets a 3 exactly 9 times. She predicts that her 60th roll will be a 3.

Solution No, this is not an appropriate use of the law of large numbers. India might reason that the outcome 3 should occur $\frac{1}{6} \times 60 = 10$ times, and that therefore, on the 60th roll, a 3 should occur for the 10th time. But the law of large numbers only describes what should happen to probabilities in the long run; it does not describe what the outcome should be for any individual trial. All six outcomes are equally likely on the 60th roll. ∎

Using Experimental Probability to Make Predictions

Example 6 It is estimated that 7% of people in the United States have diabetes. A certain screening test is 74.7% accurate for people who do have diabetes and 78% accurate for people who do not have diabetes.

At a health fair, the screening test is used to test 300 people. Use the data in the problem to make each prediction.

(A) Predict how many of the 300 people have diabetes.

Solution The experimental probability of having diabetes is 7%, or 0.07. Multiply the number of people screened by this probability: $0.07 \cdot 300 = 21$.

Prediction: It's reasonable to estimate that about 21 of the 300 people screened have diabetes. ∎

(B) Of the predicted number of people who have diabetes, predict how many will be identified by the screening test as having diabetes.

Solution The conditional probability of being accurately identified, given that a person has diabetes, is 74.7%, or 0.747. Multiply the predicted number of people who have diabetes by this probability: $0.747 \cdot 21 = 15.686$.

Prediction: The screening test will identify about 16 of the 21 people who are predicted to have diabetes. ∎

(C) Predict how many of the 300 people do not have diabetes.

Solution Not having diabetes is the complement of having diabetes, so $P(\text{not diabetes}) = 1 - P(\text{diabetes}) = 1 - 0.07 = 0.093$. Multiply the number of people screened by this probability: $0.93 \cdot 300 = 279$.

Prediction: About 279 of the 300 people screened do not have diabetes. ∎

TIP
You can also answer Example 6C by subtracting the predicted number of people with diabetes from the total number of people screened: $300 - 21 = 279$.

D Of the predicted number of people without diabetes, predict how many the screening test will inaccurately identify as having diabetes.

Solution The conditional probability of being inaccurately identified, given that a person does not have diabetes, is also a complement:

$$P(\text{inaccurate} \mid \text{not diabetes}) = 1 - P(\text{accurate} \mid \text{not diabetes})$$
$$= 1 - 0.78 = 0.22.$$

Multiply the predicted number of people without diabetes by this probability: $0.22 \cdot 279 = 61.38$.

Prediction: Of the 279 people predicted to not have diabetes, the screening test will inaccurately identify about 61 of them as having diabetes. ∎

Problem Set

The graph below shows data about a class's grade distribution on 4 tests. There are 30 students in the class. Based on the data, answer the following questions.

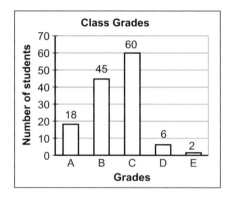

1. Predict the number of As that will occur on the next 5 tests.

2. Predict the number of Bs that will occur on the next 5 tests.

3. Predict the number of passing grades (A, B, C, or D) that will occur on the next 10 tests.

4. Predict the number of Cs that will occur on the next 10 tests.

5. Predict the number of As that will occur on the next 10 tests.

It is estimated that 9% of the people in the world have a particular genetic defect. A screening test is 80.2% accurate for people who have the defect and 92.8% accurate for people who do not have it. Nala tests 400 people for the defect.

6. Predict how many people will have the defect.

7. Of the number predicted to have the defect, predict how many will be identified by the screening test as having it.

8. Of the number predicted to have the defect, predict how many will be identified by the screening test as not having it.

9. Predict how many of the 400 people do not have the defect.

10. Of the predicted number of people without the defect, predict how many the screening test will inaccurately identify as having the defect.

Determine whether the law of large numbers is appropriately used. If not, explain why.

11. Jenny predicts getting heads about 75 times if she flips a coin 150 times.

12. Jorge flips a coin 99 times and gets tails exactly 49 times. He predicts that on his next flip, he will get tails.

13. Janette predicts getting a 6 about 150 times if she rolls a fair die 900 times.

14. Deonte rolls a fair die 119 times and gets a 4 exactly 9 times. He predicts that his next roll will be a 4.

15. Fabian draws a card from a standard deck and replaces it each time. He predicts getting a heart about 40 times if he draws 160 times.

16. Melanie draws a card from a standard deck and replaces it each time. She predicts getting a king about 10 times if she draws 130 times.

17. Maria draws a card 199 times from a standard deck and replaces the card each time. She gets a spade exactly 49 times. She predicts that her next card will be a spade.

18. Lance draws a card 259 times from a standard deck and replaces the card each time. He gets an ace exactly 19 times. He predicts that his next card will be an ace.

19. Yusuf draws a card from a standard deck and replaces it each time. He predicts getting a black card about 50 times if he draws 100 times.

20. Ellie draws a card from a standard deck and replaces it each time. She predicts getting a red card about 47 times if she draws 94 times.

The field below consists of 4 squares with side lengths of 10 meters, 14 meters, 22 meters, and 26 meters. Assume that a skydiver lands in the field at a random point. Find the probability of each event.

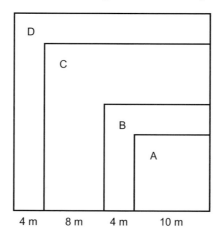

21. She lands in the small square.

22. She lands in the area labeled B.

23. She lands in the area labeled C.

24. She lands in the area labeled D.

A standard football field is in the shape of a rectangle that is 120 yards long, with two 10-yard end zones and 100 yards of field. If a ball is dropped at random on the field, find the probability of the following events.

25. The ball lands in an end zone.

26. The ball lands between one end zone and the 50-yard line.

27. The ball lands between the two 40-yard lines.

28. The ball lands between the two 20-yard lines.

Ricardo flips a coin 50 times and gets heads 32 times. Ricardo predicts that if he flips the coin 100 times, he will get about 50 heads and 50 tails.

*29. **Challenge** Is Ricardo using the law of large numbers correctly? Explain.

*30. **Challenge** Did the results of the first 50 trials match the theoretical probability? If not, does this mean that the coin is somehow faulty? Explain.

UNIT 13 Statistics

Athletes use statistics to assess and improve performance.

How high or far can a person jump? Statistics involves collecting data, using graphs and charts to present data, and using various tools to analyze data and make predictions.

Big Ideas

- You can collect, tabulate, and summarize a set of data before analyzing and interpreting the data in order to arrive at a conclusion based on the data.

- Statistics of real-world events are highly useful for making important observations and decisions.

- In statistics, it is often impossible to study an entire population, but you can select and study a sample of the population.

Unit Topics

- Foundations for Unit 13

- Measures of Center

- Variability

- Samples

- Graphs of Univariate Data

- Frequency Distributions

- The Normal Distribution

- Bivariate Data and Scatter Plots

- Lines of Best Fit

Foundations for Unit 13

Before you learn more about statistical measures and graphs, you need to know how to do the following:

▶ Evaluate a sum that is given in sigma notation.

▶ Find the average of two numbers.

▶ Graph ordered pairs.

Evaluating a Sum Given in Sigma Notation

Definition

sigma notation   a way to write a sum as follows:

$$\sum_{i=1}^{n} a_i = a_1 + a_2 + a_3 + \ldots + a_n$$

$\displaystyle\sum_{i=1}^{n} a_i$ is read as "the sum from 1 to n of a_i," where i is called the **index**, n is called the **upper limit**, and 1 is the **lower limit**. The right side of the equation is the **expanded form** of the sum.

Example 1   Write the sum in expanded form, and then evaluate the sum.

Ⓐ $\displaystyle\sum_{i=1}^{4} 3i = \underbrace{3 \cdot 1 + 3 \cdot 2 + 3 \cdot 3 + 3 \cdot 4}_{\text{Expanded Form}}$ **Ⓑ** $\displaystyle\sum_{k=2}^{5} k^3 = \underbrace{2^3 + 3^3 + 4^3 + 5^3}_{\text{Expanded Form}}$

$\phantom{\sum_{i=1}^{4} 3i}= 3 + 6 + 9 + 12$ $= 8 + 27 + 64 + 125$

$\phantom{\sum_{i=1}^{4} 3i}= 30$ $= 224$

Example 2   Show that $\displaystyle\sum_{i=0}^{4} 4(i+1)$ and $\displaystyle\sum_{i=1}^{5} 4i$ are equivalent sums.

$\displaystyle\sum_{i=0}^{4} 4(i+1) = 4(0+1) + 4(1+1) + 4(2+1) + 4(3+1) + 4(4+1)$

$\phantom{\sum_{i=0}^{4} 4(i+1)} = 4 \cdot 1 + 4 \cdot 2 + 4 \cdot 3 + 4 \cdot 4 + 4 \cdot 5$

$\phantom{\sum_{i=0}^{4} 4(i+1)} = 4 + 8 + 12 + 16 + 20$

$\phantom{\sum_{i=0}^{4} 4(i+1)} = 60$

$\displaystyle\sum_{i=1}^{5} 4i = 4 \cdot 1 + 4 \cdot 2 + 4 \cdot 3 + 4 \cdot 4 + 4 \cdot 5$

$\phantom{\sum_{i=1}^{5} 4i} = 4 + 8 + 12 + 16 + 20$

$\phantom{\sum_{i=1}^{5} 4i} = 60$

The two sums are equivalent.

Problem Set A

Expand and evaluate each sum.

1. $\displaystyle\sum_{k=1}^{5} 7k$

3. $\displaystyle\sum_{k=1}^{4} (k-3)$

5. $\displaystyle\sum_{i=1}^{4} \frac{i}{2}$

2. $\displaystyle\sum_{i=1}^{5} 2^i$

4. $\displaystyle\sum_{i=1}^{4} (3-i)$

6. $\displaystyle\sum_{j=3}^{6} \left(\frac{7-j}{2}\right)$

Show that the two sums are equivalent.

7. $\displaystyle\sum_{k=1}^{5} 2k$ and $\displaystyle\sum_{i=0}^{4} (2i+2)$

8. $\displaystyle\sum_{i=0}^{7} i$ and $\displaystyle\sum_{i=1}^{8} (8-i)$

Finding the Average of Two Numbers

To find the average of two numbers, add the numbers and divide the sum by 2.

Example 3 Find the average of each pair of numbers.

A 3 and 9

$$\frac{3+9}{2} = \frac{12}{2} = 6$$

B $\frac{1}{3}$ and $\frac{2}{3}$

$$\frac{\frac{1}{3}+\frac{2}{3}}{2} = \frac{1}{2}$$

C 21.3 and 37.8

$$\frac{21.3+37.8}{2} = \frac{59.1}{2} = 29.55$$

Problem Set B

Find the average of each pair of numbers.

9. 16 and 9

10. 7 and -5

11. 0.2 and 12

12. 0.31 and 1.57

13. 2.3 and 7.6

14. $\frac{1}{4}$ and $\frac{3}{4}$

15. $\frac{3}{4}$ and $\frac{5}{12}$

16. $\frac{7}{12}$ and $\frac{5}{16}$

Graphing Ordered Pairs

An ordered pair of numbers represents the coordinates of a point in the coordinate plane. In an ordered pair, the **x-coordinate** is the first number and the **y-coordinate** is the second number. For example, in the ordered pair $(-3, 4)$, -3 is the x-coordinate and 4 is the y-coordinate.

A point is the graph of an ordered pair, and an ordered pair contains the coordinates of a point.

Example 4 Graph each ordered pair in the same coordinate plane. For each point, identify its axis or quadrant location.

$$A(5, 0), B(3, -2), C(-2, 3), D(5, 4), E(-1, -1)$$

To locate x-coordinates, move from the origin to the right for positive values and to the left for negative values. To locate y-coordinates, move up for positive values and down for negative values.

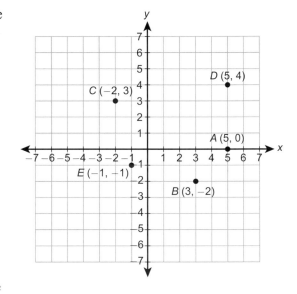

$A(5, 0)$: Start at the origin. Move 5 units to the right. The point is on the positive x-axis.

$B(3, -2)$: Start at the origin. Move 3 units to the right, and then move 2 units down. The point is located in Quadrant IV.

$C(-2, 3)$: Start at the origin. Move 2 units to the left, and then move 3 units up. The point is located in Quadrant II.

$D(5, 4)$: Start at the origin. Move 5 units to the right, and then move 4 units up. The point is located in Quadrant I.

$E(-1, -1)$: Start at the origin. Move 1 unit to the left, and then move 1 unit down. The point is located in Quadrant III.

Problem Set C

Graph each ordered pair in the same coordinate plane.
For each point, identify its axis or quadrant location.

17. $A(-4, 1)$ **20.** $D(-3, 0)$ **23.** $G(0, -5)$

18. $B(2, 0)$ **21.** $E(1, -3)$ **24.** $H(3, 5)$

19. $C(1, 6)$ **22.** $F(-2, -4)$ **25.** $K(-2, 3)$

Measures of Center

Statistics is the branch of mathematics concerned with collecting, analyzing, describing, and interpreting data.

Measures of Central Tendency

Numbers used to describe a data set are also called statistics. Some commonly used statistics are *mean, median*, and *mode*, which are measures of center, or *measures of central tendency*.

DEFINITIONS

Measures of Central Tendency

The **mean** of a data set is the statistical average. For a data set with values $x_1, x_2, \ldots, x_n$, the mean is

$$\bar{x} = \frac{\sum_{i=1}^{n} x_i}{n} = \frac{x_1 + x_2 + \ldots + x_n}{n}.$$

The **median** is the middle value when the values are ordered. If the data set has an even number of values, the median is the mean of the two middle values.

The **mode** is the value that occurs most frequently.

TIP

The symbol $\bar{x}$ is read "*x*-bar." It is used to denote the mean of a sample of data. The mean of an entire population is denoted by the Greek letter mu: μ.

A **stem-and-leaf plot** is a useful way to organize and display a data set. It shows the individual data values in increasing order, so it can be used to find the measures of central tendency. In a stem-and-leaf plot, each data value is separated into two parts: the rightmost digit is the *leaf*, and the other digit(s) form the *stem*.

Example 1 Make a stem-and-leaf plot of the following data values. Then find the mean, median, and mode.

120, 78, 99, 72, 101, 118, 78, 90, 97, 112

Solution For the stem-and-leaf plot, draw a vertical line segment. Write the stems in increasing order in a column to the left of the line segment. Write the leaves for each stem in increasing order in a row to the right of the segment. Notice that 8 is included as a stem, even though there are no leaves for it; also notice that each leaf is made up of only one digit.

```
 7 | 2  8  8
 8 |
 9 | 0  7  9
10 | 1
11 | 2  8
12 | 0
```
Key: 7 | 2 = 72

Mean: $\bar{x} = \dfrac{\sum\limits_{i=1}^{n} x_i}{n} = \dfrac{72 + 78 + 78 + 90 + 97 + 99 + 101 + 112 + 118 + 120}{10}$

$$= \frac{965}{10} = 96.5$$

Median: Look at the stem and leaf plot. There are 10 values, so the middle of the set is the average of the 5th and 6th values.

Median $= \dfrac{97 + 99}{2} = \dfrac{196}{2} = 98$

Mode: In the data set, 78 occurs twice, more than any other value, so the mode is 78. ∎

Finding a Value that Will Result in a Given Mean

You can calculate the score you need on the next test to get the average you desire.

Example 2 Sharlene earned scores of 90, 84, and 87 on the first three algebra tests. What score must Sharlene get on the fourth test in order to have an average of 90?

Solution Substitute the given values into the rule for finding $\bar{x}$.

$$\bar{x} = \frac{\sum\limits_{i=1}^{4} x_i}{4} = \frac{90 + 84 + 87 + x_4}{4} = 90$$

Solve for x_4.

$$\frac{90 + 84 + 87 + x_4}{4} = 90$$

$$90 + 84 + 87 + x_4 = 4 \cdot 90$$

$$261 + x_4 = 360$$

$$x_4 = 99$$

Sharlene must get a 99 on the fourth test in order to have an average of 90. ∎

Computing a Weighted Average

When some elements of a data set carry more importance (weight) than others, the rule for finding the average changes.

DEFINITION

The **weighted average** of a data set with values $x_1, x_2, \ldots, x_n$ that have nonnegative weights $w_1, w_2, \ldots, w_n$, respectively, is

$$\bar{x}_w = \frac{\sum\limits_{i=1}^{n} w_i x_i}{\sum\limits_{i=1}^{n} w_i} = \frac{w_1 x_1 + w_2 x_2 + \ldots + w_n x_n}{w_1 + w_2 + \ldots + w_n}.$$

Example 3   The values of letter tiles in a certain board game are as follows:

Value of Tile	0	1	2	3	4	5	8	10
Number of Tiles	2	68	7	8	10	1	2	2

What is the average value of a tile?

Solution   Multiply the number of each tile type by the value of each tile.

$$\bar{x}_w = \frac{\sum\limits_{i=1}^{8} w_i x_i}{\sum\limits_{i=1}^{8} w_i} = \frac{2 \cdot 0 + 68 \cdot 1 + 7 \cdot 2 + 8 \cdot 3 + 10 \cdot 4 + 1 \cdot 5 + 2 \cdot 8 + 2 \cdot 10}{2 + 68 + 7 + 8 + 10 + 1 + 2 + 2}$$

$$= \frac{187}{100} = 1.87$$

The weighted average value of a letter tile is 1.87. ∎

Example 4   For a class grade, tests account for 40%, quizzes account for 40%, and homework accounts for 20%. Out of 100, Carter's test score is 78 and his quiz score is 87.

A What homework score will get Carter at least an 80% for the class?

B What homework score will get Carter at least a 90% for the class?

Solution   Find the weighted average.

$$\bar{x}_w = \frac{\sum\limits_{i=1}^{3} w_i x_i}{\sum\limits_{i=1}^{3} w_i} = \frac{0.4 \cdot 78 + 0.4 \cdot 87 + 0.2 \cdot x_3}{0.4 + 0.4 + 0.2} = \frac{66 + 0.2 x_3}{1} = 66 + 0.2 x_3$$

A $66 + 0.2 x_3 \geq 80$

$0.2 x_3 \geq 14$

$x_3 \geq 70$

A homework score of 70 will get Carter an 80%. ∎

B $66 + 0.2 x_3 \geq 90$

$0.2 x_3 \geq 24$

$x_3 \geq 120$

Since a homework score of 120 is not possible, Carter cannot get a 90%. ∎

Problem Set

Find the mean, median, and mode.

1.
```
2 | 1 3
3 | 4 4
4 | 2 4
5 | 1
6 | 5
```

2.
```
0 | 6 8
1 | 2 8
2 | 3 3
3 | 4 4 9
```

3.
```
6 | 6
7 | 1 5
8 | 3 8 9
9 | 0 1
```

4.
```
 8 | 0 4
 9 | 2 5
10 | 0 4 4
11 | 0 5
12 | 0
```

5.
```
5 | 0 1
6 | 0 1
7 | 2 4 7 8
8 | 0 0
```

6.
```
20 | 5 7
21 |
22 |
23 | 1 1 3 5
24 | 4 8 9
```

Make a stem-and-leaf plot for the data. Then find the mean, median, and mode.

7. 34, 56, 22, 49, 37, 20, 61, 48, 22

8. 7, 9, 12, 3, 13, 4, 10, 11

9. 78, 82, 91, 100, 78, 92, 82, 77, 80

10. 130, 110, 121, 141, 137, 136, 103, 144

11. 66, 81, 60, 72, 79, 83, 60, 92, 68

12. 31, 89, 74, 50, 45, 56, 51, 46, 50, 72, 75, 52

13. 520, 549, 548, 531, 548, 532, 540, 533, 548

14. 4, 9, 14, 55, 21, 1, 25, 4, 24, 50, 5

Determine the indicated weighted average.

15. The cost of party favors is as follows:

	Whistle	Set of Stickers	Set of Markers	Frisbee	Water Bottle
Cost per Party Favor	0.1	0.25	0.3	0.5	0.8
Number of Party Favors	6	5	2	1	4

What is the average cost of all the party favors?

16. Canned food costs in a store are listed below:

	Corn	Lima Beans	Peas	Pinto Beans
Cost per Can	0.2	0.3	0.35	0.4
Number of Cans	10	8	3	9

What is the average cost of a can of food?

17. In a classroom, a student is given a score in four areas. Tysia's score for each area is as follows:

	Participation	Homework	Quizzes	Tests
Percent of Class Grade	10%	10%	30%	50%
Score	77	91	80	86

What is Tysia's grade for the class?

18. Sheri works on an assembly line. She earns different point values for completing tasks while she works. On the basis of the table below, what is the average number of points Sheri earned?

Point Value	1	2	3	4	5	6	7	8
Number Completed	11	12	20	7	0	15	6	8

19. In baseball, a player's slugging percentage is calculated by dividing the total bases by the number of times at bat. A single is 1 base, a double is 2 bases, a triple is 3 bases, and a home run is 4 bases.

A. If Hernandez had 30 times at bat, what is his slugging percentage?

Type of Hit	Single	Double	Triple	Home Run
Number	3	5	0	7

B. If Kowalski had 42 times at bat, what is his slugging percentage?

Type of Hit	Single	Double	Triple	Home Run
Number	10	4	5	2

Solve.

20. Omar buys five $22 shirts, three $50 pairs of pants, and six $17 ties. What is the average amount that Omar spent per article of clothing?

21. In class, a test is worth 80% of the quarter grade and homework is worth 20%. A perfect score on each test and homework assignment is 100 points. What is Vivian's quarter average if her test grades are 80, 95, 100, and 96, and her homework grades are 95, 100, 88, 92, and 97?

22. James earned scores of 77, 60, 45, and 65 on four English tests. What score must James earn on his next test in order to have a 60 average?

23. In four trips to the arcade, Jullette has collected ticket amounts of 15, 60, 78, and 94. What amount must she collect during her final visit in order to have an average ticket amount of 70?

24. Sudeep bowled 180, 250, 300, and 160 during his first four games. What must Sudeep bowl in his last game to earn a 200 bowling average?

25. Cheryl scored 500, 650, 700, and 470 on four parts of a standardized test. What must Cheryl score on the final part in order to have a 620 average?

26. During the last five weeks, Helene spent $60, $50, $80, $90, and $70, respectively. What must Helene spend this week in order to average $60 in spending during the six weeks?

27. Arun hits an average of 2 home runs per game. If he hit 5 in Game 1, 1 in Game 2, 0 in Game 3, and 0 in Game 4, how many home runs must Arun hit in Game 5 to maintain his average?

28. Edwin cuts the grass in an average of 4 hours. If he cut the grass in 4 hours 3 weeks ago, 6 hours 2 weeks ago, and 2.5 hours last week, how long should it take him to cut the grass now if he wants to maintain his average?

29. Judea exercises an average of 5 hours per week. On this month's schedule, he recorded 4 hours for Week 1, 3.5 hours for Week 2, and 0 hours for Week 3. How long must Judea exercise this week if he wishes to maintain his average?

*30. **Challenge** The average of 75, 80, 70, 60, and x is equal to the average of 60, 85, 90, 88, x, and 79. What is the value of x?

*31. **Challenge** The average of 90, 60, and x, minus the average of 23, 30, 45, 60, and x is 20. What is the value of x?

Variability

Measures of variability describe how data are spread out.

A simple measure of variability is *range*. Other statistics used to describe variability are *quartiles*, *variance*, and *standard deviation*.

> **TIP**
>
> Measures of variability are also called *measures of spread* and *measures of dispersion*.

Defining Measures of Variability

Certain statistics measure the spread of a data set.

> **DEFINITIONS**
>
> The **range** of a data set is the difference between its greatest value **(maximum)** and its least value **(minimum)**.
>
> The **second quartile, Q_2,** is the median of the entire data set. It separates the ordered data set into a lower subset and an upper subset.
>
> The **first quartile, Q_1,** is the median of the lower subset.
>
> The **third quartile, Q_3,** is the median of the upper subset.
> The three quartiles separate the ordered data set into four parts, each part having the same number of values.
>
> The minimum, the maximum, and the three quartiles are called the **five-number summary**.

Making a Box-and-Whisker Plot

A box-and-whisker plot shows how data are spread out. The "box" extends from Q_1 to Q_3. The median is on the vertical line in the box. The "whiskers" extend from the first quartile to the minimum and from the third quartile to the maximum.

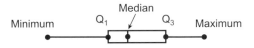

Example 1 Colin, an employee at Game Zone, recorded the number of computer games he sold each week for the past 9 weeks: 15, 20, 21, 9, 3, 16, 9, 14, 17.

Ⓐ Identify the five-number summary.

Ⓑ Find the range.

Ⓒ Draw a box-and-whisker plot.

Solution

A Make a stem-and-leaf plot of the data, then use it to identify Q_2, the median of the entire data set. Then identify Q_1 and Q_3.

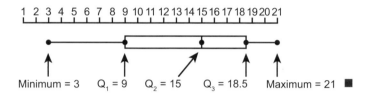

The five-number summary is minimum $= 3$, first quartile $= 9$, second quartile (median) $= 15$, third quartile $= 18.5$, maximum $= 21$.

B Range = Maximum − Minimum = $21 - 3 = 18$.

C For the box-and-whisker plot, draw five dots above or below a number line to correspond to the numbers in the five-number summary. Draw a box from Q_1 to Q_3. Inside the box, draw a short vertical line segment ($|$) through the dot at Q_2. Finally, draw the whiskers—horizontal line segments from the minimum to Q_1 and from Q_3 to the maximum.

> **TIP**
>
> In a stem-and-leaf plot, circle the median and use a short segment to indicate the first and third quartiles.

1 2 3 4 5 6 7 8 9 10 11 12 13 14 15 16 17 18 19 20 21

Minimum = 3 Q_1 = 9 Q_2 = 15 Q_3 = 18.5   Maximum = 21 ■

Notice that the left whisker is longer than the right whisker, and the left portion of the box is longer than the right portion. These features show that the lower subset of the data is more spread out than the upper subset.

Computing Variance and Standard Deviation

Two other measures of variability are *variance* and *standard deviation*.

> **DEFINITIONS**
>
> For a data set with values $x_1, x_2, \ldots, x_n$, the **variance** is
>
> $$s^2 = \frac{\sum_{i=1}^{n}(x_i - \bar{x})^2}{n - 1}.$$
>
> Each difference $x_i - \bar{x}$ is called a **deviation**.
>
> **Standard deviation** is the square root of the variance.
>
> $$s = \sqrt{s^2}$$

Example 2 Compute the variance and standard deviation of the following data set: 10, 14, 35, 11, 4, 26, 20, 32.

Solution

Step 1 Compute the mean:

$$\bar{x} = \frac{10 + 14 + 35 + 11 + 4 + 26 + 20 + 32}{8} = \frac{152}{8} = 19$$

Step 2 Find all the deviations $x_i - \bar{x}$. In this case, $\bar{x} = 19$, so find all the differences $x_i - 19$. Then find all the squares of the deviations $(x_i - \bar{x})^2$. Calculate the sum of those squares. Organize your values in a table.

Step 3 Divide the sum by $n - 1$. In this case, $n = 8$, so divide by 7.

$$s^2 = \frac{\sum_{i=1}^{n}(x_i - \bar{x})^2}{n - 1} = \frac{870}{7} \approx 124.3$$

The variance is about 124.3.

Step 4 To find the standard deviation, find the square root of the variance.

$$s = \sqrt{s^2} = \sqrt{\frac{870}{7}} \approx 11.1$$

The standard deviation is about 11.1. ■

x_i	$x_i - \bar{x}$	$(x_i - \bar{x})^2$
10	−9	81
14	−5	25
35	16	256
11	−8	64
4	−15	225
26	7	49
20	1	1
32	13	169
		Sum: 870

Comparing Standard Deviations Without Computing

Standard deviation is a measure of how far the data values are from the mean. The less spread out the data values, the closer they are to the mean, and the lower the standard deviation.

Example 3 Without computing, determine which data set has the greatest standard deviation and which has the least standard deviation.

A Set A: 1, 5, 9, 10, 15
Set B: 19, 20, 22, 24, 26
Set C: 96, 99, 99, 100, 102

Solution The numbers in Set A are the most spread out, so Set A has the greatest standard deviation. The numbers in Set C are the least spread out, so Set C has the least standard deviation. ■

B

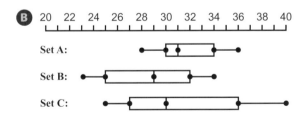

Solution The box-and-whisker plot for Set A is the least spread out, so Set A has the least standard deviation. Set B has more spread than Set A, but still has less than Set C. Set C has the greatest standard deviation. ■

Comparing Data Sets by Using Standard Deviations and Box Plots

Example 4 Compare Sets A and C from Example 3A by using standard deviations and box plots.

Solution **Set A**   **Set C**

$$\bar{x} = \frac{1 + 5 + 9 + 10 + 15}{5} = \frac{40}{5} = 8 \qquad \bar{x} = \frac{96 + 99 + 99 + 100 + 102}{5} = \frac{496}{5} = 99.2$$

x_i	$x_i - \bar{x}$	$(x_i - \bar{x})^2$
1	-7	49
5	-3	9
9	1	1
10	2	4
15	7	49
		Sum: 112

x_i	$x_i - \bar{x}$	$(x_i - \bar{x})^2$
96	-3.2	10.24
99	-0.2	0.04
99	-0.2	0.04
100	0.8	0.64
102	2.8	7.84
		Sum: 18.8

$$s^2 = \frac{112}{5 - 1} = 28 \qquad\qquad s^2 = \frac{18.8}{5 - 1} = 4.7$$

$$s = \sqrt{28} \approx 5.29 \qquad\qquad s = \sqrt{4.7} \approx 2.17$$

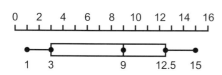

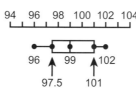

The standard deviations and box plots indicate that Set A is more spread out. ∎

Problem Set

Find the range of each data set.

1. 7, 4, 6, 2, 8, 1, 10, 5

2. 28, 20, 25, 28, 100, 25, 30

3. 44, 47, 48, 45, 50, 44, 48, 42

4. 212, 223, 219, 231, 229, 226, 236, 247

Draw a box-and-whisker plot and identify the five-number summary for each data set.

5. 30, 6, 16, 20, 22, 25, 26, 6, 19, 20, 21

6. 90, 85, 88, 95, 100, 77, 85, 100, 87, 80, 90

7. 6, 9, 16, 11, 12, 16, 5, 14, 5

8. 15, 17, 23, 21, 19, 20, 14, 25, 15, 24

9. 36, 34, 37, 29, 27, 39, 37, 25, 31, 32, 28

10. 102, 105, 112, 115, 109, 116, 116, 107, 113, 120, 118, 104, 109

Calculate the variance and standard deviation, to the nearest tenth, for each data set.

11. 19, 25, 28, 20, 27, 8, 25

12. 55, 59, 52, 65, 56, 59, 58

13. 17, 18, 22, 16, 18, 14, 13, 23, 20

14. 127, 126, 130, 125, 132, 129, 136, 140

15. 188, 190, 199, 181, 173, 192, 184, 196

*16. **Challenge** $\frac{1}{2}, \frac{1}{4}, \frac{3}{8}, \frac{3}{4}, \frac{7}{10}, \frac{5}{8}, 1\frac{3}{5}$

Without computing, determine which data set in each pair has the greater standard deviation.

17. **Set A:** 6, 7, 7, 8, 9, 10, 11, 12
    Set B: 12, 14, 14, 18, 19, 20, 23

18. **Set A:** 5, 6, 8, 10, 13, 16, 19, 29
    Set B: 5, 7, 9, 13, 15, 18, 19, 20

19. **Set A:** 101, 114, 125, 136, 147, 159, 162, 170
    Set B: 205, 215, 225, 230, 239, 245, 252, 260

*20. **Challenge Set A:** 110, 215, 314, 425, 523, 634
    Set B: 105, 250, 380, 454, 572, 694

Find the standard deviation for each set, and then compare the three sets by ranking them from least spread out (1) to most spread out (3).

21. **Set A:** 810, 807, 813, 815, 819, 806, 812, 814
    Set B: 9.4, 9.9, 9.9, 9.9, 10.0, 10.2, 10.2, 10.5
    Set C: 60, 68, 75, 78, 152, 63, 72, 62

22. **Set A:** 3.1, 2.7, 6.0, 5.6, 2.3, 2.0, 1.3, 1.6
    Set B: 634, 685, 647, 635, 699, 700, 620, 612
    Set C: 12, 43, 35, 56, 34, 67, 38, 84

Compare the three sets by ranking them from least spread out (1) to most spread out (3).

23.
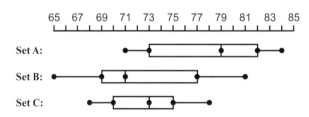

Use the graph to answer the questions.

24. A box-and-whisker plot is shown below.
   A. What percent of the data fall after 34?
   B. What percent of the data fall before 28?
   C. What percent of the data fall between 28 and 48?

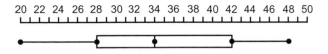

25. A box-and-whisker plot is shown below.
   A. What percent of the data fall after 40?
   B. What percent of the data fall before 40?
   C. What percent of the data fall between 5 and 35?

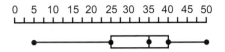

Solve.

26. Sandra got the following scores on her math tests this quarter: 87, 86, 93, 79, 96, 100, 89, 97, and 92. Find the following:
   A. the mean score
   B. the median score
   C. the standard deviation to the nearest hundredth

Samples

In statistics, it is important to understand the difference between a *population* and a *sample*.

Comparing Sampling Methods

> **DEFINITIONS**
>
> A **population** is the complete group that is being studied. A **sample** is a subset of the population.

A population is often a group of people (such as all American citizens, or all women in the world, or all ninth graders in Texas), but it doesn't have to be. In manufacturing, a population could consist of all the items manufactured on an assembly line in one day. It is often difficult or impossible to collect data about every member of a population because many populations are large. So, instead, data are collected from a sample, and conclusions are drawn about the population. The different ways to choose samples from populations are called *sampling methods*.

In **convenience sampling**, sample members are chosen that are most convenient, or readily available. For example, a surveyor might stand on a corner and choose people who happen to walk by. Or a student might survey students who take the same classes she does.

In a **voluntary response sample**, participants choose themselves. For example, a question appears on-screen during a television newscast, and viewers can choose to go online to answer it.

In **systematic sampling**, every *n*th item is chosen. This could mean choosing every 5th person on a list or selecting every 100th hammer on an assembly line.

In a **simple random sample**, every member of the population has an equal chance of being chosen. For example, suppose the population consists of all 867 students in a high school. A simple random sample can be obtained by assigning each student a different number from 1 to 867, and having a calculator or computer generate random numbers from 1 to 867, eliminating any numbers that are repeated.

In a **stratified random sample**, the population is first classified into two or more groups, or strata. For example, if the population consists of all the students in a high school, the strata could be 9th, 10th, 11th, and 12th grade students. If the population is the set of all T-shirts produced in a factory, the strata could be the T-shirt sizes: small, medium, and large. After strata are identified, a simple random sample is chosen from each stratum.

Identifying Sampling Methods and Biased Samples

> **DEFINITION**
>
> A **biased sample** is a sample for which not all members of the population are equally likely to be included.

In a biased sample, not all members of the population are equally represented. An unbiased sample is more likely than a biased sample to have the same characteristics of the population. Therefore, an unbiased sample is better for drawing conclusions about a population. Systematic, simple random, and stratified random samples are more likely to be unbiased than are convenience and voluntary response samples.

Example 1 For each scenario, identify the sampling method used. Then state whether the sample is biased, and identify possible sources of bias.

A The residents of a county are divided into renters and homeowners. Then 50 residents from each group are randomly selected and called at their home phone numbers between 8 a.m. and 4 p.m. to answer a survey. (Population: all county residents)

Solution A stratified sampling method is used. The method is biased because not all residents will be home between 8 a.m. and 4 p.m. Different people have different routines. In this case, residents with day jobs will likely be underrepresented, and residents who do not have day jobs will likely be overrepresented. ■

B A survey question in a magazine asks readers to text their response to the following question: "Do you support the president?" Standard text-messaging rates apply. (Population: all voters in the United States)

Solution A voluntary response sampling method is used. It is biased because those who do not read the magazine have no chance of responding. Furthermore, those who do read the magazine will respond only if they own a cell phone and are willing to pay to give their opinion. ■

C A mother writes the name of every child attending a birthday party on identical pieces of paper. She mixes up the pieces of paper in a hat and, without looking, selects three names out of the hat. (Population: all children attending the party)

Solution A simple random sampling method is used. Because every child has an equal chance of being chosen, the sample is not biased. ■

D A telephone surveyor calls every 100th number in a city phone book on a holiday weekend. (Population: all city residents)

Solution A systematic sampling method is used. The sample is biased because people with an unlisted number will not have a chance of being chosen. Also, different individuals might be more or less likely to answer the phone on a holiday weekend than on other days. ■

> **TIP**
>
> A good survey will use well-defined terms.
>
> In Example 1A, a *renter* could be defined as a person who lives in a rented dwelling. A *homeowner* could be defined as a person who owns his or her dwelling or who lives in a dwelling owned by a family member.

> **THINK ABOUT IT**
>
> In a voluntary response sample, often only those with a very strong opinion about the matter, especially on controversial topics, will respond.

E An inspector at a factory chooses 5 consecutive items that come off the assembly line for inspection. (Population: all 500 items produced on the assembly line that day)

Solution A convenience sampling method was used. It is biased because the percent of unsatisfactory items out of 5 consecutive items is not likely to be close to the percent of unsatisfactory items out of 500 items. The 5 items might have been assembled by the same group of workers. Another possibility is that a malfunctioning machine might have affected items produced before or after the 5 consecutive items. ■

Using a Sample to Make a Prediction About a Population

Samples are used to make predictions about populations.

Example 2 Radcliffe wanted to find out how many residents in his apartment complex are left-handed. There are 1240 residents in his apartment complex. Radcliffe mailed a survey to every 5th home in the complex. Of the 320 residents who responded, 72 said they were left-handed. Based on this sample, how many residents in the whole complex would Radcliffe predict are left-handed?

Solution From his sample, $\frac{72}{320} = 0.225 = 22.5\%$ of the residents are left-handed. So Radcliffe might predict that 22.5% of 1240 = 279 residents in his complex are left-handed. ■

Problem Set

Identify the sampling method used. Then state whether the sample is biased, and identify possible sources of bias.

1. A teacher selects 5 members of his class by assigning each student a number and randomly generating 5 numbers on a computer. (Population: the teacher's class)

2. A surveyor chooses every 20th manufacturing company listed under a computer search. (Population: all manufacturing companies)

3. A mall surveyor chooses the first 10 women she sees and asks them to complete a survey. (Population: all mall shoppers)

4. A survey question online asks readers if they prefer one soft drink over another. (Population: all soft-drink users)

5. City residents are divided into Democrats and Republicans. Then 100 residents from each party are randomly selected and sent a survey to complete. (Population: all city residents)

6. A class is divided into male and female groups. Then 50 members from each group are randomly selected and interviewed. (Population: all students in a class)

7. City residents are randomly selected for jury duty by generating 20 driver's license numbers. (Population: all city residents)

8. County residents are divided into sports fans and non–sports fans. Then 100 residents from each group are randomly selected and called after 6 p.m. and asked to complete a survey. (Population: all county residents)

9. A surveyor chooses the first 100 names beginning with B that are listed in the phone book. (Population: all entries in the phone book)

10. A survey arrives by mail and asks questions about the resident's hobbies. Residents return the survey by mail. (Population: all U.S. residents)

11. A television company selects every 10th completed response to its TV news survey. (Population: all television viewers)

12. A computer randomly chooses a U.S. citizen to win a sweepstakes by generating one social-security number. (Population: U.S. citizens)

Solve.

13. Gill assigns every student a number from 1 to 400. He randomly generates 100 numbers to survey. He wants to know if each selected student plays on a sports team. Out of 100 students surveyed, 56 play sports. Based on this sample, how many in the school of 1100 students would Gill predict play on a sports team?

14. In Jolee's class, a survey was distributed with completion instructions. Twenty-two students out of 30 completed the survey. Based on this sample, how many surveys would be completed by the student population of 1250?

15. Acquin asked the residents of every 6th house on Main Street if they drive a car to work. Thirty out of 40 people he surveyed said yes. Based on this sample, how many residents in Acquin's town of 150 would you predict to drive a car to work?

16. Carly assigned everyone in her address book a number. She randomly generated 20 numbers and invited the corresponding people to her party. Seven of the 20 people said they could come. If there are 100 people in Carly's address book, predict the number of people that could come to her party if she asked them all.

17. Jing wanted to know how many people in her neighborhood of 300 drive to work. She randomly selected 50 people. Of 50 people, 27 said they drive. Based on this sample, how many people in Jing's neighborhood would you predict drive to work?

18. Howie chose every 8th registered voter on the city's list. He asked if they had voted outside their party. Forty out of 45 said they had voted outside of their registered party. Based on this sample, how many of the 250,000 voters in the state would Howie predict have voted outside of party lines?

19. Gina asks every student in her son's class of 30 if they have ever had the chicken pox. Twelve students have had the chicken pox. On the basis of this sample, how many of the 500 students in the school would Gina predict have had the chicken pox?

20. A science teacher selects a random sample of water from a neighboring pond. The 2-gallon sample contains 3 fish. Based on this sample, predict how many fish are in the pond if the pond contains 4500 gallons of water.

21. A random sample was taken from patient records at a city hospital. Eighty of 95 patients admitted last week were diagnosed with the flu. Based on this sample, how many flu cases could the state report if 3000 people were admitted to state hospitals last week?

22. A random sample was taken from town accident reports last month. Twenty of the 30 accidents that occurred last week involved red cars. In the past week, 350 accidents were reported in the state. Based on this sample, predict how many of the 350 accidents involved red cars.

*23. Challenge Ramon wanted to find out how many neighbors like the local fast-food restaurant. There are 400 people in his neighborhood, so he chose every 10th house and questioned the residents. Of 150 people he sampled, 85 said they like the restaurant. Based on this sample, how many people in Ramon's neighborhood would you predict do not like the restaurant?

*24. Challenge Sasha wanted to know how many people in her school have red, blond, black, and brown hair. She randomly sampled 100 out of 300 juniors and found that 16 have red hair, 20 have blond hair, 10 have black hair, and the remainder have brown hair. On the basis of her sample, how many students in the school of 1600 should she predict to have red, blond, black, and brown hair?

Graphs of Univariate Data

When you work with data that describe the change in only *one* variable, you are using *univariate* data—data with one variable.

You can organize and present univariate data in several ways, such as a stem-and-leaf plot, a box-and-whisker plot, a bar graph, or a line graph.

Creating a Bar Graph

Example 1   The graduating seniors have various plans for further education. Their plans vary from going to a local college to attending a college in a distant part of the country, or even studying abroad. This table shows the data collected about the seniors' plans after high school.

Senior Destinations After High School				
Local	Same State	Same Region	Other Region	Other Country
30	9	6	4	1

Draw a bar graph for the data in the table.

Solution   There are five categories, so this graph will have five bars. The numbers of students range from 1 to 30, so a scale of 5 is appropriate.

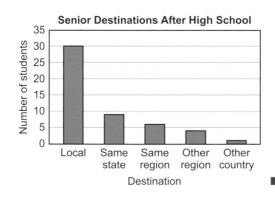

TIP

Use these labels for your graphs:

- Title

- Descriptions and scale for horizontal and vertical axes

- Numbers on the graph bars or points to make the amounts easy to read, if necessary

Creating and Interpreting a Multiple Bar Graph

Example 2 The school librarian surveyed students in grades 10, 11, and 12 about the kinds of books they had read. She counted the total number of books in these categories for each grade.

Books Students Have Read				
	Fiction	History	Biography	Science
Grade 10	3	2	5	2
Grade 11	6	5	4	3
Grade 12	8	5	7	4

REMEMBER

The bars in a bar graph can be separate, or they can touch. The bars can be vertical or horizontal.

Create a multiple bar graph from the data. Then use the bar graph to make a conjecture.

Solution

Step 1 Plan the categories and bars. Each of the four categories will have three bars, one for each grade.

Step 2 Choose the scale. A scale from 1 to 9 will include all the amounts.

Step 3 Draw the graph and bars.

Step 4 Add all the labels.

REMEMBER

Use a key to explain the different patterns for the multiple bars.

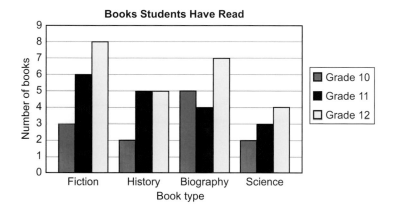

One possible conjecture is that students in the 12th grade have read more books than those in the 10th grade. ■

Bar graphs are best at comparing values. In a bar graph, the height or length of the bar shows the *frequency for a category*. The width of the bar does not matter. The order of the categories may or may not be important. In Example 1, the categories were in order of increasing distance from the high school. In Example 2, the categories were in no particular order.

Usually the numbers in a bar graph are *discrete*, or separate. For example, there are no data points between one car and two cars, or one book and two books. The items in a bar graph are usually *not grouped*. Later, you will contrast these qualities of a bar graph with the characteristics of a histogram.

Creating a Line Graph

Bar graphs can be used to show changes in categories over time, but often changes in a quantity over time are best shown by a line graph. Line graphs are good for showing a *trend* in data over time.

Example 3   The whooping crane is an endangered bird whose population was just 22 adult cranes in 1940. Since then, the population has increased and in 2008 numbered 270 birds in the only natural migratory (Western) flock.

Draw a line graph showing the changes over time for the whooping crane data in the table.

Year	1940	1960	1980	2000	2008
Cranes	22	33	76	177	270

TIP

Notice that the latest count available is 2008, so the last interval for the table is different from the previous ones.

Solution

Step 1   Plan what you will plot on the *x*-axis and on the *y*-axis. Mark intervals for years on the horizontal axis and birds on the vertical axis.

Step 2   Choose the scale: To go from 22 to 270, try intervals of 50.

Step 3   Draw the graph. Plot (*x, y*) coordinates using the two rows in the table, taking the *x*-coordinates from Row 1 as years.

Step 4   Add all the labels.

Step 5   Draw line segments from point to point on the graph.

REMEMBER

Since you do not have the data for intermediate points on the line graph, the lines you draw represent only rough approximations for the missing years.

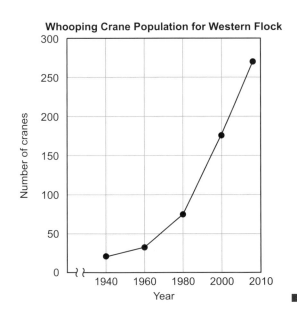

Interpreting a Line Graph

Example 4   Additional data points have been added to the original graph of the whooping crane population shown in Example 3. Use the revised graph below to answer each question.

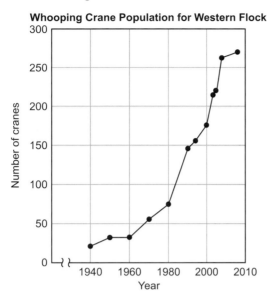

Whooping Crane Population for Western Flock

Ⓐ In general, is the population increasing or decreasing?

Ⓑ Did the population grow at the same rate from year to year?

Ⓒ Did the population ever decrease from one year to the next?

Ⓓ What might you predict for the population in 2010?

Solution

Ⓐ The *y*-value increases as the *x*-value increases, so in general, the population is increasing.

Ⓑ No. The line is steeper in some places than in others, so the rate of growth varies from year to year.

Ⓒ Because there are missing points, it could be true that the population decreased from one year to the next. As a matter of fact, it did go from 143 in 1993 to 133 in 1994, although it increased in 1995, to 158.

Ⓓ One possible prediction for 2010 would be a population of over 270. You might predict about 300. ■

Selecting the Type of Graph

Example 5   Darian wants to show the change each month during the school year for the highest and lowest temperatures in his hometown. Which of the graphs listed would be a good choice?

• stem-and-leaf plot
• box-and-whisker plot
• bar graph
• line graph

Solution   Darian could use a bar graph with two bars, one for highest temperature each month and another for the lowest. The categories along the horizontal axis could be the months from September to June. The vertical axis could have degrees of temperature with a scale that fits the data. ∎

Problem Set

Create a bar graph for each data set.

1. To determine the amount of concessions needed at future sporting events, the Parents' Association records the attendance at the Junior League's first five football games.

Attendance at Each Game					
Game	1	2	3	4	5
Attendance	100	150	89	210	195

2. Juno wants to maintain a consistent exercise schedule. The length of her workout sessions for the first five days is shown.

Length of Workout Each Day					
Day	Mon.	Tues.	Wed.	Thurs.	Fri.
Workout Time (minutes)	30	45	50	48	28

3. Jeb surveyed his class to determine how many toys his classmates owned.

Number of Toys Owned					
Toy	Balls	Blocks	Action Figures	Stuffed Animals	Trucks
Number Owned	15	48	35	24	22

4. A school published data about the number of students enrolled in each class.

Class Enrollment					
Grade	8	9	10	11	12
Number of Enrolled Students	200	300	425	225	350

5. A teacher posted the class's final exam results.

Class Test Scores					
Test Score	59 and below	60–69	70–79	80–89	90–100
Number of Students	1	2	7	20	5

Create a line graph for each data set.

6. The average temperature for a northern state was recorded for the first six months of 2008.

Average Monthly Temperature						
Month	Jan.	Feb.	Mar.	April	May	June
Average Temperature (°F)	20	17	42	55	67	76

7. The Middletown Grocery recorded its income for a six-year period, from 2000 to 2005.

Income Each Year						
Year	2000	2001	2002	2003	2004	2005
Income (thousands)	87	93	98	92	81	80

8. The government collected data regarding the number of parents who work outside the home. The data were collected in 10-year intervals beginning in 1950.

Percentage of Parents Working Outside the Home						
Year	1950	1960	1970	1980	1990	2000
Percentage	12	17	60	75	82	90

9. Mega Deals Co. recorded the number of computers it sold over the last six years.

Number of Computers Sold						
Year	2003	2004	2005	2006	2007	2008
Number	2950	3500	3780	4010	3400	1700

10. The rainfall for a South American country is recorded for the last six months of 2008.

Amount of Rainfall						
Month	July	Aug.	Sept.	Oct.	Nov.	Dec.
Rainfall (inches)	17	16.5	13	9.5	8	6.1

Solve.

11.

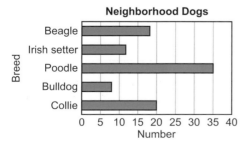

Which is the most popular breed? Which is the least popular?

12.

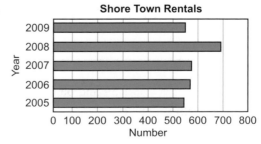

By what percentage did the number of rentals increase in 2008?

13.

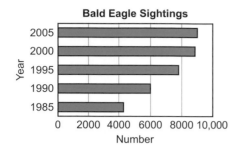

Bald Eagle Sightings

Describe how the number of bald eagle sightings have changed since 1985.

14.

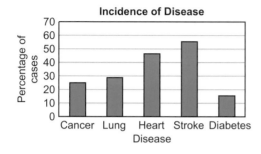

Incidence of Disease

Which two diseases have similar percentages of incidence? How close are the two percentages?

15.

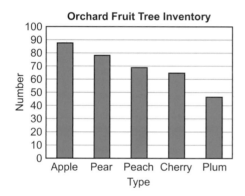

Orchard Fruit Tree Inventory

Which tree is most common? Which tree is least common?

16.

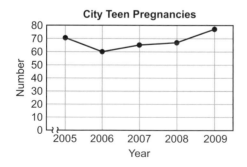

City Teen Pregnancies

Describe the general trend of city teen pregnancies over the time period from 2005 to 2009.

17.

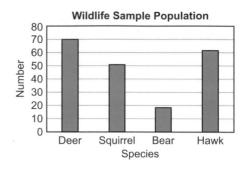

Wildlife Sample Population

How many deer are in the sample, relative to the number of bears?

18.

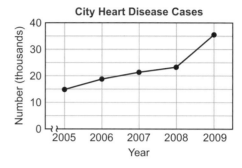

City Heart Disease Cases

By what percent did the number of cases increase in 2009?

19.

Fast-Food Restaurant Visits

Describe how the number of fast-food visits changed between 1980 and 2005.

20.

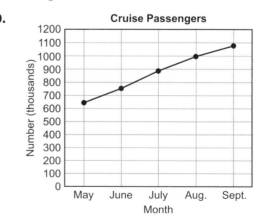

Cruise Passengers

Find the increase in the number of passengers from May to September.

Indicate the most appropriate graph type for each scenario: stem-and-leaf plot, box-and-whisker plot, bar graph, or line graph.

21. Mr. Fern has just graded the final exam. He wants to determine the distribution of grades and quickly analyze mean and quartiles.

22. Jim's Auto needs to analyze the number of sales for four car models for each of the last six months.

23. Mrs. Siegert, the track coach, organizes the sprint times of 20 runners. She is interested in individual times and in knowing how many runners will qualify for competition.

24. A state government agency is analyzing the trend of unemployment rates in the city over a 20-year period.

25. Rowen and Hicks, an investment company, wishes to analyze the trend of a stock over the last 10 years.

For each problem, do the following:

A. Create a multiple bar graph.
B. Answer the question.

26. The Browns are trying to conserve electricity. They compare last year's electricity use to this year's use over the same time period. Make a conjecture about the change in their use of electricity this year compared to the previous year's use.

The Browns' Electricity Usage					
Month	Nov.	Dec.	Jan.	Feb.	Mar.
Kilowatt Hours Used Last Year	780	1090	1300	1450	809
Kilowatt Hours Used This Year	680	999	1240	1350	750

27. Six Three Designs, Inc., tracks the number of hits on its website for two years from January to May. Make a conjecture about the number of hits for the company over the years.

Number of Website Hits					
Month	Jan.	Feb.	Mar.	April	May
Hits in 2007	69	250	2900	3400	5290
Hits in 2008	6000	4850	7800	10,000	12,000

28. Burgers & More records the number of customers during its busy season. The data for five July dates over two years are shown below. Make a conjecture about the number of customers that go to the restaurant in July over the years.

Number of Customers in July					
July Date	4	11	18	25	31
Customers in 2007	320	289	205	256	299
Customers in 2008	340	320	210	240	280

*29. **Challenge** The city government collects data on the types of energy used by businesses and consumers. The data for 1998, 2003, and 2008 are shown below. Make a conjecture about the energy used from one year to the next.

Energy Use						
Energy Type	Oil	Coal	Electric	Wind	Solar	Nuclear
Percentage of Use 1998	60	15	14	0.5	0.5	10
Percentage of Use 2003	58	5	20	2	4	10
Percentage of Use 2008	40	5	25	8	12	10

*30. **Challenge** An ongoing survey collects data regarding the subscribing habits of U.S. households. Data on magazine subscriptions were gathered for a 15-year period. The table below shows the data for 1995, 2000, and 2005. Predict the number of magazine subscriptions (in millions) for the News, Teen, and Science magazines in 2010.

Number of Magazine Subscriptions for U.S. Households						
Magazine Type	News	Sports	Women's	Teen	Science	Health
Subscriptions in 1995 (millions)	60	95	87	72	84.4	48
Subscriptions in 2000 (millions)	56	98.1	92	68	83.1	52
Subscriptions in 2005 (millions)	45.2	97	102	54.3	82	60

Frequency Distributions

A *frequency distribution* is often a useful way to organize and display a data set.

> **DEFINITIONS**
>
> A **frequency distribution** is a table or graph that describes the number of times a value or interval of values occurs in a data set. When the distribution is shown as a table, it is called a **frequency table**. One type of graph that shows a distribution is called a **histogram**.

Making a Frequency Table and a Histogram

In a frequency table or histogram, the interval sizes should be equal, and the intervals must not overlap. (That is, each data value must occur in exactly one interval.) Intervals are also called *classes*.

Example 1   Make a frequency table for the following set of test scores. Then use the table to make a histogram.

62, 88, 95, 97, 81, 78, 65, 91, 85, 84, 98, 89, 85, 89, 72, 77, 80, 93, 97, 70, 58, 66, 94, 82, 75

Solution

Step 1   Determine the number of classes you will use. As a general rule, use 5 to 15 classes. For these test scores, use 10 classes.

Step 2   Set up classes of equal width. The lowest and highest data values are 58 and 98. Convenient limits that include 58 and 98 are 50 and 100. Find the difference: $100 - 50 = 50$. Divide by the number of classes: $50 \div 10 = 5$. Finally, set up the classes, beginning at 50 and ending close to 100: 50–54, 55–59, 60–64, ..., 95–99. (Note that the first numbers of consecutive classes differ by 5: 50, 55, 60, and so on.)

Step 3   Make the frequency table. The frequency for each class is the number of times the data values in that class occur.

> **TIP**
>
> How many classes should you use for your histograms? There is no one right answer. In the first example, 10 classes worked pretty well. In general, you want to use just enough classes so you can see what is happening with the data.

Class	Frequency
50–54	0
55–59	1
60–64	1
65–69	2
70–74	2
75–79	3
80–84	4
85–89	5
90–94	3
95–99	4

Step 4 Make the histogram. Use a bar to represent the frequency of each class. The greatest frequency in the table is 5, so use a scale on the Frequency axis that goes slightly higher than 5, such as 0 to 6. There should be no spaces between bars (unless a class has a frequency of 0).

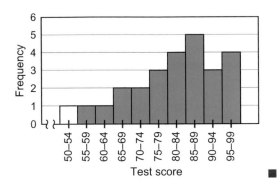

Examining Uniform, Bell-Shaped, and Skewed Distributions

The values in many data sets are distributed symmetrically. Two common symmetric distributions are the *uniform distribution* and the *bell-shaped distribution*. In a perfectly uniform distribution, all intervals have the same frequency. In a distribution that is nearly uniform or nearly bell-shaped, the mean and median are nearly equal.

THINK ABOUT IT

Real-world data sets are not likely to be perfectly uniform or bell-shaped. However, many real-world data sets are approximately uniform or bell-shaped.

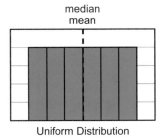

Uniform Distribution

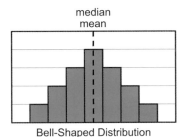

Bell-Shaped Distribution

In a *skewed distribution*, one side has lower frequencies than the other side. If the distribution is skewed to the right, the mean will be greater than the median. If the distribution is skewed to the left, the mean will be less than the median.

THINK ABOUT IT

"Skewed to the right" means mean on the *right* of median (larger).

"Skewed to the left" means mean on the *left* of median (smaller).

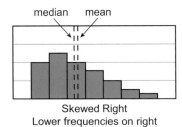

Skewed Right
Lower frequencies on right

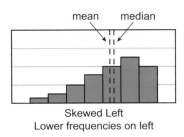

Skewed Left
Lower frequencies on left

Interpreting a Frequency Table and a Histogram

Example 2 Describe the type of distribution. Identify the relationship of the mean and the median.

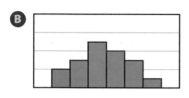

Class	Frequency
1–15	3
16–30	2
31–45	11
46–60	17
61–75	17

Solution There are fewer data values in the classes with the lower values. This distribution is skewed left. A histogram would have lower bars on the left side than on the right side. The mean of the data set is less than the median. ∎

B

Solution The histogram is nearly bell-shaped, so the mean and median are nearly equal. ∎

Example 3 The histogram shows the distance in meters jumped by the competitors in a track meet.

A Where are the data clumped together or spread out?

B Is the distribution more closely uniform, bell, skew, or none? Why?

C What is the relationship of the mean and the median?

D Isaiah jumped 6.4 meters in the meet. About what percent of people jumped farther than Isaiah?

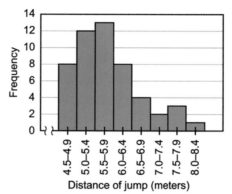

Solution

A Most of the data are clumped together in the classes on the left side of the distribution. This means that most of the competitors jumped less than a distance of 6.4 m.

B This distribution is skewed right because there are fewer data values on the right than on the left.

C The average distance jumped in the track meet will be more than the median distance jumped.

D The heights of the bars greater than 6.4 appear to be one-fourth of the height of the bars less than 6.4, so about 25% of the competitors jumped farther than Isaiah. ∎

Problem Set

Make a frequency table for each data set.

1. 34, 56, 22, 49, 37, 20, 61, 48, 22, 17, 51, 32, 50, 40, 10, 16, 20, 60, 58, 26, 33, 46, 19, 20, 34

2. 2, 3, 1, 10, 14, 22, 19, 28, 6, 11, 34, 30, 6, 18, 19, 20, 14, 29, 5, 9, 7, 9, 12, 3, 10

3. 60, 55, 52, 67, 92, 96, 60, 61, 57, 53, 66, 88, 99, 62, 96, 80, 78, 82, 91, 100, 78, 92, 82, 77, 80

4. 100, 102, 111, 106, 108, 99, 91, 122, 95, 94, 145, 150, 130, 110, 121, 141, 137, 136, 103, 144

Make a frequency table. Use the table to draw a histogram for each data set.

5. 50, 60, 71, 82, 54, 60, 88, 79, 98, 56, 71, 64, 57, 68, 85, 78, 56, 71, 62, 52, 89, 87, 70, 82, 78

6. 24, 46, 32, 39, 57, 24, 62, 58, 23, 27, 31, 42, 60, 43, 20, 34, 27, 56, 68, 36, 43, 56, 25, 30, 41

7. 5, 8, 3, 9, 10, 22, 14, 20, 2, 5, 7, 11, 10, 3, 2, 5, 15, 18, 22, 19, 18, 17, 21, 23, 21

8. 12, 23, 11, 12, 16, 23, 19, 25, 13, 11, 24, 30, 36, 18, 19, 30, 24, 29, 15, 29, 17, 39, 17, 23, 30

9. 78, 82, 98, 91, 93, 95, 94, 82, 75, 67, 99, 88, 81, 80, 72, 68, 56, 25, 58, 62, 77, 82, 93, 82, 70

10. 70, 84, 72, 65, 67, 83, 92, 98, 71, 66, 71, 88, 82, 76, 60, 70, 82, 90, 74, 77, 88, 76, 78

For each problem, do the following:

A. Describe the type of distribution.
B. Identify the relationship of the mean and the median.
C. Describe where the data are more or less spread out.

11.

Class	Frequency
1–10	20
11–20	15
21–30	13
31–40	1
41–50	3

12.

13.

Class	Frequency
1–15	1
16–30	6
31–45	18
46–60	8
61–75	3

14.

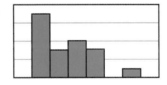

15.

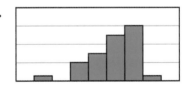

16.

Class	Frequency
1–10	2
11–20	5
21–30	11
31–40	23
41–50	25

17.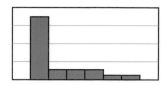

19.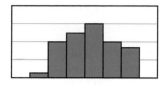

18.

Class	Frequency
1–8	5
9–16	5
17–24	4
25–32	5
33–40	6

20.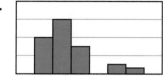

For each problem, do the following:

A. Identify the type of distribution. If none applies, explain.
B. Describe how the mean relates to the median.
C. Answer the question(s).

21. Gabriel planted several marigold seeds in his garden and, several weeks later, measured and recorded the height (in centimeters) of each plant. The data is organized in the frequency table shown. Of those planted, how many marigolds are less than 4 cm or more than 10 cm long?

Class	Frequency
1.0–3.9	1
4.0–6.9	5
7.0–9.9	6
10.0–12.9	2

22. The data organized in the frequency table represents the amount of time, in hours, Maria spent on homework each week for the past 2 months. About what percent of the time did Maria have 11 to 15 hours of homework?

Class	Frequency
1–5	1
6–10	6
11–15	1
16–20	1

23. Tomo recorded the number of basketball shots he made for each game. A frequency table of these data values are shown at right. About what percent of the total number of games played did he make more than 6 shots?

Class	Frequency
1–3	4
4–6	7
7–9	5
10–12	1

24. Serena purchased CDs from Homeless Books & CDs. The number of items she bought at each price is shown in the graph below. What percent of the CDs did she purchase for less than $5?

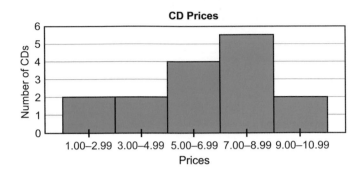

25. Derrick watched his football team during the season and recorded the team's score for each game. How many times did the team score over 50 points?

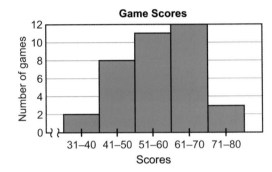

*26. **Challenge** While working at the ice rink, Chad recorded the number of skaters who came in each day during the peak month. Describe the relationship of the mean and median for each graph. Compare the mean of the two graphs. Is one mean greater than the other, or about the same? Explain.

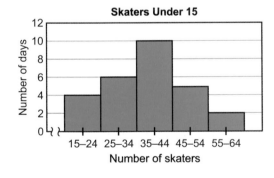
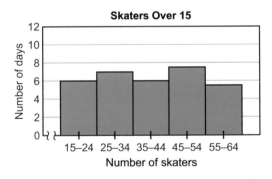

The Normal Distribution

A frequency distribution can be approximated by a curve.

Drawing a Normal Distribution

Example 1   The frequency distribution shown displays data about the heights of 1000 plants of a certain type in a nursery two weeks after seeds were planted. It shows that 2% of the plants were 3 to 4 cm tall, 6% of the plants were 5 to 6 cm tall, and so on. (Heights were rounded to the nearest centimeter before they were recorded.) The smooth curve through the tops of the bars approximates the distribution.

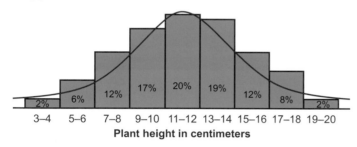

The curve for plant height is *bell-shaped*. A bell-shaped curve represents a *normal distribution* if it has the following properties.

PROPERTIES OF A NORMAL DISTRIBUTION

The data are symmetrical around the mean. The half above the mean and the half below the mean are mirror images of each other.
About 68% of the data values are within one standard deviation of the mean.
About 95% of the data values are within two standard deviations of the mean.
About 99.7% of the data values are within three standard deviations of the mean.

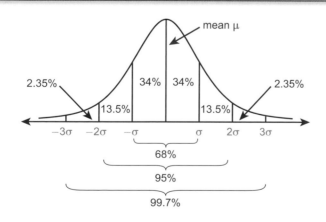

TIP

$\bar{x}$ denotes the mean of a sample.

μ (Greek letter mu) denotes the mean of a population, and is used with distribution curves.

s denotes the standard deviation of a sample.

σ (Greek letter sigma) denotes the standard deviation of a population, and is used with distribution curves.

Interpreting a Normal Distribution

A useful statistic for describing the position of a data value is *percentile*.

Example 2 A set of 2000 test scores is normally distributed with a mean of 72 and a standard deviation of 4.

A About what percent of the scores are between 68 and 80?

B Joe's score was 76. What was his percentile score?

C Estimate the number of students who scored lower than 63.

Solution

A Make a graph of a normal distribution with $\mu = 72$ and $\sigma = 4$.

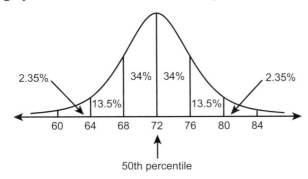

Refer to the graph: $34\% + 34\% + 13.5\% = 81.5\%$. So about 81.5% of the scores are between 68 and 80.

B The mean is 72, which is the 50th percentile. Since $50\% + 34\% = 84\%$, Joe's score of 76 is the 84th percentile.

C About 50% of the scores are less than 72. About 47.5% are between 64 and 72 (because $13.5\% + 34\% = 47.5\%$). And about 2.5% are less than 64 (because $50\% - 47.5\% = 2.5\%$). Find 2.5% of 2000: $0.025 \times 2000 = 50$. So about 50 students scored lower than 64. Therefore, fewer than 50 students scored lower than 63. ∎

Using z-Scores to Compare Two Different Normal Distributions

It is often useful to relate a normal distribution to the *standard normal distribution*. This is accomplished by using z-scores.

THE STANDARD NORMAL DISTRIBUTION AND z-SCORES

The **z-score** is the number of standard deviations that the data value is from the mean. Every data value x in a data set has a corresponding z-score, or **standard score**, obtained by the formula

$$z = \frac{x - \mu}{\sigma}.$$

If every data value in a normal distribution is converted to its corresponding z-score, a standard normal distribution is obtained. The **standard normal distribution** is the normal distribution with a mean of 0 and a standard deviation of 1.

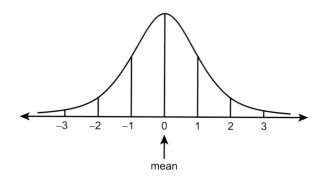

mean

Example 3 Joaquin's Math and English test scores are from different sets of normally distributed test scores. He wants to compare his scores. Which score is better, relative to the other scores in each class?

Math	
Score	86
μ_M	70
σ_M	8

English	
Score	88
μ_E	76
σ_E	10

Solution

Math score: $z_M = \dfrac{x_M - \mu_M}{\sigma_M} = \dfrac{86 - 70}{8} = \dfrac{16}{8} = 2.0$

English score: $z_E = \dfrac{x_E - \mu_E}{\sigma_E} = \dfrac{88 - 76}{10} = \dfrac{12}{10} = 1.2$

Joaquin's Math score is 2 standard deviations above the mean. His English score is 1.2 standard deviations above the mean. So Joaquin's Math score is better relative to the other scores in the class. ■

Problem Set

For each frequency distribution, draw a smooth curve through the tops of the bars and determine whether the distribution is approximately normal or not.

1.

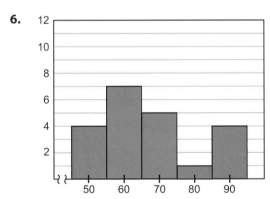

2.

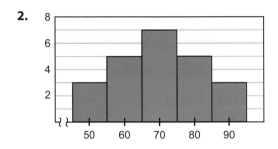

3.

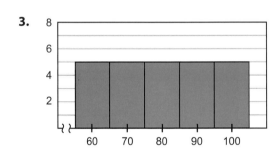

4.

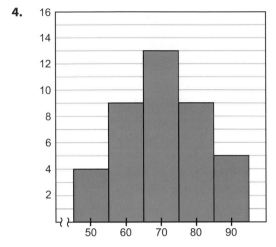

5.

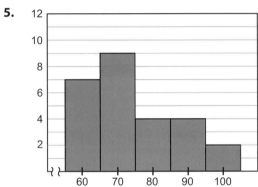

6.

A data set has a normal distribution.

7. What percent of the data are within one standard deviation of the mean?

8. What percent of the data are within two standard deviations of the mean?

9. What percent of the data are within three standard deviations of the mean?

10. What percent of the data are between one standard deviation of the mean and three standard deviations of the mean?

A set of 2000 IQ scores is normally distributed with a mean of 100 and a standard deviation of 15.

11. About what percent of the IQ scores are above 115?

12. About what percent of the IQ scores are below 85?

13. About what percent of the IQ scores are between 70 and 85?

14. Chen's IQ score was 130. What was his percentile score?

15. Elaine's IQ score was 130. What was her percentile score?

16. Estimate the number of people who scored lower than 85.

17. Estimate the number of people who scored higher than 130.

18. Estimate the number of people who scored between 85 and 115.

For a set of data, the mean was 50 and the standard deviation was 5.
Find the z-score corresponding to each score below. Express the z-scores using two decimal places.

19. $x = 60$

20. $x = 40$

21. $x = 55$

For a set of data, the mean was 100 and the standard deviation was 20.
Find the z-score corresponding to each score below. Express the z-scores using two decimal places.

22. $x = 120$

23. $x = 80$

24. $x = 105$

Answer each question.

25. Lila's Science and Government test scores are from different sets of normally distributed test scores. Which score is better, relative to the other scores in each class?

Science	
Score	90
μ_S	81
σ_S	7

Government	
Score	92
μ_G	77
σ_G	11

26. Miles and Jamal are receivers for their football teams, the Bulldozers and the Hawks, respectively. Their number of yards for a recent game are from different sets of normally distributed receiver data. Which yardage is better, relative to each team's data?

Miles	
Yards	175
μ_B	112
σ_B	30

Jamal	
Yards	200
μ_H	150
σ_H	22

27. A survey of the number of hours college students spend studying found that the mean was 8.3 hours and the standard deviation was 3.2 hours. What is the z-score corresponding to a student who studies 11 hours weekly?

*28. **Challenge** Two students took tests on emotional stability. Tavon scored 86 on a test where the mean was 80 and the standard deviation was 10. Rowanda took a test where the mean was 210 and the standard deviation was 15. If Rowanda's and Tavon's scores are the same number of standard deviations above the mean, what was Rowanda's score?

*29. **Challenge** Three people applying for a job took aptitude tests. Roxy scored 120 on a test where the mean was 100 and the standard deviation was 10. Brian scored 335 on a test where the mean was 300 and the standard deviation was 15. Ahmad scored 270 on a test where the mean was 250 and the standard deviation was 7.5. List the three applicants in order, from best to worst performance (highest to lowest z-score).

Bivariate Data and Scatter Plots

Sometimes data come in pairs, such as *age* and *height* for a group of individuals. These paired data can be called *bivariate data* because there are two variables.

Creating a Scatter Plot

A **scatter plot** is a visual display of bivariate data. The independent variable is assigned to the *x*-axis, and the dependent variable is assigned to the *y*-axis. If it is not clear which variable is independent and which is dependent, you can assign either variable to either axis.

Example 1 Make a scatter plot of the following data, which show the mileage, to the nearest thousand, and the age, in years, of 10 cars.

Age (years)	8	5	2	1	4	6	4	9	3	6
Mileage (1000s)	128	84	18	14	76	68	56	142	50	52

Solution

Step 1 Determine what goes on the *x*-axis and what goes on the *y*-axis. It is likely that mileage depends on the age of the car, so make age the independent variable and mileage the dependent variable.

Step 2 Determine the scales on the axes. Age ranges from 1 to 9, so a scale from 0 to 10 is appropriate. Mileage ranges from 14 to 142, so a scale from 0 to 150 is appropriate.

Step 3 Plot the ordered pairs (age, mileage).

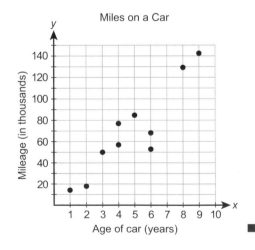

Most graphing calculators or spreadsheets make it pretty easy to create a scatter plot. For instance, if you put all your ordered pairs into a spreadsheet with one variable in column A and the other variable in column B, then you can select both columns and create a scatter plot. For instance, in some spreadsheet programs, you would Insert a Chart, then select the Scatter Plot type of chart.

	A	B
1	Age	Mileage
2	8	128
3	5	84
4	2	18
5	1	14
6	4	76
7	6	68
8	4	56
9	9	142
10	3	50
11	6	52

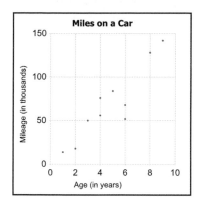

Using Correlation to Interpret Data

When you interpret a scatter plot, look for a pattern. One possible pattern is linear.

DEFINITION

Correlation indicates the strength and direction of a *linear* relationship between two variables.

If the pattern of points rises from left to right in a linear pattern, the variables have a *positive correlation*. If the pattern falls from left to right, the variables have a *negative correlation*.

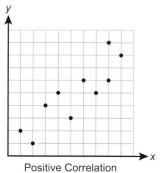

In a positive relationship, lower x-values are generally paired with lower y-values, and higher x-values are generally paired with higher y-values. In a negative relationship, lower x-values are generally paired with higher y-values, and higher x-values are generally paired with lower y-values. In Example 1, the variables show a moderate positive relationship. Mileage tends to increase as age increases.

When no linear pattern exists among the points, there is *no correlation*.

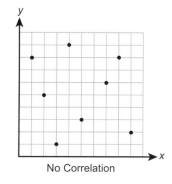

No Correlation

TIP

In a strong linear correlation, the points are close to forming a line. In a weak linear correlation, the points are more scattered.

Example 2 Determine whether there is a positive, a negative, or no correlation between the variables. If there is a correlation, describe the strength of the correlation

A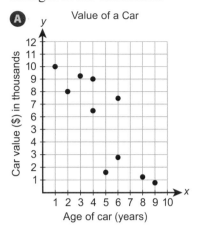

Value of a Car

Solution There is a weak to moderate negative correlation between the age of the cars and the value of the cars. As age increases, value tends to decrease. ■

B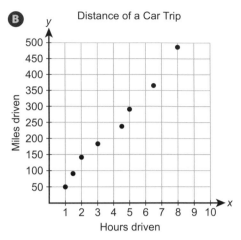

Distance of a Car Trip

Solution There is a strong positive correlation between hours and miles. As hours increase, miles tend to also increase. ■

Problem Set

Make a scatter plot for each data set.

1.

Height (inches)	Men's Shoe Size
48	10.5
56	10
60	11
64	11
70	11.5
72	12
73	12
74	12.5
75	12.5
76	13

2.

Car Age (years)	Value ($)
1	25,000
2	20,000
3	18,000
4	14,800
5	11,900
6	9000
7	6700
8	5000
9	3000

3.

Age (months)	Length (inches)
1	19
6	21
12	24
18	28
24	32
36	38
48	40
60	46
72	52
84	60

5.

Distance (miles)	Time (minutes)
0.5	3
1	15
3	60
1.5	16
2	32
4	68
3.1	59
2.5	45
5	90
1.5	20

4.

Age (years)	Doctor Visits per Year
20	1
30	3
40	5
50	7
55	5
60	8
66	10
70	15
80	13
82	9

6.

Hours Worked	Pay ($)
40	330
35	288.75
42	354.76
50	453.80
22	181.50
31	255.75
40	330
23	189.75
36	297
20	165

7.

Income Earned	Tax Owed ($)
20,000	6700
25,000	8300
30,000	11,000
40,000	13,000
50,000	17,000
60,000	20,000
70,000	22,000
80,000	28,000
90,000	32,000
100,000	40,000

9.

Year	Speed Limit (mph)
1	30
2	45
5	50
8	70
10	55
15	55
20	60
25	65
30	65
35	60

8.

Year	Cases of Flu
1	80
3	100
5	120
8	90
10	80
12	50
15	60
20	40
25	45
30	30

10.

Weeks	Weight Loss (pounds)
1	1.5
2	2
3	1.5
4	1
8	4
12	3
16	4
18	2
24	1
30	0

11.

Time (seconds)	Distance from Ground (feet)
1	50
2	48
3	45
4	40
5	38
6	34
7	30
8	28
9	24
10	20

13.

Study Time (hours)	Test Grades
1	80
2.5	95
0	60
3	84
2	90
1.5	81
3.1	83
2.8	96
0	65
4	86

12.

Distance (km)	Time (hours)
20	0.5
55	1
300	6
150	3.75
200	4
60	1.1
80	2
100	2
250	4.5
500	8.3

14.

Income ($)	Expenditures ($)
48,000	47,000
49,000	48,800
50,000	43,000
48,500	49,000
51,500	51,000
52,000	52,400
52,600	51,300
51,900	50,000
53,000	52,100
53,000	52,999

Determine whether there is a positive, a negative, or no correlation between the variables. If there is a correlation, describe the strength of the correlation.

15.

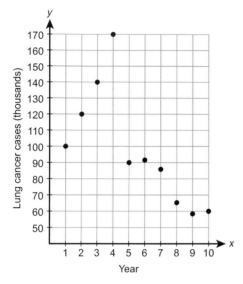

16.

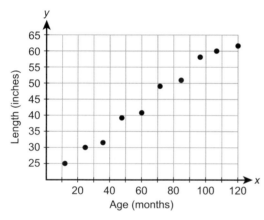

17.

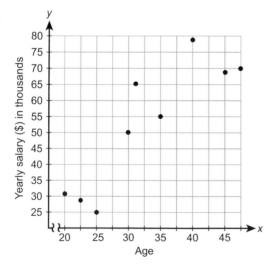

18.

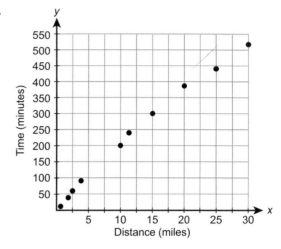

19.

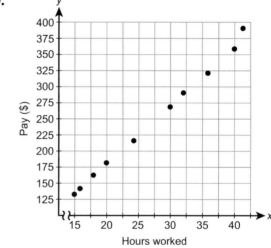

20.

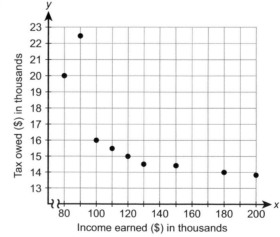

21.

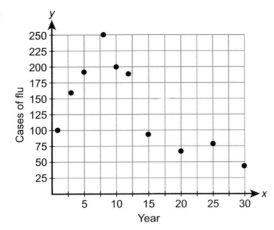

22.

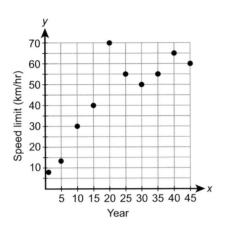

23.

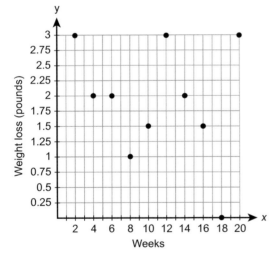

24.

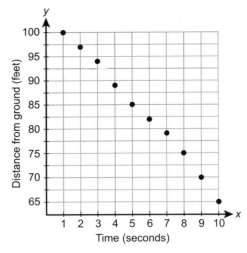

25.

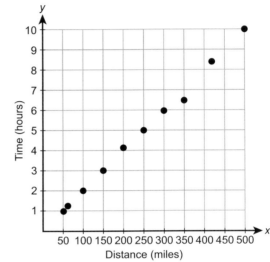

26.

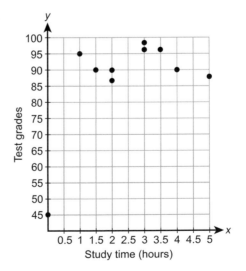

27.

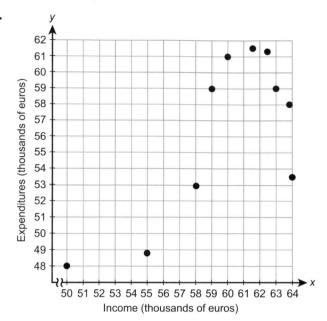

Income (thousands of euros)

*29. Challenge

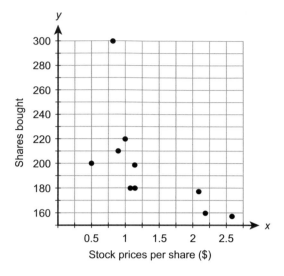

Stock prices per share ($)

*28. Challenge

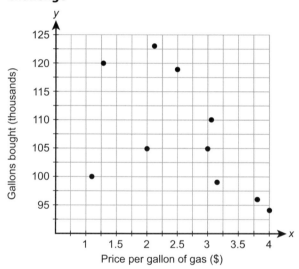

Price per gallon of gas ($)

Lines of Best Fit

A **line of fit** is a line that you can use as a model for a data set.

Choosing a Line That Best Fits Data

A line of fit can be used as a model. If an *x*-value is input into an equation of a line of fit, it should provide a reasonable value of *y* that is representative of the data. When a line of fit (also called a *fit line*) is a good model for a set of data, you can say it fits the data well.

Example 1 The ticket sales for the first five weeks of a new movie are shown below. Let *x* be the week and *y* be the ticket sales in millions of dollars.

Week	1	2	3	4	5
Ticket Sales (millions of dollars)	46	40	36	29	18

A Make a scatter plot of the ticket sales for the first five weeks.

B Select two points to sketch a line of fit.

C Use the two points selected in Example 1B to find an equation of a line of fit.

D Use the equation to predict the sales for week 7.

Solution

A Plot the points (1, 46), (2, 40), (3, 36), (4, 29), and (5, 18).

B Select two points, for example (1, 46) and (5, 18), to sketch a line of fit.

C The points selected in Example 1B are (1, 46) and (5, 18). Use the slope-intercept form to find the equation of the line.

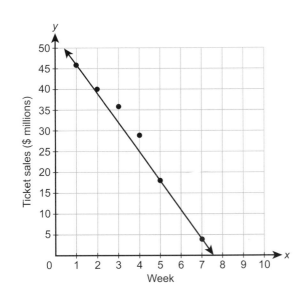

Find *m*.

$$m = \frac{y_2 - y_1}{x_2 - x_1} = \frac{46 - 18}{1 - 5} = \frac{28}{-4} = -7$$

Find *b*.

$$y = mx + b$$
$$y = -7x + b$$
$$18 = -7 \cdot 5 + b$$
$$18 = -35 + b$$
$$53 = b$$

An equation for a line of fit is $y = -7x + 53$.

THINK ABOUT IT

A relationship between variables does not imply any cause-effect relationship.

THINK ABOUT IT

The line of fit is an approximation. There are other lines that would fit the data just as well. The predicted sales depend on the line of fit that you chose. It is only a prediction.

D For week 7,

$$y = -7x + 53$$

$$y = -7 \cdot 7 + 53$$

$$y = -49 + 53$$

$$y = 4$$

The predicted ticket sales for week 7 are \$4 million. ∎

Example 2 The number of deer that live on various amounts of acreage is shown below. Let x be the number of acres in thousands and y be the number of deer.

Acres (in thousands)	2	3	4	5	6
Number of Deer	75	134	169	186	250

A Make a scatter plot of the number of deer for each number of acres.

B Select two points to sketch a line of fit.

C Use the two points selected in Example 2B to find an equation of a line of fit.

D Use the equation to predict the number of deer on 5500 acres.

Solution

A Plot the points (2, 75), (3, 134), (4, 169), (5, 186), and (6, 250).

B Select two points, for example (4, 169) and (6, 250), to sketch a line of fit.

C The points selected in Example 2B are (4, 169) and (6, 250). Use the slope-intercept form to find the equation of the line.

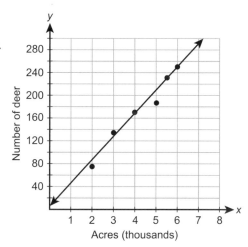

Find m.

$$m = \frac{y_2 - y_1}{x_2 - x_1} = \frac{250 - 169}{6 - 4} = \frac{81}{2} = 40.5$$

Find b.

$$y = mx + b$$

$$y = 40.5x + b$$

$$169 = 40.5 \cdot 4 + b$$

$$169 = 162 + b$$

$$7 = b$$

An equation for a line of fit is $y = 40.5x + 7$.

D For 5500 acres,

$$y = 40.5x + 7$$

$$y = 40.5 \cdot 5.5 + 7$$

$$y = 222.75 + 7$$

$$y = 229.75$$

The predicted number of deer on 5500 acres is about 230 deer. ∎

Predicting within a given range of data (Example 2) is called *interpolation*. Predicting outside a given range (Example 1) is called *extrapolation*. Use caution when extrapolating, especially as you get farther from the given data. In Example 1, the line of fit predicts negative sales for week 8, which is not likely. Also, a pattern that begins linear might not continue to be linear.

Finding an Equation of a Median-Median Line and Using It to Make a Prediction

A **median-median line** is one type of line of fit. To construct a median-median line, first order the data according to the *x*-coordinates, and then divide the data into three equal, or approximately equal, groups. For each group, find the median of the *x*-values and the median of the *y*-values. Write an ordered pair for each group, using the median *x*-value and the median *y*-value. These are called the *summary points*. Sketch the line that joins the first and third summary points. The median-median line is parallel to that line and one-third of the way toward the second summary point.

Example 3   The table shows the salaries of 12 employees at Books Unlimited Co., along with the number of years each has been employed.

Number of Years	6	3	3	5	5	2	10	16	14	14	16	10
Salary ($1000s)	70	46	34	50	57	32	80	95	87	86	89	82

A Find the equation of the median-median line for the data.

B Use the equation from Example 3A to predict the salary of a 12-year employee and the salary of a 20-year employee.

Solution

A **Step 1**   Order the data by *x*-coordinates. Then form the three groups.

Number of Years	2	3	3	5	5	6	10	10	14	14	16	16
Salary ($1000s)	32	34	46	50	57	70	80	82	86	87	89	95

Step 2   Find the three summary points.

Group 1: (3, 40)   Group 2: (8, 75)   Group 3: (15, 88)

Step 3   The slope of line *a*, through (3, 40) and (15, 88), is

$$m = \frac{88 - 40}{15 - 3} = \frac{48}{12} = 4.$$ Find the equation of line *a*.

$$y - y_1 = m(x - x_1) \Rightarrow y - 40 = 4(x - 3) \Rightarrow y = 4x + 28$$

Step 4   Find the equation of line **b** (containing (8, 75) and parallel to line *a*).

$$y - y_1 = m(x - x_1) \Rightarrow y - 75 = 4(x - 8) \Rightarrow y = 4x + 43$$

Step 5   Use the *y*-intercepts from Steps 3 and 4 to find the *y*-intercept of the median-median line (line *c*):

$$28 + \frac{1}{3}(43 - 28) = 28 + \frac{1}{3} \cdot 15 = 28 + 5 = 33.$$

The equation of the median-median line is $y = 4x + 33$.

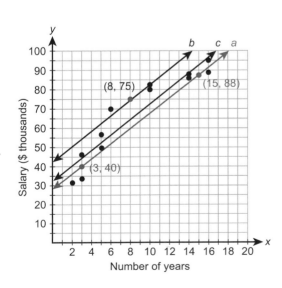

B Use the equation of the median-median line to predict the salary of a 12-year employee and a 20-year employee.

$y = 4x + 33 \Rightarrow y = 4 \cdot 12 + 33 \Rightarrow 48 + 33 = 81$

The predicted salary of a 12-year employee is $81,000.

$y = 4x + 33 \Rightarrow y = 4 \cdot 20 + 33 \Rightarrow 80 + 33 = 113$

The predicted salary of a 20-year employee is $113,000. ∎

Problem Set

For each problem, do the following:

A. Make a scatter plot of the data.
B. Select and record two points to sketch a line of fit.
C. Use the two points to find an equation of a line of fit.
D. Use the equation to calculate the indicated prediction.

1. A store manager records CD sales for the first five weeks. Predict CD sales for week 7.

Week	1	2	3	4	5
CD Sales	30	28	29	26	20

2. Bill logs his running time for the first five days. Predict Bill's running time for day 7.

Day	1	2	3	4	5
Running Time (minutes)	10	14	18	15	20

3. Jaime records her mileage for five months. Predict Jaime's car mileage for month 6.

Month	1	2	3	4	5
Mileage	22	21	19	19	17

4. A real estate company records its house sales for the first five months of the year. Predict house sales for month 7.

Month	1	2	3	4	5
House Sales	130	128	117	110	85

5. Jon scores a different number of points for the first five games. Predict the number of points Jon will score in game 7.

Game	1	2	3	4	5
Points	5	8	12	15	19

6. Kim's favorite baseball team scores a different number of points for the first six games of the season. Predict the score for game 8.

Game	1	2	3	4	5	6
Score	3	8	2	5	7	10

7. Jim's parents record their son's weight for the first six years. Predict Jim's weight for year 9.

Year	1	2	3	4	5	6
Weight (pounds)	15	23	28	35	48	50

8. Carlo records his calorie intake for the first six days of a research study. Predict Carlo's calorie consumption for day 8.

Day	1	2	3	4	5	6
Calorie Consumption	1500	1550	1610	1690	1799	2000

For each problem, do the following:

A. Make a scatter plot of the data and sketch a line of fit.
B. Use the line to make the indicated predictions.
C. Determine reasonable limits, if any, for extrapolation.

9. Distance from the ground is measured for the first six seconds of a ride. Predict the distance from the ground for the 15th and 60th seconds.

Seconds	0	10	20	30	40
Distance from Ground (meters)	1.9	3.5	5.7	7.2	5

10. Krazy Gadgets logs the company's profits for the first 18 months. Predict the company's profits for month 8 and month 24.

Month	6	9	12	15	18
Profits ($ thousands)	81	75	63	54	50

11. Ricki records the gas mileages of his semitrailer truck for different weights. Predict the truck's gas mileage for a weight of 65,000 pounds and 80,000 pounds.

Weight (pounds)	50,780	56,250	62,000	67,500	71,100
Miles per Gallon	10	8.8	7.4	5.9	5

12. The numbers of tiles that cover different areas (in sq. meters) of a floor are shown. Predict the number of tiles needed for an area of 12 sq. meters and an area of 23 sq. meters.

Area (sq. meters)	5	9	10	13	15
Number of Tiles	450	885	1020	1350	1410

13. Truly Organic Juice records its production number at certain hours. Predict the number of juice bottles produced after 12 hours and after 25 hours.

Hour	2	6	10	14	18
Number of Bottles	340	670	1020	1280	1660

14. Andy plants a tomato plant and, after a few weeks, records its height in centimeters. Predict its height for days 25 and 35.

Day	3	10	15	20	30
Height (cm)	4.1	5.5	6.8	7.2	10.3

For each problem, do the following:

A. Find the equation of the median-median line for the data.
B. Use the line to make the indicated prediction.

15. The table shows the salaries of 12 workers at a company, along with the number of years they have worked. Predict the salary of a 26-year worker.

Number of Years	8	20	5	7	5	17	10	2	15	22	9	24
Salary ($ thousands)	60	78	42	59	40	77	68	25	74	78	63	80

16. An analyst records the mileage for 12 U.S. cars and their ages. Predict the mileage of an 11-year-old car.

Age (years)	1	3	15	20	8	4	7	2	14	10	5	3
Mileage	40	27	10	9	18	22	20	35	8	15	20	25

17. A nurse records the height of 12 students and their ages. Predict the height of a 14-year-old student.

Age (years)	8	16	5	7	10	15	12	6	17	18	9	11
Height (feet)	5.1	6	3.5	4.8	4	5.8	5.2	3.8	5.6	6.5	4.7	4.8

18. A coach observes the race times and ages for 12 runners. Predict the race time for a 20-year-old runner.

Runner Age (years)	15	13	15	16	17	16	18	19	18	17	15	12
Time (minutes)	3	2	3	4.5	4.5	4	5.1	5	5.2	4.3	3.1	2

19. A race car owner records the race times and ages for 12 cars. Predict the race time for a 6-year-old car.

Car Age (years)	8	2	1	7	5	4	1	3	5	7	9	8
Race Time (minutes)	8.2	6	5	7.5	7	6.5	4.8	6.1	7.1	7.5	10	8.5

20. The table shows the price per share of 12 stocks and the number of days they have been trading. Predict the price per share on the 24th trading day.

Trading Day	2	10	5	7	8	15	20	6	18	23	5	11
Price per Share (dollars)	1	6	1.2	9	9	12	17	1.4	15	17	1.25	3.2

21. A manager of an electronic parts company keeps track of the number of defective products produced every month. Predict the number of defective products produced in month 30.

Month	8	16	5	7	10	11	12	8	17	18	9	6
Defective Products	60	120	35	55	90	100	112	75	125	126	82	51

22. A boating company records the time and distance traveled by 12 boats. Predict the time of a boat that travels 65 meters.

Distance (meters)	25	35	45	55	20	30	40	60	70	80	100	90
Time (minutes)	5.1	5.9	6.1	6.2	5	5.8	6	6.3	7	7.5	8.5	8

23. **Challenge** The table shows the income of 15 doctors and their years of experience. Predict the income of a doctor with 13 years of experience.

Experience (years)	5	1	3	7	4	6	10	12	14	15	16	16	3	8	20
Income ($ thousands)	120	80	95	129	98	121	190	200	210	250	280	285	94	130	300

24. **Challenge** The table shows the student case load of a specialist, based on years of experience. Predict the number of student cases of a specialist with 16 years' experience.

Experience (years)	2	1	6	3	8	11	7	2	5	10	11	9	10	12	14
Student Cases	45	40	100	60	110	121	100	40	90	118	125	110	120	130	140

UNIT 14   Vectors and Matrices

Knowledge of vectors and matrices is useful for animators when they create images.

Digital images are composed of numerous tiny components called pixels. Animators use lists of numbers called vectors to describe the color of every pixel of every object. They also use tables of numbers called matrices to describe the movements of each object.

Big Ideas

▶ A number is anything that obeys the laws of arithmetic; all numbers obey the laws of arithmetic.

▶ If you use a mathematical model to represent a certain situation, you can use the model to solve other problems that you might not be able to solve otherwise.

Unit Topics

▶ Foundations for Unit 14

▶ Matrices and Vectors

▶ Operations with Matrices

▶ Matrix Multiplication

▶ Transforming Points and Figures

▶ Determinants and Cramer's Rule

▶ Identity and Inverse Matrices

▶ Using Matrices to Solve Linear Systems

Foundations for Unit 14

Before you study matrix operations and learn how to solve systems of equations with matrices, you should know how to do the following:

▶ Find the reciprocal and opposite of a number.

▶ Use a coordinate rule to transform a point.

▶ Solve a system of two equations in two unknowns.

Opposites and Reciprocals

Definitions

opposites   two numbers that are the same distance from, but on opposite sides of, zero on a number line; also called *additive inverses* because their sum is 0

reciprocal   a number that when multiplied by the original number gives the multiplicative identity 1; also called *multiplicative inverse*

The opposite of a is $-a$.

The reciprocal of a is $\dfrac{1}{a}$ and the reciprocal of $\dfrac{a}{b}$ is $\dfrac{b}{a}$.

Example 1   Find the opposite and reciprocal of each number.

	Opposite	Reciprocal
A. -8	$-(-8) = 8$ **Check:** $-8 + 8 = 0$ ✓	$-\dfrac{1}{8}$ **Check:** $-8 \cdot \left(-\dfrac{1}{8}\right) = \dfrac{8}{1} \cdot \dfrac{1}{8} = 1$ ✓
B. $\dfrac{5}{6}$	$-\dfrac{5}{6}$ **Check:** $\dfrac{5}{6} + \left(-\dfrac{5}{6}\right) = 0$ ✓	$\dfrac{6}{5}$ **Check:** $\dfrac{5}{6} \cdot \dfrac{6}{5} = 1$ ✓

Problem Set A

Find the opposite and reciprocal of each number.

1. 3 **2.** $\dfrac{1}{3}$ **3.** -7 **4.** $-\dfrac{3}{4}$ **5.** 0

6. $-\dfrac{7}{15}$ **7.** 2.5 **8.** $1\dfrac{2}{3}$ **9.** 72 **10.** 1

Using Coordinate Rules to Transform Points

Use the following rules to transform points on the coordinate plane.

dilation — dilate by a scale factor of *a*: $(x, y) \rightarrow (ax, ay)$

translation — translate *h* units horizontally and *k* units vertically: $(x, y) \rightarrow (x + h, y + k)$

reflection — reflect across the *x*-axis: $(x, y) \rightarrow (x, -y)$
reflect across the *y*-axis: $(x, y) \rightarrow (-x, y)$

rotation about (0, 0) — rotate 180° (or counterclockwise 180°): $(x, y) \rightarrow (-x, -y)$
rotate 90° (or counterclockwise 270°): $(x, y) \rightarrow (y, -x)$
rotate 270° (or counterclockwise 90°): $(x, y) \rightarrow (-y, x)$

> **TIP**
> To translate, move right and up when *h* and *k* are positive; move down and left when they are negative.

Example 2 Determine the coordinates of the image point for the described transformation of the preimage point.

Ⓐ Translate $(-2, 8)$ left 4 units and up 1 unit.

Solution Use $h = -4$ and $k = 1$.

$$(x, y) \rightarrow (x + h, y + k)$$
$$(-2, 8) \rightarrow (-2 + (-4), 8 + 1)$$
$$\rightarrow (-6, 9)$$

The coordinates of the image point are $(-6, 9)$.

Ⓑ Reflect $(3, 4)$ across the *x*-axis and across the *y*-axis. Graph the points.

Solution

Across the *x*-axis: $(x, y) \rightarrow (x, -y)$
$(3, 4) \rightarrow (3, -4)$

Across the *y*-axis: $(x, y) \rightarrow (-x, y)$
$(3, 4) \rightarrow (-3, 4)$

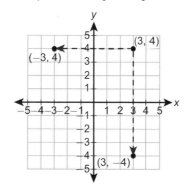

Problem Set B

Determine the coordinates of the image point for the described transformation of the preimage point.

11. Dilate $(1, 4)$ by a scale factor of 5.

12. Translate $(-2, 5)$ right 2 units and down 3 units.

13. Rotate $(-2, -6)$ 180° about the origin.

14. Translate $(3, 10)$ up 12 units.

15. Dilate $(14, -26)$ by a scale factor of $\dfrac{1}{2}$.

16. Reflect $(8, 9)$ across the *x*-axis.

17. Translate $(0, -4)$ left 8 units and down 4 units.

18. Rotate $(-1, -9)$ counterclockwise 90° about the origin.

Solving a System of Two Equations in Two Unknowns

Definition

linear combination   a method of solving a system of equations by using addition or subtraction to eliminate a variable

Example 3   Use linear combination to solve the system of equations.

$$\begin{cases} 3x - 4y = -23 \\ x + 7y = 9 \end{cases}$$

Because you want one of the variable terms to be eliminated, multiply the second equation by -3 so that the coefficients of the x-terms are opposites.

$$\begin{cases} 3x - 4y = -23 \\ x + 7y = 9 \end{cases} \Rightarrow \begin{cases} 3x - 4y = -23 \\ -3(x + 7y = 9) \end{cases} \Rightarrow \begin{cases} 3x - 4y = -23 \\ -3x - 21y = -27 \end{cases}$$

Now add the equations and solve for the remaining variable, y.

$$\begin{array}{r} 3x - 4y = -23 \\ -3x - 21y = -27 \\ \hline 0 - 25y = -50 \\ -25y = -50 \\ y = 2 \end{array}$$

To find x, substitute 2 for y in either of the original equations. Solve for x.

$$\begin{aligned} x + 7y &= 9 \\ x + 7 \cdot 2 &= 9 \\ x + 14 &= 9 \\ x &= -5 \end{aligned}$$

The solution is $x = -5$ and $y = 2$, or $(-5, 2)$.

Problem Set C

Use linear combination to solve each system of equations.

19. $\begin{cases} x + y = 8 \\ x - y = 4 \end{cases}$

20. $\begin{cases} -10x - 2y = -18 \\ x + y = 1 \end{cases}$

21. $\begin{cases} x - y = 3 \\ -3x + y = 1 \end{cases}$

22. $\begin{cases} 2x + y = 5 \\ -4x + 6y = -2 \end{cases}$

23. $\begin{cases} 4x - y = 1 \\ 8x - 2y = 11 \end{cases}$

24. $\begin{cases} 2x - y = 0 \\ 3x + 2y = 7 \end{cases}$

Matrices and Vectors

A matrix is a type of table and can display real-world data in an organized way.

<table>
<tr><td>

DEFINITIONS

A **matrix** is a table of numbers or expressions arranged in rows and columns. Each number or expression in the matrix is called an **element** of the matrix. The element in row i and column j of matrix A is typically denoted a_{ij}.

The **dimensions** of a matrix are the numbers of rows and columns. For example, if a matrix has 2 rows and 3 columns, its dimensions are 2 by 3, written 2×3.

A **vector** is a matrix with only 1 row or only 1 column.

</td><td>

TIP

You can use the dimensions of a matrix to find the number of elements in the matrix. Simply multiply the number of rows by the number of columns. For example, a 5×4 matrix has $5 \cdot 4 = 20$ elements.

</td></tr>
</table>

A matrix is named by an uppercase letter, such as A. The elements of a matrix are usually enclosed in a set of brackets. The plural of *matrix* is *matrices*.

Matrix A below has 3 rows and 4 columns, so its dimensions are 3×4.

$$A = \begin{bmatrix} -2 & 3 & 11 & 4 \\ 1 & 2 & 7 & -1 \\ 0 & -8 & 3 & 0 \end{bmatrix} \left.\vphantom{\begin{matrix}1\\1\\1\end{matrix}}\right\} \text{3 rows}$$

$\underbrace{}_{\text{4 columns}}$

Finding the Dimensions of a Matrix and Identifying a Vector

Example 1 Find the dimensions of each matrix. Tell which matrices are vectors.

A $\begin{bmatrix} 3 & -1.5 \\ 8 & 0 \\ -5 & 15 \end{bmatrix}$

B $[2 \quad 5 \quad 7 \quad 8]$

Solution The matrix has 3 rows and 2 columns, so its dimensions are 3×2. ∎

Solution The matrix has 1 row and 4 columns so its dimensions are 1×4. The matrix has only 1 row, so it is a vector. ∎

$$\text{C} \begin{bmatrix} 1+4 & -3+0 \\ 3+8 & -9+0 \end{bmatrix}$$

$$\text{D} \begin{bmatrix} x \\ y \\ z \end{bmatrix}$$

Solution The elements are sums. The matrix has 2 rows and 2 columns, so its dimensions are 2×2. ∎

Solution The matrix has 3 rows and 1 column, so its dimensions are 3×1. The matrix has only 1 column, so it is a vector. ∎

Identifying the Location of an Element

To identify the address, or location, of an element in a matrix, write the row number and column number as subscripts to the right of the matrix name in lowercase form.

3 is in row 1, column 2, so it is element a_{12}.

$$A = \begin{bmatrix} -2 & 3 & 11 & 4 \\ 1 & 2 & 7 & -1 \\ 0 & -8 & 3 & 0 \end{bmatrix}$$

row 1   column 2

Just as a_{ij} is the element in row i, column j of matrix A, b_{ij} is the element in row i, column j of matrix B, c_{ij} is the element in row i, column j of matrix C, and so on.

Example 2 Use the matrices to answer the questions.

$$F = \begin{bmatrix} 6 & 9 \\ -3 & 2 \\ 16 & 0 \\ 11 & 21 \end{bmatrix} \qquad G = \begin{bmatrix} -14 & 8 & 17 & 7 & 4 \end{bmatrix}$$

A What is the address of the element 0?

Solution The number 0 appears in row 3, column 2 of matrix F. Its address is f_{32}. ∎

B What is the address of the element 7?

Solution The number 7 appears in row 1, column 4 of matrix G. Its address is g_{14}. ∎

C What is the element with address f_{21}?

Solution The address f_{21} refers to row 2, column 1 of matrix F. Its element is -3. ∎

D What is the element with address g_{12}?

Solution The address g_{12} refers to row 1, column 2 of matrix G. Its element is 8. ∎

Interpreting a Real-World Application with a Matrix

A matrix can be a handy way to represent data.

Example 3   Matrix A below shows attendances at three movies during a one-week period at a theater.

	Mon	Tues	Wed	Thurs	Fri	Sat	Sun
Movie 1	250	178	305	524	678	780	300
Movie 2	120	345	189	300	425	455	426
Movie 3	322	367	400	356	489	560	455

$= A$

A What are the dimensions of the matrix?

B What is element a_{24}? What does that element represent?

C What is element a_{31}? What does that element represent?

D What is the total number of people who attended Movies 1, 2, and 3 on Wednesday?

E What is the average daily attendance for Movie 2 during the one-week period?

Solution

A The matrix has 3 rows and 7 columns, so it is a 3×7 matrix.

B Element a_{24} is the element in row 2, column 4, which is 300. It represents the number of people who attended Movie 2 on Thursday.

C Element a_{31} is the element in row 3, column 1, which is 322. It represents the number of people who attended Movie 3 on Monday.

D Find the sum of the elements in column 3 of the matrix.

$305 + 189 + 400 = 894$

A total of 894 people attended the three movies on Wednesday.

E Find the sum of the elements in row 2 of the matrix.

$120 + 345 + 189 + 300 + 425 + 455 + 426 = 2260$

Then divide the sum by the number of elements.

$2260 \div 7 \approx 322.9$

The average daily attendance for Movie 2 was about 323 people. ■

Problem Set

Find the dimensions of each matrix. State which matrices are vectors.

1. $\begin{bmatrix} 4 & 8 \\ 7 & 9 \end{bmatrix}$

2. $\begin{bmatrix} 0 & 12 & 9 \\ 22 & 37 & 6 \end{bmatrix}$

3. $\begin{bmatrix} -4 \\ -9 \\ 11 \end{bmatrix}$

4. $\begin{bmatrix} 1 & 0 \\ 0 & 3 \\ -18 & 5 \\ 7 & -10 \end{bmatrix}$

5. $\begin{bmatrix} -5 & 21 \end{bmatrix}$

6. $\begin{bmatrix} 1 & 0 & 0 & 0 \\ 0 & 1 & 0 & 0 \\ 0 & 0 & 1 & 0 \\ 0 & 0 & 0 & 1 \end{bmatrix}$

7. $\begin{bmatrix} -12 & 18 & 0 & 100 \\ 14 & 37 & 88 & 2 \end{bmatrix}$

8. $\begin{bmatrix} -42 \\ 6 \end{bmatrix}$

9. $\begin{bmatrix} x & y & z \\ w & q & x \\ z & v & c \end{bmatrix}$

10. $\begin{bmatrix} 17 \\ 9 \\ 104 \\ -8 \end{bmatrix}$

11. $\begin{bmatrix} 2+7 & 6-1 & 8 \cdot (-1) \end{bmatrix}$

12. $\begin{bmatrix} -1 & -1 \\ -1 & -1 \\ -1 & -1 \end{bmatrix}$

Use matrices A and B to find the address of the element with the given value.

$A = \begin{bmatrix} 0 & 30 \\ -5 & 12 \\ -29 & 4 \\ x & 7 \end{bmatrix}$ $\qquad B = \begin{bmatrix} 17 \\ -1 \\ 44 \\ 3 \end{bmatrix}$

13. 44

14. -29

15. x

16. 7

17. 17

18. -5

Use matrices C and D to find the value of the given element.

$C = \begin{bmatrix} 1 & r \\ 0.5 & -10 \\ 40 & 3 \\ -8 & 19 \end{bmatrix}$ $\qquad D = \begin{bmatrix} 22 \\ -9 \\ s \\ 15 \end{bmatrix}$

19. c_{11}

20. d_{21}

21. c_{32}

22. c_{22}

23. d_{41}

24. c_{12}

Solve.

25. Matrix C below shows the costs ($) of cars at four car dealerships.

	Model 1	**Model 2**	**Model 3**
Dealer 1	10,800	25,200	38,500
Dealer 2	12,200	25,100	35,200
Dealer 3	11,500	23,900	33,000
Dealer 4	15,100	24,500	39,900

$= C$

    A. What are the dimensions of the matrix?

    B. What is element c_{32}? What does that element represent?

    C. What is the address of the element whose value is 15,100?

    D. What is the average cost of a Model 2 across the four dealerships?

26. Brian's Pizzeria sells three sizes of pizzas: small, medium, and large. The number of each type of pizza sold for the months of May, June, and July is given below.

May: Small: 9223   Medium: 13,215   Large: 11,550

June: Small: 10,105   Medium: 15,714   Large: 9485

July: Small: 12,558   Medium: 12,902   Large: 10,371

    A. Organize this information by using a matrix.

    B. How many pizzas were sold in June?

    C. How many more large pizzas were sold in July than in June?

    D. During which month was the greatest number of pizzas sold?

    E. Phoebe adds the values of all the elements in the first column of the matrix. What does that number represent?

    F. Phoebe adds the values of all the elements in the second row of the matrix. What does that number represent?

    G. Phoebe adds the values of all the elements in the matrix. What does that number represent?

27. Matrix A below shows the number and type of medals won by countries during the 2008 Summer Olympic games.

	Gold	**Silver**	**Bronze**
China	51	21	28
United States	36	38	36
Russian Fed.	23	21	28
Great Britain	19	13	15
Germany	16	10	15

$= A$

    A. Sujan wants to use a matrix to show the total number of medals won by each of these countries. What would the dimensions of the matrix be?

    B. Write the matrix.

Operations with Matrices

A matrix isn't the same as a single real number, but you can perform operations on matrices that are similar to operations on real numbers.

Adding and Subtracting Matrices

MATRIX ADDITION

If A and B are both $m \times n$ matrices, then $A + B$ is the $m \times n$ matrix C, where each element in C is the sum of corresponding elements in A and B. That is, $A + B = C$ if and only if $a_{ij} + b_{ij} = c_{ij}$ for all values of i and j in matrices A, B, and C.

Here is an example of adding two 2×2 matrices:

$$A = \begin{bmatrix} a_{11} & a_{12} \\ a_{21} & a_{22} \end{bmatrix} \quad B = \begin{bmatrix} b_{11} & b_{12} \\ b_{21} & b_{22} \end{bmatrix} \quad A + B = \begin{bmatrix} a_{11} + b_{11} & a_{12} + b_{12} \\ a_{21} + b_{21} & a_{22} + b_{22} \end{bmatrix}$$

REMEMBER

We use subscripts to indicate the row and column of an element in a matrix. For instance, a_{ij} is the element in row i, column j of matrix A.

MATRIX SUBTRACTION

If A and B are both $m \times n$ matrices, then $A - B$ is the $m \times n$ matrix D, where each element in D is the difference of corresponding elements in A and B. That is, $A - B = D$ if and only if $a_{ij} - b_{ij} = d_{ij}$ for all values of i and j in matrices A, B, and D.

Here is an example of subtracting two 2×2 matrices:

$$A = \begin{bmatrix} a_{11} & a_{12} \\ a_{21} & a_{22} \end{bmatrix} \quad B = \begin{bmatrix} b_{11} & b_{12} \\ b_{21} & b_{22} \end{bmatrix} \quad A - B = \begin{bmatrix} a_{11} - b_{11} & a_{12} - b_{12} \\ a_{21} - b_{21} & a_{22} - b_{22} \end{bmatrix}$$

You can only add or subtract matrices that have exactly the same dimensions.

Example 1 Let $A = \begin{bmatrix} 10 & -9 & 0 \\ 4 & -12 & -2 \end{bmatrix}$, $B = \begin{bmatrix} 7 & 15 & 1 \\ -1 & 8 & 5 \end{bmatrix}$, $C = \begin{bmatrix} 3 & -5 \\ 12 & 3 \end{bmatrix}$,

and $D = \begin{bmatrix} -6 & 0 & 12 \\ 15 & 8 & -4 \end{bmatrix}$. Perform the indicated operation.

Ⓐ $A + B$

Solution

$$A + B = \begin{bmatrix} 10 & -9 & 0 \\ 4 & -12 & -2 \end{bmatrix} + \begin{bmatrix} 7 & 15 & 1 \\ -1 & 8 & 5 \end{bmatrix}$$

$$= \begin{bmatrix} 10 + 7 & -9 + 15 & 0 + 1 \\ 4 + (-1) & -12 + 8 & -2 + 5 \end{bmatrix} = \begin{bmatrix} 17 & 6 & 1 \\ 3 & -4 & 3 \end{bmatrix}\ \blacksquare$$

Ⓑ $A - B$

Solution

$$A - B = \begin{bmatrix} 10 & -9 & 0 \\ 4 & -12 & -2 \end{bmatrix} - \begin{bmatrix} 7 & 15 & 1 \\ -1 & 8 & 5 \end{bmatrix}$$

$$= \begin{bmatrix} 10 - 7 & -9 - 15 & 0 - 1 \\ 4 - (-1) & -12 - 8 & -2 - 5 \end{bmatrix} = \begin{bmatrix} 3 & -24 & -1 \\ 5 & -20 & -7 \end{bmatrix}\ \blacksquare$$

Ⓒ $A + C$

Solution A is a 2×3 matrix and C is a 2×2 matrix. Their dimensions are not the same, so they cannot be added. $\blacksquare$

Ⓓ $A + D - B$

Solution Find the sum of A and D.

$$A + D = \begin{bmatrix} 10 & -9 & 0 \\ 4 & -12 & -2 \end{bmatrix} + \begin{bmatrix} -6 & 0 & 12 \\ 15 & 8 & -4 \end{bmatrix}$$

$$= \begin{bmatrix} 10 + (-6) & -9 + 0 & 0 + 12 \\ 4 + 15 & -12 + 8 & -2 + (-4) \end{bmatrix} = \begin{bmatrix} 4 & -9 & 12 \\ 19 & -4 & -6 \end{bmatrix}$$

Now subtract B from the sum.

$$(A + D) - B = \begin{bmatrix} 4 & -9 & 12 \\ 19 & -4 & -6 \end{bmatrix} - \begin{bmatrix} 7 & 15 & 1 \\ -1 & 8 & 5 \end{bmatrix}$$

$$= \begin{bmatrix} 4 - 7 & -9 - 15 & 12 - 1 \\ 19 - (-1) & -4 - 8 & -6 - 5 \end{bmatrix} = \begin{bmatrix} -3 & -24 & 11 \\ 20 & -12 & -11 \end{bmatrix}\ \blacksquare$$

Multiplying a Matrix by a Scalar

Any matrix can be multiplied by a single number, called a **scalar**.

MATRIX SCALAR MULTIPLICATION

If A is an $m \times n$ matrix, then rA is the $m \times n$ matrix C, where each element in C is r times the corresponding element in A. That is, $rA = C$ if and only if $r \cdot a_{ij} = c_{ij}$ for all values of i and j in matrices A and C.

Here is an example of multiplying a 2×2 matrix by a scalar:

$$A = \begin{bmatrix} a_{11} & a_{12} \\ a_{21} & a_{22} \end{bmatrix} \qquad rA = \begin{bmatrix} r \cdot a_{11} & r \cdot a_{12} \\ r \cdot a_{21} & r \cdot a_{22} \end{bmatrix}$$

In short, to multiply a matrix by a scalar, multiply the scalar by each element in the matrix.

Example 2 Let $F = \begin{bmatrix} 10 & 1 \\ -4 & -2 \end{bmatrix}$. Perform the indicated operation.

Ⓐ $5F$

Solution

$5F = 5 \begin{bmatrix} 10 & 1 \\ -4 & -2 \end{bmatrix}$

$= \begin{bmatrix} 5 \cdot 10 & 5 \cdot 1 \\ 5 \cdot (-4) & 5 \cdot (-2) \end{bmatrix}$

$= \begin{bmatrix} 50 & 5 \\ -20 & -10 \end{bmatrix}$ ∎

Ⓑ $-3F$

Solution

$-3F = -3 \begin{bmatrix} 10 & 1 \\ -4 & -2 \end{bmatrix}$

$= \begin{bmatrix} -3 \cdot 10 & -3 \cdot 1 \\ -3 \cdot (-4) & -3 \cdot (-2) \end{bmatrix}$

$= \begin{bmatrix} -30 & -3 \\ 12 & 6 \end{bmatrix}$ ∎

The commutative, associative, and distributive properties hold for matrix addition and scalar multiplication. These properties can be used in solving real-world problems involving matrices.

Commutative Properties for Matrices

> ## MATRIX PROPERTIES
>
> ### Properties of Matrix Addition
> The commutative property states that if A and B are $m \times n$ matrices, then
> $$A + B = B + A.$$
> The associative property states that if A, B, and C are $m \times n$ matrices, then
> $$A + (B + C) = (A + B) + C.$$
>
> ### Properties of Scalar Multiplication
> The commutative property states that if r is a real number and A is a matrix, then
> $$rA = Ar.$$
> The associative property states that if r and s are real numbers and A is a matrix, then
> $$r(sA) = (rs)A.$$
> The distributive property states that if r and s are real numbers and A and B are matrices, then
> $$r(A + B) = rA + rB \text{ and } (r + s)A = rA + sA.$$
>
> ### Equality Property of Matrices
> If A and B are $m \times n$ matrices and each corresponding element is equal,
> if $a_{ij} = b_{ij}$ for every i and j, then $A = B$.

Example 3   Show that the addition of any 2×2 matrices is commutative.

Solution

Let $A = \begin{bmatrix} a_{11} & a_{12} \\ a_{21} & a_{22} \end{bmatrix}$ and $B = \begin{bmatrix} b_{11} & b_{12} \\ b_{21} & b_{22} \end{bmatrix}$ where all of the elements in A and B are real.

$$A + B = \begin{bmatrix} a_{11} + b_{11} & a_{12} + b_{12} \\ a_{21} + b_{21} & a_{22} + b_{22} \end{bmatrix}$$

$$B + A = \begin{bmatrix} b_{11} + a_{11} & b_{12} + a_{12} \\ b_{21} + a_{21} & b_{22} + a_{22} \end{bmatrix}$$ Since the addition of any two real numbers is commutative, you can rewrite $B + A$.

$$B + A = \begin{bmatrix} a_{11} + b_{11} & a_{12} + b_{12} \\ a_{21} + b_{21} & a_{22} + b_{22} \end{bmatrix} = A + B$$

So $A + B = B + A$. ∎

Solving a Real-World Problem with Matrices

Example 4   The matrices below show baseball and football ticket prices (in dollars) for two years at a stadium.

	Prices 2008		**Prices 2009**	
	Baseball	**Football**	**Baseball**	**Football**
Lower Deck	40	100	45	110
Mezzanine	27	85	30	92
Upper Deck	15	75	15	87

A Write a matrix that shows the changes in prices from 2008 to 2009.

B What can you conclude about the changes in ticket prices?

C Suppose stadium management plans to increase all prices by 10% from 2009 to 2010. Write and simplify a matrix expression that shows the planned 2010 ticket prices.

> **THINK ABOUT IT**
>
> As with real numbers, subtraction of matrices is not commutative.

Solution

A Subtract the 2008 matrix from the 2009 matrix.

$$\begin{bmatrix} 45 & 110 \\ 30 & 92 \\ 15 & 87 \end{bmatrix} - \begin{bmatrix} 40 & 100 \\ 27 & 85 \\ 15 & 75 \end{bmatrix} = \begin{bmatrix} 45-40 & 110-100 \\ 30-27 & 92-85 \\ 15-15 & 87-75 \end{bmatrix} = \begin{bmatrix} 5 & 10 \\ 3 & 7 \\ 0 & 12 \end{bmatrix}$$

B All ticket prices increased except for upper deck baseball seats, which remained the same.

C To find the result of a 10% increase, multiply the 2009 matrix by 1.10.

$$1.10 \begin{bmatrix} 45 & 110 \\ 30 & 92 \\ 15 & 87 \end{bmatrix} = \begin{bmatrix} 1.10 \cdot 45 & 1.10 \cdot 110 \\ 1.10 \cdot 30 & 1.10 \cdot 92 \\ 1.10 \cdot 15 & 1.10 \cdot 87 \end{bmatrix} = \begin{bmatrix} 49.50 & 121.00 \\ 33.50 & 101.20 \\ 16.50 & 95.70 \end{bmatrix}$$

The last matrix above shows the planned 2010 ticket prices. ■

Problem Set

Use the following matrices to perform each indicated operation.

$$A = \begin{bmatrix} -1 & 12 \\ 8 & 10 \end{bmatrix} \qquad B = \begin{bmatrix} 14 & 7 & 100 \\ 0 & -10 & 25 \end{bmatrix} \qquad C = \begin{bmatrix} 15 & -45 & 9 \\ 20 & -18 & 3 \end{bmatrix}$$

$$D = \begin{bmatrix} 72 & 15 & -9 \\ 4 & -25 & 30 \end{bmatrix} \qquad E = \begin{bmatrix} 35 & -20 \\ 8 & 3 \end{bmatrix} \qquad F = \begin{bmatrix} 1 & 12 & -90 \\ 14 & 7 & 82 \\ 12 & -11 & 0 \end{bmatrix}$$

$$G = \begin{bmatrix} 3 & 15 \\ -14 & 45 \end{bmatrix} \qquad H = \begin{bmatrix} 300 & -250 \\ -725 & 455 \end{bmatrix} \qquad J = \begin{bmatrix} 123 & -90 & 54 \\ 12 & -15 & 0 \end{bmatrix}$$

1.	$A + E$	9.	$4A$	17.	$G - E + A$
2.	$A + C$	10.	$6F$	18.	$J + B - C$
3.	$C - D$	11.	$-5B$	19.	$2G - E$
4.	$D + B$	12.	$10H$	20.	$D - 5B + C$
5.	$G - A$	13.	$9G$	21.	$F - 2C$
6.	$D - F$	14.	$11J$	22.	$2(G + E + 3G)$
7.	$B - D$	15.	$A + G + B$	23.	$J - H - 2J$
8.	$C + D$	16.	$C - B - D$	24.	$-3(C - D - D)$

Solve.

25. Verify the commutative property for the multiplication of any scalar r and any 2×2 matrix.

26. The matrices below show the number of hours high school students spend exercising at the local gym from Monday through Friday and on the weekends.

Hours of Exercise (Mon. – Fri.)

	Grades 9–10	Grades 11–12
Girls	750	1000
Boys	1000	1250

Hours of Exercise (Weekends)

	Grades 9–10	Grades 11–12
Girls	400	500
Boys	500	600

  A. Write a matrix that shows how many more hours the girls and boys in these grades exercise from Monday through Friday than on weekends.

  B. The gym challenges the girls and boys to double their number of hours of exercise on weekends. Write a matrix that shows the new total number of hours that the boys and girls in these grades exercise on weekends.

27. The matrices below show the number of children and adult basketball, football, and soccer fans in 2007 and 2008, according to a neighborhood survey.

2007 Survey

	Basketball	Football	Soccer
Adults	3180	2650	1090
Children	1053	743	675

2008 Survey

	Basketball	Football	Soccer
Adults	3975	3180	795
Children	1010	1215	270

  A. Write a matrix that shows the total number of adult and children fans of each sport for 2007 and 2008.

  B. Subtract the 2007 matrix from the 2008 matrix and explain what the resulting matrix represents.

28. The matrices below show the number of each of three bicycle models sold at three store locations for the years 2007 and 2008.

	Sales 2007		
	Model A	**Model B**	**Model C**
Downtown	740	152	893
West Side	623	915	1724
North Side	560	340	856

	Sales 2008		
	Model A	**Model B**	**Model C**
Downtown	980	345	654
West Side	852	1035	1924
North Side	652	255	978

A. Write a matrix that shows the changes in sales from 2007 to 2008.

B. Write a matrix that shows the total number of sales for each model at each store for 2007 and 2008.

*__29.__ **Challenge** What values of x and y make the equation true?

$$-2\begin{bmatrix} 1 & 7 \\ x & -4 \end{bmatrix} + \begin{bmatrix} y & 12 \\ -5 & x \end{bmatrix} = \begin{bmatrix} -3 & -2 \\ -13 & 12 \end{bmatrix}$$

*__30.__ **Challenge** Does the associative property hold for the subtraction of matrices? If not, provide a counterexample to show that the property does not hold.

Matrix Multiplication

You can multiply *any* matrix by a scalar, but you can multiply two matrices only when certain conditions are met.

Determining When Matrix Multiplication Is Possible

You can multiply matrix A by matrix B when the number of columns in matrix A is equal to the number of rows in matrix B. The product is a matrix with the same number of rows as matrix A and the same number of columns as matrix B.

Matrix A · Matrix B

4×2 2×3

The product exists because matrix A has 2 columns and matrix B has 2 rows.

The product has 4 rows and 3 columns.

Example 1 Let $A = \begin{bmatrix} 3 & 2 & 9 \\ -5 & 0 & -1 \end{bmatrix}$, $B = \begin{bmatrix} 5 \\ 11 \\ -7 \end{bmatrix}$, and $C = \begin{bmatrix} 14 & -8 \end{bmatrix}$.

Determine whether each product is possible. If so, give the dimensions of the product.

A AB

B AC

C BC

Solution

A Matrix A · Matrix B

     2×3 3×1

The product exists because the inner dimensions match. The product will have 2 rows and 1 column.

B Matrix A · Matrix C

     2×3 1×2

The product is not possible because the inner dimensions do not match.

C Matrix B · Matrix C

     3×1 1×2

The product exists because the inner dimensions match. The product will have 3 rows and 2 columns. ∎

If A is an $m \times n$ matrix and B is an $n \times p$ matrix, then AB is the $m \times p$ matrix C, where $c_{ij} = a_{i1}b_{1j} + a_{i2}b_{2j} + \ldots + a_{in}b_{nj}$.

In the product AB, each element is the sum of the products of the elements of a row in matrix A and the corresponding elements of a column in matrix B.

Here is an example of multiplying a 2×3 matrix by a 3×2 matrix:

$$A = \begin{bmatrix} a_{11} & a_{12} & a_{13} \\ a_{21} & a_{22} & a_{23} \end{bmatrix} \qquad B = \begin{bmatrix} b_{11} & b_{12} \\ b_{21} & b_{22} \\ b_{31} & b_{32} \end{bmatrix}$$

$$AB = \begin{bmatrix} a_{11} \cdot b_{11} + a_{12} \cdot b_{21} + a_{13} \cdot b_{31} & a_{11} \cdot b_{12} + a_{12} \cdot b_{22} + a_{13} \cdot b_{32} \\ a_{21} \cdot b_{11} + a_{22} \cdot b_{21} + a_{23} \cdot b_{31} & a_{21} \cdot b_{12} + a_{22} \cdot b_{22} + a_{23} \cdot b_{32} \end{bmatrix}.$$

Multiplying Matrices

Example 2   Let $A = \begin{bmatrix} 3 & 2 & 9 \\ -5 & 0 & -1 \end{bmatrix}$, $B = \begin{bmatrix} 5 \\ 11 \\ -7 \end{bmatrix}$, and $C = [14 \quad -8]$.

Find each product.

 AB

Solution   Matrix A ·   Matrix B
              2×3 3×1

The product is a 2×1 matrix. Set up an empty matrix for 2 rows and 1 column. To find $(ab)_{11}$, write the sum of the products of the elements in row 1 of matrix A and column 1 of matrix B.

$$AB = \begin{bmatrix} 3 & 2 & 9 \\ -5 & 0 & -1 \end{bmatrix} \cdot \begin{bmatrix} 5 \\ 11 \\ -7 \end{bmatrix} = \begin{bmatrix} 3 \cdot 5 + 2 \cdot 11 + 9 \cdot (-7) \\ \\ \end{bmatrix}$$

Find $(ab)_{21}$. Write the sum of the products of the elements in row 2 of matrix A and column 1 of matrix B.

$$AB = \begin{bmatrix} 3 & 2 & 9 \\ -5 & 0 & -1 \end{bmatrix} \cdot \begin{bmatrix} 5 \\ 11 \\ -7 \end{bmatrix} = \begin{bmatrix} 3 \cdot 5 + 2 \cdot 11 + 9 \cdot (-7) \\ -5 \cdot 5 + 0 \cdot 11 + -1 \cdot (-7) \end{bmatrix}$$

Simplify.

$$AB = \begin{bmatrix} 15 + 22 + (-63) \\ -25 + 0 + 7 \end{bmatrix} = \begin{bmatrix} -26 \\ -18 \end{bmatrix}. \blacksquare$$

B BC

Solution   Matrix B $\cdot$ Matrix C
$\qquad\qquad\;\; 3 \times 1 \qquad\quad 1 \times 2$

The product is a 3×2 matrix. Set up an empty matrix for 3 rows and 2 columns. To find $(bc)_{ij}$, write the sum of the products of the elements in row i of matrix B and column j of matrix C.

$$BC = \begin{bmatrix} 5 \\ 11 \\ -7 \end{bmatrix} \cdot [14 \quad -8] = \begin{bmatrix} 5 \cdot 14 & 5 \cdot (-8) \\ 11 \cdot 14 & 11 \cdot (-8) \\ -7 \cdot 14 & -7 \cdot (-8) \end{bmatrix}$$

Simplify.

$$BC = \begin{bmatrix} 70 & -40 \\ 154 & -88 \\ -98 & 56 \end{bmatrix} \;\blacksquare$$

Verifying that Matrix Multiplication Is Not Commutative

Unlike scalar multiplication, matrix multiplication is not commutative.

Example 3   Let $A = \begin{bmatrix} 5 & 6 \\ 3 & -8 \end{bmatrix}$ and $B = \begin{bmatrix} -9 & 10 \\ 0 & 7 \end{bmatrix}$. Show that $AB \neq BA$.

Solution   Both matrices are 2×2 matrices, so both AB and BA exist and are also 2×2 matrices.

Find AB.

$$AB = \begin{bmatrix} 5 & 6 \\ 3 & -8 \end{bmatrix} \cdot \begin{bmatrix} -9 & 10 \\ 0 & 7 \end{bmatrix} = \begin{bmatrix} 5 \cdot (-9) + 6 \cdot 0 & 5 \cdot 10 + 6 \cdot 7 \\ 3 \cdot (-9) + (-8) \cdot 0 & 3 \cdot 10 + (-8) \cdot 7 \end{bmatrix}$$

$$= \begin{bmatrix} -45 & 92 \\ -27 & -26 \end{bmatrix}$$

> **THINK ABOUT IT**
>
> For some matrices *A* and *B*, *AB* exists and *BA* does not exist.

Find BA.

$$BA = \begin{bmatrix} -9 & 10 \\ 0 & 7 \end{bmatrix} \cdot \begin{bmatrix} 5 & 6 \\ 3 & -8 \end{bmatrix} = \begin{bmatrix} -9 \cdot 5 + 10 \cdot 3 & -9 \cdot 6 + 10 \cdot (-8) \\ 0 \cdot 5 + 7 \cdot 3 & 0 \cdot 6 + 7 \cdot (-8) \end{bmatrix}$$

$$= \begin{bmatrix} -15 & -134 \\ 21 & -56 \end{bmatrix}$$

The elements in the corresponding locations in AB and BA are not the same. Since the matrices are different, $AB \neq BA$. $\blacksquare$

Left-multiplying means that a matrix should be multiplied on the left of a given matrix. Right-multiplying means that a matrix should be multiplied on the right of a given matrix. It is important to indicate when left- or right-multiplying since matrix multiplication is not commutative.

Solving a Real-World Problem by Multiplying Matrices

Example 4   Three locations of Sleep 'n' Comfort carry the same two sleeping bags. The retail cost (in dollars) of each bag is shown in the first matrix, and the inventory for each store is shown in the second.

$$\begin{array}{cc} & \textbf{20°F Bag} \quad \textbf{40°F Bag} \\ \textbf{Cost} & [215 \qquad\quad 165] \end{array}$$

$$\begin{array}{c} \\ \textbf{20°F Bag} \\ \textbf{40°F Bag} \end{array} \begin{array}{ccc} \textbf{East} & \textbf{West} & \textbf{North} \\ \begin{bmatrix} 26 & 15 & 30 \\ 54 & 29 & 51 \end{bmatrix} \end{array}$$

A Multiply the matrices.

B Which store has the greatest dollar value of sleeping bags in its inventory and what is this value?

C What does the product of the matrices tell you?

Solution

A Multiply the matrices. Since the cost matrix is 1×2 and the inventory matrix is 2×3, the product matrix is a 1×3 matrix.

$$[215 \quad 165] \cdot \begin{bmatrix} 26 & 15 & 30 \\ 54 & 29 & 51 \end{bmatrix} = [215 \cdot 26 + 165 \cdot 54 \quad 215 \cdot 15 + 165 \cdot 29 \quad 215 \cdot 30 + 165 \cdot 51]$$

$$= [14{,}500 \quad 8010 \quad 14{,}865]$$

B The North location has the greatest inventory, valued at $14,865.

C The product indicates the total cost of all bags at each store. ■

Problem Set

Problems 1–22 are based on the matrices given below.

$$A = \begin{bmatrix} 1 & 2 \\ 8 & 0 \end{bmatrix} \qquad\qquad B = \begin{bmatrix} 4 & 7 & 0 \\ 0 & -10 & 2 \end{bmatrix} \qquad\qquad C = \begin{bmatrix} 1 & 4 \\ -2 & 3 \\ 7 & 10 \end{bmatrix}$$

$$D = \begin{bmatrix} 11 & -5 & -9 \\ 4 & -2 & 30 \end{bmatrix} \qquad E = \begin{bmatrix} 0 \\ 1 \\ 1 \\ -1 \end{bmatrix} \qquad F = \begin{bmatrix} 1 & 2 & -9 \\ 4 & 7 & -8 \\ -2 & -11 & 0 \end{bmatrix}$$

$$G = \begin{bmatrix} 3 & -7 \\ -1 & 1 \end{bmatrix} \qquad H = \begin{bmatrix} 1 & 11 & -2 & -1 \\ 3 & 10 & 2 & 7 \end{bmatrix} \qquad J = \begin{bmatrix} 6 & -2 & 3 \\ 12 & -1 & 0 \end{bmatrix}$$

Write the dimensions of each product. If the product cannot be performed, write *not possible*.

1. *AB*
2. *FC*
3. *BC*

4. *CF*
5. *HE*
6. *CB*

7. *GH*
8. *DF*
9. *JF*

Find the product.

10. *CG*
11. *HE*
12. *BF*

13. *AG*
14. *DC*
15. *JF*

16. *CA*
17. *GH*
18. *DF*

Simplify.

19. *AD + GJ*
20. *DF − BF*

21. *3GA*
22. *2AG + DC*

Solve.

23. Let $A = \begin{bmatrix} -1 & 5 \\ 0 & -4 \end{bmatrix}$ and $B = \begin{bmatrix} -5 & 10 \\ 0 & 2 \end{bmatrix}$. Show $AB \neq BA$.

24. Victor, Simon, and Anya sell boxes of cookies and boxes of brownies at a charity bake sale. The cost (in dollars) of each box is shown in the first matrix, and the number of boxes each person sold is shown in the second.

	Cookies	Brownies
Cost	[5.25	6.50]

	Victor	Simon	Anya
Cookies	62	69	84
Brownies	45	42	30

   A. Multiply the matrices.

   B. Who raised the most money for charity?

   C. How much did he or she raise?

   D. What does the product of the matrices tell you?

25. Eagle Airways sells three types of tickets: economy, business, and first class. The cost (in dollars) of each ticket is shown in the first matrix. The second matrix shows the number of each ticket sold on Monday, Tuesday, and Wednesday.

	Economy	Business	First-Class
Cost	[900	1650	2200]

	Mon.	Tues.	Wed.
Economy	644	756	720
Business	200	300	252
First Class	175	197	245

   A. On which day was the greatest number of tickets sold?

   B. On which day was the greatest amount of money made? How much money was made that day?

26. Carolina wants to knit a sweater. The sweater requires three types of yarn: angora, mohair, and silk. The matrices show the number of skeins of each type of yarn needed and the cost of the yarn at three yarn stores.

	Number
Angora	3
Mohair	8
Silk	2

	Angora	Mohair	Silk
Store 1	8.50	7.75	11.95
Store 2	8.75	7.25	12.50
Store 3	7.95	8.25	11.25

A. If Carolina wants to spend as little money as possible for the sweater, where should she buy each type of yarn?

B. How much would she spend altogether?

27. The table shows the number of field goals, touchdowns, extra points, and safeties scored by two football teams during a game. Each field goal is worth 3 points. Each touchdown is worth 6 points. Each extra point is worth 1 point, and each safety is worth 2 points.

Scoring		
Type of Score	**Number for Team 1**	**Number for Team 2**
Field Goal	3	1
Touchdown	2	2
Extra Point	2	1
Safety	1	0

A. Organize the data by using two matrices. Let the first matrix show the number of points each type of score is worth. Let the second matrix show the number of each type scored by the teams, where each team is listed in a separate column.

B. Find the final score of the football game.

*28. Challenge Let $A = \begin{bmatrix} a & b \\ c & d \end{bmatrix}$, $B = \begin{bmatrix} d & e \\ f & g \end{bmatrix}$, and r be a scalar. Show $k(AB) = (kA)B$.

*29. Challenge Find two matrices A and B where $AB = BA$, $A \neq B$. What do you notice about the dimensions of A and B?

Transforming Points and Figures

You can use both scalar multiplication and matrix multiplication to transform points and figures on the coordinate plane.

For example, you can write the coordinates of a single point in a 2×1 matrix, with the x-coordinate in the first row and the y-coordinate in the second row:

$$(x, y) \rightarrow \begin{bmatrix} x \\ y \end{bmatrix}.$$

Because each column represents a point, a set of three points forms a 2×3 matrix. The matrix below shows the vertices for the given triangle.

$$\begin{bmatrix} -3 & 4 & 1 \\ 2 & 5 & -1 \end{bmatrix}$$

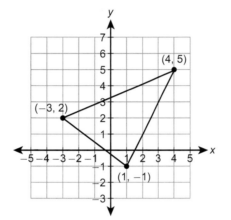

Scaling a Figure by a Single Scale Factor

To *scale* a figure is to enlarge or reduce it. If the image is similar to the preimage, the transformation is a *dilation*.

DILATING A FIGURE BY A SINGLE SCALE FACTOR

Multiplying a matrix containing coordinates of a preimage by the scale factor s gives a matrix that contains the coordinates of the scaled figure.

Here is an example with the vertices of a triangle:

$$s \cdot \begin{bmatrix} x_1 & x_2 & x_3 \\ y_1 & y_2 & y_3 \end{bmatrix} = \begin{bmatrix} sx_1 & sx_2 & sx_3 \\ sy_1 & sy_2 & sy_3 \end{bmatrix}$$

Vertices of Preimage — Vertices of Image

Example 1   The vertices of a quadrilateral are $(-2, 3)$, $(4, 2)$, $(4, -1)$, and $(-3, -2)$. Find the coordinates of the vertices after a dilation by a scale factor of 2.

Solution Write the preimage points in a matrix and multiply the matrix by 2.

$$2 \cdot \begin{bmatrix} -2 & 4 & 4 & -3 \\ 3 & 2 & -1 & -2 \end{bmatrix} = \begin{bmatrix} -4 & 8 & 8 & -6 \\ 6 & 4 & -2 & -4 \end{bmatrix}$$

The image points are $(-4, 6)$, $(8, 4)$, $(8, -2)$, and $(-6, -4)$. The image is graphed in red. ∎

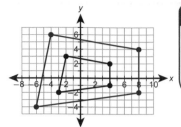

TIP

You can check your work by graphing the preimage and image figures.

Scaling Each Dimension of a Figure by a Different Scale Factor

Some real-life applications require multiplying each dimension of a figure by a different scale factor. For example, the vertical dimension of the figure may be tripled, while the horizontal dimension is halved.

THINK ABOUT IT

These transformations are *not* dilations because the images are *not* similar to the preimages.

DILATING A FIGURE BY MULTIPLE SCALE FACTORS

To scale each dimension by a different scale factor, multiply the coordinate matrix by a 2 × 2 matrix instead of by a scalar. The main diagonal of the matrix contains the scale factors and the other elements are zero.

If s_x is the horizontal scale factor and s_y is the vertical scale factor, then the image of a triangle is given by

$$\begin{bmatrix} s_x & 0 \\ 0 & s_y \end{bmatrix} \cdot \begin{bmatrix} x_1 & x_2 & x_3 \\ y_1 & y_2 & y_3 \end{bmatrix} = \begin{bmatrix} s_x \cdot x_1 + 0 & s_x \cdot x_2 + 0 & s_x \cdot x_3 + 0 \\ 0 + s_y \cdot y_1 & 0 + s_y \cdot y_2 & 0 + s_y \cdot y_3 \end{bmatrix}$$

$$= \begin{bmatrix} s_x \cdot x_1 & s_x \cdot x_2 & s_x \cdot x_3 \\ s_y \cdot y_1 & s_y \cdot y_2 & s_y \cdot y_3 \end{bmatrix}$$

Example 2 The vertices of a triangle are $(-4, 1)$, $(2, 1)$, and $(0, -3)$. Find the coordinates of the vertices after it is scaled horizontally by $\frac{1}{2}$ and vertically by 3.

Solution Use $s_x = \frac{1}{2}$ and $s_y = 3$.

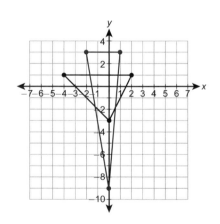

$$\begin{bmatrix} \frac{1}{2} & 0 \\ 0 & 3 \end{bmatrix} \cdot \begin{bmatrix} -4 & 2 & 0 \\ 1 & 1 & -3 \end{bmatrix} = \begin{bmatrix} \frac{1}{2} \cdot (-4) + 0 \cdot 1 & \frac{1}{2} \cdot 2 + 0 \cdot 1 & \frac{1}{2} \cdot 0 + 0 \cdot (-3) \\ 0 \cdot (-4) + 3 \cdot 1 & 0 \cdot 2 + 3 \cdot 1 & 0 \cdot 0 + 3 \cdot (-3) \end{bmatrix}$$

$$= \begin{bmatrix} -2 & 1 & 0 \\ 3 & 3 & -9 \end{bmatrix}$$

The image points are $(-2, 3)$, $(1, 3)$, and $(0, -9)$. ∎

Translating a Point

If a point (x, y) is translated t_x units horizontally and t_y units vertically, then the image point is given by

$$\begin{bmatrix} 1 & 0 & t_x \\ 0 & 1 & t_y \\ 0 & 0 & 1 \end{bmatrix} \cdot \begin{bmatrix} x \\ y \\ 1 \end{bmatrix} = \begin{bmatrix} 1 \cdot x + 0 \cdot y + t_x \cdot 1 \\ 0 \cdot x + 1 \cdot y + t_y \cdot 1 \\ 0 \cdot x + 0 \cdot y + 1 \cdot 1 \end{bmatrix} = \begin{bmatrix} x + t_x \\ y + t_y \\ 1 \end{bmatrix}$$

Notice that the preimage and image points are written as 3×1 vectors, where the element in the third row is 1. These are called *augmented vectors*. The image point is $(x + t_x, y + t_y)$.

Example 3   The coordinates of a point are $(-2, 9)$. Use augmented vectors to translate the point 7 units to the right and 3 units down.

Solution   Use $t_x = 7$ and $t_y = -3$.

$$\begin{bmatrix} 1 & 0 & 7 \\ 0 & 1 & -3 \\ 0 & 0 & 1 \end{bmatrix} \cdot \begin{bmatrix} -2 \\ 9 \\ 1 \end{bmatrix} = \begin{bmatrix} -2 + 7 \\ 9 + (-3) \\ 1 \end{bmatrix} = \begin{bmatrix} 5 \\ 6 \\ 1 \end{bmatrix}$$

The image point is $(5, 6)$. ∎

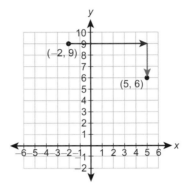

Translating a Figure

TRANSLATING A FIGURE

The formula for translating a point extends to translating a figure. For example, if (x_1, y_1), (x_2, y_2), and (x_3, y_3) are the vertices of a figure that is translated t_x units horizontally and t_y units vertically, then the vertices of the image points are given by:

$$\begin{bmatrix} 1 & 0 & t_x \\ 0 & 1 & t_y \\ 0 & 0 & 1 \end{bmatrix} \cdot \begin{bmatrix} x_1 & x_2 & x_3 \\ y_1 & y_2 & y_3 \\ 1 & 1 & 1 \end{bmatrix} = \begin{bmatrix} x_1 + t_x & x_2 + t_x & x_3 + t_x \\ y_1 + t_y & y_2 + t_y & y_3 + t_y \\ 1 & 1 & 1 \end{bmatrix}.$$

This works for any number of points. Just add as many columns to the second matrix as you need.

Example 4   The vertices of a triangle are $(-4, -1)$, $(-4, -3)$, and $(8, 2)$.
Use augmented vectors to translate the triangle 2 units left and 6 units up.

Solution   Use $t_x = -2$ and $t_y = 6$.

$$\begin{bmatrix} 1 & 0 & -2 \\ 0 & 1 & 6 \\ 0 & 0 & 1 \end{bmatrix} \cdot \begin{bmatrix} -4 & -4 & 8 \\ -1 & -3 & 2 \\ 1 & 1 & 1 \end{bmatrix} = \begin{bmatrix} -4+(-2) & -4+(-2) & 8+(-2) \\ -1+6 & -3+6 & 2+6 \\ 1 & 1 & 1 \end{bmatrix} = \begin{bmatrix} -6 & -6 & 6 \\ 5 & 3 & 8 \\ 1 & 1 & 1 \end{bmatrix}$$

The image points are $(-6, 5)$, $(-6, 3)$, and $(6, 8)$. ∎

Reflecting and Rotating Points and Figures

To reflect a point (x, y) across the x-axis, y-axis, or the line $y = x$, multiply
as shown.

Across the x-axis	Across the y-axis	Across the line y = x
$\begin{bmatrix} 1 & 0 \\ 0 & -1 \end{bmatrix} \cdot \begin{bmatrix} x \\ y \end{bmatrix} = \begin{bmatrix} x \\ -y \end{bmatrix}$	$\begin{bmatrix} -1 & 0 \\ 0 & 1 \end{bmatrix} \cdot \begin{bmatrix} x \\ y \end{bmatrix} = \begin{bmatrix} -x \\ y \end{bmatrix}$	$\begin{bmatrix} 0 & 1 \\ 1 & 0 \end{bmatrix} \cdot \begin{bmatrix} x \\ y \end{bmatrix} = \begin{bmatrix} y \\ x \end{bmatrix}$

To reflect a figure, add columns to the second matrix as needed for
additional points.

Use the following rules to rotate a point.

90° Clockwise	90° Counterclockwise	180°
$\begin{bmatrix} 0 & 1 \\ -1 & 0 \end{bmatrix} \cdot \begin{bmatrix} x \\ y \end{bmatrix} = \begin{bmatrix} y \\ -x \end{bmatrix}$	$\begin{bmatrix} 0 & -1 \\ 1 & 0 \end{bmatrix} \cdot \begin{bmatrix} x \\ y \end{bmatrix} = \begin{bmatrix} -y \\ x \end{bmatrix}$	$\begin{bmatrix} -1 & 0 \\ 0 & -1 \end{bmatrix} \cdot \begin{bmatrix} x \\ y \end{bmatrix} = \begin{bmatrix} -x \\ -y \end{bmatrix}$

To rotate a figure, add columns to the second matrix as needed.

Example 5   The vertices of a quadrilateral are $(-1, 8)$, $(-2, -3)$, $(4, 3)$,
and $(6, -5)$. Perform each transformation.

A reflection across the y-axis

B 90° clockwise rotation

Solution

A $\begin{bmatrix} -1 & 0 \\ 0 & 1 \end{bmatrix} \cdot \begin{bmatrix} -1 & -2 & 4 & 6 \\ 8 & -3 & 3 & -5 \end{bmatrix} = \begin{bmatrix} 1 & 2 & -4 & -6 \\ 8 & -3 & 3 & -5 \end{bmatrix}$

The image points are $(1, 8)$ $(2, -3)$, $(-4, 3)$, and $(-6, -5)$.

B $\begin{bmatrix} 0 & 1 \\ -1 & 0 \end{bmatrix} \cdot \begin{bmatrix} -1 & -2 & 4 & 6 \\ 8 & -3 & 3 & -5 \end{bmatrix} = \begin{bmatrix} 8 & -3 & 3 & -5 \\ 1 & 2 & -4 & -6 \end{bmatrix}$

The image points are $(8, 1)$, $(-3, 2)$, $(3, -4)$, and $(-5, -6)$. ∎

Describing a Transformation, Given a Matrix Product

Example 6 Describe the transformation represented by each product.

A $\begin{bmatrix} 1 & 0 & -3 \\ 0 & 1 & -7 \\ 0 & 0 & 1 \end{bmatrix} \cdot \begin{bmatrix} x_1 & x_2 \\ y_1 & y_2 \\ 1 & 1 \end{bmatrix}$

Solution The matrix on the right has two points, so the figure being transformed is a segment. The matrix on the left is a translation matrix for sliding the figure 3 units left and 7 units down.

$$\begin{bmatrix} 1 & 0 & -3 \\ 0 & 1 & -7 \\ 0 & 0 & 1 \end{bmatrix} \cdot \begin{bmatrix} x_1 & x_2 \\ y_1 & y_2 \\ 1 & 1 \end{bmatrix} = \begin{bmatrix} 1 \cdot x_1 + 0 \cdot y_1 + (-3) \cdot 1 & 1 \cdot x_2 + 0 \cdot y_2 + (-3) \cdot 1 \\ 0 \cdot x_1 + 1 \cdot y_1 + (-7) \cdot 1 & 0 \cdot x_2 + 1 \cdot y_2 + (-7) \cdot 1 \\ 0 \cdot x_1 + 0 \cdot y_1 + 1 \cdot 1 & 0 \cdot x_2 + 0 \cdot y_2 + 1 \cdot 1 \end{bmatrix}$$

$$= \begin{bmatrix} x_1 - 3 & x_2 - 3 \\ y_1 - 7 & y_2 - 7 \\ 1 & 1 \end{bmatrix} \blacksquare$$

B $\begin{bmatrix} 0 & 3 \\ 3 & 0 \end{bmatrix} \cdot \begin{bmatrix} x_1 & x_2 & x_3 \\ y_1 & y_2 & y_3 \end{bmatrix}$

Solution The matrix on the right has three points, so the figure being transformed is a triangle. The matrix on the left is equivalent to $3 \cdot \begin{bmatrix} 0 & 1 \\ 1 & 0 \end{bmatrix}$, so the triangle is dilated by a scale factor of 3 and reflected across the line $y = x$. $\blacksquare$

> **THINK ABOUT IT**
>
> Matrix multiplication can be used to transform a figure in more than one way with a single product.

Problem Set

For each problem, do the following:

A. Write a matrix expression to represent the transformation.
B. Evaluate the matrix expression to find the coordinates of the vertices of the transformed figure.

1. a triangle with vertices $(1, 5)$, $(2, 8)$, and $(6, 2)$, using a scale factor of 3

2. a quadrilateral with vertices $(-3, -4)$, $(-3, 5)$, $(2, 5)$, and $(2, -4)$, using a scale factor of 2

3. a quadrilateral with vertices $(0, 8)$, $(8, 0)$, $(0, -8)$, and $(-8, 0)$, using a scale factor of $\frac{1}{4}$

4. a triangle with vertices $(2, -4)$, $(-1, -5)$, and $(1, 3)$, using a scale factor of $\frac{1}{2}$

5. a triangle with vertices $(-1, 4)$, $(2, 7)$, and $(4, -4)$, scaled horizontally by 2 and vertically by 3

6. a quadrilateral with vertices $(-3, 1)$, $(3, 1)$, $(3, -1)$, and $(-3, -1)$, scaled horizontally by $\frac{1}{2}$ and vertically by 3

7. a hexagon with vertices $(-1, 2)$, $(2, 2)$, $(4, 0)$, $(2, -2)$, $(-1, -2)$, and $(-4, 0)$, scaled horizontally by 5 and vertically by $\frac{1}{2}$

8. a triangle with vertices $(-8, 1)$, $(-1, 1)$, and $(-1, 10)$, scaled horizontally by 2 and vertically by $\frac{1}{5}$

For each problem, do the following:

A. Use augmented matrices to write a matrix expression to represent the translation.
B. Evaluate the matrix expression to find the coordinates of the translated point.

9. $(2, 0)$; 5 units right and 2 units up

10. $(-4, -8)$; 7 units left and 8 units up

11. $(-12, 0)$; 5 units left and 4 units down

12. $(7, -10)$; 1 unit right and 0 units up

13. $(12, 9)$; 6 units left and 5 units down

14. $(5, -3)$; 9 units right and 14 units down

For each problem, do the following:

A. Use augmented matrices to write a matrix expression to represent the translation.
B. Evaluate the matrix expression to find the coordinates of the vertices of the transformed figure.

15. a triangle with vertices $(1, 9)$, $(2, 4)$, and $(3, -3)$, translated 4 units to the left and 2 units down

16. a quadrilateral with vertices $(1, 2)$, $(1, -1)$, $(5, -3)$, and $(-3, 2)$, translated 3 units to the right and 1 unit up

17. a triangle with vertices $(2, 0)$, $(5, -10)$, and $(-1, -4)$, translated 6 units to the right and 7 units down

18. a hexagon with vertices $(3, 4)$, $(8, 4)$, $(10, 9)$, $(10, 13)$, $(6, 14)$, and $(4, 11)$, translated 5 units to the right and 4 units up

19. a quadrilateral with vertices $(-9, -8)$, $(-4, -10)$, $(-4, 12)$, and $(10, 2)$, translated 9 units left and 6 units down

20. a pentagon with vertices $(-2, 6)$, $(-4, 3)$, $(-2, -2)$, $(3, 1)$, and $(4, 5)$, translated 6 units right and 10 units down

For each problem, do the following:

A. Use augmented matrices to write a matrix expression to represent the reflection or rotation.
B. Evaluate the matrix expression to find the coordinates of the vertices of the transformed figure.

21. a triangle with vertices $(1, 8)$, $(5, 6)$, and $(3, -4)$, reflected across the x-axis

22. a triangle with vertices $(0, 0)$, $(9, 0)$, and $(0, -10)$, rotated $180°$

23. a quadrilateral with vertices $(1, 2)$, $(4, -1)$, $(-3, -5)$, and $(-6, 2)$, rotated $90°$ counterclockwise

24. a triangle with vertices $(10, 2)$, $(-3, 7)$, and $(10, 8)$, reflected across the y-axis

25. a quadrilateral with vertices $(4, 7)$, $(-2, 9)$, $(-5, -10)$, and $(5, 0)$, rotated $90°$ clockwise

Describe the transformation represented by each product.

26. $\begin{bmatrix} 0 & 1 \\ -1 & 0 \end{bmatrix} \cdot \begin{bmatrix} 1 & 4 & -7 \\ 3 & 2 & 0 \end{bmatrix}$

27. $5 \cdot \begin{bmatrix} 9 & 1 & -2 & -3 \\ 4 & -5 & 8 & -7 \end{bmatrix}$

28. $\begin{bmatrix} 1 & 0 & -3 \\ 0 & 1 & -2 \\ 0 & 0 & 1 \end{bmatrix} \cdot \begin{bmatrix} 8 \\ 1 \\ 1 \end{bmatrix}$

Describe the transformation represented by each product. Then draw the preimage and image on a coordinate plane.

*29. Challenge $\begin{bmatrix} 0 & -\frac{1}{2} \\ \frac{1}{2} & 0 \end{bmatrix} \cdot \begin{bmatrix} -1 & 2 & -4 & 5 \\ -3 & -5 & 3 & 1 \end{bmatrix}$

*30. Challenge $\begin{bmatrix} 4 & 0 \\ 0 & -2 \end{bmatrix} \cdot \begin{bmatrix} 2 & 8 \\ 0 & -12 \end{bmatrix}$

Determinants and Cramer's Rule

Determinants can help you solve systems of equations.

Finding the Determinant of a 2 × 2 Matrix

DEFINITIONS

If a matrix has the same number of rows and columns, it is called an $n \times n$ matrix or a **square matrix**. Every square matrix has a value called a **determinant**.

If matrix $A = \begin{bmatrix} a & b \\ c & d \end{bmatrix}$, then the determinant of matrix A equals $ad - cb$.

That is, $\det A = \begin{vmatrix} a & b \\ c & d \end{vmatrix} = ad - cb$.

NOTATION

Brackets indicate a matrix, and vertical lines indicate a determinant.

Example 1 Find the determinant of each matrix.

A $\begin{bmatrix} 6 & 3 \\ 5 & 2 \end{bmatrix}$

B $\begin{bmatrix} 7 & -4 \\ -6 & 5 \end{bmatrix}$

Solution

$$\det \begin{bmatrix} 6 & 3 \\ 5 & 2 \end{bmatrix} = \begin{vmatrix} 6 & 3 \\ 5 & 2 \end{vmatrix}$$
$$= ad - cb$$
$$= 6 \cdot 2 - 5 \cdot 3$$
$$= 12 - 15 = -3 \ \blacksquare$$

Solution

$$\det \begin{bmatrix} 7 & -4 \\ -6 & 5 \end{bmatrix} = \begin{vmatrix} 7 & -4 \\ -6 & 5 \end{vmatrix}$$
$$= ad - cb$$
$$= 7 \cdot 5 - (-6) \cdot (-4)$$
$$= 35 - 24 = 11 \ \blacksquare$$

TIP

Follow the pattern below to be sure you are subtracting the products of the diagonals in the correct order.

Finding the Determinant of a 3 × 3 Matrix

Now that you know how to find the determinant of a 2 × 2 matrix, you can use the formula to find the determinant of a 3 × 3 matrix.

DEFINITION

If matrix $A = \begin{bmatrix} a & b & c \\ d & e & f \\ g & h & i \end{bmatrix}$, then

$$\det A = \begin{vmatrix} a & b & c \\ d & e & f \\ g & h & i \end{vmatrix} = a\begin{vmatrix} e & f \\ h & i \end{vmatrix} - b\begin{vmatrix} d & f \\ g & i \end{vmatrix} + c\begin{vmatrix} d & e \\ g & h \end{vmatrix}.$$

TIP

The elements in each 2 × 2 matrix of the determinant are the elements in rows 2 and 3 from matrix A that are not in the same column as the element the 2 × 2 matrix is being multiplied by.

Example 2 Find the determinant of $\begin{bmatrix} 1 & 5 & -4 \\ -3 & 2 & 1 \\ 3 & 2 & -1 \end{bmatrix}$.

TIP

Notice that the signs on the products of the 2 × 2 determinants alternate.

Solution

$$\det \begin{bmatrix} 1 & 5 & -4 \\ -3 & 2 & 1 \\ 3 & 2 & -1 \end{bmatrix} = 1\begin{vmatrix} 2 & 1 \\ 2 & -1 \end{vmatrix} - 5\begin{vmatrix} -3 & 1 \\ 3 & -1 \end{vmatrix} + (-4)\begin{vmatrix} -3 & 2 \\ 3 & 2 \end{vmatrix}$$

$$= 1[2 \cdot (-1) - 2 \cdot 1] - 5[-3 \cdot (-1) - 3 \cdot 1] - 4(-3 \cdot 2 - 3 \cdot 2)$$

$$= 1 \cdot (-4) - 5 \cdot 0 - 4 \cdot (-12)$$

$$= -4 - 0 + 48$$

$$= 44 \ \blacksquare$$

Using Cramer's Rule to Solve a System of Two Equations

Using Cramer's rule, you can solve systems of equations by using determinants of matrices. Cramer's rule uses the coefficient matrix of the system, which is the matrix formed by the coefficients of the variables when the equation is written in standard form.

REMEMBER

The standard form of a linear equation is $ax + by = c$.

System of Equations	Coefficient Matrix	Constant Vector
$\begin{cases} 2x + 3y = 16 \\ 5x - 4y = -14 \end{cases}$	$\begin{bmatrix} 2 & 3 \\ 5 & -4 \end{bmatrix}$	$\begin{bmatrix} 16 \\ -14 \end{bmatrix}$

The solution of the system $\begin{cases} a_1x + b_1y = c_1 \\ a_2x + b_2y = c_2 \end{cases}$ is the ordered pair (x, y),

where $x = \dfrac{\begin{vmatrix} c_1 & b_1 \\ c_2 & b_2 \end{vmatrix}}{\det M}$, $y = \dfrac{\begin{vmatrix} a_1 & c_1 \\ a_2 & c_2 \end{vmatrix}}{\det M}$, and M is the coefficient matrix $\begin{bmatrix} a_1 & b_1 \\ a_2 & b_2 \end{bmatrix}$.

TIP

The numerator for each variable is the determinant of the coefficient matrix with that variable's column replaced by the constant vector.

Example 3   Use Cramer's rule to solve $\begin{cases} 3x - y = -11 \\ 2x + 2y = 6 \end{cases}$.

Solution

Step 1   Find the determinant of the coefficient matrix $\begin{bmatrix} 3 & -1 \\ 2 & 2 \end{bmatrix}$.

$$
\begin{aligned}
\det M &= \begin{vmatrix} 3 & -1 \\ 2 & 2 \end{vmatrix} \\
&= 3 \cdot 2 - 2 \cdot (-1) \\
&= 6 - (-2) \\
&= 8
\end{aligned}
$$

Step 2   Find x and y. Substitute 8 for $\det M$, -11 for c_1, and 6 for c_2.

$$
\begin{aligned}
x &= \frac{\begin{vmatrix} c_1 & b_1 \\ c_2 & b_2 \end{vmatrix}}{\det M} \\
&= \frac{\begin{vmatrix} -11 & -1 \\ 6 & 2 \end{vmatrix}}{8} \\
&= \frac{-11 \cdot 2 - 6 \cdot (-1)}{8} \\
&= -2
\end{aligned}
\qquad
\begin{aligned}
y &= \frac{\begin{vmatrix} a_1 & c_1 \\ a_2 & c_2 \end{vmatrix}}{\det M} \\
&= \frac{\begin{vmatrix} 3 & -11 \\ 2 & 6 \end{vmatrix}}{8} \\
&= \frac{3 \cdot 6 - 2 \cdot (-11)}{8} \\
&= 5
\end{aligned}
$$

Step 3   Write the solution as an ordered pair. The solution is $(-2, 5)$. ■

Using Cramer's Rule to Solve a System of Three Equations

You can extend Cramer's rule to solve a system of three equations.

CRAMER'S RULE FOR A SYSTEM OF THREE EQUATIONS

The solution of the system $\begin{cases} a_1x + b_1y + c_1z = d_1 \\ a_2x + b_2y + c_2z = d_2 \\ a_3x + b_3y + c_3z = d_3 \end{cases}$ is the ordered triple (x, y, z),

where $x = \dfrac{\begin{vmatrix} d_1 & b_1 & c_1 \\ d_2 & b_2 & c_2 \\ d_3 & b_3 & c_3 \end{vmatrix}}{\det M}$, $y = \dfrac{\begin{vmatrix} a_1 & d_1 & c_1 \\ a_2 & d_2 & c_2 \\ a_3 & d_3 & c_3 \end{vmatrix}}{\det M}$, $z = \dfrac{\begin{vmatrix} a_1 & b_1 & d_1 \\ a_2 & b_2 & d_2 \\ a_3 & b_3 & d_3 \end{vmatrix}}{\det M}$, and M is

the coefficient matrix $\begin{bmatrix} a_1 & b_1 & c_1 \\ a_2 & b_2 & c_2 \\ a_3 & b_3 & c_3 \end{bmatrix}$.

Example 4 Use Cramer's rule to solve $\begin{cases} -x + y - 2z = 2 \\ 2x + 5y - z = 13 \\ 2x - 4y + 3z = -4 \end{cases}$.

Solution

Step 1 Find the determinant of the coefficient matrix.

$\det M = \begin{vmatrix} -1 & 1 & -2 \\ 2 & 5 & -1 \\ 2 & -4 & 3 \end{vmatrix} = -1\begin{vmatrix} 5 & -1 \\ -4 & 3 \end{vmatrix} - 1\begin{vmatrix} 2 & -1 \\ 2 & 3 \end{vmatrix} + (-2)\begin{vmatrix} 2 & 5 \\ 2 & -4 \end{vmatrix}$

$= -1 \cdot 11 - 1 \cdot 8 - 2 \cdot (-18) = 17$

Step 2 Find x, y, and z.

Replace the x-coefficients with the constant vector.

$x = \dfrac{\begin{vmatrix} 2 & 1 & -2 \\ 13 & 5 & -1 \\ -4 & -4 & 3 \end{vmatrix}}{17} = \dfrac{2\begin{vmatrix} 5 & -1 \\ -4 & 3 \end{vmatrix} - 1\begin{vmatrix} 13 & -1 \\ -4 & 3 \end{vmatrix} + (-2)\begin{vmatrix} 13 & 5 \\ -4 & -4 \end{vmatrix}}{17}$

$= \dfrac{2 \cdot 11 - 1 \cdot 35 - 2 \cdot (-32)}{17} = 3$

Replace the y-coefficients with the constant vector.

$y = \dfrac{\begin{vmatrix} -1 & 2 & -2 \\ 2 & 13 & -1 \\ 2 & -4 & 3 \end{vmatrix}}{17} = \dfrac{-1\begin{vmatrix} 13 & -1 \\ -4 & 3 \end{vmatrix} - 2\begin{vmatrix} 2 & -1 \\ 2 & 3 \end{vmatrix} - 2\begin{vmatrix} 2 & 13 \\ 2 & -4 \end{vmatrix}}{17}$

$= \dfrac{-1 \cdot 35 - 2 \cdot 8 - 2 \cdot (-34)}{17} = 1$

Replace the z-coefficients with the constant vector.

$$z = \frac{\begin{vmatrix} -1 & 1 & 2 \\ 2 & 5 & 13 \\ 2 & -4 & -4 \end{vmatrix}}{17} = \frac{-1\begin{vmatrix} 5 & 13 \\ -4 & -4 \end{vmatrix} - 1\begin{vmatrix} 2 & 13 \\ 2 & -4 \end{vmatrix} + 2\begin{vmatrix} 2 & 5 \\ 2 & -4 \end{vmatrix}}{17}$$

$$= \frac{-1 \cdot 32 - 1 \cdot (-34) + 2 \cdot (-18)}{17} = -2$$

Step 3   Write the solution as an ordered triple. The solution is (3, 1, –2). ∎

Determining Whether a System Has a Single Solution

You have seen how Cramer's rule can be used to find a solution to a system, but as you know, some systems have no solutions, while others have infinitely many solutions. Cramer's rule can be used to determine whether a system has a single solution.

For a system of equations, if the coefficient matrix M has a determinant of 0, then the system does *not* have a single solution.

Example 5   Use Cramer's rule to determine whether each system has a single solution.

Ⓐ $\begin{cases} -2x + y = -6 \\ -8x + 4y = -48 \end{cases}$

Solution   Find the determinant of the coefficient matrix.

$$\det\begin{bmatrix} -2 & 1 \\ -8 & 4 \end{bmatrix} = \begin{vmatrix} -2 & 1 \\ -8 & 4 \end{vmatrix} = -8 - (-8) = 0$$

No, the system does not have a single solution. ∎

Ⓑ $\begin{cases} 3y = -2x - 23 \\ 5y = -8 + x \end{cases}$

Solution   Write the equations in standard form.

$\begin{cases} 2x + 3y = -23 \\ -x + 5y = -8 \end{cases}$

$$\det\begin{bmatrix} 2 & 3 \\ -1 & 5 \end{bmatrix} = \begin{vmatrix} 2 & 3 \\ -1 & 5 \end{vmatrix} = 10 - (-3) = 13$$

Yes, the system has a single solution. ∎

THINK ABOUT IT

If the determinant of M is any value other than zero, the system has one solution.

$$\mathbf{C} \begin{cases} 2x + 3y + z = 15 \\ x - y + z = 2 \\ 6x + 9y + 3z = -18 \end{cases}$$

Solution

$$\begin{vmatrix} 2 & 3 & 1 \\ 1 & -1 & 1 \\ 6 & 9 & 3 \end{vmatrix} = 2 \begin{vmatrix} -1 & 1 \\ 9 & 3 \end{vmatrix} - 3 \begin{vmatrix} 1 & 1 \\ 6 & 3 \end{vmatrix} + 1 \begin{vmatrix} 1 & -1 \\ 6 & 9 \end{vmatrix}$$

$$= 2 \cdot (-12) - 3 \cdot (-3) + 1 \cdot 15$$

$$= 0$$

No, the system does not have a single solution. ∎

> **THINK ABOUT IT**
>
> When one row of the coefficient matrix is a multiple of another row, the system does not have a single solution.

Problem Set

Find the determinant of the matrix.

1. $\begin{bmatrix} 2 & 3 \\ 4 & 1 \end{bmatrix}$

2. $\begin{bmatrix} -2 & 10 \\ 3 & 7 \end{bmatrix}$

3. $\begin{bmatrix} 5 & 8 \\ -4 & -2 \end{bmatrix}$

4. $\begin{bmatrix} -25 & -20 \\ 12 & 8 \end{bmatrix}$

5. $\begin{bmatrix} 18 & 7 \\ 21 & -5 \end{bmatrix}$

6. $\begin{bmatrix} -9 & 6 \\ 12 & -4 \end{bmatrix}$

7. $\begin{bmatrix} 0 & 1 \\ 1 & 0 \end{bmatrix}$

8. $\begin{bmatrix} 30 & -20 \\ -10 & 10 \end{bmatrix}$

9. $\begin{bmatrix} 5 & 0 & 7 \\ -1 & -1 & 0 \\ 3 & 9 & 11 \end{bmatrix}$

10. $\begin{bmatrix} 1 & 0 & 2 \\ 3 & -5 & 0 \\ -1 & -1 & 8 \end{bmatrix}$

11. $\begin{bmatrix} -4 & 1 & 0 \\ -3 & -1 & 1 \\ 0 & 5 & 2 \end{bmatrix}$

12. $\begin{bmatrix} 5 & -2 & 12 \\ 15 & 0 & -5 \\ 2 & -8 & 20 \end{bmatrix}$

Use Cramer's rule to determine whether the system has a single solution. Write *yes* for a single solution; otherwise, write *no*.

13. $\begin{cases} 5x + 10y = 21 \\ 2x - 4y = 11 \end{cases}$

14. $\begin{cases} x - 8y = 10 \\ -2x = 12 - 16y \end{cases}$

15. $\begin{cases} 3y = 8 - 5x \\ -6y = 1 + 10x \end{cases}$

16. $\begin{cases} x - y = 9 \\ 36 = -4x + 8y \end{cases}$

17. $\begin{cases} x + y - 2z = 0 \\ 5x + 3y - 2z = 10 \\ x - 4y + z = -9 \end{cases}$

18. $\begin{cases} 2x + y + 4z = 18 \\ -4x - 2y = 20 - 8z \\ x - 3y + 2z = 8 \end{cases}$

Use Cramer's rule to solve each system of equations.

19. $\begin{cases} x + 2y = 11 \\ x - y = 2 \end{cases}$

20. $\begin{cases} 2x + y = -6 \\ 4x + 3y = -10 \end{cases}$

21. $\begin{cases} 3x + y = 25 \\ 2x - 2y = 30 \end{cases}$

22. $\begin{cases} 2x - y = -2 \\ x + 2y = 14 \end{cases}$

23. $\begin{cases} x = y - 3 \\ 2x - y = -19 \end{cases}$

24. $\begin{cases} 4x - 5y = 12 \\ -2x = 15 - 7y \end{cases}$

25. $\begin{cases} 2x + y - 2z = 8 \\ 5x + 4y - z = 1 \\ x + 2y - 3z = 9 \end{cases}$

26. $\begin{cases} x + y - z = 6 \\ x + 3y - 2z = 14 \\ 3x - 2y + z = -5 \end{cases}$

27. $\begin{cases} x + 2y + 2z = -1 \\ x + 3y + z = 4 \\ x + 3y + 2z = 3 \end{cases}$

28. $\begin{cases} x - y + 3z = 19 \\ 3x - 3y - 2z = 2 \\ -2x + 3z = 11 \end{cases}$

Solve.

***29.** **Challenge** Let A be an $n \times m$ matrix. The transpose of matrix A is the $m \times n$ matrix whose first column is the first row of A, second column is the second row of A, and so on. The transpose of matrix A is written as A^{t}.

Let $A = \begin{bmatrix} 8 & 3 \\ -1 & 2 \end{bmatrix}$.

A. Find A^{t}.

B. Show $(A^{t})^{t} = A$.

C. Show $\det A = \det A^{t}$.

***30.** **Challenge** Let $A = \begin{bmatrix} a & b \\ c & d \end{bmatrix}$ and $B = \begin{bmatrix} e & f \\ g & h \end{bmatrix}$.

Show $\det AB = \det A \cdot \det B$.

Identity and Inverse Matrices

For real numbers, the multiplicative identity is 1 and the multiplicative inverse of any real number is its reciprocal. Matrices have multiplicative identities and inverses as well, but they aren't quite as simple to define.

REMEMBER

The number 1 is the multiplicative identity for the set of real numbers because $a \cdot 1 = 1 \cdot a = a$.

Identity Matrices

MULTIPLICATIVE IDENTITY MATRIX

The **main diagonal** of a square matrix consists of the elements on the diagonal extending from the top left corner to the bottom right corner.
The **multiplicative identity matrix**, or **identity matrix**, is an $n \times n$ matrix where every element on its main diagonal is 1 and all the other elements equal 0.
The identity matrix is denoted I_n, where n is the number of rows and columns.

$$I_2 = \begin{bmatrix} 1 & 0 \\ 0 & 1 \end{bmatrix} \qquad I_3 = \begin{bmatrix} 1 & 0 & 0 \\ 0 & 1 & 0 \\ 0 & 0 & 1 \end{bmatrix}$$

If A is a square matrix, then $AI = IA = A$.

Example 1 Determine the multiplicative identity matrix for $A = \begin{bmatrix} 6 & -1 \\ -4 & 9 \end{bmatrix}$.

Solution Because A is a 2×2 matrix, the identity matrix is $I_2 = \begin{bmatrix} 1 & 0 \\ 0 & 1 \end{bmatrix}$.

Check

$$\begin{bmatrix} 6 & -1 \\ -4 & 9 \end{bmatrix} \cdot \begin{bmatrix} 1 & 0 \\ 0 & 1 \end{bmatrix} \overset{?}{=} \begin{bmatrix} 6 & -1 \\ -4 & 9 \end{bmatrix}$$

$$\begin{bmatrix} 6 \cdot 1 + (-1 \cdot 0) & 6 \cdot 0 + (-1 \cdot 1) \\ -4 \cdot 1 + 9 \cdot 0 & -4 \cdot 0 + 9 \cdot 1 \end{bmatrix} \overset{?}{=} \begin{bmatrix} 6 & -1 \\ -4 & 9 \end{bmatrix}$$

$$\begin{bmatrix} 6 & -1 \\ -4 & 9 \end{bmatrix} = \begin{bmatrix} 6 & -1 \\ -4 & 9 \end{bmatrix} \checkmark \blacksquare$$

THINK ABOUT IT

You should also check that the identity matrix works when multiplying on the left side.

Matrix Inverses

Any nonzero real number, multiplied by its multiplicative inverse, is equal to the multiplicative identity. The multiplicative inverse of a can be written as a fraction, $\frac{1}{a}$, or as a power, a^{-1}.

$$a \cdot a^{-1} = 1 \quad \longleftarrow \text{multiplicative identity}$$
$$\uparrow$$
$$\text{multiplicative inverse}$$

Not all matrices have a multiplicative inverse. In fact, only square matrices may possibly have an inverse, but not all square matrices have an inverse.

DEFINITION

If it exists, the **multiplicative inverse matrix**, or **inverse matrix**, of $n \times n$ matrix A is A^{-1}, such that $A \cdot A^{-1} = A^{-1} \cdot A = I_n$.

To verify that two square matrices A and B are inverses, you must show that $AB = I_n$ and $BA = I_n$.

> **REMEMBER**
>
> Matrix multiplication is not commutative.

Example 2 Determine whether the given matrices are inverses.

A $A = \begin{bmatrix} 4 & 2 \\ 6 & 2 \end{bmatrix}$ $\qquad B = \begin{bmatrix} -\dfrac{1}{2} & \dfrac{1}{2} \\ \dfrac{3}{2} & -1 \end{bmatrix}$

Solution

$$AB = \begin{bmatrix} 4 & 2 \\ 6 & 2 \end{bmatrix} \cdot \begin{bmatrix} -\dfrac{1}{2} & \dfrac{1}{2} \\ \dfrac{3}{2} & -1 \end{bmatrix} = \begin{bmatrix} 4 \cdot \left(-\dfrac{1}{2}\right) + 2 \cdot \dfrac{3}{2} & 4 \cdot \dfrac{1}{2} + 2 \cdot (-1) \\ 6 \cdot \left(-\dfrac{1}{2}\right) + 2 \cdot \dfrac{3}{2} & 6 \cdot \dfrac{1}{2} + 2 \cdot (-1) \end{bmatrix} = \begin{bmatrix} 1 & 0 \\ 0 & 1 \end{bmatrix}$$

$$BA = \begin{bmatrix} -\dfrac{1}{2} & \dfrac{1}{2} \\ \dfrac{3}{2} & -1 \end{bmatrix} \cdot \begin{bmatrix} 4 & 2 \\ 6 & 2 \end{bmatrix} = \begin{bmatrix} -\dfrac{1}{2} \cdot 4 + \dfrac{1}{2} \cdot 6 & -\dfrac{1}{2} \cdot 2 + \dfrac{1}{2} \cdot 2 \\ \dfrac{3}{2} \cdot 4 + (-1) \cdot 6 & \dfrac{3}{2} \cdot 2 + (-1) \cdot 2 \end{bmatrix} = \begin{bmatrix} 1 & 0 \\ 0 & 1 \end{bmatrix}$$

Because $AB = BA = I_2$, A and B are inverses. ∎

> **THINK ABOUT IT**
>
> In Example 2A, you can write $A^{-1} = B$ and $B^{-1} = A$.

B $A = \begin{bmatrix} 2 & -1 \\ -2 & \dfrac{3}{2} \end{bmatrix}$ $\qquad B = \begin{bmatrix} 3 & 2 \\ 5 & 4 \end{bmatrix}$

Solution

$$AB = \begin{bmatrix} 2 & -1 \\ -2 & \dfrac{3}{2} \end{bmatrix} \cdot \begin{bmatrix} 3 & 2 \\ 5 & 4 \end{bmatrix} = \begin{bmatrix} 2 \cdot 3 + (-1) \cdot 5 & 2 \cdot 2 + (-1) \cdot 4 \\ -2 \cdot 3 + \dfrac{3}{2} \cdot 5 & -2 \cdot 2 + \dfrac{3}{2} \cdot 4 \end{bmatrix} = \begin{bmatrix} 1 & 0 \\ \dfrac{3}{2} & 2 \end{bmatrix}$$

Because $AB \neq I_2$, there is no need to check BA. Matrices A and B are not inverses. ∎

Using a Formula to Find the Inverse of a 2 × 2 Matrix

REMEMBER

$\det A = ad - cb$

Example 3 Find the inverse of each matrix, if it exists.

A $A = \begin{bmatrix} 1 & -1 \\ 2 & -3 \end{bmatrix}$

Solution Find the determinant of the matrix. Then substitute in the formula.

$\det A = 1 \cdot (-3) - 2 \cdot (-1) = -3 - (-2) = -1$

$A^{-1} = \dfrac{1}{\det A} \begin{bmatrix} d & -b \\ -c & a \end{bmatrix} = -1 \begin{bmatrix} -3 & 1 \\ -2 & 1 \end{bmatrix} = \begin{bmatrix} 3 & -1 \\ 2 & -1 \end{bmatrix}.$ ∎

TIP

To create the matrix in the formula from the original matrix, switch *a* and *d*, and then take the opposites of *b* and *c*.

B $B = \begin{bmatrix} 4 & -8 \\ -1 & 2 \end{bmatrix}$

Solution $\det B = 4 \cdot 2 - (-1) \cdot (-8) = 8 - 8 = 0$

Because the determinant of B is 0, B^{-1} does not exist. ∎

C $C = \begin{bmatrix} 2 & 5 \\ 1 & 5 \end{bmatrix}$

Solution $\det C = 10 - 5 = 5$

$C^{-1} = \dfrac{1}{\det C} \begin{bmatrix} d & -b \\ -c & a \end{bmatrix} = \dfrac{1}{5} \begin{bmatrix} 5 & -5 \\ -1 & 2 \end{bmatrix} = \begin{bmatrix} 1 & -1 \\ -\dfrac{1}{5} & \dfrac{2}{5} \end{bmatrix}.$ ∎

REMEMBER

To check C^{-1}, verify that $C \cdot C^{-1} = I_2$ and $C^{-1} \cdot C = I_2$.

Using Technology to Find an Inverse Matrix

There are several online tools and graphing calculators that can help you find the inverse of a square matrix of any size, if it exists.

HOW TO FIND AN INVERSE MATRIX ON A GRAPHING CALCULATOR

Step 1 Create a new matrix.

Step 2 Edit the values of the matrix.

Step 3 Go to the main screen, enter the name of the matrix, and then hit the inverse key ($^{-1}$).

TIP

Check the instructions on how to find the inverse of a matrix for the tool you will be using.

Example 4 Use a graphing calculator to find the inverse of each matrix, if it exists.

A $\begin{bmatrix} 6 & -5 \\ -2 & 10 \end{bmatrix}$

Solution

```
MATRIX [A]  2 ×2
[ 6   -5        ]
[ -2  10        ]

2, 2 = 10
```

```
[A]⁻¹
  [ [.2   .1 ]
    [.04 .12] ]
```

The inverse is $\begin{bmatrix} 0.2 & 0.1 \\ 0.04 & 0.12 \end{bmatrix}$. ■

B $\begin{bmatrix} -3 & \dfrac{3}{2} \\ 4 & -2 \end{bmatrix}$

Solution

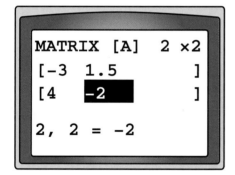

```
MATRIX [A]  2 ×2
[-3 1.5        ]
[4  -2         ]

2, 2 = -2
```

```
ERR: SINGULAR
MAT
1: Quit
2: Goto
```

> **TIP**
> A *singular matrix* is a matrix that does not have an inverse. If you receive this error message, press 1 to quit.

The matrix does not have an inverse. ■

C $\begin{bmatrix} 2 & 1 & 2 \\ 1 & 0 & 2 \\ 2 & -1 & 3 \end{bmatrix}$

Solution

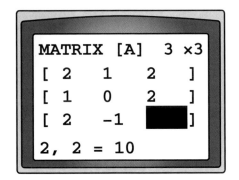

TIP
You may need to press the arrow keys to see all the elements.

The inverse is $\begin{bmatrix} \dfrac{2}{3} & -\dfrac{5}{3} & \dfrac{2}{3} \\ \dfrac{1}{3} & \dfrac{2}{3} & -\dfrac{2}{3} \\ -\dfrac{1}{3} & \dfrac{4}{3} & -\dfrac{1}{3} \end{bmatrix}$. ■

Problem Set

· ·

Determine the multiplicative identity matrix for each matrix.

1. $\begin{bmatrix} 8 & 15 \\ -3 & 1 \end{bmatrix}$

2. $\begin{bmatrix} 1 & 10 & 3 \\ -9 & -7 & -2 \\ 0 & 0 & 25 \end{bmatrix}$

3. $\begin{bmatrix} 1 & 0 & -2 & -5 \\ 12 & 3 & 0 & -10 \\ -3 & -8 & 17 & 21 \\ 2 & -12 & 14 & 1 \end{bmatrix}$

Determine whether the two matrices are inverses of each other. Write *yes* or *no*.

4. $\begin{bmatrix} 2 & 3 \\ 5 & 7 \end{bmatrix}$ and $\begin{bmatrix} -7 & 3 \\ 5 & -2 \end{bmatrix}$

8. $\begin{bmatrix} 3 & 2 \\ 2 & 2 \end{bmatrix}$ and $\begin{bmatrix} 1 & -1 \\ -1 & \dfrac{3}{2} \end{bmatrix}$

5. $\begin{bmatrix} 3 & \dfrac{5}{2} \\ -2 & -\dfrac{3}{2} \end{bmatrix}$ and $\begin{bmatrix} -3 & -5 \\ 4 & 6 \end{bmatrix}$

9. $\begin{bmatrix} 9 & 8 \\ 7 & 6 \end{bmatrix}$ and $\begin{bmatrix} \dfrac{9}{2} & \dfrac{7}{2} \\ 4 & -3 \end{bmatrix}$

6. $\begin{bmatrix} 1 & 2 \\ 4 & 9 \end{bmatrix}$ and $\begin{bmatrix} 9 & -4 \\ -2 & 1 \end{bmatrix}$

10. $\begin{bmatrix} 2 & -4 \\ 2 & 0 \end{bmatrix}$ and $\begin{bmatrix} 0 & \dfrac{1}{4} \\ -\dfrac{1}{4} & \dfrac{1}{2} \end{bmatrix}$

7. $\begin{bmatrix} 3 & 5 \\ 1 & 2 \end{bmatrix}$ and $\begin{bmatrix} 2 & -5 \\ -1 & 3 \end{bmatrix}$

11. $\begin{bmatrix} -\dfrac{1}{2} & \dfrac{3}{2} \\ 1 & -2 \end{bmatrix}$ and $\begin{bmatrix} 4 & 3 \\ 2 & 1 \end{bmatrix}$

12. $\begin{bmatrix} 1 & 0 & 2 \\ 2 & -1 & 3 \\ 4 & 1 & 8 \end{bmatrix}$ and $\begin{bmatrix} -11 & 2 & 2 \\ -4 & 0 & 1 \\ 6 & -1 & -1 \end{bmatrix}$

13. $\begin{bmatrix} 2 & 1 & 3 \\ 0 & 1 & 2 \\ 0 & 0 & 3 \end{bmatrix}$ and $\begin{bmatrix} \frac{1}{2} & \frac{1}{2} & -\frac{1}{6} \\ 1 & 0 & \frac{2}{3} \\ 0 & 0 & \frac{1}{3} \end{bmatrix}$

Use an online tool or graphing calculator to find the inverse of each matrix.

14. $\begin{bmatrix} 2 & 0 \\ 1 & 1 \end{bmatrix}$

15. $\begin{bmatrix} 5 & -1 \\ -6 & 1 \end{bmatrix}$

16. $\begin{bmatrix} -1 & 2 \\ 3 & -5 \end{bmatrix}$

17. $\begin{bmatrix} 5 & -6 \\ 3 & -2 \end{bmatrix}$

18. $\begin{bmatrix} 10 & -3 \\ 16 & -5 \end{bmatrix}$

19. $\begin{bmatrix} 4 & 1 \\ -2 & 2 \end{bmatrix}$

20. $\begin{bmatrix} 1 & 2 & 1 \\ 1 & 1 & 1 \\ 3 & -1 & 1 \end{bmatrix}$

21. $\begin{bmatrix} 1 & 1 & 6 \\ 5 & 2 & -3 \\ -2 & -1 & 2 \end{bmatrix}$

22. $\begin{bmatrix} 0 & 1 & 1 \\ 2 & -3 & -3 \\ 1 & 0.2 & -0.2 \end{bmatrix}$

Use the formula $A^{-1} = \dfrac{1}{\det A}\begin{bmatrix} d & -b \\ -c & a \end{bmatrix}$, **where** $A = \begin{bmatrix} a & b \\ c & d \end{bmatrix}$, **to find the inverse of each matrix, if it exists.**

23. $\begin{bmatrix} 0 & -1 \\ -1 & 5 \end{bmatrix}$

24. $\begin{bmatrix} -2 & 3 \\ 8 & -11 \end{bmatrix}$

25. $\begin{bmatrix} -1 & 2 \\ -1 & 3 \end{bmatrix}$

26. $\begin{bmatrix} -2 & 3 \\ 3 & -5 \end{bmatrix}$

27. $\begin{bmatrix} 10 & -5 \\ -2 & 1 \end{bmatrix}$

28. $\begin{bmatrix} 5 & -5 \\ 5 & -6 \end{bmatrix}$

Solve.

*29. **Challenge** Let $A = \begin{bmatrix} 1 & 2 \\ 1 & 3 \end{bmatrix}$ and $B = \begin{bmatrix} 2 & 0 \\ 4 & 1 \end{bmatrix}$.

Show that $(AB)^{-1} = B^{-1}A^{-1}$.

*30. **Challenge** Let $A = \begin{bmatrix} a & b \\ c & d \end{bmatrix}$. Show that the

formula for finding the inverse of A,

$A^{-1} = \dfrac{1}{\det A} \begin{bmatrix} d & -b \\ -c & a \end{bmatrix}$, is correct by showing

$AA^{-1} = I_2$ and $A^{-1}A = I_2$.

(Remember: $\det A = ad - bc$.)

Using Matrices to Solve Linear Systems

You can use matrix multiplication to model a system of equations.

Writing Matrix Equations

DEFINITIONS

A **coefficient matrix** is the matrix formed by the coefficients of the variables of a system of equations when the equations are written in standard form.

A **variable matrix** is the matrix that contains the variables used in a system of equations.

A **constant matrix** is the matrix that contains the constants used in a system of equations.

A **matrix equation** is an equation of the form $AX = B$, where A is the coefficient matrix, X is the variable matrix, and B is the constant matrix.

REMEMBER

You used the coefficient matrix when you solved a system of equations with Cramer's rule.

System of Equations	Matrix Representation
$\begin{cases} 2x - 3y = 24 \\ x + 5y = 53 \end{cases}$	$\begin{array}{ccccc} A & \cdot & X & = & B \end{array}$ $\begin{bmatrix} 2 & -3 \\ 1 & 5 \end{bmatrix} \begin{bmatrix} x \\ y \end{bmatrix} = \begin{bmatrix} -24 \\ 53 \end{bmatrix}$

Example 1 Write a matrix equation to represent each system.

A $\begin{cases} y = 2x + 7 \\ 3x = y - 9 \end{cases}$

Solution Write the equations in standard form, $ax + by = c$.

$\begin{cases} -2x + y = 7 \\ 3x - y = -9 \end{cases}$

The matrix equation is $\begin{bmatrix} -2 & 1 \\ 3 & -1 \end{bmatrix} \cdot \begin{bmatrix} x \\ y \end{bmatrix} = \begin{bmatrix} 7 \\ -9 \end{bmatrix}$. ∎

B $\begin{cases} 2x - y + 3z = 11 \\ 3x + 2z = 16 \\ x + 5y - z = 17 \end{cases}$

TIP

You can check the placement of elements in the coefficient matrix by multiplying it by the variable matrix. The result should be the left side of each equation in the system.

Solution Use 0 to represent $0y$ in the second equation.

The matrix equation is $\begin{bmatrix} 2 & -1 & 3 \\ 3 & 0 & 2 \\ 1 & 5 & -1 \end{bmatrix} \cdot \begin{bmatrix} x \\ y \\ z \end{bmatrix} = \begin{bmatrix} 11 \\ 16 \\ 17 \end{bmatrix}$. ∎

Using an Inverse Matrix to Solve a System of Equations

To solve an equation of the form $ax = c$, you can multiply both sides of the equation by the multiplicative inverse of a. Similarly, you can solve the matrix equation $AX = B$ by multiplying both sides of the equation by the multiplicative inverse of A, which is A^{-1}.

Solving $ax = c$	Solving $AX = B$	Description
$5x = 20$	$AX = B$	
$\frac{1}{5} \cdot 5x = \frac{1}{5} \cdot 20$	$A^{-1} \cdot AX = A^{-1} \cdot B$	Multiply both sides by the inverse.
$1x = \frac{1}{5} \cdot 20$	$I_n X = A^{-1} \cdot B$	Definition of inverse
$x = 4$	$X = A^{-1}B$	Definition of multiplicative identity

Because matrix multiplication is *not* commutative, you must be careful when you multiply both sides of the equation by the inverse matrix. Here, you want to left-multiply by the inverse of A. Notice above that A^{-1} is the first factor in each expression in the second line.

REMEMBER

$A^{-1} \cdot B \neq B \cdot A^{-1}$

Example 2 Solve each system by using a matrix equation.

A $\begin{cases} 3x - y = -21 \\ 2x + 2y = 10 \end{cases}$

Solution

Step 1 Write the matrix equation: $\begin{bmatrix} 3 & -1 \\ 2 & 2 \end{bmatrix} \cdot \begin{bmatrix} x \\ y \end{bmatrix} = \begin{bmatrix} -21 \\ 10 \end{bmatrix}$.

Step 2 Use the inverse of the coefficient matrix, A^{-1}, to find $A^{-1}B$.

$A^{-1} = \begin{bmatrix} \frac{1}{4} & \frac{1}{8} \\ -\frac{1}{4} & \frac{3}{8} \end{bmatrix}$
$\qquad$
$A^{-1}B = \begin{bmatrix} \frac{1}{4} & \frac{1}{8} \\ -\frac{1}{4} & \frac{3}{8} \end{bmatrix} \cdot \begin{bmatrix} -21 \\ 10 \end{bmatrix} = \begin{bmatrix} -4 \\ 9 \end{bmatrix}$

Because $\begin{bmatrix} x \\ y \end{bmatrix} = \begin{bmatrix} -4 \\ 9 \end{bmatrix}$, the solution is $x = -4$ and $y = 9$, or $(-4, 9)$. ∎

B $\begin{cases} 3x = 2y - 1 \\ 5 = -6x + 4y \end{cases}$

Solution

Step 1   Write the equations in standard form: $\begin{cases} 3x - 2y = -1 \\ -6x + 4y = 5 \end{cases}$.

Step 2   Write the matrix equation: $\begin{bmatrix} 3 & -2 \\ -6 & 4 \end{bmatrix} \cdot \begin{bmatrix} x \\ y \end{bmatrix} = \begin{bmatrix} -1 \\ 5 \end{bmatrix}$.

Step 3   If you use determinants or a graphing calculator to find A^{-1}, the inverse of the coefficient matrix, you will see that A's determinant is zero, so the inverse does not exist.

The system does not have a single solution.   ■

```
ERR: SINGULAR
MAT
1: Quit
2: Goto
```

C $\begin{cases} x + y + 2z = 7 \\ x + y = 3 \\ y - 4z = 2 \end{cases}$

Solution

Step 1   Write the matrix equation: $\begin{bmatrix} 1 & 1 & 2 \\ 1 & 1 & 0 \\ 0 & 1 & -4 \end{bmatrix} \cdot \begin{bmatrix} x \\ y \\ z \end{bmatrix} = \begin{bmatrix} 7 \\ 3 \\ 2 \end{bmatrix}$.

Step 2   Find A^{-1}, the inverse of the coefficient matrix.

```
[A]⁻¹
[[-2   3    -1]
 [2   -2    1 ]
 [.5  -.5   0 ]]
```

Step 3   Find $A^{-1}B$. $\begin{bmatrix} -2 & 3 & -1 \\ 2 & -2 & 1 \\ 0.5 & -0.5 & 0 \end{bmatrix} \cdot \begin{bmatrix} 7 \\ 3 \\ 2 \end{bmatrix} = \begin{bmatrix} -7 \\ 10 \\ 2 \end{bmatrix}$

Because $\begin{bmatrix} x \\ y \\ z \end{bmatrix} = \begin{bmatrix} -7 \\ 10 \\ 2 \end{bmatrix}$, the solution is $x = -7$, $y = 10$, and $z = 2$, or

$(-7, 10, 2)$.   ■

Problem Set

Write a matrix equation to represent each system of equations.

1. $\begin{cases} x + y = 5 \\ x - y = 3 \end{cases}$

2. $\begin{cases} 2x - y = -4 \\ -x + 5y = 20 \end{cases}$

3. $\begin{cases} 3x - 6y = 2 \\ 5x + 4y = 1 \end{cases}$

4. $\begin{cases} x + 3y = -2 \\ 7y = -6 - 2x \end{cases}$

5. $\begin{cases} 3x = 24 \\ x - 5y = 3 \end{cases}$

6. $\begin{cases} 6x = 5y - 9 \\ 6y = 2x + 8 \end{cases}$

7. $\begin{cases} 2x + 3y - z = 0 \\ -x + 2y + z = 5 \\ 6x - 8y - 2 = 2 \end{cases}$

8. $\begin{cases} x + 2y = 3 - z \\ 2x = -4 - 5y + z \\ 3x - 2y - z = 5 \end{cases}$

9. $\begin{cases} x + 5y = 12 \\ 2x - 3y + 4z = 18 \\ 6y = 10 - 7z \end{cases}$

10. $\begin{cases} x - y - z = 15 \\ x + 12 = z - 8y \\ 6x = 4 - 12z \end{cases}$

Solve each system by writing and solving a matrix equation.

11. $\begin{cases} x + 2y = 21 \\ x - y = -6 \end{cases}$

12. $\begin{cases} 2x + 2y = 18 \\ -3x - y = -19 \end{cases}$

13. $\begin{cases} x = 8 + y \\ -4y = -4x + 3 \end{cases}$

14. $\begin{cases} 2x = 5 + y \\ -2x - y = -11 \end{cases}$

15. $\begin{cases} x + 4y = 2 \\ 2x - y = -2 \end{cases}$

16. $\begin{cases} y = x - 3 \\ y = 3x + 1 \end{cases}$

17. $\begin{cases} 0.3x + 0.6y = -0.4 \\ 0.2x + 0.4y = 1.2 \end{cases}$

18. $\begin{cases} 4x + y = 1 \\ x = -5 + 2y \end{cases}$

19. $\begin{cases} 13.5y = 21.6 - 5.4x \\ 10.8x + 8.1y = -32.4 \end{cases}$

20. $\begin{cases} 7x = -28 \\ 2x - 3y = 2 \end{cases}$

21. $\begin{cases} -4 = x + 2y \\ 8 = x - 2y \end{cases}$

22. $\begin{cases} 1.3x + 2.6y = 5.2 \\ 0.2x + 0.4y = 0.8 \end{cases}$

23. $\begin{cases} 4x - 4y + 6z = 12 \\ 4x - 3y + 2z = 6 \\ -2x + 3y - 7z = 1 \end{cases}$

24. $\begin{cases} x + 2y - z = 6 \\ 3x + 8y + 9z = 10 \\ 2x - y + 2z = -2 \end{cases}$

25. $\begin{cases} x - y + z = 9 \\ 2x - y = 6 \\ -2x - y - z = -7 \end{cases}$

26. $\begin{cases} 2x + 6y - z = -1 \\ -2x - 4y + 5z = -4 \\ -x - y - 3z = 3 \end{cases}$

28. $\begin{cases} 3x - 2y + 4z = -7 \\ 4 = x - 5y + z \\ x + y = -8 + z \end{cases}$

27. $\begin{cases} x = 8 - y - z \\ -2x - 2y + 2z = -16 \\ 5x + 2y = 1 \end{cases}$

*29. **Challenge** $\begin{cases} -w + x - y + 2z = 9 \\ 2w + x + y + z = 5 \\ -2w + 2x - y - z = 1 \\ w + x - y - z = 4 \end{cases}$

Solve.

*30. **Challenge** The Coffee Dream Café sells small, medium, and large coffee drinks. The tables show the number of each size of drink sold for three consecutive days and the total sales amounts for each day.

Number of Coffee Drinks Sold			
Day	Small	Medium	Large
1	220	250	300
2	180	230	190
3	230	150	180

Total Sales Amounts	
Day	Amount
1	$1447.50
2	$1117.50
3	$1015.50

A. Write a matrix equation to represent this situation.

B. Find the cost of each size of drink.

UNIT 15   Conic Sections

The telescopes at the W.M. Keck Observatory in Hawaii use hyperbolic mirrors.

Astronomers use telescopes with optics that use the properties of conic sections. Cassegrain reflectors, for example, consist of two conic-shaped mirrors.

Big Ideas

- ▶ Conic sections have useful applications in the physical world—for example, in antenna design, optics, architecture, and structural engineering.

- ▶ If you can create a mathematical model for a situation, you can use the model to solve other problems that you might not be able to solve otherwise.

Unit Topics

- ▶ Foundations for Unit 15
- ▶ Introduction to Conic Sections
- ▶ Circles
- ▶ Ellipses
- ▶ Hyperbolas
- ▶ Parabolas
- ▶ Putting Conics into Graphing Form

Foundations for Unit 15

Before you learn more about conic sections, make sure you know how to do the following:

▶ Use the geometric definition of a circle and its parts.

▶ Find coordinates on a plane when given a description.

▶ Use square roots to solve simple equations.

Using the Geometric Definition of a Circle and Its Parts

Definitions

circle	the set of all points in a plane that are the same distance r from a given point in the plane
radius	a line segment that connects the center of a circle to a point on the circle
chord	a line segment that connects two points on a circle
diameter	a line segment that connects two points on a circle and contains the center of the circle; the length of the diameter d is two times the length of a radius r: $d = 2r$ or $r = \dfrac{d}{2}$

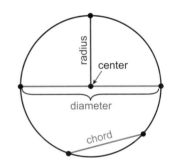

Example 1   Find the radius r and diameter d of each circle.

A

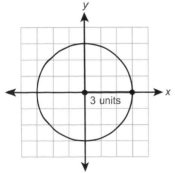

The radius is 3 units long, so $r = 3$. The diameter is twice the radius, so $d = 6$.

B

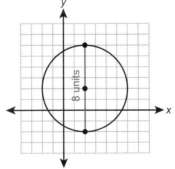

The diameter is 8 units long, so $d = 8$. The radius is half the diameter, so $r = 4$.

Problem Set A

Find the radius *r* and diameter *d* of each circle.

1.

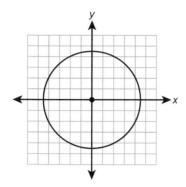

3.

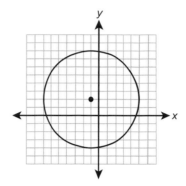

2.

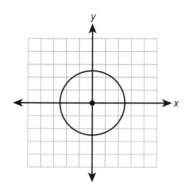

4.

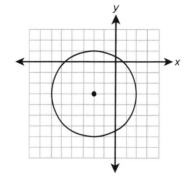

Using Symmetry to Find Coordinates of a Point

A figure has *line symmetry* if there is a line on which the figure may be folded so that two parts of the figure are mirror images of each other.

SPECIAL LINES OF SYMMETRY

Line of Symmetry	Symmetric Points
x-axis	(x, y) is symmetric to $(x, -y)$
y-axis	(x, y) is symmetric to $(-x, y)$
$y = x$	(x, y) is symmetric to (y, x)
$y = -x$	(x, y) is symmetric to $(-y, -x)$

If point *A* is symmetric to point *A'* with respect to line *m*, the midpoint of $\overline{AA'}$ is point *M*, the intersection of $\overline{AA'}$ and line *m*. Therefore, $AM = MA$.

Example 2 For each of the following, A is symmetric to A' with respect to the given line. Find the coordinates of point A'.

Ⓐ $A(-4, -2)$, line of symmetry: y-axis
(x, y) is symmetric to $(-x, y)$ with respect to the y-axis. So $A(-4, -2)$ is symmetric to $A'(4, -2)$.

Ⓑ $A(-1, 5)$, line of symmetry: $y = x$
(x, y) is symmetric to (y, x) with respect to the line $y = x$. So $A(-1, 5)$ is symmetric to $A'(5, -1)$.

Ⓒ $A(3, 1)$ is symmetric to A' with respect to the line $x = 4$.
Create a graph.

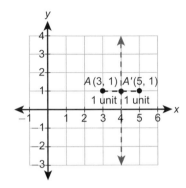

Point A' is located at $(5, 1)$.

Problem Set B

For each of the following, A is symmetric to A' with respect to the given line. Find the coordinates of point A'.

5. $A(5, -3)$, line of symmetry: x-axis
6. $A(-4, -6)$, line of symmetry: y-axis
7. $A(7, 3)$, line of symmetry: $y = x$
8. $A(2, 4)$, line of symmetry: $y = -x$
9. $A(6, 2)$, line of symmetry: $x = -5$
10. $A(-2, -1)$, line of symmetry: $y = -3$

Solving Equations of the Form $x^2 = d$

SQUARE ROOT PROPERTY

If $d > 0$, then $x^2 = d$ has two real number solutions, $x = \sqrt{d}$ and $x = -\sqrt{d}$.

Example 3 Solve the equation. Put the result in simplified radical form.

Ⓐ $n^2 = 20$
$n = \pm\sqrt{20}$
$n = \pm\sqrt{4 \cdot 5}$
$n = \pm 2\sqrt{5}$

Ⓑ $z^2 = 250$
$z = \pm\sqrt{250}$
$z = \pm\sqrt{25 \cdot 10}$
$z = \pm 5\sqrt{10}$

THINK ABOUT IT

The square root property is sometimes written, "If $x^2 = d$, then $x = \pm\sqrt{d}$."

Problem Set C

Solve each equation. Put the result in simplified radical form.

11. $x^2 = 121$
12. $x^2 = 81$
13. $x^2 = 35$
14. $x^2 = 72$
15. $x^2 = 112$
16. $x^2 = 138$
17. $x^2 = 57$
18. $x^2 = 1024$
19. $x^2 = 32$

Introduction to Conic Sections

As the name suggests, a conic section is a cross-section of a cone.

Identifying Conic Sections

DEFINITIONS

A **conic section** (or **conic**) is a two-dimensional graph that can be formed by the intersection of a plane with a double-napped cone.

A **double-napped cone** is formed as follows:

One line, called the **generating line**, intersects and revolves around another line, called the **axis**. The axis is stationary, and the two lines cannot be perpendicular. The point where the lines intersect is the **vertex** of the cone.

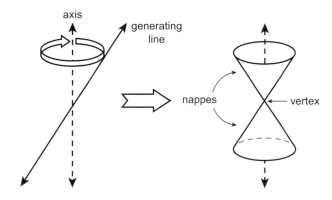

THINK ABOUT IT

A *nappe* is one of two equal pieces of a cone when the cone is divided at the vertex by a plane perpendicular to the axis.

Note: The double-napped cone described above is a surface without any bases. If a circular base were added to one nappe, the resulting figure would be the familiar cone that you study in geometry.

There are four important types of conic sections.

Circle	Ellipse	Parabola	Hyperbola
A **circle** is a conic section formed when a plane intersects only one nappe, perpendicular to the axis.	An **ellipse** is a conic section formed when a plane intersects only one nappe, not parallel to the generating line. A circle can be considered a special kind of ellipse.	A **parabola** is a conic section formed when a plane intersects only one nappe, parallel to the generating line.	A **hyperbola** is a conic section formed when a plane intersects bothnappes.

There are also three types of *degenerate conic sections*.

Degenerate Conic Sections		
A **degenerate conic section** is formed when a plane intersects the vertex of the double-napped cone. There are three degenerate cases.		
Point	**Line**	**Pair of Intersecting Lines**
The plane intersects only the vertex. This is a degenerate ellipse.	The plane contains the generating line. This is a degenerate parabola.	The plane intersects both nappes through the vertex. This is a degenerate hyperbola.

> **TIP**
>
> In mathematics, *degenerate* cases are cases that are simpler than normal cases. Points and lines are degenerate conic sections because they are simpler than the other conic sections.

Example 1 Identify the conic that will be formed by the intersection of the plane and the cone.

A Given: Plane A intersects line m, is not perpendicular to m, and is not parallel to n. The conic is an ellipse. ■

B Given: Plane B is parallel to line n. The conic is a parabola. ■

C Given: Plane C is perpendicular to line m and at the center of the cone. The conic is a degenerate ellipse (a point). ■

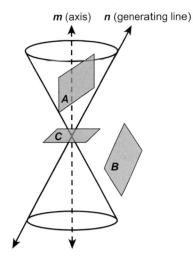

m (axis)   *n* (generating line)

REMEMBER

A line extends without end in one dimension.

A plane extends without end in two dimensions.

Using Tools of Analytic Geometry: The Distance Formula

Analytic geometry (also called **coordinate geometry**) is the study of geometry using the tools of algebra. You'll use the tools of analytic geometry to study conic sections.

The *distance formula* is one important tool in analytic geometry.

The distance formula is based on the Pythagorean theorem. To find an expression for the distance d from A to B, form right triangle ABC and use the Pythagorean theorem.

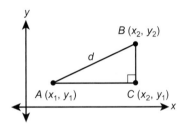

$(AB)^2 = (AC)^2 + (BC)^2$

$d^2 = (x_2 - x_1)^2 + (y_2 - y_1)^2$

$d = \sqrt{(x_2 - x_1)^2 + (y_2 - y_1)^2}$

DISTANCE FORMULA

The distance d between two points (x_1, y_1) and (x_2, y_2) is

$$d = \sqrt{(x_2 - x_1)^2 + (y_2 - y_1)^2}.$$

Example 2 Find the length of $\overline{AB}$.

Solution Let $A(1, 4)$ be (x_1, y_1) and $B(6, 2)$ be (x_2, y_2).

$AB = \sqrt{(x_2 - x_1)^2 + (y_2 - y_1)^2}$

$= \sqrt{(6 - 1)^2 + (2 - 4)^2}$

$= \sqrt{5^2 + (-2)^2}$

$= \sqrt{25 + 4}$

$= \sqrt{29}$ ■

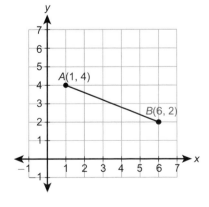

REMEMBER

The length of $\overline{AB}$ is denoted AB.

Using Tools of Analytic Geometry: The Midpoint Formula

The *midpoint formula*, another useful tool in analytic geometry, helps you determine the coordinates of the midpoint of a segment.

> **MIDPOINT FORMULA**
>
> The coordinates of the midpoint M of the segment with endpoints (x_1, y_1) and (x_2, y_2) is
> $$M = \left(\frac{x_1 + x_2}{2}, \frac{y_1 + y_2}{2} \right).$$

Example 3

A Find the coordinates of M, the midpoint of $\overline{AB}$ in Example 2.

Solution

$$\left(\frac{x_1 + x_2}{2}, \frac{y_1 + y_2}{2} \right) = \left(\frac{1 + 6}{2}, \frac{4 + 2}{2} \right)$$

The coordinates of M are $(3.5, 3)$. ■

B A line segment $\overline{CD}$ has one endpoint D at $(2, 4)$ and a midpoint M at $(0, 2.5)$. Find the coordinates of the other endpoint C.

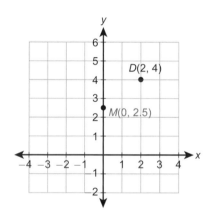

Solution

$$\left(\frac{x + 2}{2}, \frac{y + 4}{2} \right) = (0, 2.5)$$

Substitute the coordinates of the given endpoint $(2, 4)$ and the midpoint $(0, 2.5)$ into the formula.

$$\frac{x + 2}{2} = 0 \qquad \frac{y + 4}{2} = 2.5$$
$$x + 2 = 0 \qquad y + 4 = 5$$
$$x = -2 \qquad y = 1$$

Set each expression equal to its corresponding coordinate, and then solve for x and y.

The coordinates of C are $(-2, 1)$. ■

> **THINK ABOUT IT**
>
> You can use the distance formula to verify that M is the midpoint. Show that $AM = MB$.
>
> $AM = \sqrt{(3.5 - 1)^2 + (3 - 4)^2}$
> $= \sqrt{7.25}$
>
> $MB = \sqrt{(6 - 3.5)^2 + (2 - 3)^2}$
> $= \sqrt{7.25}$

Problem Set

Identify the conic that will be formed by the intersection of the plane described and the cone below.

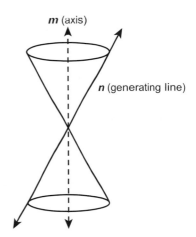

1. Given: The plane is perpendicular to *m* and above the vertex.

2. Given: The plane intersects *m* and *n* at the same point.

3. Given: The plane contains *n*.

4. Given: The plane is parallel to *n* and intersects one nappe.

5. Given: The plane intersects only one nappe and is neither perpendicular to *m* nor parallel to *n*.

6. Given: The plane intersects both nappes.

7. Given: The plane intersects both nappes through the vertex.

Find the exact length of $\overline{AB}$. Express your answer in simplified radical form.

8. $A(1, 5), B(-3, 2)$

9. $A(-2, 2), B(4, -10)$

10. $A(-4, 4), B(-6, 9)$

11. $A(-6, -9), B(7, 5)$

12. $A(3, -6), B(1, 8)$

13. $A(3, -9), B(8, -6)$

14. $A(-9, 8), B(-5, 8)$

15. $A(-4, 4), B(-10, -2)$

*16. **Challenge** $A(-2.4, 5.3),$ $B(-6.5, -6)$

Find the coordinates of midpoint *M* of $\overline{AB}$.

17. $A(6, -8), B(6, -9)$

18. $A(6, 4), B(8, -7)$

19. $A(-3, -10), B(-2, 3)$

20. $A(-2, -10), B(2, 10)$

21. $A(1, -2), B(1, 4)$

22. $A(-6, 7), B(-2, 6)$

Find the coordinates of endpoint *B* of $\overline{AB}$, given midpoint *M* and endpoint *A*.

23. $A(-10, 0), M(-1, 0)$

24. $A(-4, 3), M(-7, 3)$

25. $A(6, -1), M(1, 0)$

26. $A(6, 4), M(-3, 1)$

27. $A(-3, 1), M(-5, 5)$

28. $A(2, -4), M(0, 2)$

Solve.

*29. **Challenge** A right triangle has vertices $A(-5, 2), B(-3, 8),$ and $C(-3, 2)$. The triangle is then rotated 180° to the right. Find the coordinates of the vertices of the new triangle by using the midpoint formula.

Circles

The circle is the simplest and most familiar conic section.

Deriving an Equation of a Circle from the Definition

> **DEFINITION**
>
> A **circle** is the set of all points in a plane that are a fixed distance r (the **radius**) from a given point (the **center**).

> **TIP**
>
> The word *radius* can mean either a line segment from the center to the circle, or the length of such a line segment.

In a coordinate plane, a circle is a set of points (x, y). For any circle, r has the same value, no matter where (x, y) is on the circle.

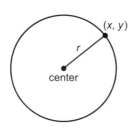

Example 1   Derive an equation of the circle with the given center and radius.

Ⓐ center $= (0, 0)$, $r = 6$

Solution   For any point (x, y) on the circle, the distance from the center $(0, 0)$ is 6.

$$\sqrt{(x_2 - x_1)^2 + (y_2 - y_1)^2} = d$$ Distance Formula

$$\sqrt{(x - 0)^2 + (y - 0)^2} = 6$$ The distance between $(0, 0)$ and any point (x, y) on the circle is 6.

$$(x - 0)^2 + (y - 0)^2 = 36$$ Square each side.

$$x^2 + y^2 = 36$$ Simplify. ■

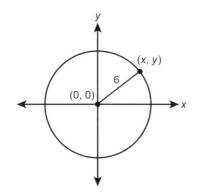

Ⓑ center $= (2, 5)$, $r = 3$

Solution   For any point (x, y) on the circle, the distance from the center $(2, 5)$ is 3.

$$\sqrt{(x - 2)^2 + (y - 5)^2} = 3$$ The distance between $(2, 5)$ and any point (x, y) on the circle is 3.

$$(x - 2)^2 + (y - 5)^2 = 9$$ Square each side. ■

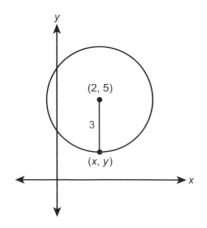

Writing an Equation of a Circle, Given Its Graph

There are different forms for the equation of a circle, but one common form is a helpful one to use when you want to graph the circle.

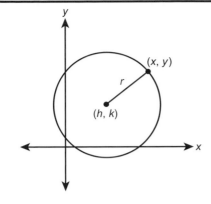

EQUATION OF A CIRCLE

The **equation in graphing form** of the circle with center (h, k) and radius r is $(x - h)^2 + (y - k)^2 = r^2$.

Example 2 Write the equation in graphing form of the circle shown at right.

Solution The center is $(-3, 6)$, so $h = -3$ and $k = 6$.

To find the radius, calculate the distance between the center $(-3, 6)$ and the point $(0, 2)$ on the circle:

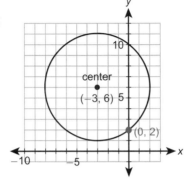

$$r = \sqrt{(0 - (-3))^2 + (2 - 6)^2} = \sqrt{9 + 16} = \sqrt{25} = 5.$$

Substitute h, k, and r into the equation in graphing form:

$$(x - h)^2 + (y - k)^2 = r^2$$
$$(x - (-3))^2 + (y - 6)^2 = 5^2$$
$$(x + 3)^2 + (y - 6)^2 = 25 \quad \blacksquare$$

Finding the Center, Radius, and Diameter of a Circle, Given Its Equation in Graphing Form

Example 3 Find the center, radius, and diameter of the circle with equation $(x + 1)^2 + (y + 3)^2 = 16$.

Solution Rewrite the equation as $(x - (-1))^2 + (y - (-3))^2 = 4^2$ to identify h, k, and r.

The circle is in graphing form with $h = -1$, $k = -3$, and $r = 4$.

The center of the circle (h, k) is $(-1, -3)$.

The radius r is 4, so the diameter is $4 \cdot 2 = 8$. $\quad \blacksquare$

Graphing a Circle, Given Its Equation in Graphing Form

Example 4 Graph the circle with equation $(x - 4)^2 + (y + 1)^2 = 4$.

Solution The equation is in graphing form with $h = 4$, $k = -1$, and $r = 2$.

Step 1 Plot the center (h, k) at $(4, -1)$.

Step 2 The radius is 2, so every point on the circle is 2 units from the center. Count 2 units left, right, up, and down from the center to find four points on the circle: $(2, -1)$, $(6, -1)$, $(4, 1)$, and $(4, -3)$.

Step 3 Draw the circle through the four points.

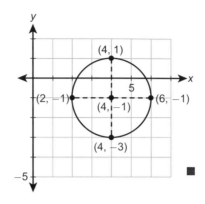

> **TIP**
>
> When you draw a circle, use a compass to improve your accuracy.

Finding the Equation of a Circle, Given Three Points

Example 5 Find the equation of the circle that contains $A(-3, 6)$, $B(3, 4)$, and $C(5, 0)$.

Solution You need the center and radius. To find the center, find the point of intersection of the perpendicular bisectors of two chords of the circle.

Step 1 Identify two chords, say $\overline{AB}$ and $\overline{BC}$. Find the slope of each chord. Then find the slope of each perpendicular bisector by using the opposite reciprocal.

> **REMEMBER**
>
> A chord is a segment that connects two points of a circle. A theorem of geometry states that the perpendicular bisector of any chord of a circle passes through the center of the circle.

Chord	Slope of Chord	Slope of Perpendicular Bisector
$\overline{AB}$	$\dfrac{4 - 6}{3 - (-3)} = \dfrac{-2}{6} = -\dfrac{1}{3}$	3
$\overline{BC}$	$\dfrac{0 - 4}{5 - 3} = \dfrac{-4}{2} = -2$	$\dfrac{1}{2}$

Step 2 Find the midpoint of each chord.

Midpoint of $\overline{AB}$: $\left(\dfrac{-3 + 3}{2}, \dfrac{6 + 4}{2}\right) = \left(\dfrac{0}{2}, \dfrac{10}{2}\right) = (0, 5)$

Midpoint of $\overline{BC}$: $\left(\dfrac{3 + 5}{2}, \dfrac{4 + 0}{2}\right) = \left(\dfrac{8}{2}, \dfrac{4}{2}\right) = (4, 2)$

Step 3 Find the equations of the perpendicular bisectors. Use the point-slope form $y - y_1 = m(x - x_1)$. Use the slopes from Step 1 and the midpoints from Step 2.

Perpendicular bisector of $\overline{AB}$:
$y - 5 = 3(x - 0)$, or $y = 3x + 5$.

Perpendicular bisector of $\overline{BC}$:
$y - 2 = \dfrac{1}{2}(x - 4)$, or $y = \dfrac{1}{2}x$.

> **TIP**
>
> This problem does not require a graph, but a sketch helps you visualize what is happening.
>
>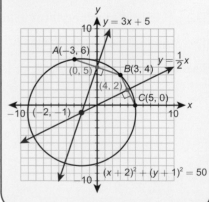

Step 4 Solve the system of linear equations.

$$y = 3x + 5 \qquad \text{Perpendicular bisector of } \overline{AB}$$

$$\frac{1}{2}x = 3x + 5 \qquad \text{Substitute } \frac{1}{2}x \text{ for } y.$$

$$x = -2 \qquad \text{Solve for } x.$$

$$y = \frac{1}{2} \cdot (-2) = -1 \qquad \text{Substitute and solve for } y.$$

So the solution to the system is $(-2, -1)$.
This is the center of the circle, so $(h, k) = (-2, -1)$.

Step 5 Calculate the radius. Use the center $(-2, -1)$ and any point on the circle, say $A(-3, 6)$.

$$r = \sqrt{(-3 - (-2))^2 + (6 - (-1))^2} = \sqrt{1 + 49} = \sqrt{50}$$

Step 6 Use the center and radius to write the equation in graphing form.

$$(x - h)^2 + (y - k)^2 = r^2$$

$$(x - (-2))^2 + (y - (-1))^2 = (\sqrt{50})^2$$

$$(x + 2)^2 + (y + 1)^2 = 50 \blacksquare$$

Problem Set

Find the equation of each circle.

1. center at $(3, 1)$ and radius 5

2. center at $(-5, -2)$ and radius 2

3.

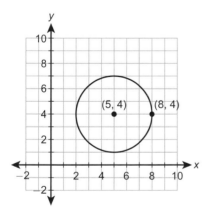

4.

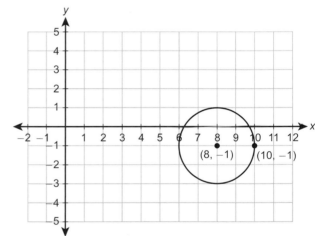

5. center at $(-4, 7)$ and radius 3.5

6. center at $(7, 9)$ and radius 10

7.

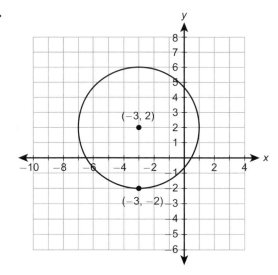

8.

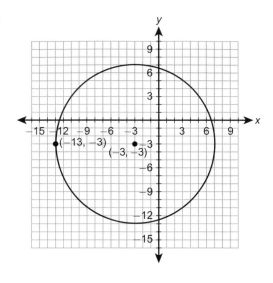

For each problem, do the following:

A. Find the center, radius, and diameter of the circle.

B. Graph the circle.

9. $(x - 2)^2 + (y - 4)^2 = 1$

10. $(x - 4)^2 + (y + 8)^2 = 64$

11. $(x + 10)^2 + (y + 9)^2 = 100$

12. $(x - 1)^2 + (y - 2)^2 = 25$

13. $x^2 + (y + 4)^2 = 36$

14. $(x - 7)^2 + (y + 2)^2 = 3$

15. $x^2 + y^2 = 49$

16. $(x - 11)^2 = 50 - y^2$

17. $(x - 1)^2 + (y - 6)^2 = 4$

18. $(x + 8)^2 + (y - 5)^2 = 16$

19. $(x + 5)^2 + (y + 7)^2 = 81$

20. $(x - 1)^2 + y^2 = 1$

Find the equation of the circle that contains the given points.

21. $A(2, 9), B(12, -1), C(8, 7)$

22. $A(-2, -3), B(-1, 4), C(6, 3)$

23. $A(0, 0), B(-1, 1), C(-1, -3)$

24. $A(-3, -4), B(9, 0), C(1, 8)$

Solve.

25. A satellite travels in a circular orbit around the earth at a distance of 26,199 miles from the earth's center.

    A. Assume that the earth's center is positioned at $(0, 0)$ in the solar system. Write an equation for the path of the satellite's orbit around the earth.

    B. Write an equation of the path of the satellite if the earth's center is positioned at $(-2000, 1300)$ in the solar system.

26. An airport's luggage carousel moves in a circular path, as shown in the graph.

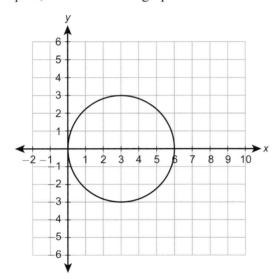

    A. Write an equation for the path of the luggage carousel.

    B. The luggage comes up in the center of the circle and moves to the circular path in a straight line. What is the distance a piece of luggage travels before it hits the circular path?

27. A ride in an amusement park takes people in a circular loop represented by the equation $(x + 3)^2 + (y + 2)^2 = 64$, with the center of the park at $(0, 0)$.

    A. A waterfall is located at the center of the ride. What are the coordinates of the waterfall's location in the amusement park?

    B. What is the distance between the center of the ride and the center of the park?

28. A radio signal reaches all locations within a 100-mile distance from the radio tower, located at $(-150, 50)$.

    A. Write an equation that represents the locations within a 100-mile distance from the radio tower.

    B. A house is located at $(-120, -40)$. How far away is the house from the radio tower? Will the radio signal reach the house?

*29. **Challenge** Write the equation of a circle with a circumference of 14π and center $(-3, 8)$.

*30. **Challenge** A line is tangent to a circle if it intersects the circle in exactly one point. Write the equation of the line that is tangent to the circle $(x + 1)^2 + (y + 2)^2 = 50$ at the point $(6, -1)$.

Ellipses

When the general second-degree equation $Ax^2 + Bxy + Cy^2 + Dx + Ey + F = 0$ has the same signs for A and C ($A \neq 0$ and $C \neq 0$), the equation is that of an ellipse.

In this topic, you'll work only with ellipses that have $B = 0$.

Deriving an Equation of an Ellipse from the Definition

<table>
<tr>
<td>

DEFINITION

An **ellipse** is the set of all points in a plane such that the sum of the distances from two fixed points (the **foci**) is constant.

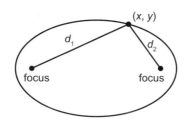

$d_1 + d_2$ is constant, no matter where (x, y) is on the ellipse.

</td>
<td>

TIP

Focus (fō-kəs) is singular.

Foci (fō-sī) is plural.

Vertex (vər-teks) is singular.

Vertices (vərt-ə-sēz) is plural.

</td>
</tr>
</table>

The **major axis** of an ellipse is the segment that passes through the foci, with endpoints on the ellipse; those endpoints are called **vertices**. The **minor axis** is the perpendicular bisector of the major axis; its endpoints are also on the ellipse and are called **covertices**. The intersection of the axes is the **center** of the ellipse. The center is the midpoint of both axes: Each half of the major axis is a **semimajor axis**; each half of the minor axis is a **semiminor axis**. The major axis is the longer axis.

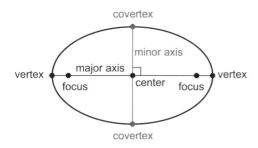

Below, F_1 and F_2 are foci, V_1 and V_2 are vertices, $\overline{V_1V_2}$ is the major axis, C_1 and C_2 are covertices, $\overline{C_1C_2}$ is the minor axis, and (h, k) is the center.

Ellipse with **horizontal** major axis:

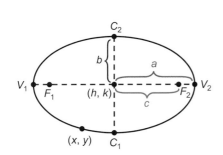

Ellipse with **vertical** major axis:

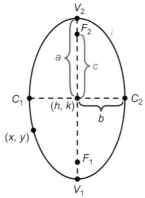

Equation in Graphing Form:

$$\frac{(x-h)^2}{a^2} + \frac{(y-k)^2}{b^2} = 1$$

Equation in Graphing Form:

$$\frac{(x-h)^2}{b^2} + \frac{(y-k)^2}{a^2} = 1$$

PROPERTIES OF ELLIPSES

Length of **major axis** (V_1V_2 in the diagrams) $= \mathbf{2a}$
Length of semimajor axis (center to either vertex) $= \mathbf{a}$

Length of **minor axis** (C_1C_2 in the diagrams) $= \mathbf{2b}$
Length of semiminor axis (center to either covertex) $= \mathbf{b}$

Distance from center to either focus $= \mathbf{c}$

$\mathbf{c^2 = a^2 - b^2}$ (or $\mathbf{a^2 = b^2 + c^2}$) $\mathbf{a > b}$ (But a^2 may be in either denominator.)	Sum of distances from the two foci to any point on the ellipse: $\mathbf{d_1 + d_2 = 2a}$.

The ellipse at right has foci $(-4, 0)$ and $(4, 0)$ and constant sum 10. The equation in graphing form of this ellipse can be derived by using the definition of an ellipse. For any point (x, y) on the ellipse, the sum of the distances from the foci is 10.

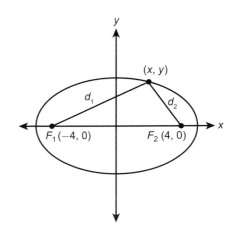

$$d_1 + d_2 = 10 \qquad \text{The sum of the distances is constant.}$$

$$\sqrt{(x+4)^2 + (y-0)^2} + \sqrt{(x-4)^2 + (y-0)^2} = 10 \qquad \text{Distance Formula}$$

$$\sqrt{x^2 + 8x + 16 + y^2} + \sqrt{x^2 - 8x + 16 + y^2} = 10 \qquad \text{Expand binomials.}$$

$$\sqrt{x^2 + 8x + 16 + y^2} = 10 - \sqrt{x^2 - 8x + 16 + y^2} \qquad \text{Isolate one radical.}$$

$$x^2 + 8x + 16 + y^2 = 100 - 20\sqrt{x^2 - 8x + 16 + y^2} \qquad \text{Square both sides.}$$
$$+ \; x^2 - 8x + 16 + y^2$$

$$16x - 100 = -20\sqrt{x^2 - 8x + 16 + y^2} \qquad \text{Isolate the remaining radical.}$$

$$256x^2 - 3200x + 10{,}000 = 400(x^2 - 8x + 16 + y^2) \qquad \text{Square both sides.}$$

$$256x^2 - 3200x + 10{,}000 = 400x^2 - 3200x + 6400 + 400y^2 \qquad \text{Distribute.}$$

$$-144x^2 - 400y^2 = -3600 \qquad \text{Isolate the constant.}$$

$$\frac{x^2}{25} + \frac{y^2}{9} = 1 \qquad \text{Divide both sides by } -3600.$$

Finding the Length of the Major and Minor Axes and the Center of an Ellipse, Given Its Graph

Example 1   Given the ellipse in the graph at right, find the following:

A the lengths of the major and minor axes

B the coordinates of the center

Solution

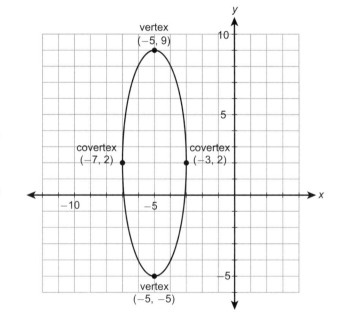

A The endpoints of the major axis are $(-5, 9)$ and $(-5, -5)$, so its length is $9 - (-5) = 14$. The length of the semimajor axis is $a = 7$.

The endpoints of the minor axis are $(-7, 2)$ and $(-3, 2)$, so its length is $-3 - (-7) = 4$. The length of the semiminor axis is $b = 2$.

B The center (h, k) is the midpoint of either axis:

$$(h, k) = \left(\frac{-5 - 5}{2}, \frac{-5 + 9}{2}\right) = (-5, 2) \text{ or}$$

$$(h, k) = \left(\frac{-7 - 3}{2}, \frac{2 + 2}{2}\right) = (-5, 2). \; \blacksquare$$

Writing an Equation of an Ellipse, Given Its Graph

Example 2   Write the equation in graphing form of the ellipse shown.

Solution   The values of h, k, a^2, and b^2 are needed for the equation. The center is the midpoint of the minor axis connecting the covertices, so the center is $(h, k) = (3, -6)$.
The length of the semiminor axis is $b = 5$, so $b^2 = 25$.
The length of the semimajor axis is $a = 8$, so $a^2 = 64$.
Substitute a^2, b^2, h, and k into the equation in graphing form.
The major axis is vertical, so use $\dfrac{(x-h)^2}{b^2} + \dfrac{(y-k)^2}{a^2} = 1$.
The equation is $\dfrac{(x-3)^2}{25} + \dfrac{(y+6)^2}{64} = 1$. ∎

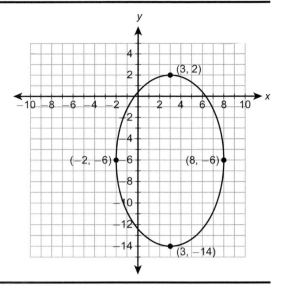

Graphing an Ellipse, Given Its Equation

Example 3   Graph the ellipse with equation $\dfrac{(x-1)^2}{81} + \dfrac{(y+7)^2}{16} = 1$.

Solution   In an ellipse, $a > b$, so $a^2 = 81$, and the equation is in graphing form $\dfrac{(x-h)^2}{a^2} + \dfrac{(y-k)^2}{b^2} = 1$. Therefore, the major axis is horizontal, $h = 1$, $k = -7$, $a = \sqrt{81} = 9$, and $b = \sqrt{16} = 4$.

Step 1   Plot the center (h, k) at $(1, -7)$.

Step 2   The major axis is horizontal. Count 9 units left and 9 units right from the center. Plot the vertices at $(-8, -7)$ and $(10, -7)$.

Step 3   The minor axis is vertical. Count 4 units down and 4 units up from the center. Plot the covertices at $(1, -11)$ and $(1, -3)$.

Step 4   Sketch the ellipse through the vertices and covertices.

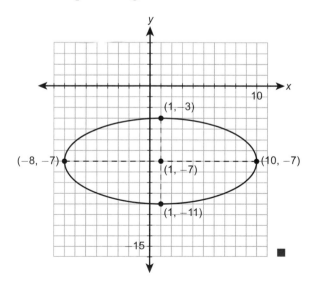

Finding the Eccentricity and Foci of an Ellipse

All conic sections have a ratio e, called *eccentricity*. For ellipses, the value of e determines the shape of the ellipse. (You will see later that the value of e also determines the shape of a hyperbola.)

DEFINITION

The **eccentricity** of an ellipse is the ratio $e = \frac{c}{a}$.

Properties of Eccentricity for Ellipses

- $0 < e < 1$ (or $0 \leq e < 1$ if a circle is considered to be an ellipse.)
- If e is near 0, then c is near 0, and the ellipse looks nearly circular. (The foci are near the center.)
- If e is near 1, then c and a are close in value, and the ellipse looks elongated. (The foci get closer to the vertices.)

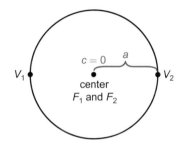

Eccentricity is 0.
Ellipse is a circle.

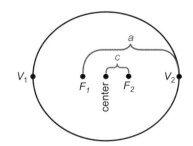

Eccentricity is closer to 0.
Ellipse is more "circular."

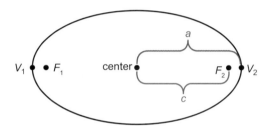

Eccentricity is closer to 1.
Ellipse is less "circular."

Example 4 For the equation $\dfrac{(x+3)^2}{25} + \dfrac{(y-5)^2}{4} = 1$, do the following:

A Find the coordinates of the foci.

B Find the eccentricity.

Solution The equation is in graphing form $\dfrac{(x-h)^2}{a^2} + \dfrac{(y-k)^2}{b^2} = 1$, with a horizontal major axis.

A Calculate c to find the coordinates of the foci:
$c^2 = a^2 - b^2 = 25 - 4 = 21$, so $c = \sqrt{21}$.

The distance from the center to each focus is $\sqrt{21}$. The major axis is horizontal, so the foci are left and right of the center at $(-3 - \sqrt{21}, 5)$ and $(-3 + \sqrt{21}, 5)$, or about $(-7.6, 5)$ and $(1.6, 5)$.

B Calculate a:
$a = \sqrt{25} = 5$

Substitute the values for c and a: $e = \dfrac{c}{a} = \dfrac{\sqrt{21}}{5} \approx 0.92$. ∎

> **THINK ABOUT IT**
>
> For an ellipse, $c^2 = a^2 - b^2$. If $a = b$, then the major axis and minor axis have equal lengths, forming a circle. Then $c^2 = 0$, $c = 0$, and $e = \dfrac{c}{a} = \dfrac{0}{a} = 0$.

Problem Set

Find the equation of the ellipse.

1.

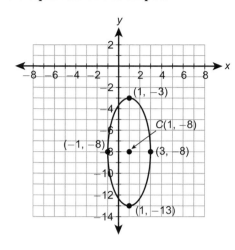

2.

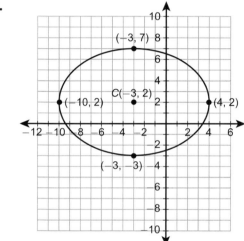

3.

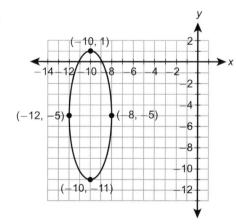

4.

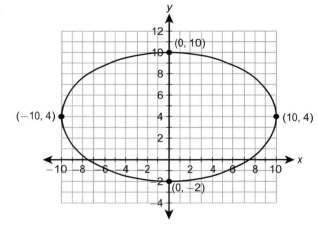

5.

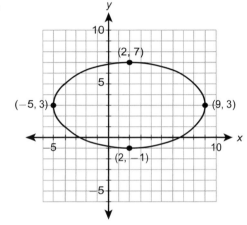

6.

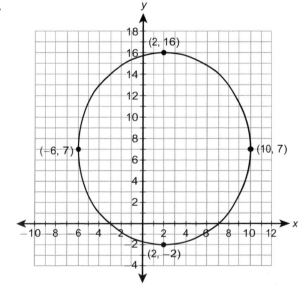

For each problem, do the following:

A. Find the coordinates of the center.
B. Find the length of the major axis.
C. Find the length of the minor axis.
D. Graph the ellipse.

7. $\dfrac{x^2}{4} + \dfrac{y^2}{9} = 1$

8. $\dfrac{x^2}{9} + \dfrac{y^2}{25} = 1$

9. $\dfrac{(x-1)^2}{16} + \dfrac{y^2}{36} = 1$

10. $\dfrac{x^2}{16} + \dfrac{(y-9)^2}{4} = 1$

11. $\dfrac{(x-3)^2}{25} + \dfrac{(y-6)^2}{4} = 1$

12. $\dfrac{(x+12)^2}{100} + \dfrac{(y-15)^2}{64} = 1$

13. $\dfrac{(x-6)^2}{169} + \dfrac{(y+3)^2}{225} = 1$

14. $\dfrac{(x+7)^2}{81} + \dfrac{(y+10)^2}{16} = 1$

15. $\dfrac{(x-1)^2}{16} + \dfrac{(y-8)^2}{49} = 1$

16. $\dfrac{(x-5)^2}{100} + \dfrac{(y-4)^2}{81} = 1$

17. $\dfrac{(x+1)^2}{54} + \dfrac{(y-6)^2}{144} = 1$

18. $\dfrac{(x-8)^2}{20} + \dfrac{(y+10)^2}{64} = 1$

Find the coordinates of the foci of the ellipse.

19. $\dfrac{(x-4)^2}{100} + \dfrac{(y-8)^2}{64} = 1$

20. $\dfrac{(x+4)^2}{46} + \dfrac{(y-9)^2}{50} = 1$

21. $\dfrac{(x+2)^2}{4} + \dfrac{(y+8)^2}{16} = 1$

22. $\dfrac{(x+10)^2}{49} + \dfrac{y^2}{4} = 1$

23. $\dfrac{(x-2)^2}{9} + \dfrac{(y-3)^2}{25} = 1$

24. $\dfrac{(x+5)^2}{64} + \dfrac{(y-4)^2}{49} = 1$

Find the eccentricity of the ellipse.

25. $\dfrac{(x+2)^2}{100} + \dfrac{(y-7)^2}{81} = 1$

27. $\dfrac{(x-9)^2}{64} + \dfrac{(y+8)^2}{144} = 1$

26.

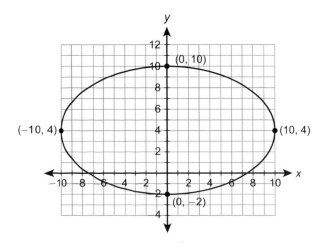

28.

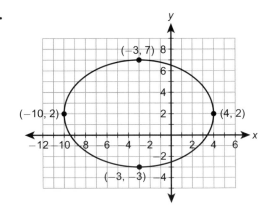

Solve.

29. An elliptical mirror reflects light from one focus toward the other focus. A designer installs an elliptical mirror modeled by the equation

    $$\frac{(x + 4)^2}{16} + \frac{y^2}{25} = 1.$$

    A. Graph the elliptical mirror.

    B. A light ray that passes through one focus will pass through the other. What two points will this light ray pass through?

30. A tunnel has an elliptical opening that is 60 feet high and 80 feet wide.

    A. Write an equation that models the tunnel.

    B. Find the foci of the ellipse.

    C. Find the eccentricity of the ellipse. What does this indicate about the shape of the ellipse?

31. A whispering gallery is enclosed in an elliptical area. If a person stands at one focus and whispers, the sound will reflect directly to the other focus. Emma and Jamal are in an elliptical whispering gallery that is 324 feet long and 196 feet wide.

    A. What are the lengths of the semimajor and semiminor axes?

    B. Write the distance that Emma should stand from Jamal so that she will hear Jamal's whisper.

    C. Write an equation of an ellipse that models the whispering gallery.

32. A standing tin of chocolates has an elliptical opening that is 36 centimeters wide and 16 centimeters high.

    A. Write an equation that models the tin.

    B. Find the foci of the ellipse.

    C. Find the eccentricity of the ellipse. What does this eccentricity indicate about the shape of the ellipse?

*33. **Challenge** The earth is at one focus of the elliptical orbit of a satellite. The length of the major axis is 30,000 miles, and the earth's center is 9000 miles from the center of the ellipse. Write the equation for the path of the satellite.

*34. **Challenge** The "whisper chamber" in the United States Capitol is shaped like an ellipse. If Yasmine stands at one focus and whispers, Sharika, who is standing at the other focus, can hear her distinctly. Find the equation of the shape of the room given the length of the horizontal major axis of the chamber is 96 feet and the two girls are standing $10\sqrt{71}$ feet apart. Assume the chamber is centered at the origin.

Hyperbolas

When the general second-degree equation
$Ax^2 + Bxy + Cy^2 + Dx + Ey + F = 0$ has opposite
signs for A and C, then the equation is that of a
hyperbola.

Deriving an Equation of a Hyperbola from the Definition

> ### DEFINITION
>
> A **hyperbola** is the set of all points in a plane such that the absolute
> value of the difference of the distances from two fixed points (the **foci**)
> is constant.

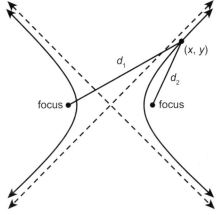

$|d_2 - d_1|$ is constant, no matter
where (x, y) is on the hyperbola.

Every hyperbola has two separate **branches**. The line through the foci
intersects the hyperbola at two **vertices**. The **transverse axis** is the line
segment joining the vertices. The midpoint of the transverse axis is the
center of the hyperbola. Every hyperbola has an **associated rectangle**.
The diagonals of the associated rectangle pass through the center. The lines
containing these diagonals are **asymptotes** of the hyperbola. As a point
in the hyperbola gets farther from either vertex, it approaches—but never
touches—one of the asymptotes. The **conjugate axis** is the line segment
through the center, perpendicular to the transverse axis, with endpoints on
the associated rectangle. A hyperbola is symmetric with respect to both its
transverse axis and its conjugate axis.

In each diagram below, F_1 and F_2 are foci, V_1 and V_2 are vertices, $\overline{V_1 V_2}$ is the transverse axis, and (h, k) is the center.

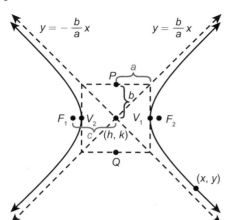

Hyperbola with **horizontal** transverse axis:

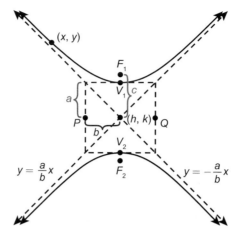

Hyperbola with **vertical** transverse axis:

Equation in Graphing Form:
$$\frac{(x - h)^2}{a^2} - \frac{(y - k)^2}{b^2} = 1$$

Slopes of Asymptotes: $\pm \dfrac{b}{a}$

Equation in Graphing Form:
$$\frac{(y - k)^2}{a^2} - \frac{(x - h)^2}{b^2} = 1$$

Slopes of Asymptotes: $\pm \dfrac{a}{b}$

PROPERTIES OF HYPERBOLAS

Length of transverse axis = **2a** (V_1V_2 in the diagrams above)
Distance from center to either vertex = **a**

Length of conjugate axis = **2b** (PQ in the diagrams above)

Distance from center to either focus = **c**
$c^2 = a^2 + b^2$
In the equation in graphing form, a^2 is always the first denominator.
Any of these are possible: $a > b$, $a = b$, or $a < b$.

The hyperbola to the right has foci $(0, 5)$ and $(0, -5)$ and constant difference 6. The equation in graphing form of this hyperbola can be derived by using the definition of a hyperbola. For any point (x, y) on the hyperbola, the absolute value of the difference of the distances from the foci is 6.

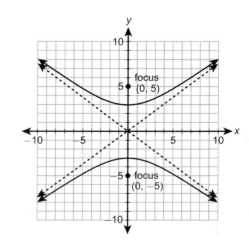

$$\begin{aligned}
d_2 \qquad - \qquad d_1 \qquad &= \pm 6 \\
\sqrt{(x-0)^2 + (y+5)^2} - \sqrt{(x-0)^2 + (y-5)^2} &= \pm 6 \\
\sqrt{x^2 + y^2 + 10y + 25} - \sqrt{x^2 + y^2 - 10y + 25} &= \pm 6 \\
\sqrt{x^2 + y^2 + 10y + 25} &= \pm 6 + \sqrt{x^2 + y^2 - 10y + 25} \\
x^2 + y^2 + 10y + 25 &= 36 \pm 12\sqrt{x^2 + y^2 - 10y + 25} \\
&\quad + x^2 + y^2 - 10y + 25 \\
20y - 36 &= \pm 12\sqrt{x^2 + y^2 - 10y + 25} \\
5y - 9 &= \pm 3\sqrt{x^2 + y^2 - 10y + 25} \\
25y^2 - 90y + 81 &= 9(x^2 + y^2 - 10y + 25) \\
25y^2 - 90y + 81 &= 9x^2 + 9y^2 - 90y + 225 \\
16y^2 - 9x^2 &= 144 \\
\frac{y^2}{9} - \frac{x^2}{16} &= 1
\end{aligned}$$

If $|d_2 - d_1| = 6$, then $d_2 - d_1 = \pm 6$.

Distance Formula

Expand binomials.

Get one radical on each side.

Square both sides.

Isolate the radical term.

Divide both sides by 4.

Square both sides.

Distribute.

Isolate the constant term.

Divide both sides by 144.

Finding Everything You Want to Know About a Hyperbola, Given Its Equation

Example 1   The equation of a hyperbola is $\dfrac{y^2}{9} - \dfrac{x^2}{16} = 1$.

Ⓐ Identify the location of the center.

Ⓑ Identify the lengths of the transverse and conjugate axes.

Ⓒ Identify the equations of the asymptotes.

Ⓓ Graph the hyperbola. Label the axes and asymptotes.

Solution   Rewrite the equation as $\dfrac{(y-0)^2}{3^2} - \dfrac{(x-0)^2}{4^2} = 1$ to see that it is in the form $\dfrac{(y-k)^2}{a^2} - \dfrac{(x-h)^2}{b^2} = 1$.
This hyperbola has a vertical transverse axis.

Ⓐ In the equation, the center (h, k) is $(0, 0)$.

Ⓑ In the equation, $a = 3$ and $b = 4$. This means the length of the transverse axis is $2a = 2 \cdot 3 = 6$, and the length of the conjugate axis is $2b = 2 \cdot 4 = 8$.

Ⓒ The slopes of the asymptotes are $\pm\dfrac{a}{b} = \pm\dfrac{3}{4}$, so the equations of the asymptotes are $y = \dfrac{3}{4}x$ and $y = -\dfrac{3}{4}x$.

Ⓓ

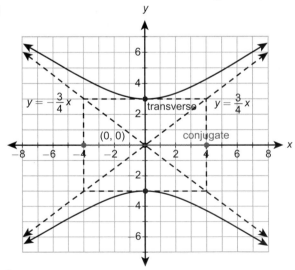

Writing an Equation of a Hyperbola, Given Its Graph

Example 2 Write the standard equation of the hyperbola shown at the right.

Solution The center is the midpoint of the line segment connecting the vertices, so the center is (3, 2), and $h = 3$ and $k = 2$.

The distance between the vertices is 6, so $a = 3$. Since the length of the conjugate axis $2b$ is 10, b is 5.

The transverse axis is horizontal, so the equation has the form $\dfrac{(x - h)^2}{a^2} - \dfrac{(y - k)^2}{b^2} = 1$. The equation is $\dfrac{(x - 3)^2}{9} - \dfrac{(y - 2)^2}{25} = 1$. ∎

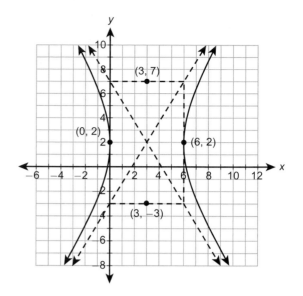

Graphing a Hyperbola, Given Its Equation

Example 3 Graph the hyperbola with equation $\dfrac{(y - 3)^2}{4} - \dfrac{(x + 2)^2}{9} = 1$.

Solution The equation is in the graphing form $\dfrac{(y - k)^2}{a^2} - \dfrac{(x - h)^2}{b^2} = 1$, so the transverse axis is vertical. In the equation, $k = 3$ and $h = -2$, so the center (h, k) is $(-2, 3)$. Also, $a^2 = 4$ and $b^2 = 9$, so $a = 2$ and $b = 3$.

Step 1 Graph the center. To graph the vertices, count 2 units up and 2 units down from the center. The vertices are $(-2, 5)$ and $(-2, 1)$.

Step 2 Use the values of a and b to sketch the associated rectangle. The dimensions of the rectangle are $2a = 4$ and $2b = 6$.

Step 3 Sketch the lines containing the diagonals of the rectangle; these lines will be the asymptotes of the hyperbola.

Verify that the slopes of the asymptotes are $\pm \dfrac{a}{b} = \pm \dfrac{2}{3}$.

Step 4 Sketch the two branches of the hyperbola, using the asymptotes as a guide.

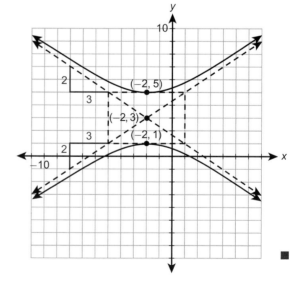

∎

Finding the Eccentricity of a Hyperbola

Eccentricity is a ratio that indicates the appearance of a conic.

DEFINITION

The **eccentricity** e of a hyperbola is the ratio $e = \frac{c}{a}$.

PROPERTIES OF ECCENTRICITY FOR HYPERBOLAS

- For all hyperbolas, $e > 1$ because $c > a$.
- If c is much greater than a, then e is large, and the branches of the hyperbola are wide.
- If c is close to a, then e is close to 1, and the branches of the hyperbola are narrow.

TIP

Ellipses and hyperbolas have the same ratio for eccentricity.

$$e = \frac{c}{a}$$

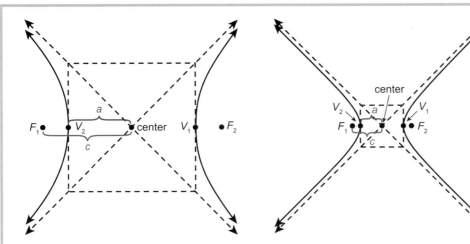

The values of c and e are large. The hyperbola has wide branches.

The values of c and e are close to 1. The hyperbola has narrow branches.

Example 4 For the equation $\dfrac{(y-2)^2}{16} - \dfrac{(x+4)^2}{16} = 1$, do the following:

A Find the coordinates of the foci.

B Find the eccentricity.

Solution The equation is in graphing form $\dfrac{(y-k)^2}{a^2} - \dfrac{(x-h)^2}{b^2} = 1$ and indicates that the hyperbola has a vertical transverse axis.

A To find the coordinates of the foci, find c.
$a^2 = b^2 = 16$, so $a = b = 4$. To find c, substitute these values into the equation: $c^2 = a^2 + b^2 = 16 + 16 = 32$. So $c = \sqrt{32} \approx 5.66$. The coordinates of the foci are approximately $(-4, 7.66)$ and $(-4, -3.66)$.

B The eccentricity for this hyperbola is $e = \dfrac{c}{a} = \dfrac{\sqrt{32}}{4} \approx 1.4$. ∎

Problem Set

Find the equation of the hyperbola.

1.

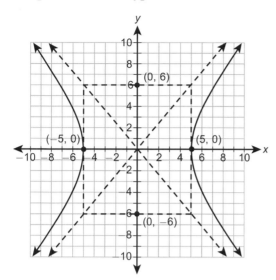

2.

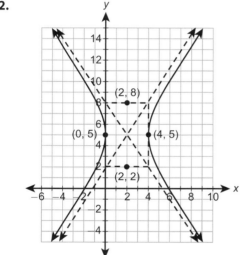

3.

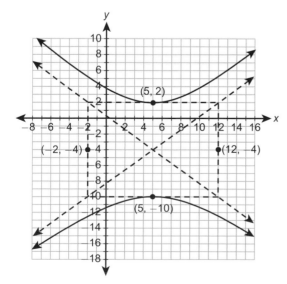

4.

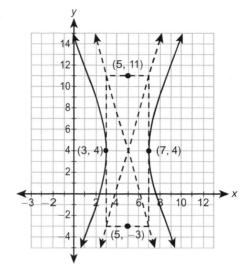

5.

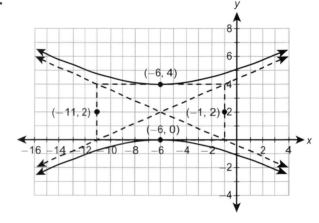

6.

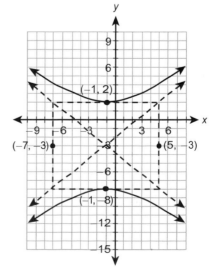

For each problem, do the following:

A. Find the coordinates of the center.
B. Find the length of the transverse axis.
C. Find the length of the conjugate axis.
D. Find the equations of the asymptotes.
E. Graph the hyperbola.

7. $\dfrac{x^2}{100} - \dfrac{y^2}{25} = 1$

8. $\dfrac{x^2}{49} - \dfrac{y^2}{64} = 1$

9. $\dfrac{y^2}{81} - \dfrac{x^2}{16} = 1$

10. $\dfrac{x^2}{4} - \dfrac{(y-11)^2}{9} = 1$

11. $\dfrac{(x-2)^2}{9} - \dfrac{y^2}{4} = 1$

12. $\dfrac{(y+3)^2}{16} - \dfrac{(x-5)^2}{81} = 1$

13. $\dfrac{(x-12)^2}{36} - \dfrac{(y-10)^2}{49} = 1$

14. $\dfrac{(x+4)^2}{121} - \dfrac{(y-1)^2}{100} = 1$

15. $\dfrac{(y-2)^2}{81} - \dfrac{(x+10)^2}{9} = 1$

16. $\dfrac{(y-1)^2}{25} - \dfrac{(x+1)^2}{16} = 1$

17. $\dfrac{(x+9)^2}{49} - \dfrac{(y+5)^2}{85} = 1$

18. $\dfrac{(y-1)^2}{24} - \dfrac{(x-2)^2}{36} = 1$

Find the coordinates of the foci of the hyperbola.

19. $\dfrac{y^2}{64} - \dfrac{(x-1)^2}{36} = 1$

20. $\dfrac{(x+7)^2}{16} - \dfrac{y^2}{9} = 1$

21. $\dfrac{(x+8)^2}{4} - \dfrac{(y+4)^2}{9} = 1$

22. $\dfrac{(y-12)^2}{16} - \dfrac{(x-3)^2}{4} = 1$

Find the eccentricity of the hyperbola.

23. $\dfrac{y^2}{36} - \dfrac{x^2}{64} = 1$

25. $\dfrac{(x-3)^2}{4} - \dfrac{(y-8)^2}{25} = 1$

24.

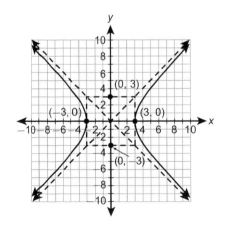

26.

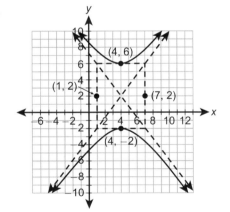

Answer each question.

27. The paths of two comets are represented by the hyperbola with equation $\frac{x^2}{16} - \frac{y^2}{49} = 1$. Each branch represents the path of one comet. Find one point along each path at which the comets' paths are closest.

28. The shapes of a pair of hyperbolic mirrors can be described by the graph of $\frac{(y-2)^2}{4} - \frac{(x-3)^2}{9} = 1$. An object is placed in the center between the mirrors. Find the location of the object.

29. If a part of a satellite's path can be modeled by the graph of a hyperbola, find the equation of the hyperbola, given $a = 220{,}531$ km and $c = 525{,}231$ km. Assume the center of the hyperbola is at the origin and the hyperbola has a horizontal transverse axis.

30. During stormy conditions, an airplane is forced to travel along the path modeled by the right branch of the hyperbola with equation $\frac{x^2}{16} - \frac{y^2}{25} = 1$. Find the originally planned path if it corresponds to the positively sloped asymptote.

*31. **Challenge** A meteor travels along the path of a hyperbola with the equation $\frac{(y-4)^2}{900} - \frac{x^2}{2500} = 1$. Find each of the following:

   A. the lengths of the transverse and conjugate axes

   B. the location of the center of the hyperbola

   C. the coordinates of the foci

   D. the slopes of the asymptotes

*32. **Challenge** Using the diagram, show that $|d_2 - d_1| = 2a$. Hint: Choose a vertex of the hyperbola for the point (x, y).

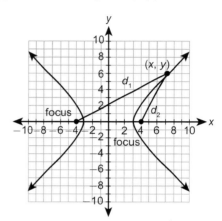

Parabolas

You have learned that the graph of a quadratic function is a parabola that opens upward or downward. Now you'll learn more about parabolas, including those that open left and right (and therefore do not represent functions).

Deriving an Equation of a Parabola from the Definition

DEFINITIONS

A **parabola** is the set of all points in a plane that are equidistant from a fixed line (the **directrix**) and a fixed point (the **focus**).

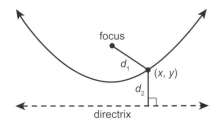

$d_1 = d_2$ for any point (x, y) on the parabola.

The standard equation of a parabola can be derived by using the definition. The parabola below has focus $(0, 3)$ and directrix $y = -3$. The distance from a point to a line is the length of the line segment from the point perpendicular to the line. So the distance from (x, y) to the horizontal directrix is the vertical distance from (x, y) to $(x, -3)$.

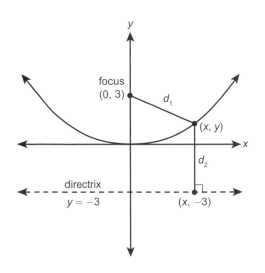

$$d_1 = d_2$$

$$\sqrt{(x - 0)^2 + (y - 3)^2} = \sqrt{(x - x)^2 + (y + 3)^2} \qquad \text{Distance Formula}$$

$$\sqrt{x^2 + y^2 - 6y + 9} = \sqrt{y^2 + 6y + 9} \qquad \text{Expand binomials.}$$

$$x^2 + y^2 - 6y + 9 = y^2 + 6y + 9 \qquad \text{Square each side.}$$

$$x^2 = 12y \qquad \text{Simplify.}$$

Writing an Equation of a Parabola, Given Its Graph

There are many equivalent ways to write the equation $x^2 = 12y$. You could write it in the general form of a second-degree equation: $x^2 - 12y = 0$. Or, because the parabola represents a function, you could also write it in the standard form of a quadratic function: $y = \frac{1}{12}x^2$.

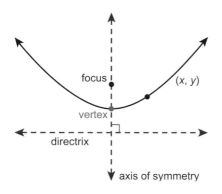

Every parabola has a single **vertex** that lies halfway between the focus and directrix. The **axis of symmetry** is the line that passes through the focus and vertex, perpendicular to the directrix. The axis of symmetry separates the graph into two halves that are reflection images of each other.

In the diagrams below, V is the vertex with coordinates (h, k), F is the focus, and f is the *directed* distance from V to F (positive for right or up; negative for left or down).

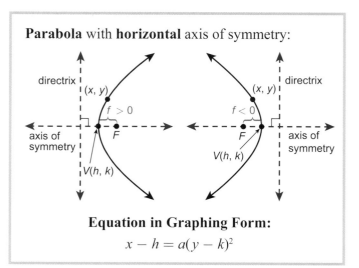

Parabola with horizontal axis of symmetry:

Equation in Graphing Form:
$$x - h = a(y - k)^2$$

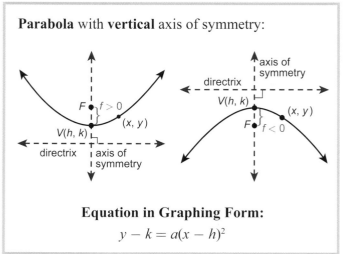

Parabola with vertical axis of symmetry:

Equation in Graphing Form:
$$y - k = a(x - h)^2$$

PROPERTIES OF PARABOLAS

If the directed distance from vertex to focus (the **focal distance**) is represented by f, then the directed distance from vertex to directrix is $-f$, and $a = \dfrac{1}{4f}$ $\left(\text{or } f = \dfrac{1}{4a}\right)$.

- $f \neq 0$ and $a \neq 0$.
- $f > 0$ and $a > 0$ if the parabola opens right or up.
- $f < 0$ and $a < 0$ if the parabola opens left or down.
- The **eccentricity** of a parabola is $e = 1$.

TIP

The eccentricity of a parabola is $e = \dfrac{XF}{XD}$, where X is any point on the parabola, F is the focus, and D is the directrix. Because $XF = XD$ for any point X on a parabola, $e = 1$.

Example 1 Write the equation in graphing form of the parabola shown.

Solution The axis of symmetry has the equation $y = -1$, and it intersects the directrix at $(0.625, -1)$.

The vertex (h, k) is halfway between the focus and directrix, so it is the midpoint of the segment from $(0.375, -1)$ to $(0.625, -1)$:

$$(h, k) = \left(\frac{0.375 + 0.625}{2}, \frac{-1 + (-1)}{2} \right) = \left(\frac{1}{2}, \frac{-2}{2} \right) = (0.5, -1).$$

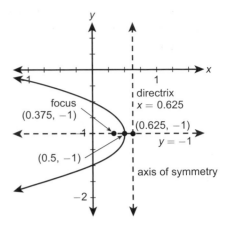

The focus is 0.125 unit left of the vertex, so $f = -0.125$. Find a.

$$a = \frac{1}{4f} = \frac{1}{4(-0.125)} = -2$$

Substitute h, k, and a into the equation in graphing form for a horizontal parabola.

$$x - h = a(y - k)^2$$
$$x - 0.5 = -2(y + 1)^2 \quad \blacksquare$$

Graphing a Parabola, Given Its Equation in Graphing Form

Example 2 Graph the parabola with equation $x - 3 = 2(y - 4)^2$.

Solution Use the same techniques that you learned to graph the vertex form of a quadratic function.

The equation is in the graphing form $x - h = a(y - k)^2$, so the parabola has a horizontal axis of symmetry. Since the value of a is positive, the parabola opens to the right.

Step 1 Plot the vertex $(3, 4)$ and sketch the axis of symmetry $y = 4$.

Step 2 Find and plot two more solutions to the equation $x - 3 = 2(y - 4)^2$, such as $(5, 5)$ and $(8, 5.58)$.

Step 3 Reflect the points you found in Step 2 across the axis of symmetry to find two points on the other side: $(5, 3)$ and $(3, 3.58)$.

Step 4 Draw a smooth curve through all the points.

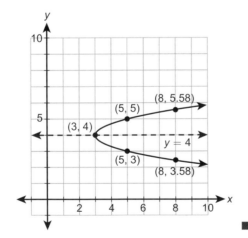

> **THINK ABOUT IT**
>
> In the study of conic sections, $x - h = a(y - k)^2$ and $y - k = a(x - h)^2$ are called equations in graphing form of parabolas. Equations of the form $y - k = a(x - h)^2$ represent functions and can be rewritten in the form $y = ax^2 + bx + c$, which is called standard form in the study of quadratic functions. (Try it. You should find that $b = -2ah$ and $c = ah^2 + k$.)

> **TIP**
>
> The focus, directrix, and axis of symmetry are not really part of the graph, but they provide important information. If you identify them in a problem, it is useful to include them in the graph.

Identifying the Vertex, Focal Length, Focus, and Directrix of a Parabola, Given Its Equation

Example 3 The equation of a parabola is $y - 4 = 0.125(x + 3)^2$.

A Identify the coordinates of the vertex.

B Identify the focal length and the coordinates of the focus.

C Identify the equation of the directrix.

D Graph the parabola. Label the vertex, focus, axis of symmetry, directrix, and two other points on the curve.

Solution The value of a is positive, so the parabola opens upward.

A The equation is in the graphing form $y - k = a(x - h)^2$, with $h = -3$, $k = 4$, and $a = 0.125$. So the vertex (h, k) is at $(-3, 4)$.

B The distance from the vertex to the focus is $f = \dfrac{1}{4a} = \dfrac{1}{4 \cdot 0.125} = \dfrac{1}{0.5} = 2$.

Because $f = 2$, the focus is 2 units above the vertex at $F(-3, 6)$.

C Because $-f = -2$, the directrix is 2 units below the vertex and passes through $(-3, 2)$. The axis of symmetry is vertical, so the directrix is horizontal. The equation of the directrix is $y = 2$.

D

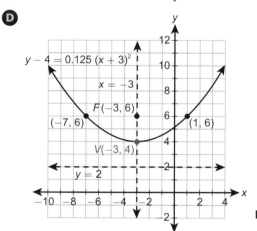

Problem Set

Find the equation of the parabola.

1.

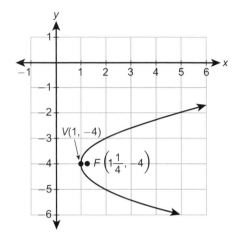

2.

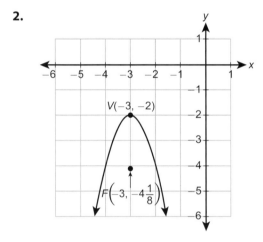

3.

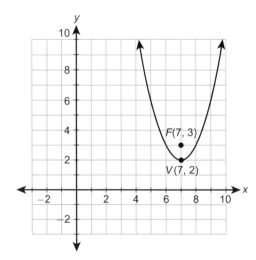

4.

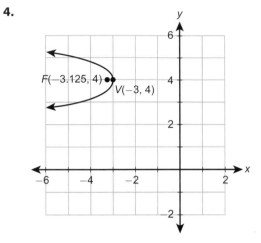

5.

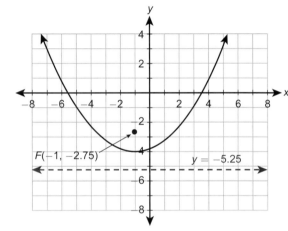

6.

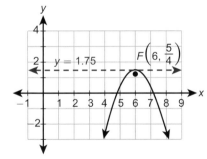

For each problem, do the following:

A. Identify the coordinates of the vertex.
B. Graph the parabola.

7. $y = -x^2$

8. $x = 2(y + 3)^2$

9. $x + 1.4 = -(y - 7)^2$

10. $y + 10 = -5(x - 4)^2$

11. $y - 25 = (x - 36)^2$

12. $x = (y - 12)^2$

13. $y - 1 = -2x^2$

14. $y + 4 = -\frac{1}{2}(x - 2)^2$

15. $x + 4 = (y + 16)^2$

16. $y + 1.5 = 5(x - 7)^2$

For each problem, do the following:

A. Identify the focal length.
B. Identify the coordinates of the focus.
C. Find the equation of the directrix.

17. $y - 1 = 3(x + 1)^2$

18. $y = -2(x - 2.5)^2$

19. $y = \frac{1}{5}(x - 9)^2$

20. $x - 1 = -\frac{1}{2}(y - 8)^2$

21. $y + 20 = 0.2(x - 2)^2$

22. $x = -0.75(y + 5)^2$

23. $x + 7 = 5(y - 1)^2$

24. $y + 24 = -\frac{1}{8}(x - 3)^2$

Solve.

25. The flame of the Olympic torch is sparked using a parabolic mirror. If the shape of the parabolic mirror is modeled by the equation $y + 2 = 0.5(x - 3)^2$, find the coordinates of the focus.

26. A parabolic reflector in a telescope is modeled by the equation $y - 2 = 0.25(x + 1)^2$. Graph the parabola and label its focus point.

27. Olivia hits a game-winning home run. The ball travels in the parabolic path shown in the graph. Write an equation for the path of the baseball in the air.

28. Andrew launches a toy rocket into the air and watches it travel along a parabolic path modeled by the equation $y - 256 = -5(x - 4)^2$. Find the vertex, focus, and directrix of the parabola.

*****29.** **Challenge** The focus of a parabola is $(-1, 2)$ and the directrix is $y = -1$. Write the equation of the parabola in graphing form.

30. Jeremy is building a bird feeder like the one shown. The wire he is using to hang the bird feeder passes through the focus of each end. Write the equation representing the shape of each end of the bird feeder.

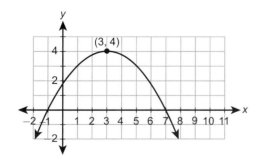

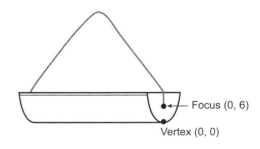

Putting Conics into Graphing Form

Conic sections have many applications in science and technology.

PROPERTIES OF $Ax^2 + Bxy + Cy^2 + Dx + Ey + F = 0$

The general form of the equation for any conic section is
$$Ax^2 + Bxy + Cy^2 + Dx + Ey + F = 0$$
where x, y, A, B, C, D, E, and F are all real numbers.

Use the value of the discriminant $B^2 - 4AC$ to determine the type of conic described by the general form.

Discriminant Value	Conic Section
$B^2 - 4AC > 0$	Hyperbola
$B^2 - 4AC = 0$	Parabola
$B^2 - 4AC < 0$	Ellipse if $A \neq C$ Circle if $A = C$

THINK ABOUT IT

This definition of the value of the discriminant is different than the one used for determining the type of roots of a parabola.

Identifying a Conic from Its Equation in General Form

Example 1   Use the discriminant to identify the conic section in each equation.

A $4x^2 + 4y^2 + 24x - 12y - 35 = 0$

Solution

$A = 4$, $B = 0$, $C = 4$

$B^2 - 4AC = 0^2 - 4 \cdot 4 \cdot 4$

$\qquad\qquad = 0 - 64 = -64 < 0$

$A = C = 4$

The graph is a circle. ∎

B $5x^2 + 2y^2 - 100x - 12y + 498 = 0$

Solution

$A = 5$, $B = 0$, $C = 2$

$B^2 - 4AC = 0^2 - 4 \cdot 5 \cdot 2$

$\qquad\qquad = 0 - 40 = -40 < 0$

$A = 5 \neq 2 = C$

The graph is an ellipse. ∎

C $4x^2 - 9y^2 - 24x - 18y - 9 = 0$

Solution

$A = 4$, $B = 0$, $C = -9$

$B^2 - 4AC = 0^2 - 4 \cdot 4 \cdot (-9)$

$\qquad\qquad = 0 + 144 = 144 > 0$

The graph is a hyperbola. ∎

D $3y^2 - x - 12y + 13 = 0$

Solution

$A = 0$, $B = 0$, $C = 3$

$B^2 - 4AC = 0^2 - 4 \cdot 0 \cdot 3$

$\qquad\qquad = 0 - 0 = 0$

The graph is a parabola. ∎

Converting an Equation of a Circle from General Form to Graphing Form

When the general second-degree equation $Ax^2 + Bxy + Cy^2 + Dx + Ey + F = 0$ has $B^2 - 4AC < 0$ and $A = C$ (but not zero), the equation is that of a circle. Converting from general form to graphing form will help you find the center and radius of the circle.

Example 2   An equation of a circle is $4x^2 + 4y^2 + 24x - 16y - 12 = 0$.

Ⓐ Write the equation of the circle in graphing form.

Ⓑ Graph the circle.

Solution
The equation is in general second-degree form with $B^2 - 4AC < 0$ and $A = C$, so this is an equation of a circle.

Ⓐ To write the equation in graphing form, complete the square for each variable.

$4x^2 + 4y^2 + 24x - 16y - 12 = 0$	Equation in general form
$4x^2 + 4y^2 + 24x - 16y \quad = 12$	Isolate the constant.
$4x^2 + 24x \quad + 4y^2 - 16y \quad = 12$	Group like terms.
$4(x^2 + 6x \quad) + 4(y^2 - 4y \quad) = 12$	Factor to get leading terms x^2 and y^2.
$4(x^2 + 6x + 9) + 4(y^2 - 4y + 4) = 12 + 36 + 16$	Complete the squares. Because you added 9 and 4 inside the parentheses, you are really adding $4 \cdot 9 = 36$ and $4 \cdot 4 = 16$.
$4(x + 3)^2 + 4(y - 2)^2 = 64$	Write the trinomials as squared binomials.
$(x + 3)^2 + (y - 2)^2 = 16$	Divide ea ch side by 4.

Ⓑ In graphing form, $h = -3$, $k = 2$, and $r = 4$.

Step 1   First plot the center (h, k) at $(-3, 2)$.

Step 2   Count 4 units left, right, up, and down from the center to find the approximate locations of four points on the circle.

Step 3   Draw the circle through the four points.

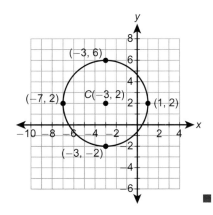

Converting an Equation of an Ellipse from General Form to Graphing Form

When the general second-degree equation $Ax^2 + Bxy + Cy^2 + Dx + Ey + F = 0$ has $B^2 - 4AC < 0$ and $A \neq C$, the equation is that of an ellipse. To find the center of the ellipse and the length of the major and minor axes, convert from general form to graphing form.

Example 3 The equation of an ellipse is $5x^2 + 2y^2 - 40x - 12y + 78 = 0$.

A Write the equation in graphing form.

B Graph the ellipse.

Solution

A The equation is in general second-degree form with $B^2 - 4AC < 0$ and $A \neq C$. This is an equation of an ellipse. To write the equation in graphing form, complete the square for each variable.

<table>
<tr><td>$5x^2 + 2y^2 - 40x - 12y + 78 = 0$</td><td>Equation in general form</td></tr>
<tr><td>$5x^2 + 2y^2 - 40x - 12y = -78$</td><td>Isolate the constant.</td></tr>
<tr><td>$5x^2 - 40x \qquad + 2y^2 - 12y = -78$</td><td>Group like terms.</td></tr>
<tr><td>$5(x^2 - 8x \quad) + 2(y^2 - 6y \quad) = -78$</td><td>Factor to get leading terms x^2 and y^2.</td></tr>
<tr><td>$5(x^2 - 8x + 16) + 2(y^2 - 6y + 9) = -78 + 80 + 18$</td><td>Complete the squares. Note that you are adding 80 and 18 to both sides.</td></tr>
<tr><td>$5(x - 4)^2 + 2(y - 3)^2 = 20$</td><td>Write the trinomials as squared binomials.</td></tr>
<tr><td>$\dfrac{5(x - 4)^2}{20} + \dfrac{2(y - 3)^2}{20} = \dfrac{20}{20}$</td><td>Divide each side by 20.</td></tr>
<tr><td>$\dfrac{(x - 4)^2}{4} + \dfrac{(y - 3)^2}{10} = 1$</td><td>Simplify.</td></tr>
</table>

B In graphing form, $h = 4$, $k = 3$, $a = \sqrt{10} \approx 3.16$, and $b = \sqrt{4} = 2$.

Step 1 Plot the center (h, k) at $(4, 3)$.

Step 2 The length of the major axis $2a$ is about 6.32, so count 3.16 units up and down from the center. Plot the covertices at $(4, 6.16)$ and $(4, 0.16)$.

Step 3 The length of the minor axis $2b$ is 4, so count 2 units left and right from the center. Plot the covertices at $(2, 3)$ and $(6, 3)$.

Step 4 Draw the ellipse through the four points.

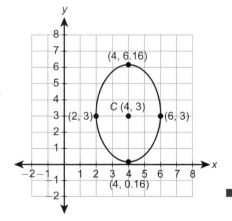

> ### REMEMBER
> To graph an ellipse when you are given the equation in general form, rewrite it in graphing form by following the method used in Example 2.

Converting an Equation of a Hyperbola from General Form to Graphing Form

When the general second-degree equation $Ax^2 + Bxy + Cy^2 + Dx + Ey + F = 0$ has $B^2 - 4AC > 0$, the equation is that of a hyperbola. Converting from general form to graphing form will enable you to find the center of the hyperbola and the length of the conjugate and transverse axes so you can draw the asymptotes.

Example 4   The equation of a hyperbola is $4x^2 - 9y^2 - 24x - 18y - 9 = 0$.

A   Write the equation in graphing form.

B   Graph the hyperbola.

Solution

A   The given equation is in general second-degree form, with $B = 0$.
To write the equation in graphing form, complete the square for each variable.

$4x^2 - 9y^2 - 24x - 18y - 9 = 0$	Equation in general form
$4x^2 - 9y^2 - 24x - 18y = 9$	Isolate the constant.
$4x^2 - 24x \quad - 9y^2 - 18y = 9$	Group like terms.
$4(x^2 - 6x \quad) - 9(y^2 + 2y \quad) = 9$	Factor to get leading terms x^2 and y^2.
$4(x^2 - 6x + 9) - 9(y^2 + 2y + 1) = 9 + 36 - 9$	Complete the squares. Note that you are adding 36 and -9 to each side.
$4(x - 3)^2 - 9(y + 1)^2 = 36$	Write the trinomials as squared binomials.
$\dfrac{4(x - 3)^2}{36} - \dfrac{9(y + 1)^2}{36} = \dfrac{36}{36}$	Divide each side by 36.
$\dfrac{(x - 3)^2}{9} - \dfrac{(y + 1)^2}{4} = 1$	Simplify.

B   The equation is in the graphing form, $\dfrac{(x - h)^2}{a^2} - \dfrac{(y - k)^2}{b^2} = 1$,

so the transverse axis is horizontal. In the equation, $h = 3$, $k = -1$, $a = \sqrt{9} = 3$, and $b = \sqrt{4} = 2$.

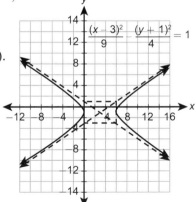

Step 1   Plot the center (h, k) at $(3, -1)$. Count 3 units left and right from the center. Plot the vertices at $(0, -1)$ and $(6, -1)$.

Step 2   Use the values of a and b to sketch the associated rectangle with dimensions $2a = 6$ and $2b = 4$.

Step 3   Sketch the lines that go through the diagonals of the rectangle and are the asymptotes of the hyperbola. Verify that the slopes of the asymptotes are $\pm\dfrac{2}{3}$.

Step 4   Sketch the branches of the hyperbola. ∎

Converting an Equation of a Parabola from General Form to Graphing Form

When the general second-degree equation $Ax^2 + Bxy + Cy^2 + Dx + Ey + F = 0$ has $B^2 - 4AC = 0$, the equation is that of a parabola. Converting from general form to graphing form will help you identify the vertex and axis of symmetry of the parabola.

Example 5 The equation of a parabola is $3y^2 - x - 12y + 13 = 0$.

Ⓐ Write the equation in graphing form.

Ⓑ Graph the parabola.

Solution

Ⓐ To write the equation in standard form, complete the square for the variable that has a squared term.

$3y^2 - x - 12y + 13 = 0$	Given equation in general form
$3y^2 - 12y \quad\quad = x - 13$	Isolate the y-terms because the equation has y^2.
$3(y^2 - 4y \quad) = x - 13$	Factor to get leading term y^2.
$3(y^2 - 4y + 4) = x - 13 + 12$	Complete the square.
$3(y - 2)^2 = x - 1$	Write the trinomial as a squared binomial.
$x - 1 = 3(y - 2)^2$	Write in graphing form $x - h = a(y - k)^2$.

Ⓑ The parabola has a horizontal axis of symmetry, and in the equation, $h = 1$, $k = 2$, and $a = 3$.

Step 1 First plot the vertex (h, k) at $(1, 2)$ and sketch the axis of symmetry, $y = 2$.

Step 2 Find two solutions to the equation, such as $(4, 3)$ and $(13, 4)$. To do this, you can pick y-values and solve for the corresponding x-values.

Step 3 Use reflection across the axis of symmetry to find $(4, 1)$ and $(13, 0)$.

Step 4 Draw a smooth curve through the points.

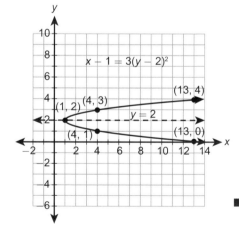

TIP

Many graphing calculators will graph functions in the form "$y =$" only. To graph $x - 1 = 3(y - 2)^2$ on a calculator, solve for y and enter the resulting equations as these two functions:

$y_1 = 2 + \sqrt{\dfrac{x - 1}{3}}$ and

$y_2 = 2 - \sqrt{\dfrac{x - 1}{3}}$.

Problem Set

Identify the type of conic section (circle, ellipse, hyperbola, or parabola) for each equation.

1. $x^2 + 4y^2 + 2x - 24y + 33 = 0$

2. $18y^2 - 36x = 0$

3. $x^2 + y^2 + 2x - 10 = 0$

4. $4x^2 - 25y^2 - 8x + 100y - 196 = 0$

5. $100x^2 + 25y^2 - 100 = 0$

6. $3x^2 - 12y^2 + 45x + 60y + 60 = 0$

For each problem, do the following:

A. Convert the given equation to graphing form.
B. Draw the graph.

7. $2x^2 - 4y^2 - 16x - 16y - 36 = 0$

8. $x^2 + y^2 + 2x - 8y + 13 = 0$

9. $x^2 - 4y^2 + 2x - 24y - 71 = 0$

10. $9x^2 + 4y^2 = 36$

11. $x^2 - 2y^2 - 2 = 0$

12. $x^2 + y^2 + 14x + 6y - 23 = 0$

13. $3x^2 - 24x - y + 50 = 0$

14. $21x^2 + 25y^2 - 42x - 250y + 121 = 0$

15. $x^2 - 2x - y + 5 = 0$

16. $-16x^2 + 9y^2 - 64x - 72y - 64 = 0$

17. $5x^2 + y^2 + 20x + 18y + 26 = 0$

18. $2y^2 - x + 20y + 58 = 0$

19. $x^2 + y^2 + 8x - 6y = 0$

20. $4x^2 + y^2 - 10y + 9 = 0$

21. $x^2 + y^2 - 6x - 16y + 53 = 0$

22. $5y^2 - x - 25y + 25.75 = 0$

Graph and solve the given quadratic system.

*23. **Challenge** $\begin{cases} x^2 + y^2 = 1 \\ y^2 + x = 1 \end{cases}$

*24. **Challenge** $\begin{cases} y^2 - x - 6y + 7 \geq 0 \\ x^2 - y - 4 \leq 0 \end{cases}$

Pronunciation Guide

The table below provides sample words to explain the sounds associated with specific letters and letter combinations used in the respellings in this book. For example, *a* represents the short "a" sound in *cat*, while *ay* represents the long "a" sound in *day*.

Letter combinations are used to approximate certain more complex sounds. For example, in the respelling of *trapezoid*—TRA-puh-zoyd—the letters *uh* represent the vowel sound you hear in *shut* and *other*.

Vowels

a	short a: apple, cat
ay	long a: cane, day
e, eh	short e: hen, bed
ee	long e: feed, team
i, ih	short i: lip, active
iy	long i: try, might
ah	short o: hot, father
oh	long o: home, throw
uh	short u: shut, other
yoo	long u: union, cute

Letter Combinations

ch	chin, ancient
sh	show, mission
zh	vision, azure
th	thin, health
th	then, heather
ur	bird, further, word
us	bus, crust
or	court, formal
ehr	error, care
oo	cool, true, rule
ow	now, out
ou	look, pull, would
oy	coin, toy
aw	saw, maul, fall
ng	song, finger
air	Aristotle, barrister
ahr	cart, martyr

Consonants

b	butter, baby
d	dog, cradle
f	fun, phone
g	grade, angle
h	hat, ahead
j	judge, gorge
k	kite, car, black
l	lily, mile
m	mom, camel
n	next, candid
p	price, copper
r	rubber, free
s	small, circle, hassle
t	ton, pottery
v	vase, vivid
w	wall, away
y	yellow, kayak
z	zebra, haze

Glossary

absolute value the distance of a number's graph from the origin; the absolute value of 0 is 0; the absolute value of a number a is denoted by $|a|$

absolute value function a function whose rule contains an absolute value expression

analytic geometry the study of geometry using the tools of algebra; also called *coordinate geometry*

arithmetic sequence a type of sequence where the difference between consecutive terms is a constant

arithmetic series the sum of consecutive terms of an arithmetic sequence

asymptote a line that a graph of a given function approaches without touching

bar graph a graph that uses bars to display and compare data

base (in a power) a number, variable, or expression that is a factor in a power; in the power a^n, the base is a

biased sample a sample for which not every member of the population is equally likely to be included

binomial experiment a probability experiment in which there are a fixed number of independent trials, each outcome for each trial is labeled either success or failure—where success and failure are complementary events—and the probability p of success is the same for each trial; the probability of failure for each trial is $1 - p$

bivariate data data for which each item is described with two dimensions

boundary line the line in the graph of a linear inequality that divides the coordinate plane into two half-planes

bounded closed interval the set of all real numbers between two numbers, including the endpoints

bounded half-open interval the set of all real numbers between two numbers, including one and only one endpoint

bounded interval the set of all real numbers between two numbers (endpoints)

bounded open interval the set of all real numbers between two numbers, excluding both endpoints

box-and-whisker plot a method of showing the distribution or spread of data; it uses the minimum, the maximum, and the three quartiles of the data

circle the set of all points in a plane that are equidistant from a given point in the plane called the *center*

closed half-plane a figure that consists of all the points on either side of a solid line that divides a plane

closed set a set such that, under an operation, the result of the operation on any two elements of the set is also an element of the set

coefficient the numerical factor of a term

coefficient matrix the matrix formed by the coefficients of the variables of a system of equations when the equations are written in standard form

combination a collection of items in which the order of the items is not important

common difference the difference between a term and the previous term of an arithmetic sequence or series

common logarithm a logarithm with base 10; usually written as $\log x$

common ratio the quotient of a term and the previous term of a geometric sequence or series

complementary events two events such that one must occur, but both cannot occur at the same time

completing the square adding a real number to a quadratic expression so that it becomes a perfect square trinomial

complex conjugates two complex numbers of the form $a + bi$ and $a - bi$

complex number any number of the form $a + bi$, where a and b are real numbers and i is the imaginary unit

complex plane the plane used to graph complex numbers; the horizontal axis is the real axis and the vertical axis is the imaginary axis

compound event (in probability) an event that consists of two or more simple events

compound fraction a fraction that has at least one fraction in the numerator or denominator

compound inequality a pair of inequalities joined by the word *and* or the word *or*

conditional equation an equation that is true for some values of the variable but not others

conditional probability the probability of one event, given that another event has occurred

conic section a two-dimensional graph that can be formed by the intersection of a plane and a double-napped cone

conjugate binomials two binomials that can be written in the form $(a + b)$ and $(a - b)$

conjunction a compound statement that has two statements connected by the word *and*; a conjunction is true only if both statements are true

constant matrix the matrix that contains the constants used in a system of equations

constraints the set of conditions, in the form of linear inequalities, that must be satisfied in a linear programming problem

correlation indicator of the strength and direction of a linear relationship between two variables

counting number any whole number greater than zero $\{1, 2, 3, 4, \ldots\}$; the set of counting numbers is denoted by $\mathbb{N}$; also called a *natural number*

degenerate conic section a figure formed when a plane intersects the vertex of a double-napped cone; the three degenerate cases are a point, a line, and a pair of intersecting lines

degree of a monomial the sum of the exponents of the variables in the monomial

degree of a polynomial the degree of the monomial with the greatest degree in a polynomial

dependent events two events related in such a way that knowing about one event's occurrence has an effect on the probability of the other event

dependent variable the output variable for a function

diameter a segment that passes through the center of a circle and has endpoints on the circle; the length of this segment is also called the diameter

dilation a transformation that changes the size but not the shape of an image

dimension of a matrix the number of rows or columns in a matrix

discriminant a value used to determine the number and types of roots for a given polynomial; for a quadratic of the form $ax^2 + bx + c$, the discriminant is $b^2 - 4ac$

disjunction a compound statement that has two statements connected by the word *or*; a disjunction is false only when both statements are false

domain in a relation, the set of allowable inputs

double-napped cone a figure formed when a line, called the generating line, revolves around a stationary line, or the axis; the two lines cannot be parallel or perpendicular

eccentricity the ratio e that describes the shape of a conic section

element of a matrix each number or expression in the matrix

element of a set a member of a set

ellipse the set of all points in a plane such that the sum of the distances from two fixed points (the foci) is constant; a circle can be considered a special kind of ellipse

empty set the set with no members; denoted $\{ \}$ or $\varnothing$

end behavior how a function behaves when the domain values increase or decrease without bound

even function a function in which $f(-x) = f(x)$; the graph of any even function is symmetric about the y-axis

event a set of one or more outcomes; an event is a subset of the sample space

experiment any process or action that has a result

experimental probability probability based on actual observations or results of an experiment

exponent a number or variable that indicates how many times the base is used as a factor; in the power a^n, the exponent is n

exponential function a function that has an equation of the form $f(x) = ab^{x-h} + k$, where $a \neq 0$, $b > 0$, and $b \neq 1$

expression a group of mathematical symbols that represent a numerical value; most expressions contain numerals as well as operation signs, grouping symbols, or a combination of these elements; an expression containing one or more variables is called a *variable expression* or *algebraic expression*

extraneous solution an apparent solution that does not make the original equation true

factored form of a quadratic function quadratic function in the form $f(x) = a(x - r_1)(x - r_2)$

factorial for a positive integer n, the product of all positive integers less than or equal to n; denoted $n!$; also, $0! = 1$

family of functions a group of functions with the same fundamental characteristics

feasible region the set of all the points that satisfy the constraints and are possible solutions to a linear programming problem

Fibonacci sequence the sequence 1, 1, 2, 3, 5, 8, 13, 21, ..., where each term is the sum of the previous two terms

finite set a set that has a countable number of elements

five-number summary in a data set, the minimum, the maximum, and the three quartiles

FOIL a mnemonic used for a method to perform the distributive property when multiplying binomials: first-outer-inner-last

frequency distribution a graph or table that describes the number of times a value or interval of values occurs in a data set

function a relation that assigns to each member of the domain exactly one member of the range

function composition a mapping in which each element of the range of one function is the domain of another function; if f and g are functions of x, the composition of f with g is denoted by $f \cdot g$ and is defined as $f(g(x))$

geometric sequence a sequence for which the ratio between consecutive terms is a constant

geometric series the sum of consecutive terms of a geometric sequence

greatest integer function a function that assigns the greatest integer less than or equal to each real number in an interval; denoted by $f(x) = \lfloor x \rfloor$; also called the *floor function*

half-life the length of time it takes for one half of a radioactive substance to decay

half-plane a figure that consists of all the points on either side of a line that divides a plane

histogram a bar graph that displays the frequency of data values that occur within certain intervals; the height of each bar gives the frequency in the respective interval

hyperbola the set of all points in a plane such that the absolute value of the difference of the distances from two fixed points (the foci) is constant

imaginary number any number that can be written in the form ai, where a is any real number and i is the imaginary unit

independent events two events related in such a way that one event's occurrence has no effect on the probability of the other event

independent variable the input variable for a function

index an integer greater than 1 that denotes the number of times a radicand is multiplied

inequality a mathematical sentence that includes one of the symbols $<$, $>$, $\leq$, or $\geq$

infinite set a set that does not have a countable number of elements

integer any whole number, its opposite, or zero $\{..., -3, -2, -1, 0, 1, 2, 3, ...\}$; the set of integers is denoted by $\mathbb{Z}$

intersection elements common to two or more sets

interval notation notation used to express an inequality with brackets and/or parentheses

inverse of a relation a relation that interchanges members of the ordered pairs of the original relation; the domain of the inverse relation is the range of the original relation, and the range of the inverse relation is the domain of the original relation

inverse function one of two functions f and g that "undo" each other; if you start with a value x, apply f, and then apply g, the result is the original value x; the inverse function is denoted by f^{-1}

inverse matrix two square $n \times n$ matrices A and B are inverses when $AB = I_n$ and $BA = I_n$

irrational number any real number that cannot be written in the form $\frac{a}{b}$ for any integers a and b; in decimal form, all irrational numbers are nonterminating and nonrepeating; the set of irrational numbers is denoted by $\mathbb{I}$

iterative rule a rule that can be used to find the nth term of a sequence without calculating previous terms of the sequence

least integer function a function that assigns the greatest integer less than or equal to each real number in an interval; denoted by $f(x) = \lceil x \rceil$; also called the *ceiling function*

like terms terms that contain the same variables raised to the same powers

line of fit a line that can be used as a model for a data set

line of symmetry the line over which you can flip a given figure, leaving the figure unchanged, or the line that divides a given figure into two congruent (mirror-image) halves; a figure for which there is a line of symmetry is said to have line or reflection symmetry

linear equation an equation whose graph is a line

linear inequality a statement relating two variables using an inequality symbol

linear programming the process of maximizing or minimizing an objective function that satisfies a set of conditions

literal equation an equation with two or more variables

logarithm the exponent to which a base would have to be raised to result in a given value; $\log_b a = x$ if and only if $b^x = a$, where $b > 0$, $b \neq 1$, and $a > 0$

logarithmic function an equation of the form $f(x) = \log_b (x - h) + k$, where $x - h > 0$, $b > 0$, and $b \neq 1$

main diagonal of a square matrix the elements on the diagonal extending from the top left corner to the bottom right corner

matrix a table of numbers or expressions arranged in rows and columns

matrix equation an equation of the form $AX = B$, where A is the coefficient matrix, X is the variable matrix, and B is the constant matrix

mean (average) the sum of the values in a data set divided by the number of values

median for a data set with an odd number of values, the middle value after the values have been ordered from least to greatest; for a data set with an even number of values, the mean of the two middle values after the values have been ordered from least to greatest

median-median line line of fit that is parallel to the line connecting the first and third summary points and one-third of the way toward the second summary point

mode the data value(s) occurring most often in a data set

modulus a nonnegative real number representing the distance between the complex number, $a + bi$, and the origin on the complex plane, denoted by $|a + bi|$

monomial a number, a variable, or the product of a number and one or more variables

multiplicative identity matrix an $n \times n$ matrix such that for any $m \times n$ matrix A and any $n \times p$ matrix B, $AI = A$ and $IB = B$; every element on its main diagonal is 1 and all the other elements equal 0; denoted I_n, where n is the number of rows and columns

multiplicity for a root a of $p(x) = 0$, the number of times the factor $x - a$ occurs in the factorization of any polynomial $p(x)$

mutually exclusive events events that cannot happen at the same time

natural logarithm a logarithm with base e; often written using the notation $\ln x$

natural number any whole number greater than zero $\{1, 2, 3, 4, ...\}$; the set of natural numbers is denoted by $\mathbb{N}$; also called a *counting number*

nearest integer function denoted by $f(x) = \text{nint}(x)$; a function that assigns the nearest integer to each real number in an interval

normal distribution bell-shaped distribution, centered around the mean, whose area obeys the empirical rule

nth partial sum the sum of the first n terms of a series

nth root of a any number x such that $x^n = a$ for a natural number $n > 1$

objective function a linear function that is to be optimized (maximized or minimized), subject to the constraints of a linear programming problem

odd function a function in which $f(-x) = -f(x)$; the graph of any odd function is symmetric about the origin

open half-plane a figure that consists of all the points on either side of (but not including) a dashed line that divides a plane

optimization the process of finding a maximum or minimum

outcome the result in a probability experiment

parabola the shape of the graph of a quadratic function

parent function the basic function in a family of functions

percentile the percent of a population that a given value is greater than

permutation an arrangement of items in which the order of the items is important

piecewise function a function that is defined using different rules for different intervals of the domain

point-slope form (of a linear equation) an equation of a line that passes through the points (x_1, y_1), has a slope m, and is given by $y - y_1 = m(x - x_1)$

polynomial a monomial or the sum or difference of two or more monomials

population a group of individuals or objects about which information is wanted

power a type of product that is the result of repeated multiplication by the same factor; a power has a *base* and an *exponent*; in the power a^n, the base is a and the exponent is n (which indicates the number of times the base is repeatedly multiplied)

power function a function that can be written in the form $f(x) = ax^n + b$, where n is a positive integer, a is any nonzero real number, and b is any real number

principal square root the nonnegative square root of a nonnegative real number

probability a number from 0 to 1, inclusive, that describes how likely an event is to occur

proper subset a set whose elements are contained within another set, without the two sets being equal; denoted by $\subset$

quadrant one of the four regions into which the coordinate axes separate the coordinate plane

quadratic equation a second-degree polynomial equation that can be written in the standard form $ax^2 + bx + c = 0$, where $a \neq 0$

quadratic function second-degree polynomial function

quadratic inequality a quadratic expression containing an inequality symbol $<$, $>$, $\leq$, $\geq$, or $\neq$

quartile one of three values that separate an ordered data set into four equal parts; the second quartile Q_2 is the median of the data set; the first quartile Q_1 is the median of the lower half of the data set; the third quartile Q_3 is the median of the upper half of the data set

radical equation an equation that contains at least one radical expression with a variable in the radicand

radical expression an expression that contains a radical sign

radical function a function of the form $f(x) = a\sqrt[n]{x - h} + k$, where n is an integer greater than 1

radicand an expression under a radical sign

radius a segment that connects the center of a circle to a point on the circle; the length of that segment is also called the radius

range in a relation the set of possible outputs

range of a data set the difference of the maximum and minimum values in the data set

rational equation an equation that contains one or more rational expressions

rational expression a quotient of two polynomials

rational function a function of the form $f(x) = \dfrac{p(x)}{q(x)}$, where $p(x)$ and $q(x)$ are polynomial functions

rational number any number that can be expressed as a ratio $\left(\dfrac{a}{b}\right)$, where a and b are integers and $b \neq 0$; the set of rational numbers is represented by $\mathbb{Q}$

real number any number that can be written as a decimal; the set of real numbers is denoted by $\mathbb{R}$

reciprocal a number that when multiplied by the number gives the multiplicative identity 1; also called the *multiplicative inverse*

reciprocal power function a power function that has the power of x in the denominator of a rational function

recursive rule a rule for generating terms of a sequence that depends on one or more previous terms of the sequence

relation any set of ordered pairs

root of a function for a function $f(x)$, any value of the variable x that makes $f(x) = 0$ a true statement

sample part of a population

sample space the set of all possible outcomes of an experiment

scalar a quantity without dimensions, as opposed to a matrix or a vector

scatter plot a graph that displays two-dimensional data as points; scatter-plot points represent ordered pairs

sequence a function whose domain is the set of natural numbers

series the sum of consecutive terms of a sequence

set a collection of objects

skewed distribution distribution in which one side has lower frequencies than the other side

simple event a single outcome of an experiment (a single element of a sample space)

simplified form of a polynomial a polynomial with no like terms; each term is in simplest form, and its terms are in order of decreasing degree with respect to a variable

simplified radical form a radical expression with radical index n, where the radicand is not a fraction, there are no radicals in the denominator, and no factors are a perfect nth power

slope a number that describes the steepness of a line, computed as the ratio of the change in the y-coordinates to the change in the x-coordinates when moving from one point on a line to another point on the same line

slope-intercept form (of a linear equation) an equation of the form $y = mx + b$, where m is the slope of the line and b is the y-intercept

square matrix a matrix that has the same number of rows and columns

square root a factor of a number that when multiplied by itself results in the number

standard deviation a measure of variability of a data set; calculated as the square root of the variance

standard form (of a linear equation) an equation in the form $Ax + By = C$, where A, B, and C are integers, and A and B are not both zero

standard form (of a quadratic equation) an equation in the form $ax^2 + bx + c = 0$, where $a \neq 0$

standard normal distribution the normal distribution with a mean of 0 and a standard deviation of 1

stem-and-leaf plot a graph used to organize and display data; its benefits include showing the distribution of the data as well as the individual values

step function a function defined using a rule that produces a constant value for each designated interval of the domain

subset a set whose elements are contained within another set; denoted $\subseteq$

synthetic division a shorthand method for polynomial long division; the divisor is a binomial in the form $x - k$, where k is a constant; the coefficients of the dividend appear in the top row and the coefficients of the quotient appear with the remainder in the bottom row

system of linear equations two or more linear equations with the same variables

system of linear inequalities a set of two or more linear inequalities using the same variables

term part of an expression that is added or subtracted

transformation a one-to-one correspondence between two sets of points

translation the sliding of a figure in a straight path

unbounded interval the set of all real numbers on one side of a number

uniform distribution distribution in which all the data intervals have the same frequency

union the set of elements that are in either of two sets

univariate data data with one variable

variable matrix a matrix that contains the variables used in a system of equations

variance a measure of variability of a data set relative to its mean

vector an object that has both magnitude and direction; a matrix with only one row or only one column

Venn diagram a diagram that uses simple closed regions to show relationships between sets; overlapping regions represent intersections of the sets

vertex form of a quadratic function quadratic function in the form $f(x) = a(x - h)^2 + k$, where $a \neq 0$

vertical line test a method of determining whether a relation is a function by verifying that there is only one y value for every x value, performed by sliding a vertical line across the function from left to right; if a vertical line can hit the graph at more than one point, then the relation is not a function

weighted average a weighted mean for which some elements of a data set carry more importance (weight) than others

whole number any number that is a natural number or zero $\{0, 1, 2, 3, 4, ...\}$; the set of whole numbers is denoted by $\mathbb{W}$

x-axis the horizontal number line in the coordinate plane

x-coordinate the first number in an ordered pair of numbers that designates the location of a point on the coordinate plane; also called the *abscissa* (ab-SIH-suh)

x-intercept the x-coordinate of a point where a graph intersects the x-axis

y-axis the vertical line in the coordinate plane

y-coordinate the second number in an ordered pair of numbers that designates the location of a point on the coordinate plane; also called the *ordinate* (OR-duh-nuht)

y-intercept the y-coordinate of a point where a graph intersects the y-axis

z-score the number of standard deviations that a data value is from the mean

zero of a function the value or values of x that make $f(x) = 0$

Symbols

|	such that	$\log x$	logarithm with base 10
$\in$	is an element of	$\log_b a$	log base b of a
$\varnothing$ or { }	null or empty set	a_n	nth element of a sequence
$\subset$	is a proper subset of	π	pi
$\subseteq$	is a subset of	σ	standard deviation of a population
$\cap$	intersection	S_n	the sum of the first n terms of a series
$\cup$	union	$\sum\limits_{i=1}^{n} a_i$	the sum from 1 to n of a_i
$-a$	the opposite of a		
∞	infinity	$n!$	factorial of a nonnegative integer n
$\sqrt{}$	radical sign; the principle square root	$_nP_r = P(n, r)$	permutation of n objects taken r at a time
$\sqrt[n]{x}$	nth root of x	$_nC_r = C(n, r) = \binom{n}{r}$	combination of n objects taken r at a time
i	imaginary unit		
$\mathbb{N}$	the set of natural numbers	$\overline{x}$	sample mean
$\mathbb{Z}$	the set of integers	$\approx$	is approximately equal to
$\mathbb{Q}$	the set of rational numbers	$=$	is equal to
$\mathbb{R}$	the set of real numbers	$\neq$	is not equal to
$\mathbb{I}$	the set of irrational numbers	$<$	is less than
$\mathbb{W}$	the set of whole numbers	$>$	is greater than
$\mathbb{C}$	the set of complex numbers	$\leq$	is less than or equal to
e	base of the natural logarithm	$\geq$	is greater than or equal to
$\ln x$	logarithm with base e; natural logarithm	$f(x)$	f is a function of x

$\lfloor x \rfloor$	greatest integer function; also floor function	$\{x \mid \text{condition}\}$	the set of all x that satisfy the given condition; set-builder notation
$\lceil x \rceil$	least integer function; also ceiling function		
$\text{nint}(x)$	nearest integer function; also round function	$\begin{bmatrix} a & b \\ c & d \end{bmatrix}$	matrix
$f \circ g$	the composition of function f with function g		
f^{-1}	inverse of a function f	$\begin{vmatrix} a & b \\ c & d \end{vmatrix}$	determinant of a matrix
$|x|$	absolute value of x	I_n	identity matrix
$\{\ldots\}$	description or list of all elements in a set; roster notation		

Formulary

Geometric Formulas

Circle

Circumference $\quad C = \pi d = 2\pi r$

Area $\quad A = \pi r^2$

Cylinder

Volume $\quad V = Bh = \pi r^2 h$

Surface area $\quad S = 2\pi rh + 2\pi r^2$

Prism: Cube

Volume $\quad V = s^3$

Surface area $\quad S = 6s^2$

Prism: Rectangular

Volume $\quad V = lwh$

Surface area $\quad S = 2lw + 2lh + 2lw$

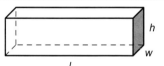

Rectangle

Area $\quad A = lw$

Perimeter $\quad P = 2l + 2w$

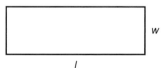

Square

Area $\quad A = s^2$

Perimeter $\quad P = 4s$

Triangle: General

Area $A = \frac{1}{2}bh$

Perimeter $P = a + b + c$

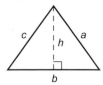

Triangle: Right

Pythagorean theorem $a^2 + b^2 = c^2$

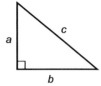

Coordinate Geometry

Distance formula The distance between points (x_1, y_1) and (x_2, y_2) is
$$d = \sqrt{(x_2 - x_1)^2 + (y_2 - y_1)^2}.$$

Midpoint formula $M = \left(\dfrac{x_1 + x_2}{2}, \dfrac{y_1 + y_2}{2} \right)$

Line

Slope $m = \dfrac{\text{rise}}{\text{run}} = \dfrac{\text{vertical change}}{\text{horizontal change}} = \dfrac{y_2 - y_1}{x_2 - x_1}$

Equation Forms

Standard: $Ax + By = C$

Slope-intercept: $y = mx + b$

Point-slope: $y - y_1 = m(x - x_1)$

Circle

Equation in graphing form: $(x - h)^2 + (y - k)^2 = r^2$

Center (h, k) and radius r

Parabola

Graphing Forms:

Vertical axis of symmetry: $y - k = a(x - h)^2$
(axis of symmetry $x = h$)

Horizontal axis of symmetry: $x - h = a(y - k)^2$
(axis of symmetry $y = k$)

Vertex: (h, k)

Focal distance: $f = \dfrac{1}{4a}$

Eccentricity: $e = 1$

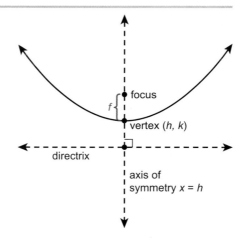

Ellipse

Graphing Forms:

Horizontal major axis: $\dfrac{(x - h)^2}{a^2} + \dfrac{(y - k)^2}{b^2} = 1$

Vertical major axis: $\dfrac{(x - h)^2}{b^2} + \dfrac{(y - k)^2}{a^2} = 1$

Center: (h, k)

Major axis length: $2a$

Minor axis length: $2b$

Formula for focal length c: $c^2 = a^2 - b^2$

Eccentricity: $e = \dfrac{c}{a}$

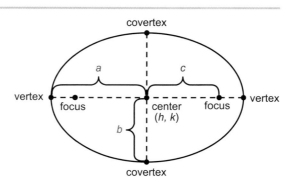

Hyperbola

Graphing Forms:

Horizontal transverse axis: $\dfrac{(x - h)^2}{a^2} - \dfrac{(y - k)^2}{b^2} = 1;$

Slopes of asymptotes: $\pm \dfrac{b}{a}$

Vertical transverse axis: $\dfrac{(y - k)^2}{a^2} - \dfrac{(x - h)^2}{b^2} = 1;$

Slopes of asymptotes: $\pm \dfrac{a}{b}$

Center: (h, k)

Transverse axis length: $2a$

Conjugate axis length: $2b$

Formula for focal length c: $c^2 = a^2 + b^2$

Eccentricity: $e = \dfrac{c}{a}$

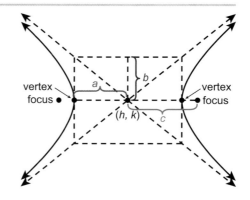

Other Formulas

Solving Quadratics

Completing the square   Given the equation $ax^2 + bx = c$, add $\left(\dfrac{b}{2a}\right)^2$ to both sides.

Discriminant   Given the equation $ax^2 + bx + c = 0$, the discriminant is $b^2 - 4ac$.

Quadratic formula   The solutions of the equation $ax^2 + bx + c = 0$, where $a \neq 0$, are

$$x = \frac{-b \pm \sqrt{b^2 - 4ac}}{2a}.$$

Exponents and Logarithms

Exponential decay formula   If a quantity is decaying exponentially from initial amount b, for time t and with decay rate r, then the amount y remaining after t time periods is

$$y = b(1 - r)^t.$$

Exponential growth formula   If a quantity is growing exponentially from the initial amount b, where r is the fixed percent expressed as a decimal and t is the time period, then the total amount y after t time periods is

$$y = b(1 + r)^t.$$

Compound interest formula   The total amount A of an investment with initial principle P, earning compound interest at an annual interest rate r and compounded n times per year for t years, is

$$A = P\left(1 + \frac{r}{n}\right)^{nt}.$$

Half-life formula   The amount y of a radioactive substance after t time periods, where b is the initial amount and h is the half-life, is

$$y = b\left(\frac{1}{2}\right)^{\frac{t}{h}}.$$

General Applications

Distance   For uniform motion, where d is distance, r is rate, and t is time,
$$d = rt.$$

Projectile motion   The height of an object, *in meters*, after t seconds, with initial vertical velocity v_0 and initial height h_0, is given by
$$h(t) = -4.9t^2 + v_0 t + h_0.$$

The height of an object, in feet, after t seconds, with initial vertical velocity v_0 and initial height h_0, is given by
$$h(t) = -16t^2 + v_0 t + h_0.$$

Simple interest   The amount of simple interest I earned, where P is the principal (amount borrowed, deposited, or invested), r is the annual interest rate, and t is the time in years, is given by
$$I = Prt.$$

Temperature conversion $F = \dfrac{9}{5}C + 32$, where F is degrees Fahrenheit and C is degrees Celsius

Sequences and Series

Sequences: arithmetic
common difference of an arithmetic sequence: $d = a_n - a_{n-1}$
iterative rule for an arithmetic sequence: $a_n = a_1 + (n-1)d$
recursive rule for an arithmetic sequence: $a_n = a_{n-1} + d$

Sequences: geometric
common ratio of a geometric sequence: $r = \dfrac{a_n}{a_{n-1}}$

iterative rule for a geometric sequence: $a_n = a_1 \cdot r^{n-1}$
recursive rule for a geometric sequence: $a_n = r \cdot a_{n-1}$

General formula for the sum of a series:

Sigma Notation   The sum of the first n terms of a sequence can be written as

$$S_n = \sum_{i=1}^{n} a_i = a_1 + a_2 + a_3 + \ldots + a_n,$$

where i is the index, 1 is the lower limit, and n is the upper limit.

Arithmetic series   The nth partial sum of an arithmetic series a with common difference d is

$$S_n = \frac{n}{2}(a_1 + a_2) \text{ or } S_n = \frac{n}{2}(2a_1 + (n-1)d).$$

Geometric series   The nth partial sum of a geometric series a with common ratio r is

$$S_n = \frac{a_1(1 - r^n)}{1 - r}, \text{ or } S_n = \frac{a_1 - a_n r}{1 - r}, \text{ where } r \neq 1.$$

Counting and Probability

Factorial
$n! = n \cdot (n-1) \cdot (n-2) \cdot \ldots \cdot 1$ (n factors)
$0! = 1$

Permutations
The number of permutations of n objects taken r at a time is

$$_nP_r = P(n, r) = \frac{n!}{(n-r)!}.$$

The number of permutations n objects of which p are alike and q are alike is

$$\frac{_nP_n}{p!\,q!}.$$

where $p \leq n$ and $q \leq n$.

The number of permutations of n objects arranged in a circle is

$$(n-1)!.$$

Combinations   The number of combinations of n objects taken r at a time, with $r \leq n$, is

$$_nC_r = C(n, r) = \binom{n}{r} = \frac{n!}{r!(n-r)!}.$$

Binomial theorem   Given a binomial of the form $(x + y)$ and an integer $n \geq 0$, the expansion of $(x + y)^n$ is

$$(x + y)^n = \sum_{r=0}^{n} {_nC_r}\, x^{n-r} y^r = {_nC_0}\, x^n y^0 + {_nC_1}\, x^{n-1} y^1 + {_nC_2}\, x^{n-2} y^2 + \ldots + {_nC_n}\, x^0 y^n.$$

Binomial probability   For a binomial experiment with n trials and p probability of success in each trial, the probability of exactly r successes is

$$P(\text{exactly } r \text{ successes}) = {}_nC_r\, p^r (1-p)^{n-r}.$$

Simple theoretical probability

$$P(E) = \frac{\text{number of outcomes in event } E}{\text{total number of outcomes in sample space } S} = \frac{n(E)}{n(S)}$$

Probability of dependent events $P(A \text{ and } B) = P(A) \cdot P(B|A)$

Probability of independent events $P(A \text{ and } B) = P(A) \cdot P(B)$

Probability of mutually exclusive events $P(A \text{ or } B) = P(A) + P(B)$

Probability of complementary events $P(A) = 1 - P(B)$

Experimental probability of event E

$$P(E) = \frac{\text{number of times event } E \text{ has occurred}}{n}$$

Statistics

Mean   For a data set with n elements, the mean is

$$\bar{x} = \frac{x_1 + x_2 + \ldots + x_n}{n}.$$

Median
Arrange the values in order from least to greatest.
For an *odd* number of values, the median is the middle value.
For an *even* number of values, the median is the average of the middle two values.

Mode
The mode is the value that occurs most often in a set of data. If no one value occurs most often, then there is no mode for the set.

Weighted average   If each element, x_i, of a data set has weight (importance) w_i, then the weighted average is

$$\bar{x}_w = \frac{\displaystyle\sum_{i=1}^{n} w_i x_i}{\displaystyle\sum_{i=1}^{n} w_i} = \frac{w_1 x_1 + w_2 x_2 + \ldots + w_n x_n}{w_1 + w_2 + \ldots + w_n}$$

for a data set with values $x_1, x_2, \ldots, x_n$ that have nonnegative weights $w_1, w_2, \ldots, w_n$, respectively.

Variance   For a data set with values $x_1, x_2, \ldots, x_n$, the variance is

$$s^2 = \frac{\displaystyle\sum_{i=1}^{n} (x_i - \bar{x})^2}{n-1}.$$

Standard deviation   For a data set with values $x_1, x_2, \ldots, x_n$, the standard deviation is the square root of the variance:

$$s = \sqrt{s^2}.$$

Matrices

Adding matrices
$A + B = C$ if and only if $a_{ij} + b_{ij} = c_{ij}$ for all values of i and j in matrices A, B, and C.

$$A = \begin{bmatrix} a_{11} & a_{12} \\ a_{21} & a_{22} \end{bmatrix} \qquad B = \begin{bmatrix} b_{11} & b_{12} \\ b_{21} & b_{22} \end{bmatrix} \qquad C = A + B = \begin{bmatrix} a_{11} + b_{11} & a_{12} + b_{12} \\ a_{21} + b_{21} & a_{22} + b_{22} \end{bmatrix}$$

Subtracting matrices
$A - B = D$ if and only if $a_{ij} - b_{ij} = d_{ij}$ for all values of i and j in matrices A, B, and D.

$$A = \begin{bmatrix} a_{11} & a_{12} \\ a_{21} & a_{22} \end{bmatrix} \qquad B = \begin{bmatrix} b_{11} & b_{12} \\ b_{21} & b_{22} \end{bmatrix} \qquad D = A - B = \begin{bmatrix} a_{11} - b_{11} & a_{12} - b_{12} \\ a_{21} - b_{21} & a_{22} - b_{22} \end{bmatrix}$$

Multiplying matrices by a scalar
$rA = C$ if and only if $r \cdot a_{ij} = c_{ij}$ for all values of i and j in matrices A and C.

$$A = \begin{bmatrix} a_{11} & a_{12} \\ a_{21} & a_{22} \end{bmatrix} \qquad C = rA = \begin{bmatrix} r \cdot a_{11} & r \cdot a_{12} \\ r \cdot a_{21} & r \cdot a_{22} \end{bmatrix}$$

Matrix multiplication
If A is an $m \times n$ matrix and B is an $n \times p$ matrix, then AB is the $m \times p$ matrix C, where $c_{ij} = a_{i1}b_{1j} + a_{i2}b_{2j} + \ldots + a_{in}b_{nj}$.

$$A = \begin{bmatrix} a_{11} & a_{12} & a_{13} \\ a_{21} & a_{22} & a_{23} \end{bmatrix} \qquad B = \begin{bmatrix} b_{11} & b_{12} \\ b_{21} & b_{22} \\ b_{31} & b_{32} \end{bmatrix}$$

$$C = AB = \begin{bmatrix} a_{11} \cdot b_{11} + a_{12} \cdot b_{21} + a_{13} \cdot b_{31} & a_{11} \cdot b_{12} + a_{12} \cdot b_{22} + a_{13} \cdot b_{32} \\ a_{21} \cdot b_{11} + a_{22} \cdot b_{21} + a_{23} \cdot b_{31} & a_{21} \cdot b_{12} + a_{22} \cdot b_{22} + a_{23} \cdot b_{32} \end{bmatrix}$$

Determinant of a 2 × 2 matrix
If matrix $A = \begin{bmatrix} a & b \\ c & d \end{bmatrix}$, then the determinant of matrix A equals $ad - cb$.

That is, $\det A = \begin{vmatrix} a & b \\ c & d \end{vmatrix} = ad - cb$.

Determinant of a 3 × 3 matrix
If matrix $A = \begin{bmatrix} a & b & c \\ d & e & f \\ g & h & i \end{bmatrix}$, then

$$\det A = \begin{vmatrix} a & b & c \\ d & e & f \\ g & h & i \end{vmatrix} = a \begin{vmatrix} e & f \\ h & i \end{vmatrix} - b \begin{vmatrix} d & f \\ g & i \end{vmatrix} + c \begin{vmatrix} d & e \\ g & h \end{vmatrix}.$$

Cramer's rule for a system of two equations
The solution of the system $\begin{cases} a_1 x + b_1 y = c_1 \\ a_2 x + b_2 y = c_2 \end{cases}$ is the ordered pair (x, y), where $x = \dfrac{\begin{vmatrix} c_1 & b_1 \\ c_2 & b_2 \end{vmatrix}}{\det M}$, $y = \dfrac{\begin{vmatrix} a_1 & c_1 \\ a_2 & c_2 \end{vmatrix}}{\det M}$,

and M is the coefficient matrix $\begin{bmatrix} a_1 & b_1 \\ a_2 & b_2 \end{bmatrix}$.

Selected Answers

UNIT 1   Numbers, Expressions, and Equations

Pages 4–6

1. A. The coordinate of A is -4.   **B.** The coordinate of B is $-\frac{1}{2}$ or -0.5.   **C.** The coordinate of C is $\frac{3}{2}$, $1\frac{1}{2}$, or 1.5.
D. The coordinate of D is 3.   **3. A.** The coordinate of A is $-\frac{5}{2}$, $-2\frac{1}{2}$, or -2.5.   **B.** The coordinate of B is -1.   **C.** The coordinate of C is $\frac{5}{4}$, $1\frac{1}{4}$, or 1.25.   **D.** The coordinate of D is $\frac{5}{2}$, $2\frac{1}{2}$, or 2.5.

5.

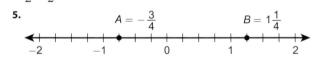

7. -13 **9.** -18 **11.** $\frac{-31}{6}$ or $-5\frac{1}{6}$ **13.** 5.17 **15.** 1.14
17. -4 **19.** $-\frac{49}{5}$ or $-9\frac{4}{5}$ **21.** 12 **23.** 5.054

Pages 11–13

1. natural numbers, whole numbers, integers, rational numbers, real numbers   **3.** rational numbers, real numbers   **5.** irrational numbers, real numbers   **7.** irrational numbers, real numbers   **9.** irrational numbers, real numbers   **11.** $A = \{-9, -6, -3, 0, 3, 6, 9\}$; $A = \left\{x \mid -10 \le x \le 10 \text{ and } \frac{x}{3} \in \mathbb{Z}\right\}$ **13.** M is the set of natural numbers greater than -5; $M = \{1, 2, 3, \dots\}$

15. A.

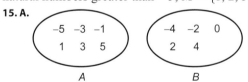

B. $A \cap B = \{\}$ **C.** $A \cup B = \{-5, -4, -3, -2, -1, 0, 1, 2, 3, 4, 5\}$ **D.** Neither is a subset of the other.

17. A.

B. $\mathbb{N} \cap \mathbb{W} = \mathbb{N}$ **C.** $\mathbb{N} \cup \mathbb{W} = \mathbb{W}$ **D.** The natural numbers are a proper subset of the whole numbers.

19. A. $\{5, 10\}$ **B.** $\{10\}$ **C.** $\{10\}$ **D.** $\{-10, 0, 5, 10, 15, 20, 25\}$ **E.** $\{-10, -5, 0, 5, 10, 15, 20, 25\}$ **F.** $\{-10, -5, 0, 5, 10, 15, 20, 25\}$ **21.** Answers will vary. Sample answers: $-1, -5$ **23.** Not possible   **25. A.** $\{-3, -1, 3, 6, 9\}$ **B.** $\{-3, -2, -1, 0, 1\}$ **C.** $\{-3, -1\}$ **27. A.** The union is swimming, sun bathing, yoga, shuffle board, video game arcade, pilates, dancing, cooking class, movie theater, and sauna; this represents all of the activities that the cruise offers.   **B.** The intersection is empty; this represents the fact that there are no activities open for the entire day.   **C.** No, it is not possible because there are four activities offered in the evening that are not offered at any other time; answers will vary. Sample answer: Morning: yoga, swimming, sunbathing; Afternoon: pilates, shuffleboard, video game arcade; Evening: dancing, movie theater, cooking class, sauna.
29. A and B are both null sets.   **31. A.** $\{4\}$ **B.** $\{1\}$ **C.** $\{1, 4\}$

Pages 17–18

1. A. -12 **B.** $\frac{1}{2}$ **C.** $-\sqrt{5}$ **3.** 8 **5.** $1\frac{19}{40}$ **7.** 7 **9.** 9
11. 13 **13.** -10 **15.** 15 **17.** $>$ **19.** $=$ **21.** 10
23. 5.8 **25.** 5.75 **27.** -0.5 **29.** 5.0725 **31.** Friday had the greatest overall change in stock value.

Pages 23–25

1. Commutative Property of Multiplication   **3.** Identity Property of Addition   **5.** Commutative Property of Addition   **7.** Inverse Property of Addition   **9.** Commutative Property of Addition   **11.** Identity Property of Multiplication   **13. A.** Associative Property of Multiplication   **B.** Commutative Property of Multiplication   **C.** Associative Property of Multiplication
15. A. $\frac{1}{3} \cdot x + 1 + (-1)$ **B.** $\frac{1}{3}x + 0$ **C.** Identity Property of Addition   **17.** $4x^2 - 17x - 10$ **19.** $10.5k^2 - 7.5k + 15.2$
21. -125 **23.** 81 **25.** $6p - 24$ **27.** $2x^3y$ **29.** $-1\frac{1}{2}x$
31. A. Closed. Subtracting two integers results in another integer.   **B.** Not closed; 1 and 2 are integers; However, $\frac{1}{2}$ is not an integer.   **33. A.** Associative Property of Addition   **B.** Commutative Property of Addition   **C.** Distributive Property   **D.** $(a + b) + 1 \in \mathbb{Z}$ **E.** even integer

1. 22.7   **3.** $\frac{1}{4}$ **5.** 15.65   **7.** 5   **9.** 0   **11.** -6 **13.** 24

15. 4   **17.** 11.15   **19.** $3\frac{16}{25}$ **21.** $21 > 9$ **23.** $35 < 125$

25. $-8 < \frac{13}{15}$ **27.** $2\frac{1}{2} < 30$ **29.** $9 = 9$ **31. A.** $30x + 10y$

B. $140   **33. A.** $10.99p + 3.49r$ **B.** $5.07

35. A. $g \cdot (m + 2)$ **B.** $2175   **37.** Answers will vary.
Sample answers: **A.** $(8 + 2) \cdot (4 - 1)$ **B.** $(8 - 5 + 7) \cdot 3$
C. $(4 \cdot 4 - 1) \cdot 2$

Page 35

1. $\{3\}$ **3.** $\{18\}$ **5.** $\{60\}$ **7.** $\left\{\frac{1}{5}\right\}$ **9.** $\{-6\}$ **11.** $\{5\}$

13. $\{0.85\}$ **15.** $\left\{\frac{2}{5}\right\}$ **17.** $\{-6\}$ **19.** $\{\}$

21. $x = -\frac{24}{9}$; **A.** $x = -\frac{24}{9}$ **B.** $\{\}$ **C.** $\{\}$ **23.** $x = 0$;   **A.** $\{0\}$

B. $\{0\}$ **C.** $\{\}$ **25. A.** Let m be the time in minutes that Benito
rides the carousel. The domain is $\{m \in$ real numbers$\}$.
B. $6.5m = 39$ **C.** $m = 6$ **D.** Benito's carousel ride lasted 6
minutes.   **27. A.** Let x be the amount of time Casey works at
the $7 per hour job. Then $15 - x$ is the amount of time she
works at the $8 per hour job. The domain is $\{m \in$ real
numbers$\}$ **B.** $7x + 8(15 - x) = 115$ **C.** $x = 5$ **D.** Casey
should work 5 hours at the $7 per hour job and 10 hours at
the $8 per hour job.   **29. A.** Let m be the number of times
Shar goes to the movies. Then $7 - m$ is the number of times
she goes to the smoothie place. The domain is $\{m \in$ whole
numbers$\}$ **B.** $10m + 3(7 - m) = 35$ **C.** $m = 2$ **D.** Shar will
attend a movie 2 times and visit the smoothie place 5 times.

Pages 38–39

1. $x = \pm 12$ **3.** $w = 0$ **5.** $y = 5$ **7.** $k = \pm 4$ **9.** $\{\}$
11. $p = 15$ or $p = 9$ **13.** $\{\}$ **15.** $y = -4$ or $y = -12$
17. $n = 12$ or $n = 0$ **19.** $x = 7$ **21.** $x = 2$ **23.** $x = 0.3$ or

$x = -3.5$ **25.** $x = 0.5$ **27.** $x = -\frac{2}{3}$ or $x = 4$

29. A. $x = 7$ or $x = 3$ **B.** The solution set is $\{-5, 11\}$.
C. The solution set is $\{-7, -1\}$.

Pages 44–45

1. A. 12 in.   **B.** 73 cm   **C.** 5 km   **D.** 18.75 ft   **3. A.** 93.6 yd²

B. 242 in²   **C.** about 9.5 m   **D.** 1.2 mi   **5.** $l = \frac{A}{w}$

7. $r = \frac{I}{Pt}$ **9.** $C = \frac{5}{9}(F - 32)$ **11.** $\sigma = \frac{x - \mu}{z}$ **13. A.** $s = \frac{P}{5}$

B. The side lengths are 6 cm, 5.2 cm, and 4.4 cm,
respectively.   **15.** The area of the dog run is 150 square
meters.   **17.** Hong needs to deposit $4444.44.   **19. A.** The
bullet train trip is approximately 0.73 hours.   **B.** To the
nearest minute, the bullet train trip is 44 minutes.

21. A. $w = \frac{S - 2hl}{2(l + h)}$ **B.** The width of the rectangular prism is

$3\frac{1}{10}$ inches.

UNIT 2   Linear Equations and Systems

Pages 49–50

1.   3.   5.

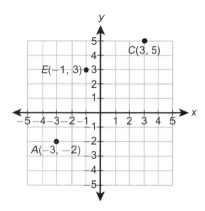

7.   9.   11.

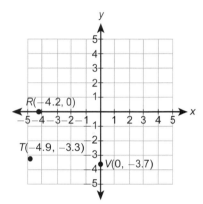

13. $A(3, 4)$ **15.** $C(2, -1)$ **17.** $E(-4, -1)$ **19.** $R(0, 4)$
21. $T(4, -2)$ **23.** $V(4, -5.5)$ **25.** $A(-3, -2)$ lies in
QIII.   **27.** $C(3, 5)$ lies in QI.   **29.** $E(-1, 3)$ lies in QII.
31. $R(-4, 0)$ lies on the negative x-axis.   **33.** $T(-4, -3)$ lies
in QIII.   **35.** $V(0, -3)$ lies on the negative y-axis.
37. The x-coordinate is negative in QII and QIII.   **39.** The
y-coordinate is negative in QIII and QIV.

Pages 55–56

1. x-intercept: -4; y-intercept: -4 **3.** x-intercept: -15;

y-intercept: -3 **5.** x-intercept: $\frac{11}{2}$; y-intercept: $\frac{11}{3}$

7. Yes   **9.** Yes   **11.** -3 **13.** -5 **15.** $-\frac{1}{8}$ **17.** $-\frac{4}{7}$

19.

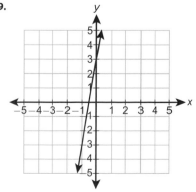

21.

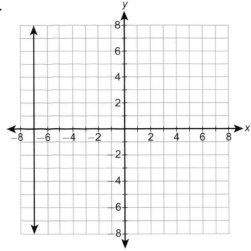

23.

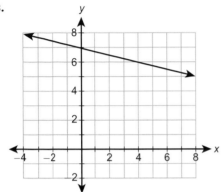

25.

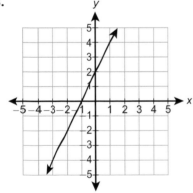

27. Zero   **29.** Negative   **31.** $y = -16$ **33.** $x = 1$

Page 60

1. $y = -\dfrac{2}{5}x + 4$ **3.** $y = \dfrac{5}{2}x + 4$ **5.** $x - 3y = -11$

7. $x - 9y = -7$

9.

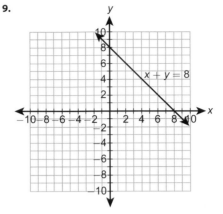

11.

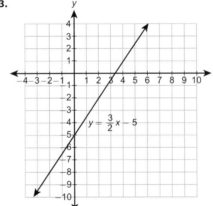

13.

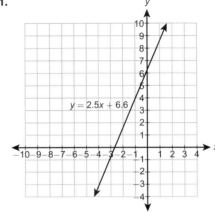

15.

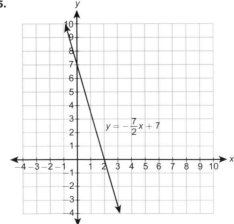

17.

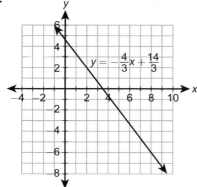

$y = -\frac{4}{3}x + \frac{14}{3}$

19.

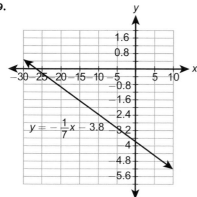

$y = -\frac{1}{7}x - 3.8$

21.

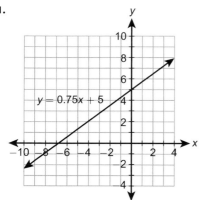

$y = 0.75x + 5$

23.

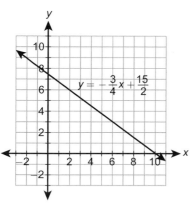

$y = -\frac{3}{4}x + \frac{15}{2}$

25.

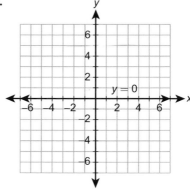

$y = 0$

27.

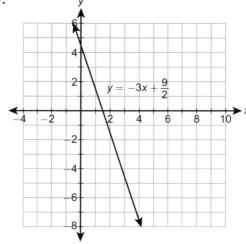

$y = -3x + \frac{9}{2}$

29.

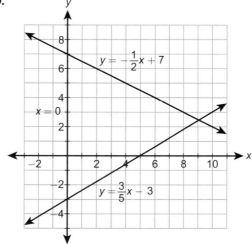

$y = -\frac{1}{2}x + 7$

$x = 0$

$y = \frac{3}{5}x - 3$

31. When a is positive, increasing a increases the slope. When a is negative, increasing a, for example, from -3 to -2, decreases the slope.

Pages 64–65

1. $y = -\frac{1}{2}x + 3$ **3.** $y = 3x + 10$ **5.** $y = -4x + 34$

7. $y = \frac{1}{3}$ **9.** $y = \frac{4}{5}x - \frac{3}{7}$ **11.** $y = -\frac{1}{3}x + 2$ **13.** $x = -5$

15. $x = 7$ **17. A.** $y - 4 = 4(x - 3)$ or $y - 0 = 4(x - 2)$
B. $4x - y = 8$ **C.** $y = 4x - 8$ **19. A.** $y - 8 = -1(x - 3)$ or

$y - 5 = -1(x - 6)$ **B.** $x + y = 11$ **C.** $y = -x + 11$
21. A. $y - (-1) = -0.925(x - 8.3)$ or $y - 7.6 = -0.925(x - (-1))$ **B.** $0.925x + y = 6.675$
C. $y = -0.925 + 6.675$ **23.** Parallel **25.** Perpendicular
27. Perpendicular, even though the product of the slopes is undefined. **29.** $y = -\dfrac{3}{2}x - \dfrac{1}{2}$

Pages 70–72

1. A. Let r = rewards and t = tasks completed. **B.** $r = t - 2$
C.

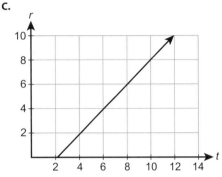

D. 12 tasks **3. A.** Let d = number of decorations and f = number of favors. **B.** $2d + 4.5f \le 40$
C.

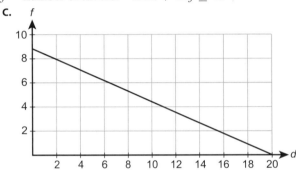

D. 5 favors **5.** Let x = total number of running minutes and y = number of miles run. **A.** $y = \dfrac{1}{13}x$ **B.** Slope equals the
constant running rate (mi/min). **C.** 340.6 minutes
7. Let x = days and y = tables. **A.** $y = 3x$ **B.** The slope represents how many tables the carpenter can make per day.
C. 30 tables **9.** Let x = number of days from Sept. 15, and y = stock value. **A.** $y = 121 + -\dfrac{21}{5}x$, where $m = -\dfrac{21}{5}$
B. The slope is the rate the value increases (or decreases).
C. \$58.00 **11.** Let x = number of hours over 40 and y = desire total earnings where $y > 430$. **A.** $y = 16.25x + 430$
B. The slope is the hourly rate of overtime pay. **C.** about 45 hrs **13.** Let x = total number of phone jacks and y = cost. **A.** $y = 40(x - 1) + 100$ **B.** The slope is the installation cost per jack. **C.** 9 **15.** Answers will vary.
Sample answer: **A.** Let x = the year and y = average hours spent with child. **B.** $y = -0.02x + 41.1$ **C.** 0.90
17. Answers will vary. Sample answer: **A.** Let x = the year and y = percent of filed income tax returns.
B. $y = 0.44x - 835.78$ **C.** 48.62 **19.** Answers will vary.

Sample answer: **A.** Let x = the year and y = percent of filed income tax returns. **B.** $y = 0.4011904762x - 796.4214286$
C. 2007

Page 78

1. Yes **3.** Yes **5.** Yes **7.** Yes **9.** Yes
11. $(2, 2)$

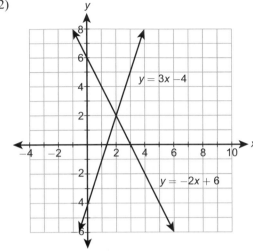

13. $(2, -1)$

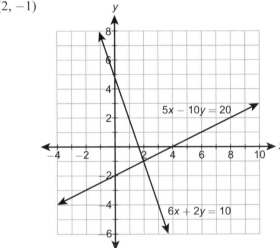

15. $(5, 1)$ **17.** $\left(\dfrac{21}{17}, -\dfrac{81}{34}\right)$ **19.** $(5, -1)$ **21.** $\left(\dfrac{5}{2}, -1\right)$
23. $(-4.09714, -0.73142)$ **25.** $\left(2, \dfrac{1}{2}, 4\right)$ **27.** No solution

Pages 82–83

1. A. Let x = amount invested earning 4% and y = amount invested at 6.5%. **B.** $\begin{cases} x + y = 4500 \\ 0.04x + 0.065y = 220 \end{cases}$ **C.** $x = \$2900$;
$y = \$1600$ **D.** Tyler invested \$2900 at 4% and \$1600 at 6.5%.
3. A. Let x = adult tickets purchased and y = child tickets purchased. **B.** $\begin{cases} x + y = 350 \\ 10x + 6y = 3292 \end{cases}$ **C.** $x = 298$; $y = 52$
D. There were 298 adults and 52 children at the showing.
5. A. Let x = amount invested at 3% and y = amount invested at 4%. **B.** $\begin{cases} x + y = 6000 \\ 0.03x + 0.04y = 225 \end{cases}$ **C.** $x = \$1500$;
$y = \$4500$ **D.** Kiana invested \$1500 at 3% and \$4500 at 4%.

7. A. Let $x =$ Chang's minutes and $y =$ Min's minutes.
B. $\begin{cases} x + y = 500 \\ 0.2x + 0.25y = 111 \end{cases}$ **C.** $x = 280; y = 220$ **D.** Chang used 280 minutes and Min used 220 minutes.
9. A. Let $x =$ computers from Company A and $y =$ computers from Company B. **B.** $\begin{cases} x + y = 1000 \\ 0.015x + 0.02y = 18 \end{cases}$ **C.** $x = 400$; $y = 600$ **D.** Perfect Electronics purchased 400 Company A computers and 600 Company B computers.
11. A. Let $x =$ bushels of corn and $y =$ bushels of wheat.
B. $\begin{cases} x + y = 1000 \\ 3x + 4.5y = 3781.50 \end{cases}$ **C.** $x = 479; y = 521$
D. The farmer purchased 479 bushel of corn and 521 bushels of wheat. **13. A.** Let $x =$ bagels and $y =$ muffins.
B. $\begin{cases} y - x = 25 \\ 1.29x + 1.5y = 316.50 \end{cases}$ **C.** $x = 100; y = 125$
D. The coffee shop sold 100 bagels and 125 muffins.
15. A. Let $x =$ quarters and $y =$ dimes.
B. $\begin{cases} x + y = 72 \\ 0.25x + 0.10y = 13.5 \end{cases}$ **C.** $x = 42; y = 30$
D. The meter held 42 quarters and 30 dimes.
17. A. Let $x =$ adults at the fair and $y =$ children at the fair.
B. $\begin{cases} 3x = y \\ x + y = 528 \end{cases}$ **C.** $x = 132$ and $y = 396$ **D.** There were 132 adults and 396 children at the fair. **19. A.** Let $x =$ amount invested at 5%, $y =$ amount invested at 7.5%, and $z =$ amount invested at 6.25%. **B.** $\begin{cases} x - y = 300 \\ x + y + z = 4000 \\ 0.05x + 0.075y + 0.0625z = 246.25 \end{cases}$
C. $x = 300; y = 0; z = 3700$ **D.** Casey invested $300 at 5%, $0 at 7.5%, and $3700 at 6.25%. **21. A.** Let $Q =$ number of quarters, $D =$ number of dimes, and $N =$ number of nickels.
B. $\begin{cases} Q + D + N = 120 \\ Q = 5D \\ 0.25Q + 0.10D + 0.05N = 16.50 \end{cases}$
C. $Q = 50; D = 10; N = 60$ **D.** There are 50 quarters, 10 dimes, and 60 nickels. **23. A.** Let $C =$ pounds of cheese, $T =$ pounds of turkey, and $S =$ pounds of salami.
B. $\begin{cases} C + T + S = 26 \\ T = 2S \\ 1.99C + 2.49T + 1.89S = 57.14 \end{cases}$ **C.** $C = 8; T = 12;$
$S = 6$ **D.** The deli sold 8 lbs of cheese, 12 lbs of turkey, and 6 lbs of salami.

UNIT 3 Functions

Pages 87–88

1. Mapping Diagram   Table   Graph

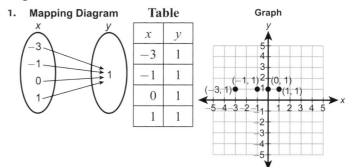

3. Mapping Diagram   Table   Graph

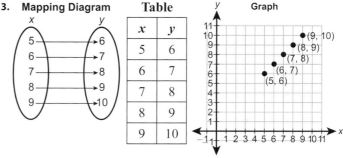

5. domain: $\{5, 6, 7, 8\}$; range: $\{3, 4, 5, 6\}$ **7.** domain: $\{x: x \neq 3\}$; range: $\{y: y \neq 0\}$ **9.** domain: $\{x \in \text{real numbers}\}$; range: $\{y \in \text{real numbers}\}$ **11.** domain: $\{x \in \text{real numbers}\}$; range: $\{y: y \geq 0\}$

Pages 92–95

1. Yes. Each x-value is assigned to only one y-value.
3. No. Jill is assigned to both fruit and vegetables.
5. Yes. Each x-value is assigned to only one y-value.
7. No. The x-value 2 is assigned to 3 different values.
9. domain: $\{x \in \text{real numbers}\}$; range: $\{y \in \text{real numbers}\}$
11. domain: $\{x \mid x \geq 6\}$; range: $\{y \mid y \geq 0\}$
13. domain: $\{x \in \text{real numbers}\}$; range: $\{y \in \text{real numbers}\}$
15. domain: $\{x: x \neq 3\}$; range: $\{y: y \neq 0\}$
17. Yes **19.** No **21.** No **23.** No
25.

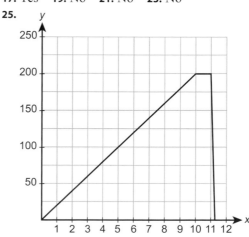

27.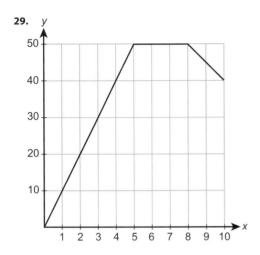

29.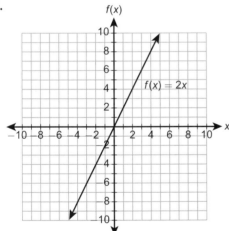

9.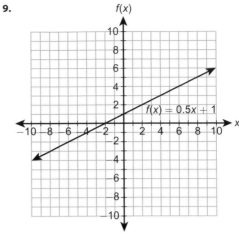

11. domain: $\{x \in$ real numbers$\}$; range: $\{f(x) \in$ real numbers$\}$
13. domain: $\{x \in$ real numbers$\}$; range: $\{f(x)|\ y \geq -4\}$
15. domain: $\{n \in$ real numbers$\}$; range: $\{b(n) \in$ real numbers$\}$
17. domain: $\{a \in$ real numbers$\}$; range: $\{q(a)|\ q(a) \geq 0\}$
19. domain: $\{y|\ y \geq 0\}$; range: $\{t(y)|\ t(y) \geq 0\}$
21. Independent variable: amount of fertilizer; Dependent variable: number of tomatoes **23.** Independent variable: number of games won; Dependent variable: place in the standings **25.** Independent variable: size of vehicle; Dependent variable: number of miles per gallon
27. Independent variable: temperature of the water; Dependent variable: amount of sugar dissolved
29. Independent variable: distance from person being called; Dependent variable: cost of phone call

Pages 98–99

1. $1, -1$ **3.** $-2, -3$ **5.** $0, 1$

7.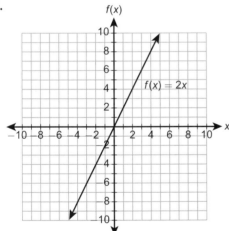

Pages 104–105

1.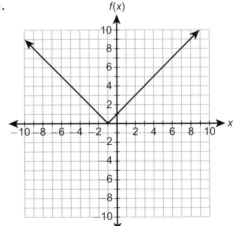

3.

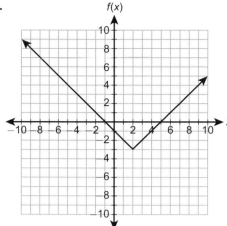

5.

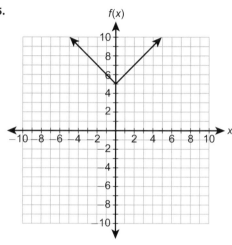

7. narrower   **9.** 1 unit down; upside–down V; wider
11. $(1, 0)$ **13.** $(-5, -1)$ **15.** $f(x) = |x + 6| + 2$
17. $f(x) = -|x + 7| - 1$ **19.** $f(x) = |x - 8|$
21. $f(x) = -|x + 12|$ **23.** domain: $\{x \in$ real numbers$\}$;
range: $\{y: y \geq -3\}$ **25.** domain: $\{x \in$ real numbers$\}$;
range: $\{y: y \geq 0\}$ **27.** $-50|x - 5| + 200$

Pages 109–112

1. $f(x) = \begin{cases} -3x \text{ if } x \leq 0 \\ 3x \text{ if } x > 0 \end{cases}$ **3.** $f(x) = \begin{cases} 2x \text{ if } x \leq 0 \\ -2x \text{ if } x > 0 \end{cases}$

5. $f(x) = \begin{cases} -x + 3 \text{ if } x \leq 3 \\ x - 3 \text{ if } x > 3 \end{cases}$ **7.** $f(x) = \begin{cases} -1 \text{ if } x < 2 \\ 1 \text{ if } x \geq 2 \end{cases}$

9. $f(x) = \begin{cases} 5 \text{ if } x \leq -2 \\ 2x \text{ if } -2 < x < 2 \\ -5 \text{ if } x \geq 2 \end{cases}$ **11.** $f(x) = \begin{cases} 4 \text{ if } x \leq -2 \\ x \text{ if } -2 < x \leq 2 \\ -5 \text{ if } x > 2 \end{cases}$

13. $f(x) = \begin{cases} -x \text{ if } x \leq -2 \\ 2x \text{ if } x > -2 \end{cases}$ **15.** $f(x) = \begin{cases} -2x \text{ if } x < 2 \\ 0 \text{ if } x = 2 \\ -x \text{ if } x > 2 \end{cases}$

17. $f(x) = \begin{cases} -x \text{ if } x < 0 \\ 2x + 2 \text{ if } x \geq 0 \end{cases}$

19.

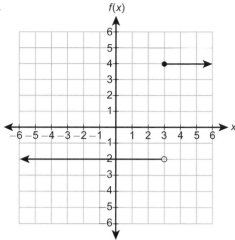

21.

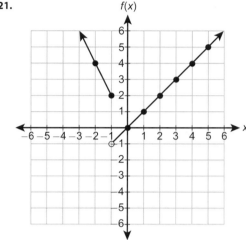

23.

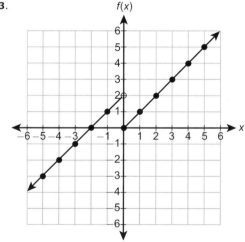

25. $-4, -4, 3$ **27.** $7, 0, 3.25, 13$ **29.** $-2, -3, 8, 4$

Pages 116–118

1. $f(x) = -1, 0, 1, 2, 2$ **3.** $f(x) = -1, -1, 0, 1, 2$

5.

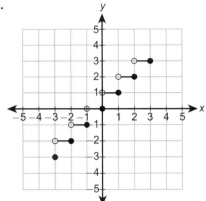

7.

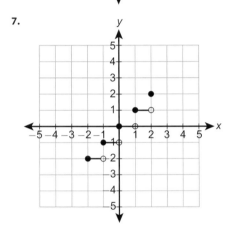

9.

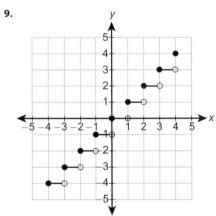

11. $f(x) = \begin{cases} -1 \text{ if } -3 \leq x < -2 \\ 0 \text{ if } -2 \leq x < -1 \\ 1 \text{ if } -1 \leq x < 0 \\ 2 \text{ if } 0 \leq x < 1 \end{cases}$

13. $f(x) = \begin{cases} -2 \text{ if } -5 < x \leq -4 \\ -1 \text{ if } -4 < x \leq -3 \\ 0 \text{ if } -3 < x \leq -2 \\ 1 \text{ if } -2 < x \leq -1 \end{cases}$

15. $f(x) = \begin{cases} -4 \text{ if } -3 < x \leq -2 \\ -2 \text{ if } -2 < x \leq -1 \\ 0 \text{ if } -1 < x \leq 0 \\ 2 \text{ if } 0 < x \leq 1 \\ 4 \text{ if } 1 < x \leq 2 \end{cases}$

17. A. domain: $\{x \in \text{real numbers}\}$; range: $\{y \in \ldots -4, -2, 0, 2, 4, \ldots\}$ **B.** Multiplying by 2 stretches the graph vertically by a factor of 2. **C.** No other graph is the same.
19. A. domain: $\{x \in \text{real numbers}\}$; range: $\{y \in \ldots -1.5, -1, -0.5, 0, 0.5, 1, 1.5, \ldots\}$ **B.** Multiplying by $\frac{1}{2}$ compresses the graph vertically by a factor of $\frac{1}{2}$. **C.** No other graph is the same. **21. A.** domain: $\{x \in \text{real numbers}\}$; range: $\{y \in \ldots -5, -2, 1, 4, 7, \ldots\}$ **B.** Multiplying by 3 stretches the graph vertically by a factor of 3. Adding 1 moves the parent graph up 1 unit. **C.** No other graph is the same.
23. A. domain: $\{x \in \text{real numbers}\}$; range: $\{y \in \ldots -5, -3, -1, 1, 3, \ldots\}$ **B.** Multiplying by 2 stretches the graph vertically by a factor of 2. Subtracting 3 moves the parent graph down 3 units. **C.** No other graph is the same.
25. A. domain: $\{x \in \text{real numbers}\}$; range: $\{y \in \ldots -1.5, -1, -0.5, 0, 0.5, 1, 1.5 \ldots\}$ **B.** Multiplying by 0.5 compresses the graph vertically by a factor of 0.5. Adding 6 moves the parent graph up 6 units. **C.** No other graph is the same.
27. A. domain: $\{x \in \text{real numbers}\}$; range: $\{y \in \text{integers}\}$;
B. Adding 2 moves the parent graph up 2 units.
C. This graph is the same as $f(x) = \lceil x \rceil + 1$ but with different endpoints.

29.

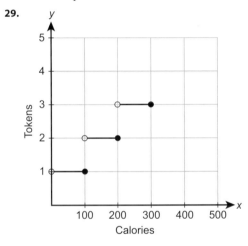

$f(x) = \begin{cases} 1 \text{ if } 0 < x \leq 100 \\ 2 \text{ if } 100 < x \leq 200 \\ 3 \text{ if } 200 < x \leq 300 \end{cases}$

Pages 122–123

1. A. $x^2 + x - 6$ **B.** $x^2 - x - 12$ **C.** $x^3 + 3x^2 - 9x - 27$
D. $x - 3 \ (x \neq -3)$ **3. A.** $2x^2 + 3x + 1$ **B.** $2x^2 - x - 1$
C. $4x^3 + 4x^2 + x$ **D.** $x \left(x \neq -\frac{1}{2} \right)$ **5. A.** $16x^2 + 1$
B. $4x^2 + 4$ **7. A.** $-12x^2 - 4$ **B.** $-6x^2 - 8$ **9.** 15
11. 950 **13.** $\{x \mid -2 \leq x \leq 1\}$ **15.** $\{x \mid -4 \leq x < 4\}$
17. A. -16 **B.** 4 **19. A.** 10 **B.** 15 **21.** $h(x) = 2x - 8$
23. $h(x) = \frac{9}{2}x - 8$ **25.** $(f \cdot g)(x) = 3^{\frac{4}{x}}$; domain of $(f \cdot g)$
and domain of g: $\{x \mid x \neq 0\}$; range of $f \cdot g$ and range of
f: $\{y \mid y > 0\}$; domain of f: $\{\text{real numbers}\}$; range of

$g: \{y \mid y \neq 0\}$ **27.** $(f \cdot g)(x) = \left|\frac{1}{x}\right|$; domain of $f \cdot g$ and domain of g: $\{x \mid x \neq 0\}$; range of $f \cdot g$: $\{y \mid y > 0\}$; range of f: $\{y \mid y \geq 0\}$; domain of f: $\{x \in \text{real numbers}\}$; range of g: $\{y \mid y \neq 0\}$ **29.** $(f \cdot g)(x) = (g \cdot f)(x) = x$; $f(x)$ and $g(x)$ are inverses

Pages 128–129

1. $y = \frac{1}{2}x - 2$; domain: $\{x \in \text{real numbers}\}$; range: $\{y \in \text{real numbers}\}$ **3.** $x = 3$; domain: $x = 3$; range: $\{y \in \text{real numbers}\}$ **5. A.** $f^{-1}(x) = \frac{1}{7}x - \frac{11}{7}$;

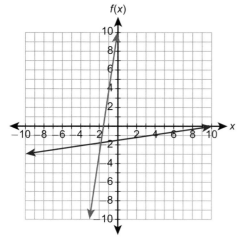

B. Function   **C.** domain: $\{x \in \text{real numbers}\}$; range: $\{y \in \text{real numbers}\}$ **7. A.** $y = \pm\sqrt{x + 3}$;

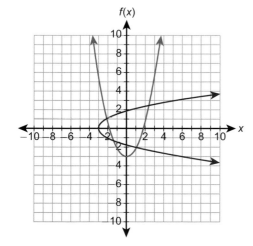

B. not a function   **C.** domain: $\{x \mid x \geq -3\}$; range: $\{y \in \text{real numbers}\}$ **9. A.** $f^{-1}(x) = \sqrt{x - 1}$;

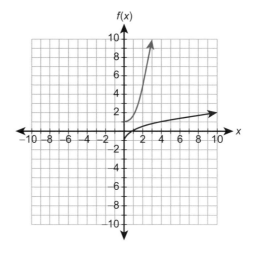

B. Function   **C.** domain: $\{x \mid x \geq 1\}$; range: $\{y \mid y \geq 0\}$
11. A. $f^{-1}(x) = \sqrt{16 - x^2}$; $0 \leq x \leq 4$; $0 \leq y \leq 4$;

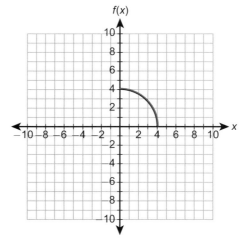

B. Function   **C.** domain: $-4 \leq x \leq 4$; range: $0 \leq y \leq 4$ **13. A.** $f^{-1}(x) = -\sqrt{x - 4}$;

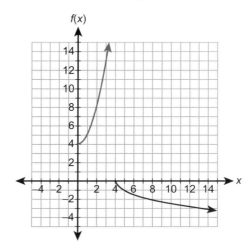

B. Function **C.** domain: $\{x \mid x \geq 4\}$; range: $\{y \mid y \leq 0\}$;

15. $(f \circ g)(x) = f\left(-\dfrac{4}{3}x + \dfrac{8}{3}\right) = -\dfrac{3}{4}\left(-\dfrac{4}{3}x + \dfrac{8}{3}\right) + 2 =$
$x - 2 + 2 = x$; $(g \circ f)x = g\left(-\dfrac{3}{4}x + 2\right) =$
$-\dfrac{4}{3}\left(-\dfrac{3}{4}x + 2\right) + \dfrac{8}{3} = x - \dfrac{8}{3} + \dfrac{8}{3} = x$; $(f \circ g)(x) =$
$(g \circ f)x$ **17.** $(f \circ g)(x) = f(\sqrt{x+9}) = (\sqrt{x+9})^2 - 9 =$
$x + 9 - 9 = x$; $(g \circ f)x = g(x^2 - 9) = \sqrt{(x^2 - 9) + 9} =$
$\sqrt{x^2} = x$; $(f \circ g)(x) = (g \circ f)x$ **19.** $\dfrac{9}{2}$ **21.** $\dfrac{39}{100}$

23. Undefined **25.** $-\dfrac{1}{15}$ **27.** $-\dfrac{1}{4}$ **29.** about 5000 miles

UNIT 4 Inequalities

Pages 133–134

1. True **3.** False **5.** True **7.** True **9.** True

11.

13.

15.

17.

19.

21. $x \geq -3$ **23.** $x > 1$ **25.** $x < -4.5$

Page 139

1. $t \in [2, \infty)$ **3.** $x \in (-\infty, 5)$ **5.** $x \in (7, \infty)$
7. $x \in (-\infty, 0)$ **9.** $x \in (-4, \infty)$
11. A. $b \in (-\infty, 10)$,

B. $b \in \{\dots, 7, 8, 9\}$,

C. $b \in \{0, 1, 2, 3, 4, 5, 6, 7, 8, 9\}$,

13. A. $p \in (-\infty, 7]$,

B. $p \in \{\dots -1, 0, 1, 2, 3, 4, 5, 6, 7\}$,

C. $p \in \{0, 1, 2, 3, 4, 5, 6, 7\}$,

15. A. $x \in [4, \infty)$,

B. $x \in \{4, 5, 6 \dots\}$,

C. $x \in \{4, 5, 6, \dots\}$,

17. A. $t \in (-\infty, 10)$,

B. $x \in \{\dots, -1, 0, 1, 2, 3, 4, 5, 6, 7, 8, 9\}$,

C. $x \in \{1, 0, 1, 2, 3, 4, 5, 6, 7, 8, 9\}$,

19. A. $x \in \left(-\infty, 2\dfrac{1}{6}\right)$,

B. $x \in \{\dots -1, 0, 1, 2\}$,

C. $x \in \{0, 1, 2\}$,

21. A. $h \in \left(-\infty, \dfrac{1}{6}\right)$,

B. $h \in \{\dots, -3, -2, -1, 0\}$,

C. $h \in \{0\}$,

23. A. $x \in [4, \infty)$,

B. $x \in \{4, 5, 6, 7, 8, 9, 10 \ldots\}$,

(number line 0–10)

C. $x \in \{4, 5, 6, 7, 8, 9, 10 \ldots\}$,

(number line 0–10)

25. The width of the garden must be less than 11.5 meters.

Page 143

1. (number line 0–10),

$x \in (3, 6]$

3. (number line −6 to 4),

no solution

5. (number line 0–10),

$x \in (-\infty, 5)$

7. (number line 0–10),

$r \in (-\infty, 2] \cup r \in [5, \infty)$

9. (number line −5 to 5),

$x \in (-\infty, \infty)$ or $x \in \{\text{real numbers}\}$

11. (number line −5 to 5),

$x \in (-3, \infty)$

13. $-4 \leq x \leq 4; x \in [-4, 4]$

15. $-1 < x \leq 3; x \in (-1, 3]$

17. $x > 3; x \in (3, \infty)$

19. $x < 2$ or $x > 2; x \in (-\infty, 2) \cup x \in (2, \infty)$

21. $x > 5$ or $x > 11$;

(number line 0–12)

23. $x < 3$ or $x \geq 2$;

(number line 0–10)

25. $-\dfrac{7}{3} \leq x \leq \dfrac{4}{3}$;

(number line −5 to 5)

27. $x \geq \dfrac{7}{3}$ and $x \leq \dfrac{3}{2}$, no solution,

(number line 0–10)

29. $-\dfrac{7}{2} \leq x \leq 5$;

(number line −5 to 5)

31. $x \in (26{,}557.03, \; 26{,}649.64)$

Page 146

1. Conjunction **3.** Disjunction

5. A. $x > -5$ and $x < 5$ **B.** $x \in (-5, 5)$

C.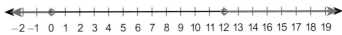
(number line −5 to 5)

7. A. $m \geq -2$ and $m \leq 2$ **B.** $m \, [-2, 2]$

C. (number line −5 to 5)

9. $-7 < a < 3$;

(number line −7 to 4)

11. $-\dfrac{1}{7} < r < \dfrac{9}{7}$;

(number line −1 to 2)

13. $x > \dfrac{9}{5}$ or $x < -\dfrac{11}{5}$;

(number line −5 to 5)

15. $f < 0$ or $f > 12$;

(number line −2 to 19)

17. $n < -\dfrac{3}{2}$ or $n > \dfrac{9}{2}$;

(number line −4 to 6)

19. $t \geq 44$ or $t \leq -52$;

(number line −60 to 60)

21. no solution;

(number line −5 to 5)

23. $x < -4$ or $x > -2$;

(number line −5 to 5)

25. $g \geq 1$ and $g \leq 17$;

(number line −1 to 20)

27. $x > -2$ and $x < 6$;

(number line −3 to 7)

29. $|x - 20| \leq 0.25; x \geq 19.75$ and $x \leq 20.25$

1.

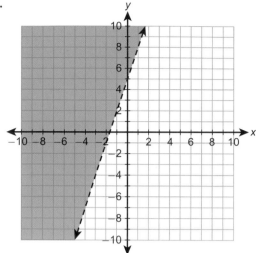

3.

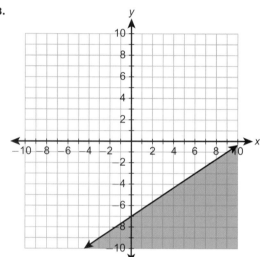

5.

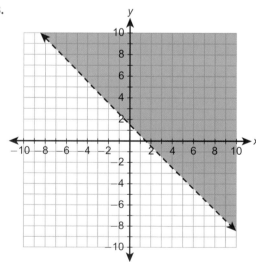

7.

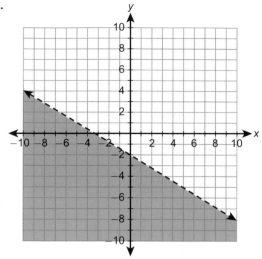

9.

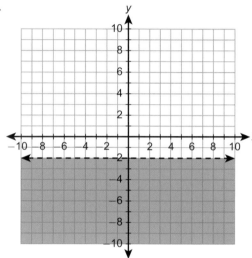

11.

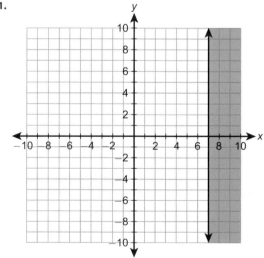

13.

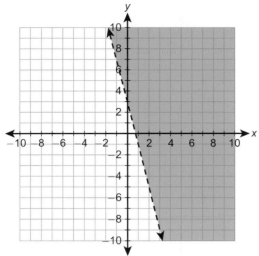

15.

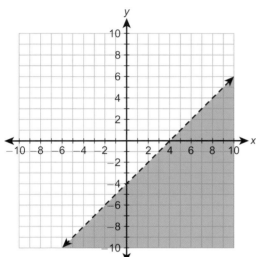

17.

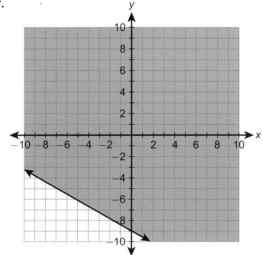

19. $y > 2.5$ **21.** $x > 4$ **23.** $y > 6x - 5$

25. $2y < 3x + 14$ **27.** $y > 7x + 5$ **29.** Answers will vary. Sample answer: $y \geq 4$,

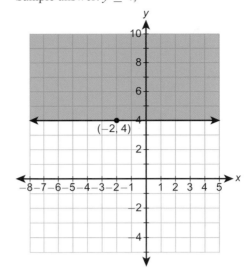

$x \leq -2$,

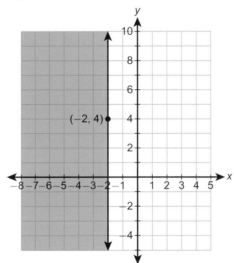

$y \leq x + 6$,

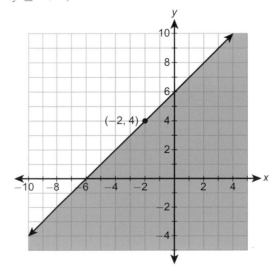

Pages 156–158

1. Yes **3.** No **5.** No

7.

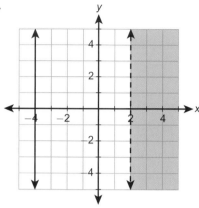

9.

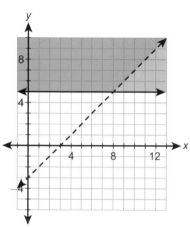

11.

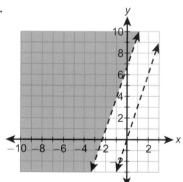

13.

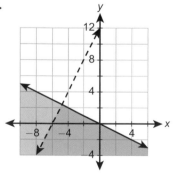

15.

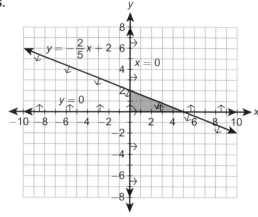

17.

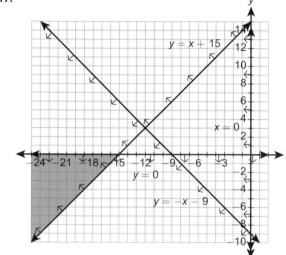

19.

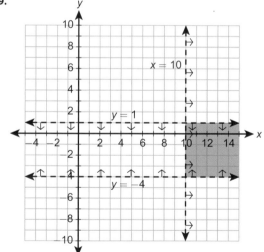

21.

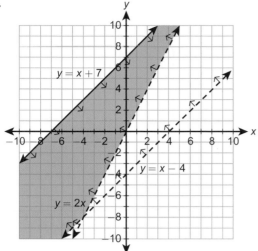

23. $\begin{cases} x \geq 4 \\ y \leq -6 \end{cases}$ **25.** $\begin{cases} y > 2x + 3 \\ y \geq \frac{1}{2}x - 3 \end{cases}$ **27.** $\begin{cases} y \geq -2x + 1 \\ y \leq x + 5 \\ x \geq 0 \end{cases}$

29.

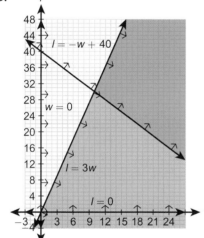

$\begin{cases} l \leq 3w \\ 2w + 2l \geq 80 \\ w \geq 0 \\ l \geq 0 \end{cases}$

Three possibilities for the width and length are 10 and 30, 11 and 32, and 12 and 35.

Pages 163–165

1. A. Let $l =$ number of large pizzas; $s =$ number of small pizzas; $15l + 10s \leq 60$; $45l + 15s \leq 135$; $l \geq 0$; $s \geq 0$

B.

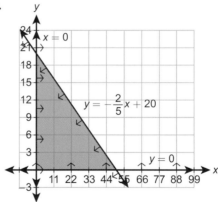

C. Stacy can sell 1 large and 3 small pizzas or 2 large and 1 small pizzas.   **3. A.** Let x be the number of packets of cashews and y be the number of packets of almonds; $5x + 8y \leq 50$; $y \geq \frac{1}{2}x$; $x \geq 0$; $y \geq 0$

B.

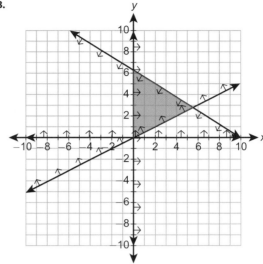

C. Jessie can buy 2 packets each of cashews and almonds or 3 packets each of cashews and almonds.   **5. A.** If Dorian rides x km at 25 km/hr and y km at 40 km/hr, then $2x + 5y \leq 100$; $x \geq 0$; $y \geq 0$

B.

C. Dorian can ride 22 kilometers at 25 kilometers per hour and then 6 kilometers at 40 kilometers per hour. He could also ride 11 kilometers at 25 kilometers per hour and then 9 kilometers at 40 kilometers per hour.

7. A.

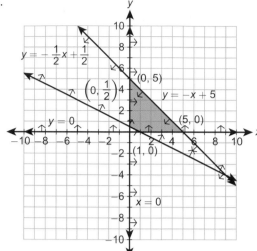

B. Optimal solution: (0, 5)

9. A.

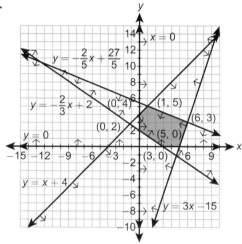

B. Optimal solution (6, 3)

11. A.

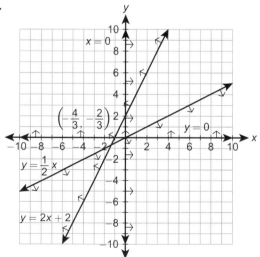

B. There is no region of feasibility.

13. A. $7x + 5y \geq 15; 2x + 2y \geq 6; 3x + 2y \geq 8; x \geq 0, y \geq 0$

B.

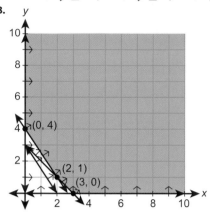

C. $C = 7x + 4y$　**D.** To minimize her cost, Liza should buy 0 X pills and 4 Y pills for a total cost of \$16.　**15. A.** $x + y \geq 36;$ $y \geq 2x; x \geq 0, y \geq 0$

B.

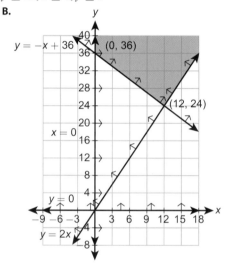

C. $P = 15x + 25y$　**D.** To earn a minimum of \$780, Jiao should tutor 12 hours and teach 24 hours.

17. A. $250 \le x \le 500$; $200 \le y \le 500$; $x + y \ge 600$

B.

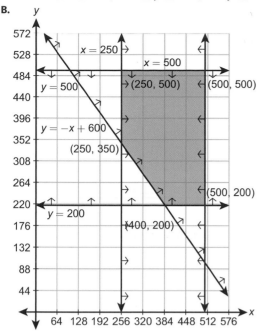

C. $P = -3x + 5y$ **D.** Optimal solution is for Auto World to produce 250 front wipers and 500 back wipers each week.

UNIT 5   Polynomials and Power Functions

Pages 169–170

1. 8   **3.** $2abc$ **5.** $\dfrac{16}{25}$ **7.** $3^{10} = 59{,}049$ **9.** x^2 **11.** xy^4 **13.** y^2

15. $\dfrac{f^4}{d}$ **17.** 9   **19.** $8m^3$ **21.** $5x^2y^7$ **23.** $2s^{13}t^6$

Page 175

1. Yes.   **3.** No; it has a variable with a negative exponent.

5. $6d$ and $\dfrac{1}{4}d$; c^3 and $25c^3$ **7.** $10y$ and $-5y$; $5xy$ and $30xy$

9. binomial, degree 1   **11.** binomial, degree 2   **13.** $3z - 7$

15. $\dfrac{8}{5}c^3 + 4c^2 - 18$ **17.** degree: 2, leading coefficient: 3, constant: 0   **19.** degree: 5, leading coefficient: 3, constant: 4

21. $-3m^2 + 4m + 3$ **23.** $-4a^3 - 5a^2 + 4a - 3$

25. $-3z^2 + 4z - 4$ **27.** $-2x^3 + 2x + 5$ **29.** $8n^2 + 18n + 22$

Pages 178–179

1. $8x^4y^3z^3$ **3.** $-3x^3 + 5x^2$ **5.** $18y^4 + 6y^3 - 12y^2 - 18y$

7. $2y^2 - 13y + 20$ **9.** $12m^2 + 20m - 8$

11. $4y^4 - 3y^3 - 6y^2 + 6y - 4$ **13.** $x^2 - 8x + 16$

15. $25x^2 - 70x + 49$ **17.** $a^3 + b^3$ **19.** $4z^2 + 16z + 16$

21. $-12x^3 - 6x^2y - 16x - 8y$ **23.** $6z^3 + 17z^2 - 3z$

25. $3\sqrt{2}m^2 - 14m + 4\sqrt{2}$ **27.** $4x^2 + 7\sqrt{2}xy - 30y^2$

29. $-2h^2 + h + 45$ **31.** $75\pi a^2 - 60\pi a + 12\pi$

Page 185

1. $9(a^2 + 2a - 4)$ **3.** $-3c(2c^3 + 5c + 3)$

5. $7mn(m^2 - 3n^2 + 2)$ **7.** $(n - 9)(n + 9)$ **9.** Not factorable

11. Not factorable   **13.** $(w + 6)(w^2 - 6w + 36)$

15. $(c + 10)(c - 5)$ **17.** Not factorable   **19.** $(3x - 2)(x + 3)$

21. $(3c - 2)(3c - 2)$ or $(3c - 2)^2$ **23.** $6r(r + 9)$

25. $-3(2n - 1)(6n - 5)$ **27.** $3(x^2 - 4)(x^2 - 16)$

29. $3(2y + 5)^2$

Page 189

1. Yes.   **3.** No; 4 is not a perfect cube.   **5.** No; 6 is not a perfect cube   **7.** $(c^3 + 5)(c^6 - 5c^3 + 25)$ **9.** $(4 - x)(16 + 4x + x^2)$

11. $\left(m^3 + \dfrac{1}{2}\right)\left(m^6 - \dfrac{1}{2}m^3 + \dfrac{1}{4}\right)$ **13.** $(a + b)(c - 4)$

15. $(x - 3y)(4x + 1)$ **17.** $(x - 3)(x + 7)$ **19.** $(3x + 2)(2x - 5)$

21. $(y + 3)(y - 3)(y - 1)$ **23.** $4a(a - 3)(a + 9)$

25. $4(3x - 4)(x + 2y)$ **27.** $3(y + 2)(y - 2)(y^4 + 4y^2 + 16)$

29. $4x\,(4x + 5)(4x - 5)(x + 2)$

Page 193

1. $\{-2, 3\}$ **3.** $\left\{-\dfrac{5}{2}, 3\right\}$ **5.** $\left\{\dfrac{3}{4}, 2\right\}$ **7.** $\left\{-\dfrac{1}{2}, \dfrac{11}{8}\right\}$

9. $\left\{-\dfrac{3}{2}, 12\right\}$ **11.** $\{-6, 6\}$ **13.** $\left\{0, \dfrac{1}{5}\right\}$ **15.** $\left\{0, \dfrac{1}{6}\right\}$

17. $\left\{-\dfrac{3}{5}, \dfrac{3}{5}\right\}$ **19.** $\left\{0, \dfrac{1}{6}\right\}$ **21.** $\left\{-\dfrac{1}{2}, \dfrac{1}{2}\right\}$ **23.** $\left\{-\dfrac{1}{3}, \dfrac{1}{3}\right\}$ **25.** $\left\{0, \dfrac{3}{2}\right\}$

27. $\left\{-\dfrac{3}{4}, -\dfrac{1}{4}, \dfrac{1}{4}\right\}$ **29.** $\left\{-\dfrac{11}{6}, \dfrac{7}{18}\right\}$

Pages 200–201

1. Linear   **3.** Quadratic

5.

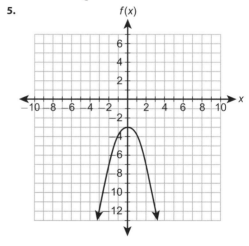

7.

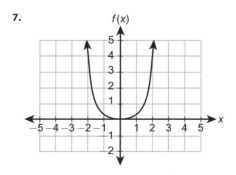

9.

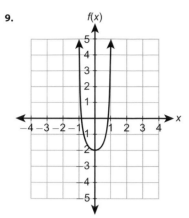

11.

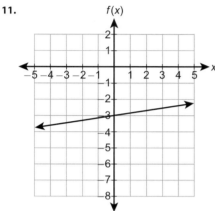

13.

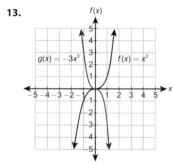

Increasing the absolute value of a causes the graph to contract; when a is negative, the graph is reflected across the y-axis.

15.

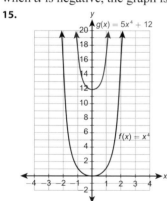

Increasing the absolute value of a causes the graph to contract; increasing the parameter b causes the graph to shift up b units.   **17.** $p(x) = \frac{2}{3}x^3$ **19.** $p(x) = -3x$

21. A. Even   **B.** The function is a quadratic function and the leading coefficient is negative, so as x increases without bound, $f(x)$ eventually decreases without bound, and as x decreases without bound, $f(x)$ eventually decreases without bound.   **23. A.** Neither   **B.** The function is a linear function and the leading coefficient is positive, so as x increases without bound, $f(x)$ increases without bound, and as x decreases without bound, $f(x)$ decreases without bound.
25. A. Odd   **B.** The function is a cubic function and the leading coefficient is positive, so as x increases without bound, $f(x)$ eventually increases without bound, and as x decreases without bound, $f(x)$ eventually decreases without bound.   **27.** Linear   **29.** Cannot be determined, but at least quartic.   **31.** As time increases, the ball's height increases; after reaching its maximum height, the ball's height decreases as time increases until it reaches zero (on the ground).

UNIT 6   Rational Equations

Pages 205–206

1. $\frac{1}{2}$ **3.** $\frac{a+c}{b}$ **5.** $\frac{xb+ay}{by}$ **7.** $\frac{3}{16}$ **9.** $\frac{7}{12}$ **11.** $\frac{uw}{vx}$

13. 3   **15.** 2   **17.** $\frac{cf}{de}$ **19.** $\frac{1}{216}$ **21.** $\frac{32}{243}$ **23.** c^{x-y}

Pages 209–210

1. $x \neq 0, y \neq 0$ **3.** $t \neq -\frac{5}{2}$ **5.** $d \neq -2$

7. $x \neq -4, x \neq 2$ **9.** $r \neq -4, r \neq 3$ **11. A.** $p \neq 0, q \neq 0$

B. $\frac{q^6}{7p^3}$ **13. A.** $x \neq 2, x \neq 3$ **B.** $\frac{x+5}{x-3}$ **15. A.** $n \neq -5, n \neq 3$

B. -1 **17. A.** $t \neq 0$ **B.** $t - 3 + \frac{4}{t}$ **19. A.** $r \neq 0$

B. $2r^2 + 3r + 5$ **21. A.** $f \neq 0$ **B.** $2f^4 + 4f^2 + 1$

23. A. $a \neq 3, a \neq -3$ **B.** $\frac{a-2}{a-3}$ **25. A.** $v \neq 3$ **B.** $v + 5$

27. A. $h \neq -4$ **B.** $h + 5$ **29. A.** $c \neq 5, c > -2$ **B.** $\sqrt{c+2}$

Pages 214–215

1. $\frac{2x^2 + x + 7}{2x - 1}$ **3.** $\frac{-q-3}{q^2}$ **5.** $\frac{2(b^2 - 10b + 2)}{3b - 5}$

7. $\frac{-11x^2 + 20x}{5x^2 + 6x - 8}$ **9.** $\frac{x^2 - 5x + 18}{x^3 - 2x^2 - 16x + 32}$ or

$\frac{x^2 - 5x + 18}{(x+4)(x-4)(x-2)}$

11. $\frac{-3x + 122}{10x(x^2 + 1)}$ or $\frac{-3x + 122}{10x^3 + 10x}$ **13.** $\frac{2x + 5}{3x(x+2)}$ or

$\frac{2x+5}{3x^2 + 6x}$ **15.** $\frac{x}{x-3}$ **17.** $5x$ **19.** $18w$

21. $\frac{3x^2 - 2x}{9}$ or $\frac{x(3x-2)}{9}$ **23.** $\frac{3d^2 + 15d}{d+3}$ or $\frac{3d(d+5)}{d+3}$

25. $\frac{3}{4}$ **27.** $\frac{3x-1}{12x}$ **29.** $\frac{11k^2 + 44k + 41}{(k+3)^2(k-1)}$

Pages 218–219

1. $\frac{2}{3}$ **3.** $\frac{3}{50}$ **5.** $-\frac{5}{3}$ **7.** $\frac{y}{2x}$ **9.** $\frac{3a^2}{b^2}$ **11.** $\frac{5}{9}$ **13.** $1\frac{6}{7}$

15. $\frac{6}{5}$ **17.** $\frac{2-20x}{2x+3}$ **19.** $\frac{40y-20}{6-15y}$ **21.** $\frac{3x+4}{3x}$

23. $\frac{5y-6}{2-y}$ **25.** $\frac{2x+y+10}{5}$ **27.** $\frac{5x+3y+5xy+3}{-4x-7y-7xy-4}$

29. $\frac{29}{9x+55}$

Pages 224–225

1. $\{12\}, h \neq -4, h \neq 0$ **3.** $\{1\}$ **5.** $\left(-\frac{3}{26}\right), a \neq -3, a \neq 0$

7. $\{-1, -8\}, x \neq -2, x \neq 0$ **9.** $\{-6, -2\}, q \neq -3, q \neq 0$

11. $\{7\}, n \neq 0, n \neq 4$ **13.** $\{7\}, c \neq -5, c \neq -1$

15. $\{-1\}, r \neq -2, r \neq 2$ **17.** $\{ \}, g \neq -3, g \neq \frac{1}{2}$

19. A. Let x = hours it takes Sun to build a fence alone;
$\frac{6}{10} + \frac{6}{x} = 1$ **B.** $x = 15$ **C.** It would take Sun 15 hours to
make the fence alone. **21. A.** Let x = hours it takes Julio to
stain the fence alone. $\frac{1}{x} + \frac{1}{3x} = \frac{1}{3}$ **B.** $x = 4$
C. Julio takes 4 hours; Samuel takes 3 times longer, or 12
hours. **23. A.** Let x = hours for Company B to install a heat
pump alone; $\frac{9}{12} + \frac{9}{x} = 1$ **B.** $x = 36$ **C.** It takes Company
B 36 hours to install the heat pump alone.

25. A. Let x = hours for B&T to fix a car; $\frac{15}{20} + \frac{15}{x} = 1$
B. $x = 60$ **C.** It takes B&T 60 hours to fix the car alone.
27. A. Let x = hours for scouts to deliver baskets;
scouts deliver $\frac{1}{x}$ baskets per hour; $\frac{8}{18} + \frac{8}{x} = 1$ **B.** $x = 14.4$
C. It takes the scouts 14.4 hours to deliver the baskets.
29. A. Let x = hours it takes both companies to produce 500
books if PP starts 1 hour after PIC starts.
$100 + 100x + \frac{500}{3}x = 500$ **B.** $x = 1.5$ **C.** It takes 2.5
hours to produce 500 books.

Pages 230–232

1. domain: $\{x \mid x \in \mathbb{R}, x \neq 0\}$;
range: $\{f(x) \mid f(x) \in \mathbb{R}, f(x) \neq 0\}$
3. domain: $\{q \mid q \in \mathbb{R}, q \neq 0\}$; range: $\{s(q) \mid s(q) > 0\}$
5.

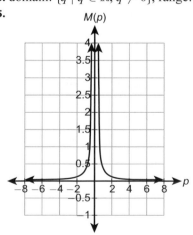

7.

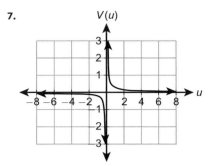

9.

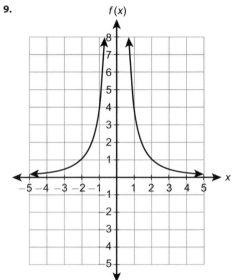

11.

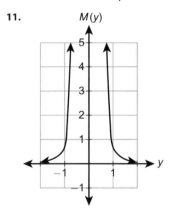

13.

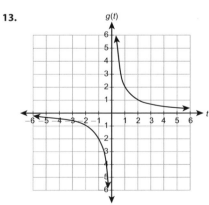

15.

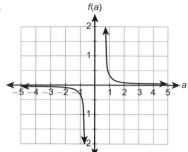

17. $g(x) = \dfrac{1}{8x^2}$ **19.** $T(x) = -\dfrac{5}{x}$ **21.** $f(x) = \dfrac{243}{4x^6}$

23. $f(x) = \dfrac{4}{x^2}$ **25.** $h(x) = \dfrac{-8}{x}$ **27.** $f(x) = \dfrac{3}{x^2}$

29. Answers will vary. Sample answer:

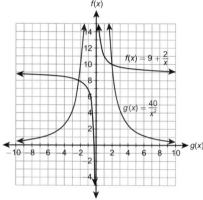

One is the graph of $g(x) = \dfrac{40}{x^2}$, and another is the graph of $f(x) = 9 + \dfrac{2}{x}$. Both graphs have a vertical asymptote at $x = 0$. The graph of $f(x) = 9 + \dfrac{2}{x}$ has a horizontal asymptote at $y = 9$, while the graph of $g(x) = \dfrac{40}{x^2}$ has a horizontal asymptote at $y = 0$. The range of $g(x) = \dfrac{40}{x^2}$ is $\{g(x) \mid g(x) > 0\}$, while the range of $f(x) = 9 + \dfrac{2}{x}$ is $\{f(x) \mid f(x) \in \mathbb{R}, f(x) \neq 0\}$.

Pages 237–239

1. $\{x \mid x \in \mathbb{R}, x \neq -1 \text{ and } x \neq 2\}$ **3.** $\{x \mid x \in \mathbb{R}\}$
5. $x = 5$ and $y = 0$ **7.** $x = 2$ and $y = 4$
9. A.

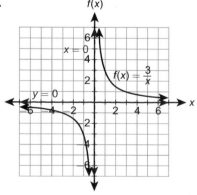

B. domain: $\{x \mid x \in \mathbb{R}, x \neq 0\}$; qx: $\{y \mid y \in \mathbb{R}, y \neq 0\}$

11. A.

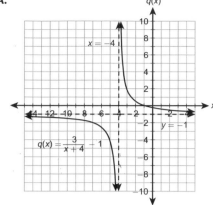

B. domain: $\{x \mid x \in \mathbb{R}, x \neq -4\}$; range: $\{y \mid y \in \mathbb{R}, y \neq -1\}$

13. A.

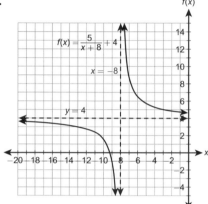

B. domain: $\{x \mid x \in \mathbb{R}, x \neq -8\}$;
range: $\{y \mid y \in \mathbb{R}, y \neq 4$ **15.** $f(x) = \dfrac{1}{x + 1} + 2$

17. $b(x) = \dfrac{1}{x + 2} - 3$ **19.** $f(x) = \dfrac{2}{3(x + 7)} + 2$

21. $N(x) = \dfrac{-2}{(x - 1)} + 6$

23.

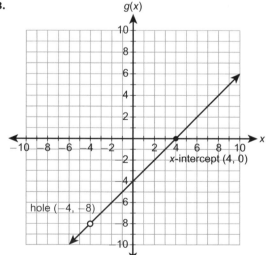

25.

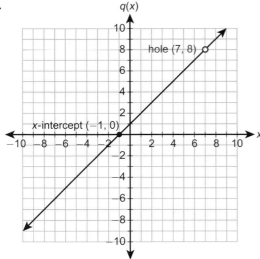

27.

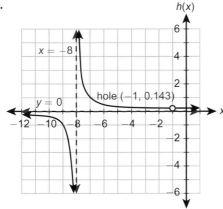

29. A. $f(x) = \dfrac{500}{x} + 2$ where $500 = $ distance, $x = $ rate and $f(x) = $ time,

B. *time (hours)*

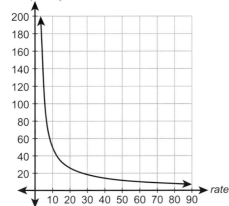

Pages 243–244

1. ± 18 **3.** ± 1.6 **5.** $\pm\dfrac{17}{19}$ **7.** ± 60 **9.** ± 48 **11.** -6

13. Undefined   **15.** 32   **17.** $x = \pm\dfrac{15}{8}$ **19.** $c = \pm\dfrac{6}{7}$

21. $x = \pm 4$ **23.** $c = \pm 8$ **25.** $x = \pm 2$ **27.** $x = 4$ or $x = -12$ **29.** $x = 25$ or $x = -15$

Pages 249–250

1. $5\sqrt{2}$ **3.** $\sqrt{33}$ **5.** $\dfrac{\sqrt{10}}{10}$ **7.** $\dfrac{\sqrt{7}}{8}$ **9.** $\dfrac{\sqrt{5}}{7}$ **11.** $2b\sqrt{5ab}$

13. $x^2\sqrt{19y}$ **15.** $a^5b^6\sqrt{5ab}$ **17.** $\dfrac{2}{b^9}$ **19.** $\dfrac{1}{m}$ **21.** $\dfrac{\sqrt{n}}{n^2}$

23. $x^4\sqrt{x}$ **25.** 18   **27.** 80   **29.** 60   **31.** $15h^3g^4\sqrt{35g}$

33. $80x^6y^2\sqrt{15xy}$ **35.** $3 + 2\sqrt{6} + \sqrt{15} + 2\sqrt{10}$

37. $65 - 9\sqrt{33}$ **39.** $\sqrt{195} - 3\sqrt{182} - 2\sqrt{105} + 42\sqrt{2}$

41. $-2\sqrt{11} + \sqrt{13}$ **43.** $9\sqrt{19} - 6\sqrt{3}$ **45.** $-14\sqrt{2}$

47. $-52\sqrt{3}$ **49.** $-244\sqrt{10}$ **51.** $4x\sqrt{5} + 4\sqrt{5}$

53. $-42x^2\sqrt{2x} - 80\sqrt{2x}$ **55.** $-8 - 4\sqrt{5}$ **57.** $\dfrac{9 + \sqrt{7}}{37}$

59. $\dfrac{18n + 9\sqrt{3n}}{16n^2 - 12n}$ **61.** $\dfrac{2a + 2\sqrt{3a}}{a^2 - 3a}$ **63.** $\dfrac{11x + 11\sqrt{23xy}}{x^2 - 23xy}$

65. $\dfrac{-6m - 2\sqrt{3n}}{9m^2 - 3n}$ **67.** $\dfrac{-10\sqrt{2xy}}{18 - xy}$

Page 254

1. 3   **3.** 2   **5.** -3 **7.** $17^{\frac{1}{4}}$ **9.** $(x - 2)^{\frac{3}{2}}$ **11.** $(t^2 + 4)^{\frac{3}{4}}$

13. $\sqrt[3]{25}$ **15.** $4\sqrt[3]{a^2}$ **17.** $\sqrt[5]{9a^2b^2}$ **19.** -27 **21.** $3\sqrt[4]{27}$

23. x^2 **25.** $3h^2g\sqrt[4]{g}$ **27.** $\sqrt[5]{xy^3}$ **29.** $\dfrac{2xy^2z\sqrt[3]{y^2z}}{3a^3b^6}$

Pages 257–258

1. $c = 44$ **3.** $x = -67$ **5.** $a = 22$ **7.** $a = 126.5$ **9.** $z = 1$

11. $s = \dfrac{3}{5}$ **13.** $x = 3$ **15.** $x = -3$ or $x = -1$ **17.** $x = \dfrac{1}{4}$

19. $b = 2$; extraneous: 13   **21.** $x = \dfrac{2}{3}$ **23.** $x = 2$; extraneous: -3 **25.** $x = 9$; extraneous: 1   **27.** $g = 2$ or $x = \dfrac{10}{9}$ **29.** $4\sqrt{6}$ cm^2

Pages 263–265

1. A. $\{x \mid x \geq 0\}$ **B.** $\{y \mid y \leq 0\}$

C.

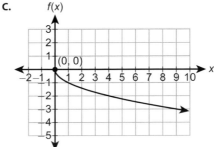

3. A. $\{x \mid x \geq 0\}$ **B.** $\{y \mid y \geq -1\}$

C.

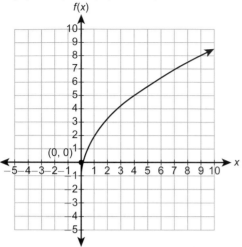

5. A. $\{x \mid x \in \mathbb{R}\}$ **B.** $\{y \mid y \in \mathbb{R}\}$

C.

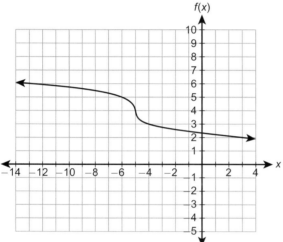

7. A. $\{x \mid x \geq 0\}$ **B.** $\{y \mid y \geq 0\}$

C.

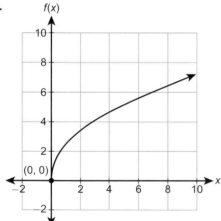

9. A. $\{x \mid x \geq 1\}$ **B.** $\{y \mid y \geq 2\}$

C.

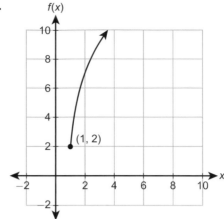

11. A. $\{x \mid x \geq 3\}$ **B.** $\{y \mid y \leq -1\}$

C.

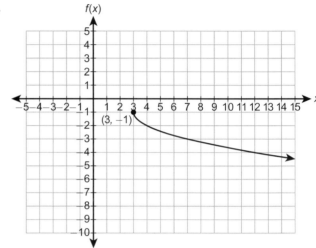

13. Reflect the graph over the x-axis and translate 10 units up. **15.** Stretch vertically by a factor of 8, translate 5 units to the left and 9 units up. **17.** Stretch vertically by a factor of 6, translate 3 units to the right and 12 units up.

19. $f(x) = \sqrt{x} - 2$ **21.** $f(x) = 3\sqrt{x + 2} + 1$

23. $f(x) = 4\sqrt{x - 5} - 1$ **25.** $f(x) = -\sqrt{x + 4}$

27.

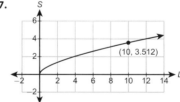

A full swing takes about 3.512 seconds.

Page 269

1. $5i$ **3.** $11i$ **5.** $6i\sqrt{5}$ **7.** $45i$ **9.** $1.1i$ **11.** $1.8i$ **13.** 28
15. -20 **17.** $-8i$ **19.** If ai and bi are any two imaginary numbers, then you can use the distributive property to write $ai - bi$ as $(a - b)i$. Because the real numbers are closed under subtraction, $a - b$ is a real number (say d), so the

difference is di. This is a product of a real number and the imaginary unit, so di is an imaginary number, and the set of imaginary numbers is closed under subtraction.

21. 1 **23.** i **25.** -2 **27.** -6 **29.** $\frac{1}{4}$

Page 274

1. $10 + i$ **3.** $3 + 7i$ **5.** $-4i$

7. A.

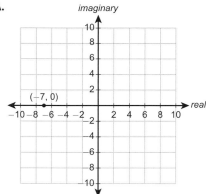

B. 7

9. A.

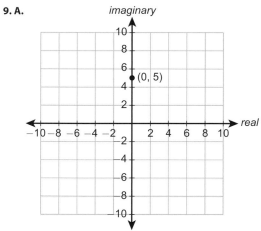

B. 5

11. A.

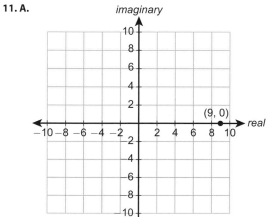

B. 9

13. A.

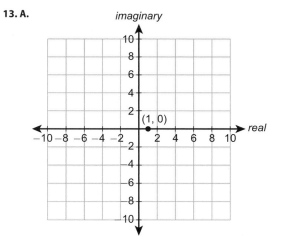

B. 1

15. A.

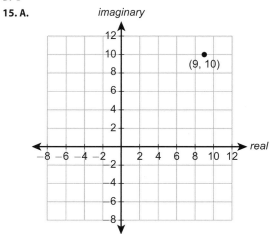

B. $\sqrt{181} \approx 13.5$

17. A.

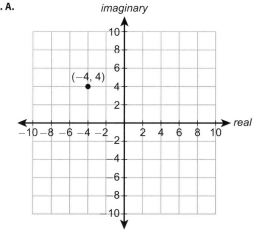

B. $4\sqrt{2} \approx 5.7$

19. A.

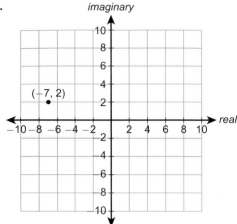

B. $\sqrt{53} \approx 7.3$

21. A.

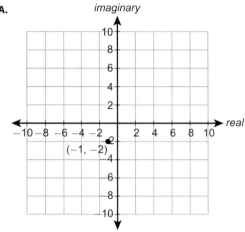

B. $\sqrt{5} \approx 2.2$ **23.** $\sqrt{10} \approx 3.2$

Page 278

1. $6 - 18i$ **3.** $6 + 10i$ **5.** $-7 + 26i$ **7.** $87 + 37i$

9. $-9 + 19i$ **11. A.** $4 + 6i$ **B.** 52 **13. A.** $\dfrac{\sqrt{5}}{7} - i$

B. $\dfrac{54}{49}$ **15. A.** $-2 - 9i$ **B.** 85 **17.** $\dfrac{-1 + 6i}{37}$

19. $\dfrac{25 - 62i}{41}$ **21.** $\dfrac{-7 - 16i}{10}$ **23.** $\dfrac{61 - 33i}{74}$

25. A. $3\sqrt{5} \approx 6.71$

B.

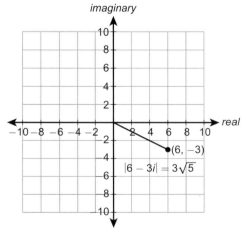

27. A. $4\sqrt{2} \approx 5.66$

B.

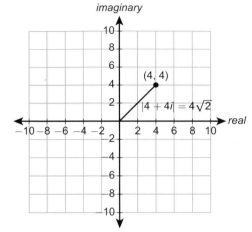

29. A. $3\sqrt{122} \approx 33.14$

B.

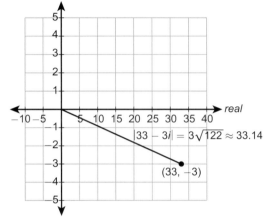

Page 281

1. $y = \pm 12$ **3.** $x = \pm 2\sqrt{3}$ **5.** $c = \pm 10$ **7.** $p = \pm\sqrt{71}$

9. $r = 1 \pm \sqrt{2}$ **11.** $y = -2 \pm \sqrt{\dfrac{13}{2}}$ **13.** $t = \pm i\sqrt{38}$

15. $b = \pm 2i\sqrt{3}$ **17.** $s = -2 \pm \sqrt{6}$ **19.** $w = -4 \pm \sqrt{12}$

21. $x = \dfrac{3}{4} \pm \dfrac{i}{4}\sqrt{7}$ **23.** $z^2 + 121 = 0$ **25.** $z^2 + 144 = 0$

27. $z^2 + 90 = 0$ **29.** $z^2 + 432 = 0$ **31.** $z^2 + 4z + 84 = 0$

33. $z^2 + 10z + 275 = 0$

UNIT 8   Quadratic Functions

Pages 287–288

1. $x = -0.5, y = 2$ **3.** no line of symmetry   **5.** $f(2) = 9$

7. $f(4) = 1, f(2) = 1$ **9.** $h(1) = 5$ **11.** $y = -|x| + 8$

13. $y = -|x + 2| - 3$

Pages 293–294

1. A.

x	-2	-1	0	1	2
y	8	3	0	-1	0

B.

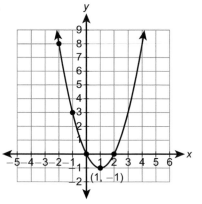

3. A.

x	−2	−1	0	1	2
y	6	3	2	3	6

B.

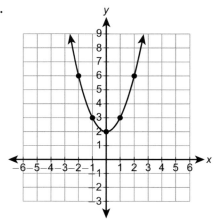

5. A.

x	−2	−1	0	1	2
y	−6	−6	−4	0	6

B.

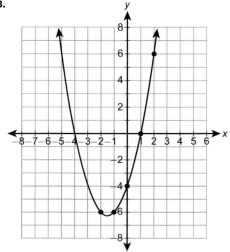

7. −3   **9.** −8

11.

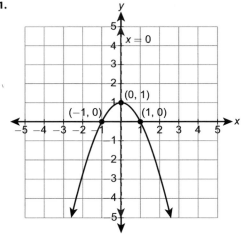

13.

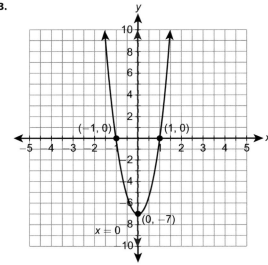

15. two real zeros;

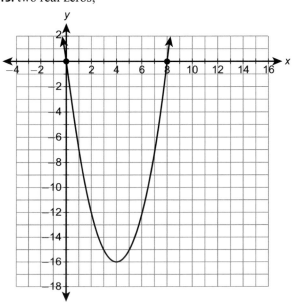

17. no real zeros;

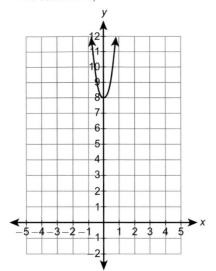

19. two real zeros;

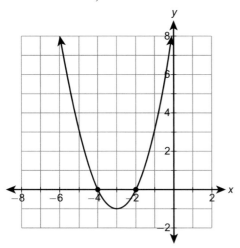

21.

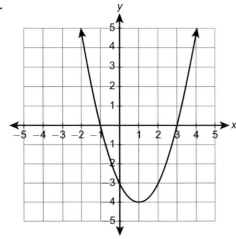

23.

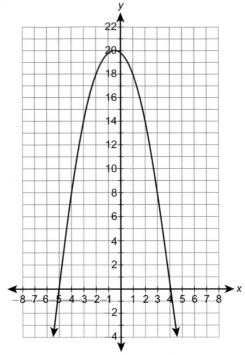

25.

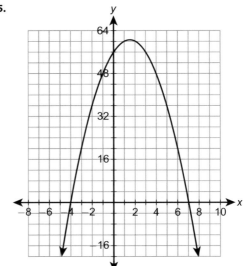

27.

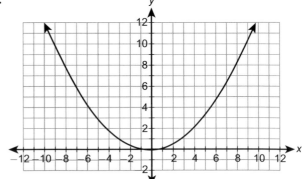

29.

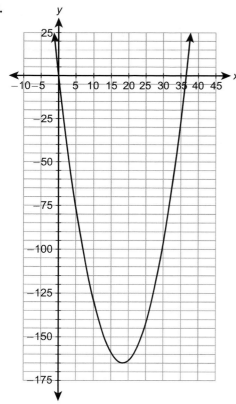

Pages 298–299

1.

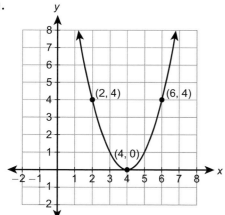

3.

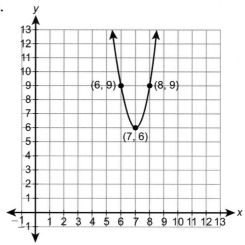

5.

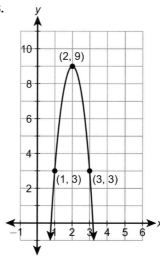

7. $y = 3(x - 1)^2 + 1$ **9.** $y = 2(x - 2)^2 - 2$ **11.** $y = -x^2 + 7$

13. $y = x^2 + 2$ **15.** $y = \frac{1}{4}(x - 4)^2 - 3$ **17.** $y = -x^2 + 9x - 14$

19. $y = 9x^2 - 12x + 4$ **21.** $y = 9x^2 - 12x + 1$

23. $y = (x - 2)^2$ **25.** $y = (x - 4)^2 - 6$

27. $y = 2(x + 6)^2 - 47$ **29.** $y = 4\left(x - \frac{1}{3}\right)^2 - \frac{10}{3}$

Pages 304–305

1. $-2.22, 0.22$ **3.** $-0.28, 1.78$ **5.** $\{1\}$ **7.** $\left\{-\frac{1}{2}, 3\right\}$

9. $\{3, 2\}$ **11.** $\{3, -2\}$ **13.** $\{4 + i\sqrt{6}, 4 - i\sqrt{6}\}$ **15.** $\{3, -10\}$

17. $\left\{1, \frac{5}{2}\right\}$ **19.** $\{5, -1\}$ **21.** $\left\{\dfrac{-1 + i\sqrt{23}}{4}, \dfrac{-1 - i\sqrt{23}}{4}\right\}$

23. two complex roots   **25.** one real root   **27.** two real roots

Pages 310–311

1. no; no; yes   **3.** yes; yes; yes   **5.** yes; yes   **7.** no; no
9. no; yes   **11.** $\{x \mid x \leq -4 \text{ or } x \geq 1\}$;

$$\begin{array}{c}
\longleftarrow\!\!\mid\!\!+\!\!+\!\!\bullet\!\!+\!\!+\!\!+\!\!+\!\!+\!\!\bullet\!\!+\!\!+\!\!\mid\!\!\longrightarrow \\
-6 \;\; -5 \;\; -4 \;\; -3 \;\; -2 \;\; -1 \;\;\; 0 \;\;\; 1 \;\;\; 2 \;\;\; 3
\end{array}$$

13. $\left\{x \mid -1 \le x \le \frac{4}{3}\right\}$;

15. $\{x \mid -1 < x < 5\}$;

17. $\left\{x \mid -1 \le x \le \frac{1}{2}\right\}$;

19.

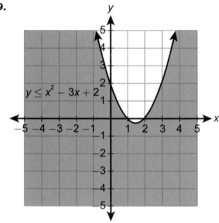

$y \le x^2 - 3x + 2$

21.

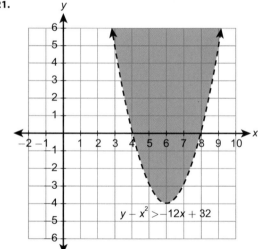

$y - x^2 > -12x + 32$

23.

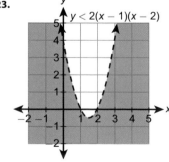

$y < 2(x-1)(x-2)$

25.

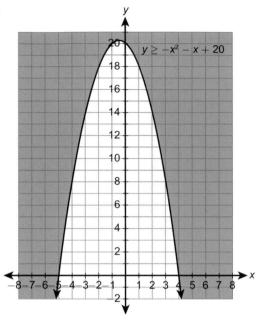

$y \ge -x^2 - x + 20$

27.

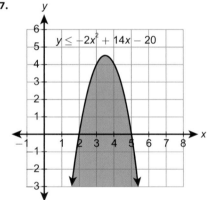

$y \le -2x^2 + 14x - 20$

29. The ball reaches a height of 25 meters or greater between 0.98 and 2.08 seconds after it is launched. **31.** Wind speeds of less than 52.6 miles per hour will result in a pressure of less than 10 pounds of force per square inch.

33. $\begin{cases} y > -\dfrac{1}{2}x \\ y \le -(x+3)^2 + 4 \end{cases}$

Page 315

1. $y = 2x^2 - 4x - 6$ **3.** $y = x^2 + 2x - 3$ **5.** $y = x^2 - 3x - 4$
7. $y = -x^2 + 6x - 8$ **9.** $y = \dfrac{1}{2}x^2 - \dfrac{11}{4}x + 3$
11. $y = x^2 + 2x - 1$ **13.** $y = 2x^2 - 8x + 7$
15. $y = -x^2 - 4x - 5$ **17.** $y = -3x^2 + 6x - 4$
19. $y = x^2 - 2x + 2$ **21.** $y = x^2 - 3x + 4$
23. $y = x^2 + 2x - 3$ **25.** $y = 3x^2 - 2x - 3$
27. $y = 3x^2 - x - 1$ **29.** Answers will vary. Sample answer: To find a polynomial with degree n, you need $n + 1$ points.

Pages 318–319

1. The length of the farm is 20 meters.   **3.** The base of the ladder is 7 feet from the wall.   **5.** The sheep pen is 5 meters wide.   **7.** The field measures 25 km by about 60 km.

9. A. $h(t) = -16t^2 + 5$

B.

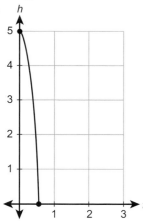

C. The plate will hit the ground at about 0.56 seconds.

11. A. $h(t) = -4.9t^2 + 3$

B.

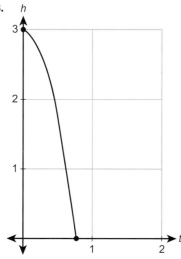

C. The paintball will hit the ground at about 0.78 seconds.

13. A. $y = -4.9t^2 - 2t$, where $h = 0$ at the top of the well (at ground level)

B.

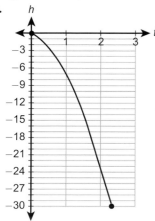

C. The bucket will hit the bottom at about 2.69 seconds.
15. The farm needs to be 500 meters by 250 meters to have maximum area.   **17.** The maximum area of the store is 10,000 square meters.   **19.** The garden has maximum area when it is 20 meters by 40 meters.   **21.** He can maximize his profits at a price of \$320.   **23.** A radius of $\sqrt{2} \approx 1.41$ meters produces the largest possible volume of the cylinder.

UNIT 9   Solving and Graphing Polynomials

Pages 323–324

1. 29 R2 or $29\frac{2}{5}$ **3.** 139 R51 or $139\frac{17}{23}$ **5.** 150 R28 or $150\frac{28}{59}$ **7.** $\{-1\}$ **9.** $\{-6\}$ **11.** $\{-6, -5\}$ **13.** $\{1, \frac{11}{2}\}$

15. $\{-8, 5\}$

17.

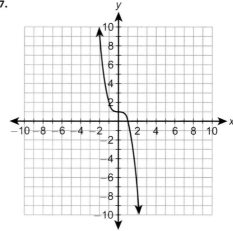

As $x \to -\infty$, $g(x) \to \infty$ and as $x \to \infty$, $g(x) \to -\infty$.

19.

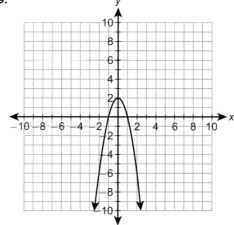

As $x \to -\infty$, $f(x) \to -\infty$ and as $x \to \infty$, $f(x) \to -\infty$.

21.

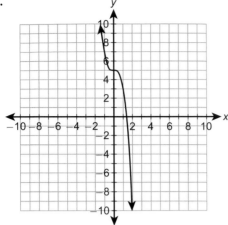

As $x \to -\infty$, $h(x) \to \infty$ and as $x \to \infty$, $h(x) \to -\infty$.

23.

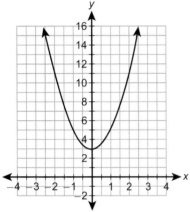

As $x \to -\infty$, $h(x) \to \infty$ and as $x \to \infty$, $h(x) \to \infty$.

Page 328

1. $x - 3$ **3.** $x + 3$, R1   **5.** $r - 2$ **7.** $q + 3$, R6
9. $2x - 1$ **11.** $3g^3 + 1$ **13.** $h^2 + h + 1$

15. $2b^2 + 1 + \dfrac{2}{b^2 + 3}$ **17.** No   **19.** Yes   **21.** No

23. Yes   **25.** $x - 1$

Page 332

1. $4a + 3$ **3.** $2v + 5$ **5.** $\dfrac{w - 9 - 10}{w + 5}$ **7.** $7x - 6$

9. $12a^2 - 48a + 199 - \dfrac{796}{a + 4}$ **11.** $q^3 + 2q^2 - 8q + 5$

13. $2m^3 + 3m^2 + 3m + 9$ **15.** $\dfrac{b + 4 - 6}{2b + 2}$

17. $\dfrac{x}{2} - \dfrac{24}{2x - 8}$ **19.** $f + \dfrac{8}{5} - \dfrac{46}{25f + 10}$ **21.** $3h - 2 + \dfrac{16}{3h + 6}$

23. $2x^2 - 4x + 12 - \dfrac{68}{3x + 6}$ **25.** $3n^3 + 2n^2 + n - 1$

27. $x^4 - x^3 + x^2 - x + 1$

Pages 335–336

1. 16   **3.** 24   **5.** -95 **7.** 15   **9.** -35 **11. A.** Answers will vary. Sample answer: $(-2, 0), (-1, -3), (0, -2), (1, 3)$

B.

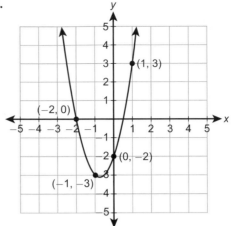

13. A. Answers will vary. Sample answer: $(-1, 7), (0, 1),$ $(1, 1), (2, 13)$

B.

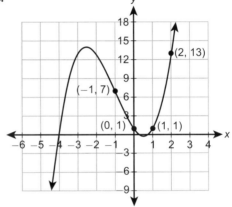

15. A. Answers will vary. Sample answer: $(-1, -12), (0, 1),$ $(1, 6), (2, 15)$

B.

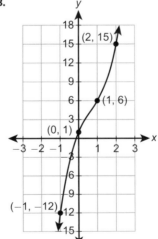

17. A. Answers will vary. Sample answer: $(-2, 7), (-1, 3),$ $(1, -5), (2, 3)$

B.

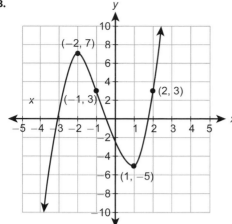

19. A. Answers will vary. Sample answer:
$(-3, -29), (-1, 15), (0, 10), (2, -24)$

B.

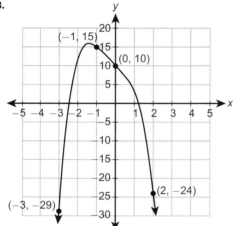

21. A. Answers will vary. Sample answer: $(-2, 2), (-1, -5),$
$(0, -2), (1, 17)$

B.

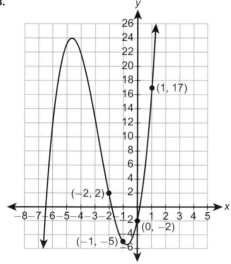

23. A. Answers will vary. Sample answer:
$(-2, 19), (0, 17), (2, -1), (3, 74)$

B.

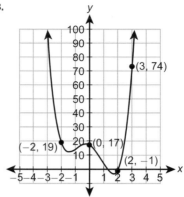

25. 27.5 degrees   **27.** 4528.2 km

Pages 340–341

1. Yes   **3.** No   **5.** Yes   **7.** Yes   **9.** $(x + 2)(x + 1)(x - 1)$
11. $(x + 3)(x + 7)(x - 1)$ **13.** $-2, 1, 2$ **15.** $-2, 2, 3$

17. $\pm\dfrac{11}{6}, \pm\dfrac{11}{3}, \pm\dfrac{11}{2}, \pm11, \pm\dfrac{1}{6}, \pm\dfrac{1}{3}, \pm\dfrac{1}{2}, \pm1$

19. $\pm\dfrac{1}{4}, \pm\dfrac{1}{2}, \pm1, \pm\dfrac{7}{4}, \pm2, \pm\dfrac{7}{2}, \pm4, \pm7, \pm14, \pm28$

21. $\pm\dfrac{1}{3}, \pm1, \pm\dfrac{5}{3}, \pm3, \pm5, \pm15$ **23.** $(x - 1)(x - 6)$

25. $(x + 1)(x^2 - 3)$ **27.** $(x + 3)(x - 2)(5x - 1)$
29. $(x + 2)(x^2 + 9)$

Pages 345–346

1. $-6, 5$ **3.** $-3, -1$ **5.** $1, 3, 5$
7. As $x \to \infty, h(x) \to \infty$; As $x \to -\infty, h(x) \to \infty$.
9. As $x \to \infty, p(x) \to \infty$; As $x \to -\infty, p(x) \to -\infty$.
11. As $x \to \infty, f(x) \to -\infty$; As $x \to -\infty, f(x) \to \infty$.
13. As $x \to \infty, h(x) \to -\infty$; As $x \to -\infty, h(x) \to -\infty$.
15.

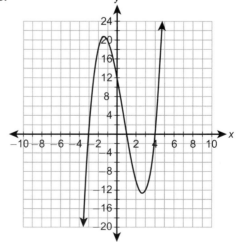

17.

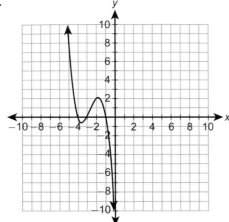

23.

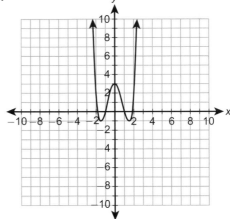

19.

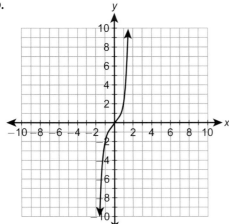

25.

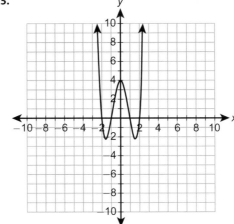

21.

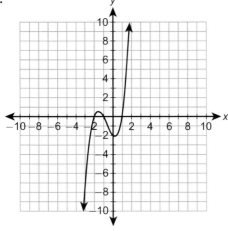

27.

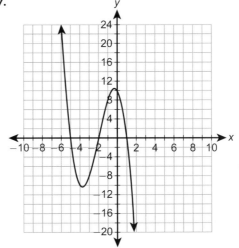

29.

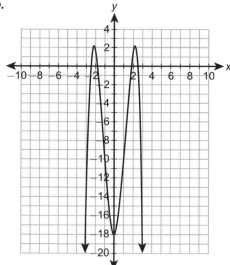

Page 350

1. 6 **3.** 4 **5.** 1 **7.** 16 **9.** The root -3 has multiplicity 1; The root -1 has multiplicity 2; The root 7 has multiplicity 1; The graph crosses the x-axis at $x = -3$ and $x = 7$. The graph touches but does not cross the x-axis at $x = -1$.
11. The root -4 has multiplicity 1; The root -2 has multiplicity 1; The root 1 has multiplicity 1; The root 3 has multiplicity 1; The graph crosses the x-axis at $x = -4$, $x = -2$, $x = 1$, and $x = 3$. **13.** four real roots; four rational roots
15. one real root; one rational root **17.** $(x - 2)(x + 3)(x + 5)$
19. $(x + 10)\left(x - \frac{2}{3}\right)\left(x - \frac{1}{2}\right)$
21. $(x - 3)(x + 3)(x + (-1 + i))(x + (-1 - i))$
23. $3\left(x - \frac{2}{3}\right)(x - (-1 + \sqrt{2}))(x - (-1 - \sqrt{2}))$
25. $-6\left(x - \left(\frac{1}{3} - \frac{\sqrt{34}}{6}\right)\right)\left(x - \left(\frac{1}{3} + \frac{\sqrt{34}}{6}\right)\right)$
27. $(x + 1)(x + 3)(x + \sqrt{2})(x - \sqrt{2})$

Pages 353–355

1. \$56.88 **3.** $x^2 - x + 30$ **5.** 24 inches **7.** 6 weeks
9. 2 seconds **11.** 1, 3, and 4 years **13.** No, because the function has a negative end behavior, so the stock is predicted to decrease in value. **15.** $f(x) = 4x^3 - 54x^2 + 180x$;

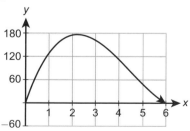

17. $x = 0$ **19.** $h = 1$ and $h = 3$ **21.** $f(x) = 4x^3 - 32x^2 + 64x$;

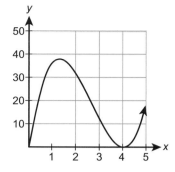

23. $x^2 + 20$

UNIT 10 Exponentials and Logarithms

Pages 358–360

1. 1 **3.** $\frac{1}{16}$ **5.** a **7.** $8x^7$ **9.** $x^6y^6z^6$ **11.** $\frac{1}{pq}$ **13.** $243a^{10}b^5$
15. 343 **17.** a^{10} **19.** $\frac{1}{a^2b^2}$ **21.** $\frac{1}{243p^8q^8}$ **23.** 729
25. $\frac{144y^{12}z^8}{x^4}$ **27.** $\frac{1}{32y^5z^5}$

Page 365

1. $4\sqrt[4]{2}$ **3.** $3\sqrt[4]{3}$ **5.** $10^{\frac{3}{5}}$ **7.** $8^{\frac{1}{4}}$ **9.** $7^{\frac{5}{3}}$ **11.** $10^{\frac{2}{5}}$ **13.** $\frac{64^{\frac{1}{8}}x}{\sqrt{y}}$
15. $\frac{3}{4}x^ty^{2t}z^{4t}$ **17.** $2\sqrt[4]{5}$ **19.** $2yz^3\sqrt[4]{x^2y^2}$ **21.** $3x^2z^5\sqrt[3]{x}$
23. $x = \frac{3}{2}$ **25.** $d = 2$ **27.** $y = \frac{1}{2}$ **29.** $x = 256$

Pages 369–371

1. Answers will vary. Sample answer:

x	-2	-1	0	1	2
$f(x)$	$\frac{1}{9}$	$\frac{1}{3}$	1	3	9

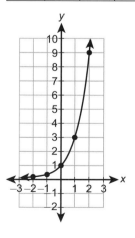

3. Answers will vary. Sample answer:

x	-2	-1	0	1	2
$f(x)$	9	3	1	$\frac{1}{3}$	$\frac{1}{9}$

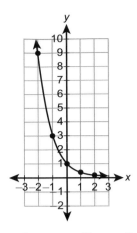

5. Answers will vary. Sample answer:

x	-2	-1	0	1	2
$b(x)$	$\frac{1}{2}$	1	2	4	8

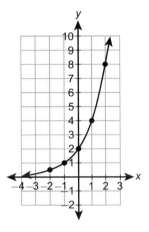

7. Answers will vary. Sample answer:

x	-2	-1	0	1	2
$g(x)$	$11.\overline{1}$	$3.\overline{3}$	1	0.3	0.09

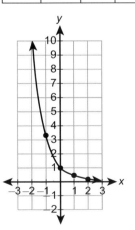

9. Answers will vary. Sample answer:

x	-2	-1	0	1	2
$h(x)$	-0.96	-0.8	0	4	24

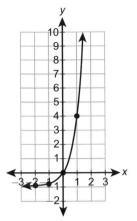

11.

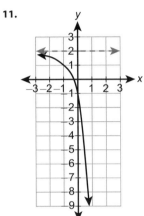

The domain is the set of real numbers; the range is the set of real numbers less than 2; the asymptote is $y = 2$.

13.

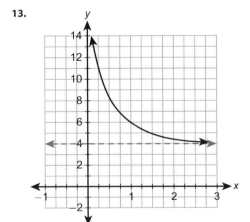

The domain is the set of real numbers; the range is the set of real numbers greater than 4; the asymptote is $y = 4$.

15.

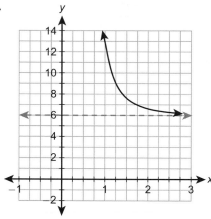

The domain is the set of real numbers; the range is the set of real numbers greater than 6; the asymptote is $y = 6$.

17. The parent graph is stretched vertically by a factor of $a = 3$.
19. The parent graph is stretched vertically by a factor of $a = 2$, shifted right $h = 3$ units, and shifted up $k = 9$ units.
21. The parent graph is stretched vertically by a factor of $a = 5$; shifted right $h = 6$ units, and shifted down $k = 10$ units.

23. $f(x) = 4 \cdot 2^x$ **25.** $f(x) = 3(0.5)^x$ **27.** $f(x) = 2 \cdot 3^x - 1$

29. $-3 \cdot (0.2)^x - 4$ **31.** $3 \cdot \left(\frac{1}{3}\right)^x - 4$

Pages 376–377

1. The population in 2012 will be approximately 16,260,150.   **3.** Juan can expect to find 20,971,520,000 bacteria after 17 hours.   **5.** After 10 hours, she should expect to find 10,035,200 bacteria. **7.** In 2020, the county population will be about 13,027.   **9.** Filipe should expect the value of the car to be about \$42,889.68 in 2012.   **11.** Zhang should expect the value of the card to be about \$244.55.
13. In 2008, the population will be about 21,525,144.
15. She should expect to find about 98.5% of normal uranium-238 levels in the rock   **17.** The total amount after 10 years is about \$34,162.89.   **19.** The total amount after 15 years is about \$75,021.86.   **21.** The total amount after 5 years is about \$11,616.17.   **23.** The interest rate paid by the account was about 2.5%.

Pages 381–382

1. $\log_6 216 = 3$ **3.** $\log_8 2 = \frac{1}{3}$ **5.** $4^3 = 64$ **7.** $16^1 = 16$
9. $\log_4 15$ **11.** $\log_8 4$ **13.** $\log_3 20$ **15.** $\log_9 4 + 5 \log_9 x$
17. $8 \log_5 x - \log_5 2$ **19.** 1   **21.** 1.1461   **23.** 0.3010
25. 2.8332   **27.** 1.4560   **29.** 1.5480   **31.** 2

Page 385

1. $x = \dfrac{\log 10}{\log 3} \approx 2.0959$ **3.** $x = \dfrac{\log 1000}{\log 5} \approx 4.2920$

5. $h = \dfrac{\log 22}{\log 7} \approx 1.5885$ **7.** $p = \dfrac{\log 50}{2 \log 7} \approx 1.0052$

9. $z = \dfrac{\log 110}{4 \log 6} \approx 0.6558$ **11.** $z = \dfrac{\log 219}{5 \log 3} \approx 0.9811$

13. $y = 0$ **15.** $x = \dfrac{\ln 4}{3} \approx 0.4621$

17. $x = \dfrac{\ln 50 - 1}{5} \approx 0.5824$ **19.** $x = \dfrac{2}{\ln 6 - 1} \approx 2.5260$

21. $x = \dfrac{3}{\ln 20 - 1} \approx 1.5032$ **23.** $b = \dfrac{1}{3 \ln 9 + 4} \approx 0.0944$

25. $x = -\dfrac{2}{3 \ln 4 - 2} \approx -0.9264$

27. $x = \dfrac{2}{5 - 3 \ln 5} \approx 11.6492$ **29.** $y = \dfrac{5}{2}, -\dfrac{1}{3}$

Page 388

1. $3^x = 81; x = 4$ **3.** $6^a = 6; a = 1$ **5.** $\left(\frac{1}{5}\right)^x = 625; x = -4$
7. $2^5 = x + 4; x = 28$ **9.** $6^4 = 2x + 8; x = 644$
11. $r = 6$ **13.** $v = 4$ **15.** $x = 1$ **17.** $x = 2$ **19.** $x = 9$
21. $y = \dfrac{3}{5}$ **23.** $q = 4$ **25.** $b = \sqrt{3}$ **27.** $x = 64$ **29.** $w = \dfrac{3}{4}$

Pages 393–394

1.

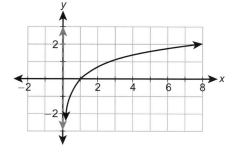

3.

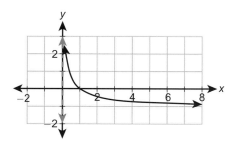

5.

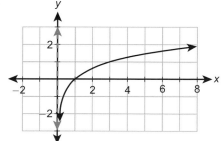

7.

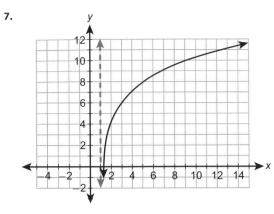

The domain is the set of real numbers greater than 1. The range is the set of all real numbers. The asymptote is $x = 1$.

9.

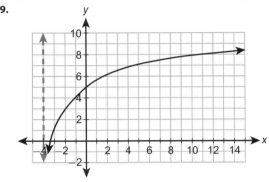

The domain is the set of real numbers greater than -4. The range is the set of all real numbers. The asymptote is $x = -4$.

11.

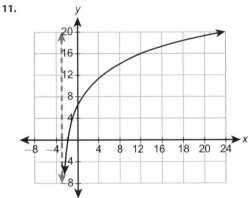

The domain is the set of real numbers greater than -3. The range is the set of all real numbers. The asymptote is $x = -3$.
13. h: shifted left 9 units   **15.** a: reflected across the x-axis; h: shifted left 5 units; k: shifted down 3 units
17. a: vertically stretched by a factor of 3; h: shifted left 11 units; k: shifted up 8 units   **19.** $f(x) = \log_4 x + 3$
21. $f(x) = \log_{\frac{1}{3}} x - 7$ **23.** $f(x) = \log_6 (x + 3) + 2$
25. $f(x) = \log_{\frac{1}{2}} (x + 3) + 3$

Page 399

1. The $[H^+]$ is about 0.0040 mole per liter.   **3.** The half-life of tritium is about 12 years.   **5.** The $[H^+]$ is 10^{-11} mole per liter.   **7.** About 4605 bacteria will be present at 10 p.m.
9. It is approximately 4223 years old.   **11.** On Day 9, there will be 12,800 bacteria.   **13.** The relative intensity of a quiet conversation is 30 decibels.   **15.** The $[H^+]$ is about 0.0063 mole per liter   **17.** The sound intensity of a train is 10^{11} times greater than the threshold of hearing.   **19.** There will be 84 insects five days after the beginning of the experiment.
21. The sound intensity of a train is 10^4 times greater than the threshold of hearing.   **23.** The time of decay is 2814 years.

UNIT 11   Sequences and Series

Pages 402–404

1. 28   **3.** 216   **5.** $\frac{2}{3}$ **7.** $\frac{6}{25}$ **9.** 21
11. domain $= \{1, 2, 3, 4\}$; range $= \{2\}$
13. domain $= \{x \mid x \geq 0\}$; range $= \{y \mid y \geq 1\}$
15. $f(1) = 1; f(2) = -1; f(3) = -3$ **17.** $g(1) = 1; g(2) = 8;$ $g(3) = 27$ **19.** $h(1) = 0; h(2) \approx 0.30; h(3) \approx 0.48$
21. $h(1) = 1; h(2) \approx 1.26; h(3) \approx 1.44$ **23.** $f(1) = 5;$ $f(2) = 10; f(3) = 10$

Pages 407–408

1. A. 5.2   **B.** 1st term   **3. A.** $\frac{3}{16}$ **B.** 10th term   **5. A.** 105
B. 13th term   **7.** 3, 18, 648, 839, 808, 1.4106×10^{12}
9. 6, 9, 12, 15, 18   **11.** 1.27, 3.81, 11.43, 34.29, 102.87
13. 126, 42, 14, $\frac{14}{3} = 4\frac{2}{3}$, $\frac{14}{9} = 1\frac{5}{9}$,   **15.** 400, 20, $\sqrt{20}$, $\sqrt{\sqrt{20}}$,
$\sqrt{\sqrt{\sqrt{20}}}$ **17.** 15   **19.** 1, 16, 81, 256   **21.** 486   **23.** 48
25. 69   **27.** $-1, 5.5$ **29. A.** $a_n = a_{n-1} + 6$ **B.** $a_n = 24 + 6n$
C. 270

Page 412

1. 11   **3.** 66   **5.** 2   **7.** 13   **9.** -6.8 **11. A.** $a_n = 2n$
B. $a_n = a_{n-1} + 2$ **C.** 12, 14   **13. A.** $a_n = 4 + 2n$
B. $a_n = a_{n-1} + 2$ **C.** 16, 18   **15. A.** $a_n = 24 - 4n$
B. $a_n = a_{n-1} - 4$ **C.** 0, -4 **17. A.** $a_n = 7 + 3.5n$
B. $a_n = a_{n-1} + 3.5$ **C.** 28, 31.5   **19. A.** $a_n = 102.3 - 7.2n$
B. $a_n = a_{n-1} - 7.2$ **C.** 59.1, 51.9
21.

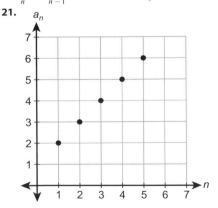

23.

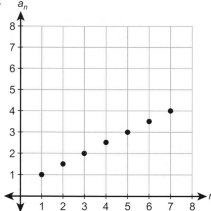

25.

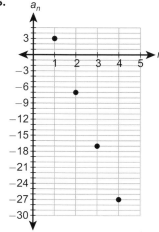

27. 35 days

Page 416

1. -32 **3.** -36 **5.** 2 **7.** 7 **9.** $-\dfrac{1}{4}$ **11.** $\dfrac{3}{2}$ **13.** $\dfrac{1}{2}$

15. A. $a_n = 3 \cdot 2^{n-1}$ **B.** $a_n = 2a_{n-1}$ **C.** 96, 192

17. A. $a_n = 216 \cdot \left(-\dfrac{1}{6}\right)^{n-1}$ **B.** $a_n = -\dfrac{1}{6}a_{n-1}$ **C.** $\dfrac{1}{6}, -\dfrac{1}{36}$

19. A. $a_n = 5 \cdot 0.3^{n-1}$ **B.** $a_n = 0.3a_{n-1}$ **C.** 0.0405, 0.0122

21. A. $a_n = 22 \cdot 4^{n-1}$ **B.** $a_n = 4a_{n-1}$ **C.** 5632, 22528

23. A. $a_n = -9 \cdot \left(-\dfrac{1}{3}\right)^{n-1}$ **B.** $a_n = -\dfrac{1}{3}a_{n-1}$ **C.** $-\dfrac{1}{9}, \dfrac{1}{27}$

25.

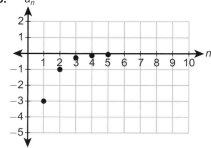

27.

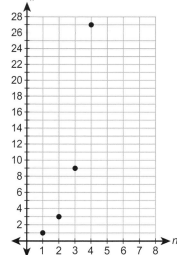

29.

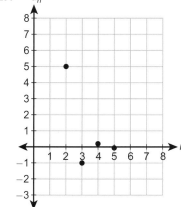

31. $a_n = 100 \cdot 1.02^{n-1}$

Page 422–423

1. A. Arithmetic   **B.** common difference: -60 **C.** -70
3. A. Geometric   **B.** common ratio: 2   **C.** 8   **5. A.** Neither
B. None   **C.** 2   **7.** Arithmetic; $32,000, $32,300, $32,600, $32,900, $33,200; Mr. Brown will make over $34,700 after 10 years.   **9.** Arithmetic; In 10 days, Kori will have 40 pictures.   **11.** Geometric; She will deposit $65.61 on the 9th day.   **13.** Arithmetic; 90, 87.5, 85, 82.5, 80, 77.5.
15. Arithmetic; $120,000, $117,750, $115,500, $113,250, $111,000; After 9 months, the balance will be less than $100,000.   **17.** Geometric; On the 6th cut, she cuts off $\dfrac{1}{4}$
meters.   **19.** Geometric; In 2005, Hampton's population will be about 8964 people.   **21.** Geometric; At the end of the 19th day, there will be about 42.3 kilograms of salt in the bin.
23. Arithmetic; Their salaries will be equal in the 12th year.

Page 426

1. $1 + 2 + 3 + 4 + 5 + 6 + 7 + 8 = 36$
3. $(3 + 1) + (3 + 2) + (3 + 3) + (3 + 4) + (3 + 5) = 30$
5. $(3 \cdot 1 - 1) + (3 \cdot 2 - 1) + (3 \cdot 3 - 1) + (3 \cdot 4 - 1) = 26$

7. $(-2 \cdot 1 + 4) + (-2 \cdot 2 + 4) + (-2 \cdot 3 + 4) +$
$(-2 \cdot 4 + 4) + (-2 \cdot 5 + 4) = -10$
9. $-2 \cdot 4 + (-2 \cdot 5) + (-2 \cdot 6) + (-2 \cdot 7) + (-2 \cdot 8) +$
$(-2 \cdot 9) + (-2 \cdot 10) + (-2 \cdot 11) = -120$
11. $\left(\frac{1}{2} \cdot 10 + \frac{5}{2}\right) + \left(\frac{1}{2} \cdot 11 + \frac{5}{2}\right) + \left(\frac{1}{2} \cdot 12 + \frac{5}{2}\right) +$
$\left(\frac{1}{2} \cdot 13 + \frac{5}{2}\right) + \left(\frac{1}{2} \cdot 14 + \frac{5}{2}\right) + \left(\frac{1}{2} \cdot 15 + \frac{5}{2}\right) +$
$\left(\frac{1}{2} \cdot 16 + \frac{5}{2}\right) + \left(\frac{1}{2} \cdot 17 + \frac{5}{2}\right) = 74$
13. $(-7 \cdot 2 - 2) + (-7 \cdot 3 - 2) + (-7 \cdot 4 - 2) +$
$(-7 \cdot 5 - 2) + (-7 \cdot 6 - 2) + (-7 \cdot 7 - 2) +$
$(-7 \cdot 8 - 2) + (-7 \cdot 9 - 2) = -324$ **15.** $\left(\frac{1}{2} \cdot 6\right) +$
$\left(\frac{1}{2} \cdot 7\right) + \left(\frac{1}{2} \cdot 8\right) + \left(\frac{1}{2} \cdot 9\right) + \left(\frac{1}{2} \cdot 10\right) + \left(\frac{1}{2} \cdot 11\right) +$
$\left(\frac{1}{2} \cdot 12\right) = 31.5$ **17.** $\sum_{i=1}^{7} 2^{i-1}$ **19.** $\sum_{i=1}^{6} 4\left(\frac{1}{4}\right)^{i-1}$
21. $\sum_{i=1}^{7} 0.5i + 3.5$ **23.** $\sum_{i=1}^{5} -64\left(\frac{1}{4}\right)^{i-1}$ **25.** $\sum_{i=1}^{5} 5^{i}$
27. $\sum_{i=1}^{5} (-3i + 12)$ **29.** $\sum_{i=1}^{5} 49\left(-\frac{1}{7}\right)^{i-1}$ **31. A.** $\sum_{i=1}^{10} 10i$
B. \$550

Page 430

1. 1275 **3.** 275 **5.** 2145 **7.** 144 **9.** -1700
11. 70 **13.** 825 **15.** 33 **17.** 810 **19.** -49 **21.** 44
23.

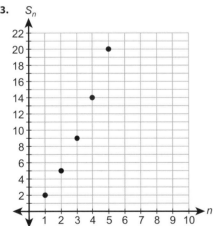

25.

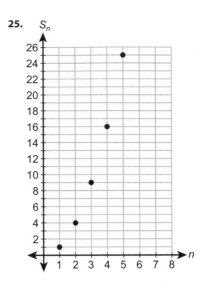

27.

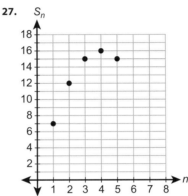

29. $\sum_{i=1}^{7} (5i + 5)$; \$175

Page 435

1. 5100 **3.** $121\frac{1}{3}$ **5.** $-3\frac{255}{256}$ **7.** $-\frac{629{,}145}{4096} \approx -153.6$
9. 625,000 **11.** $-\frac{2{,}232{,}728}{3125} \approx -714.47$ **13.** 5460 **15.** 728
17. $-\frac{13{,}107}{1024} \approx -12.80$ **19.** 55,987 **21.** -2.0496 **23.** -79.98
25.

27.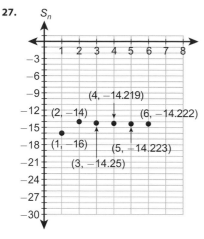

29.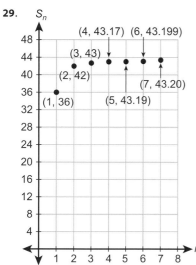

31. A. When $|r| > 1$, the distances between points gradually increase, and the points are spread out; **B.** When $|r| < 1$, the distances between points gradually decrease, and the points are close together.

Pages 439–441

1. Geometric **3.** Neither **5.** Arithmetic **7.** Arithmetic; There are 120 cans total. **9.** Geometric; The ball travels about 150 feet. **11.** Arithmetic; After 20 years, Frederic earns $976,000 total. **13.** Geometric; After 10 years, the *Denominator Gazette* serves a total of 2401 readers. **15.** Arithmetic; The balance of his account will be greater than $2000 after the 8th month. **17.** Arithmetic; There are 272 seats in rows 1 to 8. **19.** Arithmetic; after the 4th week, Theresa will reach a 60-hour work week. **21.** Geometric; After 5 minutes, the sum of the lengths is about 14.9 inches. **23.** Arithmetic; The mosaic will be finished on day 11. **25. A.** Arithmetic; Kyle would complete 51 jobs. **B.** Geometric; Kyle would complete 31.5 jobs; Plan A will enable him to accomplish more work. **27. A.** Geometric; Student would read about 83 pages. **B.** Arithmetic; Student would read 90 pages; Pattern A requires 7 fewer pages than pattern B. **29.** Child Play is arithmetic; Cool Kids is geometric. **A.** Cool Kids will exceed 300 first. **B.** The number of sale items at Cool Kids exceed the number of sale items at Child Play in the 8th week.

Pages 446–447

1. $-4, -2, 0, 2, 4, 6, 8$ **3.** $8, 2, -4, -10, -16, -22, -28$ **5.** $0.25, -4.75, -9.75, -14.75, -19.75, -24.75, -29.75$ **7.** $3, 3.75, 4.5, 5.25, 6, 6.75, 7.5$ **9.** $3, 12, 48, 192, 768, 3072, 12{,}288$ **11.** $-3, -27, -243, -2{,}187, -19{,}683, -177{,}174, -1{,}594{,}323$ **13.** $0.55, 3.85, 26.95, 188.65, 1320.55, 9243.85, 64{,}706.95$ **15.** $\frac{1}{9}, -\frac{1}{3}, 1, -3, 9, -27, 81$ **17.** $10, 23, 39, 58, 80$ **19.** $-5, -6, -3, 4, 15$ **21.** $0.6, -5.8, -19.2, -39.6, -67$ **23.** $0.88, 2.43, 4.65, 7.54, 11.1$ **25.** $-18, 54, -234, 918, -3690, 14{,}742$ **27.** $0.75, 4.5, 23.25, 117, 585.75, 2929.5$ **29.** $0.9, -5.04, 34.164, -224.6, 1483.1, -9787.8$ **31.** $-0.6923, -0.2596, -0.53, -0.361, -0.4667, -0.4006$

UNIT 12 Counting and Probability

Pages 450–452

1. $3\%; \frac{3}{100}$ **3.** $70\%; \frac{7}{10}$ **5.** $60\%; \frac{3}{5}$ **7.** $0.06; \frac{3}{50}$ **9.** $0.005; \frac{1}{200}$ **11.** $0.99; \frac{99}{100}$ **13.** $0.875; 87.5\%$ **15.** $0.39; 39\%$ **17.** $0.06; 6\%$ **19.** $\frac{9}{256}$ **21.** $\frac{1}{1000}$ **23.** 0.5625 **25.** $a^2 + 2ab + b^2$ **27.** $m^2 - 4mn + 4n^2$ **29.** $a^3 - 0.6a^2b + 0.12ab^2 - 0.008b^3$ **31.** 25 **33.** 0.0625 **35.** 1

Pages 455–456

1. 24 **3.** $604{,}800$ **5.** $\frac{1}{5940}$ **7.** 100 **9.** 9 **11.** 3 **13.** There are 6 different combinations possible. **15.** There are 12 different ways Mario can remodel the room. **17.** Addition; there are 3 ways Carrie can raise her grade. **19.** Multiplication; there are 800 ways Tanya can select her look. **21.** Multiplication; there are 277,200 different possible light patterns. **23.** There are 12 ways Sheila can choose her prize. **25.** There are 39 ways Sonny can apply for a job. **27.** There are 19 ways Mikey can become involved. **29.** There are 10^5 or 100,000 zip codes.

Pages 460–461

1. 120 **3.** 90 **5.** $40{,}320$ **7.** 144 **9.** $\frac{5}{3}$ **11.** There are 120 ways the students could fill the openings. **13.** There are 24 ways to finish the marathon. **15.** There are 24 ways to form words from the given letters. **17.** There are 210 ways to fill the top three spots. **19.** There are 40,320 ways to line up the reindeer. **21.** There are 120 ways to arrange the beads. **23.** There are 60 distinct arrangements possible.

Pages 467–468

1. 70 **3.** 1 **5.** 84 **7.** Permutation; order matters. **9.** Permutation; order matters. **11.** Combination; order does not matter. **13.** $_{12}C_2 = 66$ **15.** $_{30}C_{10} = 30{,}045{,}015$

17. 210   **19.** 1   **21.** $9x^2 - 24xy + 16y^2$
23. $125x^3 + 300x^2y + 240xy^2 + 64y^3$ **25.** $252x^5y^5$
27. $-126x^4$ **29.** $_{12}C_2 + {}_{12}C_3 + {}_{12}C_4$; There are 781 different
choices possible.   **31.** $_8C_2 + {}_8C_3 + {}_8C_4$; There are 154
different combinations of books possible.   **33.** $2 \cdot {}_{16}C_6$;
There are 16,016 possible combinations.

Pages 471–472

1. $S = \{$hearts, spades, clubs, diamonds$\}$
3. $S = \{1, 2, 3, 4, 5\}$ **5.** $S = \{1, 2, 3, 4, 5, 6, 7, 8, 9, 10, 11,$
$12\}$ **7.** $S = \{$spring, summer, fall, winter$\}$ **9.** $S = \{$red,
yellow, green$\}$ **11.** $S = \{$A, E, I, O, U$\}$ **13.** $\frac{1}{6}$ or about
17%   **15.** 25%   **17.** $\frac{1}{2}$ or about 50%   **19.** $\frac{5}{26}$ or about 19%

21. The probability of finishing oldest to youngest is $\frac{1}{24}$.

23. The probability that the arrangement spells *CROP* is $\frac{1}{24}$.

25. The probability of the DVD sets being in order by season

is $\frac{1}{120}$.   **27.** The probability of getting a pair of aces is $\frac{1}{221}$

or about 0.45%   **29.** Drew's friend's chances of winning are
1 out of 3.

Pages 475–476

1. A.

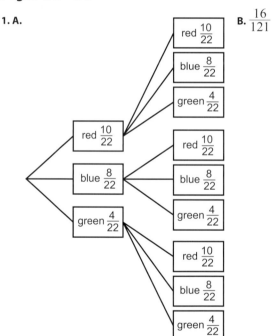

B. $\frac{16}{121}$

3. A.

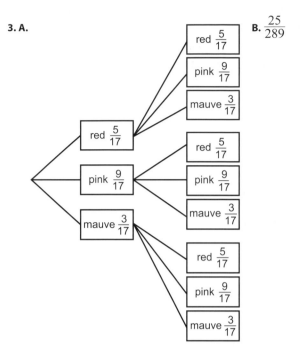

B. $\frac{25}{289}$

5. $\frac{1}{169}$ **7.** $\frac{49}{400}$ **9.** $\frac{66}{325}$ **11.** $\frac{24}{95}$ **13.** $\frac{3}{25}$ **15.** $\frac{56}{729}$

17. $\frac{6}{25}$ **19.** $\frac{3}{23}$ **21.** $\frac{125}{6859}$ **23.** $\frac{6}{169}$

Pages 479–480

1. Independent   **3.** Dependent   **5.** Independent
7. Independent   **9.** Dependent   **11.** Dependent
13. about 3.31%   **15.** 12.5%   **17.** about 1.23%   **19.** about
2.78%   **21.** about 0.46%   **23.** 0.198079%   **25.** 1.656863%
27. 0.182842%   **29.** about 2.78%

Pages 483–484

1. Yes   **3.** No; it is possible to draw a 10 of diamonds.
5. No; it is possible to draw a red marble.   **7.** Yes   **9.** Yes

11. Yes   **13.** Yes   **15.** $\frac{4}{13}$ **17.** $\frac{3}{4}$ **19.** $\frac{2}{9}$ **21.** 66%

23. 37%   **25.** 41%   **27.** 44%   **29.** If the occurrence of one
event means that the other cannot take place, then the events
are mutually exclusive.

Pages 488–489

1. No   **3.** Yes   **5.** Yes   **7.** No   **9.** Yes   **11.** Yes
13. No; the probability of success is not the same for each
trial.   **15.** No; there is no fixed number of trials.
17. 15.625%   **19.** about 5.36%   **21.** 37.5%
23. The probability that exactly half will say they prefer a
shorter shift with less promotion potential is about 20.07%.
25. The probability that exactly 2 bought black cars is 30.87%.
27. He would expect 46 people to have bought black cars.
29. A. No; it is possible to pick a green marble.   **B.** No; the
probability of success is not the same for each trial.

Pages 494–495

1. 21 As   **3.** 295 passing grades   **5.** 41 As   **7.** 29 people
9. 364 people   **11.** Yes   **13.** Yes   **15.** Yes   **17.** No; the law of large numbers does not predict the outcome of individual trials.   **19.** Yes   **21.** $\frac{25}{169}$ **23.** $\frac{24}{169}$ **25.** 16.67%

27. 16.67%   **29.** Yes; Ricardo is using the law of large numbers to predict the outcome of not a single trial but several trials.

UNIT 13   Statistics

Pages 499–500

1. $7 \cdot 1 + 7 \cdot 2 + 7 \cdot 3 + 7 \cdot 4 + 7 \cdot 5$; 105
3. $(1 - 3) + (2 - 3) + (3 - 3) + (4 - 3)$; −2

5. $\frac{1}{2} + \frac{2}{2} + \frac{3}{2} + \frac{4}{2}$; 5   **7.** $\sum_{k=1}^{5} 2k = 30$; $\sum_{i=0}^{4} (2i + 2) = 30$

9. 12.5   **11.** 6.1   **13.** 4.95   **15.** $\frac{7}{12}$

17. $A(-4, 1)$ is in Quadrant II;

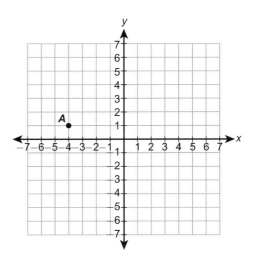

19. $C(1, 6)$ is in Quadrant I;

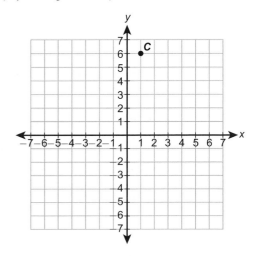

21. $E(1, -3)$ is in Quadrant IV;

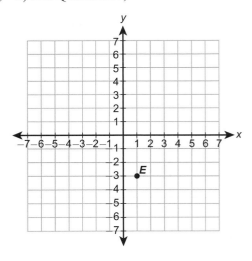

23. $G(0, -5)$ is on the negative y-axis;

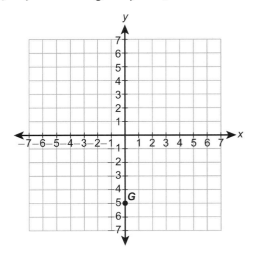

25. $K(-2, 3)$ is in Quadrant II;

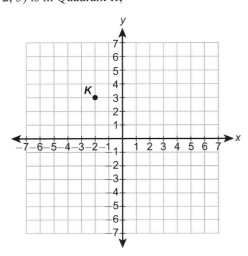

Pages 504–505

1. mean = 39.25; median = 38; mode = 34
3. mean = 81.625; median = 85.5; mode = none
5. mean = 68.3; median = 73; mode = 80

7.

2	0 2 2
3	4 7
4	8 9
5	6
6	1

mean $= 38\frac{7}{9}$ or $38.\overline{7}$; median $= 37$; mode $= 22$

9.

7	7 8 8
8	0 2 2
9	1 2
10	0

mean $= 84\frac{4}{9}$ or $84.\overline{4}$; median $= 82$; modes $= 78, 82$

11.

6	0 0 6 8
7	2 9
8	1 3
9	2

mean $= 73\frac{4}{9}$ or $73.\overline{4}$; median $= 72$; mode $= 60$

13.

52	0
53	1 2 3
54	0 8 8 8 9

mean $= 538\frac{7}{9}$ or $538.\overline{7}$; median $= 540$; mode $= 548$
15. 0.34 **17.** 83.8 **19. A.** $1\frac{11}{30}$ or $1.3\overline{6}$ **B.** $.976$ **21.** 93
23. 103 **25.** 780 **27.** 4 **29.** 12.5 hours **31.** 12

Pages 509–511

1. 9 **3.** 8

5.
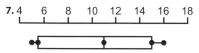

minimum $= 6$, $Q_1 = 16$, median $= 20$, $Q_3 = 25$, maximum $= 30$

7. 4 6 8 10 12 14 16 18

minimum $= 5$, $Q_1 = 5.5$, median $= 11$, $Q_3 = 15$,
maximum $= 16$

9. 24 26 28 30 32 34 36 38 40

minimum $= 25$, $Q_1 = 28$, median $= 32$, $Q_3 = 37$,
maximum $= 39$ **11.** $s^2 = 47.9$; $s = 6.9$ **13.** $s^2 = 11.4$;
$s = 3.4$ **15.** $s^2 = 70.7$; $s = 8.4$ **17.** Set B **19.** Set A
21. Set A: $s \approx 4.28$, Set B: $s \approx 0.32$, Set C: $s \approx 30.29$;
(1) Set B, (2) Set A, (3) Set C **23.** (1) Set C, (2) Set A,
(3) Set B **25. A.** 25% **B.** 75% **C.** 50%

Pages 514–515

1. Simple random sample; it is not biased because every
student has an equal chance of being selected.
3. Convenience sampling; it is biased because male mall
shoppers have no chance of being selected for the survey.
5. Stratified random sample; it is biased because not all
residents will return the mailed survey. **7.** Simple random
sample; it is biased because city residents who do not have
driver's licenses will not be selected. **9.** Convenience
sampling; it is biased because all entries in the phone book
do not have an equally likely chance of being selected.
11. Systematic sampling; it is biased because only TV
viewers who returned the survey are represented.
13. 616 **15.** 112 **17.** 162 **19.** 200 **21.** 2526 **23.** 173

Pages 520–524

1.
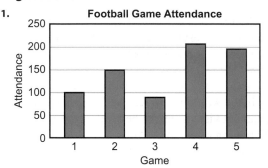

3.
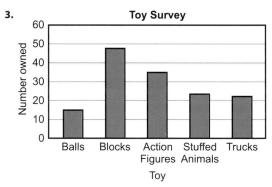

5.
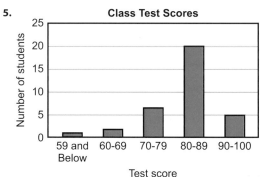

7.
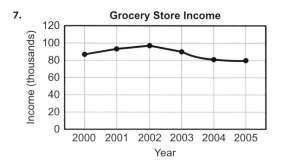

9.

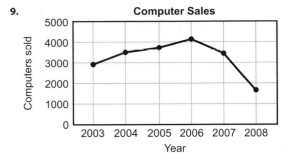

Computer Sales

11. In the neighborhood, the poodle is the most popular dog, and the bulldog is the least popular. **13.** The number of bald eagles has been increasing since 1985. **15.** The apple tree is the most common tree in the orchard and the plum tree is the least common. **17.** There are almost four times as many deer as bears in the wildlife sample. **19.** The number of fast-food restaurant visits seems to be leveling off at a little less than 900 million a year as of 2005.

21. box-and-whisker plot **23.** stem-and-leaf plot
25. line graph

27. A.

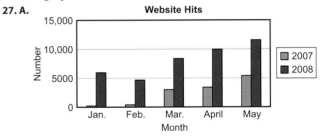

Website Hits

B. The number of hits for the company increased each month in 2007 and 2008.

29. A.

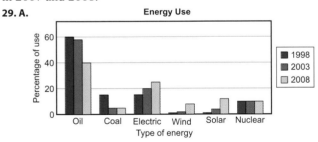

Energy Use

B. Oil and coal use decreased, while electric, wind, and solar use increased. Nuclear energy use stayed the same.

Pages 528–530

Answers may vary based on the number of classes shown.

1.

Class	Frequency	Class	Frequency
5–10	1	35–40	2
11–16	1	41–46	1
17–22	7	47–52	4
23–28	1	53–58	2
29–34	4	59–64	2

3.

Class	Frequency	Class	Frequency
50–55	3	80–85	4
56–61	4	86–91	2
62–67	3	92–97	4
68–73	0	98–103	2
74–79	3		

5.

Class	Frequency	Class	Frequency
50–54	3	75–79	3
55–59	3	80–84	2
60–64	4	85–89	4
65–69	1	90–94	0
70–74	4	95–99	1

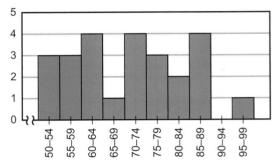

7.

Class	Frequency	Class	Frequency
0–4	4	15–19	5
5–9	6	20–24	6
10–14	4		

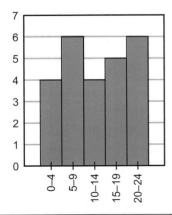

9.

Class	Frequency	Class	Frequency
25–31	1	67–73	4
32–38	0	74–80	4
39–45	0	81–87	5
46–52	0	88–94	5
53–59	2	95–101	3
60–66	1		

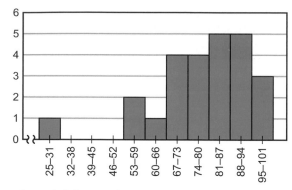

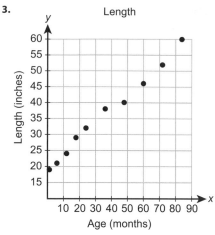

3.

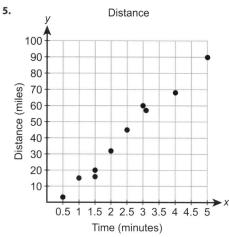

5.

11. A. skewed right **B.** The mean is greater than the median.
C. The data are clumped from 1–30 and spread out from 31–50. **13. A.** nearly bell shaped **B.** The mean and median are nearly equal. **C.** The data are clumped in the center (31−45) and more spread out near the ends (1−15 and 61−75). **15. A.** skewed left **B.** The mean is less than the median. **C.** The data are clumped to the right and spread out to the left. **17. A.** skewed right **B.** The mean is greater than the median. **C.** The data are clumped to the left and spread out to the right. **19. A.** nearly bell shaped **B.** The mean and median are nearly equal. **C.** The data are clumped in the center and spread out on either side. **21. A.** nearly bell shaped **B.** The mean and the median are nearly equal
C. 3 marigolds **23. A.** skewed right **B.** The median is less than the mean. **C.** 35% **25. A.** skewed left **B.** The mean is less than the median. **C.** 26 times

Pages 534–535

1. Not normal **3.** Not normal **5.** Not normal **7.** 68%
9. 99.7% **11.** 16% **13.** 13.5% **15.** 97.5 percentile
17. 50 **19.** 2.00 **21.** 1.00 **23.** −1.00 **25.** Lila's Government test score is better relative to the other scores in the class. **27.** 0.84375 **29.** Ahmad, Brian, Roxy

Pages 538–544

1.

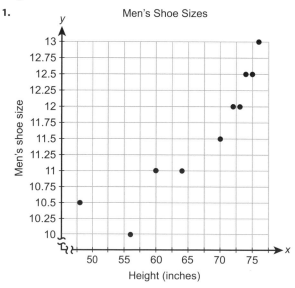

7.

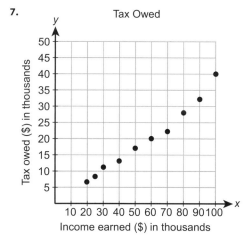

9.

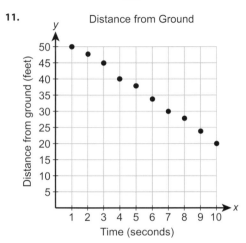

Speed Limit

11.

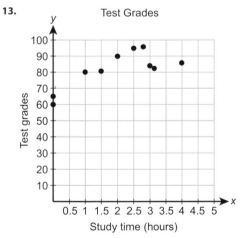

Distance from Ground

13.

Test Grades

15. There is a weak negative correlation; as the year increases, the number of lung cancer cases usually decreases.   **17.** There is a weak positive correlation; as age increases, yearly salary tends to increase.   **19.** There is a strong positive correlation; as the hours worked increases, the pay tends to increase.   **21.** There is a weak negative correlation; as the year increases, the cases of flu may decrease.   **23.** There is no correlation.   **25.** There is a strong positive correlation; as the distance increases, the time tends

to increase.   **27.** There is a weak positive correlation; as the income increases, the expenditures tends to increase.
29. There is a weak negative correlation; as the stock price per share increases, the number of shares bought tends to decrease.

Pages 548–551

1. A.

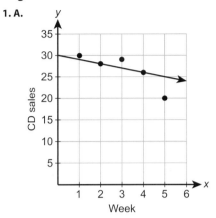

CD sales / Week

B. $(2, 28), (4, 26)$ **C.** $y = -x + 30$ **D.** 23

3. A.

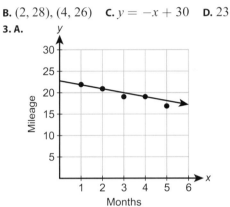

Mileage / Months

B. $(2, 21), (4, 19)$ **C.** $y = -x + 23$ **D.** 17

5. A.

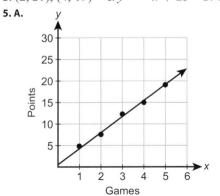

Points / Games

B. $(2, 8), (5, 19)$ **C.** $y = \frac{11}{3}x + \frac{2}{3}$ **D.** 26

7. A.

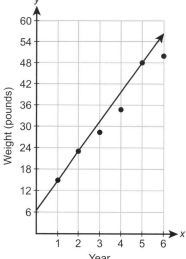

B. $(2, 23), (5, 48)$ **C.** $y = \dfrac{25}{3}x + \dfrac{19}{3}$ **D.** 81

9. A.

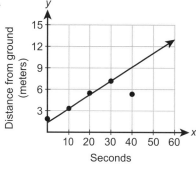

B. $(15, 4.5)$ and $(60, 13)$ **C.** The line of fit is not reasonable after 30 seconds, so the data are not consistent with a linear function after that point.

11. A.

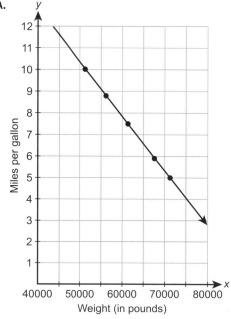

B. $(65{,}000, 6.5)$ and $(80{,}000, 2.75)$ **C.** The miles per gallon will never fall below 0, and the weight of the semitrailer truck must have a lower limit as well.

13. A.

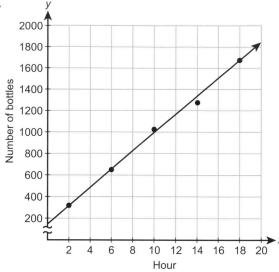

B. $(12, 1180)$ and $(25, 2300)$ **C.** The points all roughly fall on the line of fit, so any point should be able to be extrapolated.   **15. A.** $y = 2.31x + 24.74$ **B.** $\$84{,}800$
17. A. $y = 0.16x + 3.32$ **B.** 5.56 feet
19. A. $y = 0.44x + 4.84$ **B.** 7.48 minutes
21. A. $y = 6.95x + 3.775$ **B.** 212.275
23. A. $y = 14.23x + 64.36$ **B.** $\$249{,}350$

UNIT 14   Vectors and Matrices

Pages 554–556

1. $-3; \dfrac{1}{3}$ **3.** $7; -\dfrac{1}{7}$ **5.** 0; no reciprocal   **7.** $-2.5; \dfrac{2}{5}$

9. $-72; \dfrac{1}{72}$ **11.** $(5, 20)$ **13.** $(2, 6)$ **15.** $(7, -13)$

17. $(-8, -8)$ **19.** $(6, 2)$ **21.** $(-2, -5)$ **23.** no solution

Pages 560–561

1. 2×2; not a vector   **3.** 3×1; vector   **5.** 1×2; vector
7. 2×4; not a vector   **9.** 3×3; not a vector   **11.** 1×3;
vector   **13.** b_{31} **15.** a_{41} **17.** b_{11} **19.** 1 **21.** 3 **23.** 15
25. A. 4×3 **B.** $23{,}900$; cost of Dealer 3's Model 2
C. c_{41} **D.** $\$24{,}675$

27. 1×5 or 5×1; $\begin{bmatrix} 100 & 110 & 72 & 47 & 41 \end{bmatrix}$ or $\begin{bmatrix} 100 \\ 110 \\ 72 \\ 47 \\ 41 \end{bmatrix}$

Pages 566–568

1. $\begin{bmatrix} 34 & -8 \\ 16 & 13 \end{bmatrix}$ **3.** $\begin{bmatrix} -57 & -60 & 18 \\ 16 & 7 & -27 \end{bmatrix}$ **5.** $\begin{bmatrix} 4 & 3 \\ -22 & 35 \end{bmatrix}$

7. $\begin{bmatrix} -58 & -8 & 109 \\ -4 & 15 & -5 \end{bmatrix}$ **9.** $\begin{bmatrix} -4 & 48 \\ 32 & 40 \end{bmatrix}$ **11.** $\begin{bmatrix} -70 & -35 & -500 \\ 0 & 50 & -125 \end{bmatrix}$

13. $\begin{bmatrix} 27 & 135 \\ -126 & 405 \end{bmatrix}$ **15.** The matrices cannot be added

because their dimensions are different. **17.** $\begin{bmatrix} -33 & 47 \\ -14 & 52 \end{bmatrix}$

19. $\begin{bmatrix} -29 & 50 \\ -36 & 87 \end{bmatrix}$ **21.** The matrices cannot be added because

their dimensions are different. **23.** The matrices cannot be added because their dimensions are different.

25. Answers will vary. Sample answer: If $A = \begin{bmatrix} a_{11} & a_{12} \\ a_{21} & a_{22} \end{bmatrix}$,

then $rA = \begin{bmatrix} ra_{11} & ra_{12} \\ ra_{21} & ra_{22} \end{bmatrix}$ and $Ar = \begin{bmatrix} a_{11}r & a_{12}r \\ a_{21}r & a_{22}r \end{bmatrix}$. Since the

multiplication of any two real numbers is commutative, $ra_{11} = a_{11}r$, $ra_{12} = a_{12}r$, and so on for the rest of the corresponding elements of matrices rA and Ar. So, $rA = Ar$.

27. A. $\begin{bmatrix} 7155 & 5830 & 1885 \\ 2063 & 1958 & 945 \end{bmatrix}$ **B.** $\begin{bmatrix} 795 & 530 & -295 \\ -43 & 472 & -405 \end{bmatrix}$;

It represents the increase or decrease in the number of sports fans from 2007 to 2008. **29.** $x = 4$ and $y = -1$

Pages 572–574

1. 2×3 **3.** 2×2 **5.** 2×1 **7.** 2×4 **9.** 2×3

11. $\begin{bmatrix} 10 \\ 5 \end{bmatrix}$ **13.** $\begin{bmatrix} 1 & -5 \\ 24 & -56 \end{bmatrix}$ **15.** $\begin{bmatrix} -8 & -35 & -38 \\ 8 & 17 & -100 \end{bmatrix}$

17. $\begin{bmatrix} -18 & -37 & -20 & -52 \\ 2 & -1 & 4 & 8 \end{bmatrix}$ **19.** $\begin{bmatrix} -47 & -8 & 60 \\ 95 & -39 & -75 \end{bmatrix}$

21. $\begin{bmatrix} -159 & 18 \\ 21 & -6 \end{bmatrix}$ **23.** $AB = \begin{bmatrix} 5 & 0 \\ 0 & -8 \end{bmatrix}$ and $BA = \begin{bmatrix} 5 & -65 \\ 0 & -8 \end{bmatrix}$,

so $AB \neq BA$. **25. A.** Tuesday **B.** Tuesday; $1,608,800

27. A. $[3 \quad 6 \quad 1 \quad 2]$; $\begin{bmatrix} 3 & 1 \\ 2 & 2 \\ 2 & 1 \\ 1 & 0 \end{bmatrix}$ **B.** Team 1 scored 25 points

and Team 2 scored 16 points. **29.** Answers will vary.

Sample answer: $A = \begin{bmatrix} 1 & 2 \\ 3 & 4 \end{bmatrix}$ and $B = \begin{bmatrix} 1 & 0 \\ 0 & 1 \end{bmatrix}$; The

dimensions of A must be the same as the dimensions of B.

Pages 579–580

1. A. $3 \cdot \begin{bmatrix} 1 & 2 & 6 \\ 5 & 8 & 2 \end{bmatrix}$ **B.** $(3, 15)$, $(6, 24)$, and $(18, 6)$

3. A. $\frac{1}{4} \cdot \begin{bmatrix} 0 & 8 & 0 & -8 \\ 8 & 0 & -8 & 0 \end{bmatrix}$ **B.** $(0, 2)$, $(2, 0)$, $(0, -2)$, and

$(-2, 0)$ **5. A.** $\begin{bmatrix} 2 & 0 \\ 0 & 3 \end{bmatrix} \begin{bmatrix} -1 & 2 & 4 \\ 4 & 7 & -4 \end{bmatrix}$ **B.** $(-2, 12)$, $(4, 21)$,

and $(8, -12)$ **7. A.** $\begin{bmatrix} 5 & 0 \\ 0 & \frac{1}{2} \end{bmatrix} \begin{bmatrix} -1 & 2 & 4 & 2 & -1 & -4 \\ 2 & 2 & 0 & -2 & -2 & 0 \end{bmatrix}$

B. $(-5, 1)$, $(10, 1)$, $(20, 0)$, $(10, -1)$, $(-5, -1)$, and $(-20, 0)$

9. A. $\begin{bmatrix} 1 & 0 & 5 \\ 0 & 1 & 2 \\ 0 & 0 & 1 \end{bmatrix} \cdot \begin{bmatrix} 2 \\ 0 \\ 1 \end{bmatrix}$ **B.** $(7, 2)$

11. A. $\begin{bmatrix} 1 & 0 & -5 \\ 0 & 1 & -4 \\ 0 & 0 & 1 \end{bmatrix} \cdot \begin{bmatrix} -12 \\ 0 \\ 1 \end{bmatrix}$ **B.** $(-17, -4)$

13. A. $\begin{bmatrix} 1 & 0 & -6 \\ 0 & 1 & -5 \\ 0 & 0 & 1 \end{bmatrix} \cdot \begin{bmatrix} 12 \\ 9 \\ 1 \end{bmatrix}$ **B.** $(6, 4)$

15. A. $\begin{bmatrix} 1 & 0 & -4 \\ 0 & 1 & -2 \\ 0 & 0 & 1 \end{bmatrix} \cdot \begin{bmatrix} 1 & 2 & 3 \\ 9 & 4 & -3 \\ 1 & 1 & 1 \end{bmatrix}$ **B.** $(-3, 7)$, $(-2, 2)$, and

$(-1, -5)$ **17. A.** $\begin{bmatrix} 1 & 0 & 6 \\ 0 & 1 & -7 \\ 0 & 0 & 1 \end{bmatrix} \cdot \begin{bmatrix} 2 & 5 & -1 \\ 0 & -10 & -4 \\ 1 & 1 & 1 \end{bmatrix}$

B. $(8, -7)$, $(11, -17)$, $(5, -11)$

19. A. $\begin{bmatrix} 1 & 0 & -9 \\ 0 & 1 & -6 \\ 0 & 0 & 1 \end{bmatrix} \cdot \begin{bmatrix} -9 & -4 & -4 & 10 \\ -8 & -10 & 12 & 2 \\ 1 & 1 & 1 & 1 \end{bmatrix}$

B. $(-18, -14)$, $(-13, -16)$, $(-13, 6)$, and $(1, -4)$

21. A. $\begin{bmatrix} 1 & 0 \\ 0 & -1 \end{bmatrix} \begin{bmatrix} 1 & 5 & 3 \\ 8 & 6 & -4 \end{bmatrix}$ **B.** $(1, -8)$, $(5, -6)$,

and $(3, 4)$ **23. A.** $\begin{bmatrix} 0 & -1 \\ 1 & 0 \end{bmatrix} \begin{bmatrix} 1 & 4 & -3 & -6 \\ 2 & -1 & -5 & 2 \end{bmatrix}$

B. $(-2, 1)$, $(1, 4)$, $(5, -3)$, and $(-2, -6)$

25. A. $\begin{bmatrix} 0 & 1 \\ -1 & 0 \end{bmatrix} \begin{bmatrix} 4 & -2 & -5 & 5 \\ 7 & 9 & -10 & 0 \end{bmatrix}$ **B.** $(7, -4)$, $(9, 2)$,

$(-10, 5)$, and $(0, -5)$ **27.** a quadrilateral dilated by a scale factor of 5 **29.** a quadrilateral dilated by a scale factor of $\frac{1}{2}$ and rotated 90° counterclockwise

Pages 586–587

1. -10 **3.** 22 **5.** -237 **7.** -1 **9.** -97 **11.** 34
13. Yes   **15.** No   **17.** Yes   **19.** $(5, 3)$ **21.** $(10, -5)$
23. $(-16, -13)$ **25.** $(1, -2, -4)$ **27.** $(-7, 4, -1)$

29. A. $A^t = \begin{bmatrix} 8 & -1 \\ 3 & 2 \end{bmatrix}$ **B.** $(A^t)^t = \begin{bmatrix} 8 & 3 \\ -1 & 2 \end{bmatrix} = A$

C. $\det A = 8 \cdot 2 - 3 \cdot (-1) = 16 - (-3) = 19$;
$\det A^t = 8 \cdot 2 - (-1) \cdot 3 = 16 - (-3) = 19$

Pages 592–594

1. $\begin{bmatrix} 1 & 0 \\ 0 & 1 \end{bmatrix}$ **3.** $\begin{bmatrix} 1 & 0 & 0 & 0 \\ 0 & 1 & 0 & 0 \\ 0 & 0 & 1 & 0 \\ 0 & 0 & 0 & 1 \end{bmatrix}$ **5.** Yes   **7.** Yes   **9.** No

11. Yes   **13.** No   **15.** $\begin{bmatrix} -1 & -1 \\ -6 & -5 \end{bmatrix}$ **17.** $\begin{bmatrix} -0.25 & 0.75 \\ -0.375 & 0.625 \end{bmatrix}$

19. $\begin{bmatrix} 0.2 & -0.1 \\ 0.2 & 0.4 \end{bmatrix}$ **21.** $\begin{bmatrix} -0.\overline{1} & 0.\overline{8} & 1.\overline{6} \\ 0.\overline{4} & -1.\overline{5} & -3.\overline{6} \\ 0.\overline{1} & 0.\overline{1} & 0.\overline{3} \end{bmatrix}$ **23.** $\begin{bmatrix} -5 & -1 \\ -1 & 0 \end{bmatrix}$

25. $\begin{bmatrix} -3 & 2 \\ -1 & 1 \end{bmatrix}$ **27.** The inverse does not exist.

29. $AB = \begin{bmatrix} 1 & 2 \\ 1 & 3 \end{bmatrix} \begin{bmatrix} 2 & 0 \\ 4 & 1 \end{bmatrix} = \begin{bmatrix} 10 & 2 \\ 14 & 3 \end{bmatrix}$; $(AB)^{-1} = \begin{bmatrix} 1.5 & -1 \\ -7 & 5 \end{bmatrix}$;

$B^{-1}A^{-1} = \begin{bmatrix} 0.5 & 0 \\ -2 & 1 \end{bmatrix} \begin{bmatrix} 3 & -2 \\ -1 & 1 \end{bmatrix} = \begin{bmatrix} 1.5 & -1 \\ -7 & 5 \end{bmatrix}$

Pages 598–599

1. $\begin{bmatrix} 1 & 1 \\ 1 & -1 \end{bmatrix} \begin{bmatrix} x \\ y \end{bmatrix} = \begin{bmatrix} 5 \\ 3 \end{bmatrix}$ **3.** $\begin{bmatrix} 3 & -6 \\ 5 & 4 \end{bmatrix} \begin{bmatrix} x \\ y \end{bmatrix} = \begin{bmatrix} 2 \\ 1 \end{bmatrix}$

5. $\begin{bmatrix} 3 & 0 \\ 1 & -5 \end{bmatrix} \begin{bmatrix} x \\ y \end{bmatrix} = \begin{bmatrix} 24 \\ 3 \end{bmatrix}$ **7.** $\begin{bmatrix} 2 & 3 & -1 \\ -1 & 2 & 1 \\ 6 & -8 & -2 \end{bmatrix} \begin{bmatrix} x \\ y \\ z \end{bmatrix} = \begin{bmatrix} 0 \\ 5 \\ 2 \end{bmatrix}$

9. $\begin{bmatrix} 1 & 5 & 0 \\ 2 & -3 & 4 \\ 0 & 6 & 7 \end{bmatrix} \begin{bmatrix} x \\ y \\ z \end{bmatrix} = \begin{bmatrix} 12 \\ 18 \\ 10 \end{bmatrix}$ **11.** $(3, 9)$ **13.** The system

does not have a single solution.   **15.** $\left(-\frac{2}{3}, \frac{2}{3}\right)$ **17.** The

system does not have a single solution.   **19.** $(-6, 4)$
21. $(2, -3)$ **23.** The system does not have a single solution.
25. $(2, -2, 5)$ **27.** $(-5, 13, 0)$ **29.** $(1.\overline{6}, 2, -3.\overline{1}, 2.\overline{7})$

UNIT 15   Conic Sections

Pages 602–604

1. $r = 4.5$ units; $d = 9$ units   **3.** $r = 6$ units; $d = 12$ units
5. $(5, 3)$ **7.** $(3, 7)$ **9.** $(-16, 2)$ **11.** $x = \pm 11$ **13.** $x = \pm\sqrt{35}$
15. $x = \pm 4\sqrt{7}$ **17.** $x = \pm\sqrt{57}$ **19.** $x = \pm 4\sqrt{2}$

Page 609

1. Circle   **3.** Degenerate parabola (line)   **5.** Ellipse
7. Degenerate hyperbola (pair of intersecting lines)   **9.** $6\sqrt{5}$
11. $\sqrt{365}$ **13.** $\sqrt{34}$ **15.** $6\sqrt{2}$ **17.** $(6, -8.5)$ **19.** $(-2.5, -3.5)$
21. $(1, 1)$ **23.** $(8, 0)$ **25.** $(-4, 1)$ **27.** $(-7, 9)$
29. $A' = (-1, 2)$; $B' = (-3, -4)$; $C' = (-3, 2)$

Pages 613–615

1. $(x - 3)^2 + (y - 1)^2 = 25$ **3.** $(x - 5)^2 + (y - 4)^2 = 9$
5. $(x + 4)^2 + (y - 7)^2 = 12.25$ **7.** $(x + 3)^2 + (y - 2)^2 = 16$
9. A. center $= (2, 4)$; $r = 1$; $d = 2$

B.

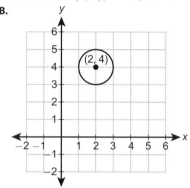

11. A. center $= (-10, -9)$; $r = 10$; $d = 20$

B.

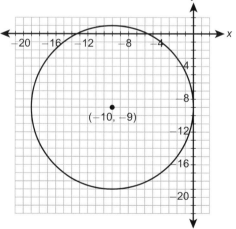

13. A. center $= (0, -4)$; $r = 6$; $d = 12$
B.
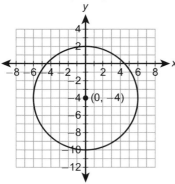

15. A. center $= (0, 0)$; $r = 7$; $d = 14$
B.
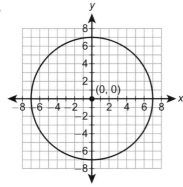

17. A. center $= (1, 6)$; $r = 2$; $d = 4$
B.
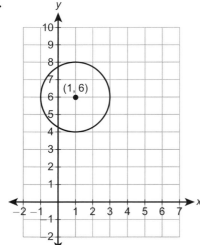

19. A. center $= (-5, -7)$; $r = 9$; $d = 18$
B.
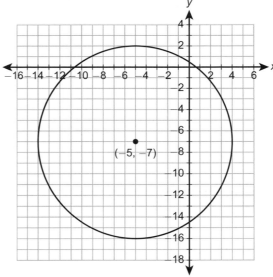

21. $(x - 2)^2 + (y + 1)^2 = 100$
23. $(x + 2)^2 + (y + 1)^2 = 5$ **25. A.** $x^2 + y^2 = 686{,}387{,}601$
B. $(x + 2000)^2 + (y - 1300)^2 = 686{,}387{,}601$ **27. A.** $(-3, -2)$
B. $\sqrt{13}$ units   **29.** $(x + 3)^2 + (y - 8)^2 = 49$

Pages 621–623

1. $\dfrac{(x - 1)^2}{4} + \dfrac{(y + 8)^2}{25} = 1$ **3.** $\dfrac{(x + 10)^2}{4} + \dfrac{(y + 5)^2}{36} = 1$

5. $\dfrac{(x - 2)^2}{49} + \dfrac{(y - 3)^2}{16} = 1$ **7. A.** $(0, 0)$ **B.** 6 **C.** 4

D.
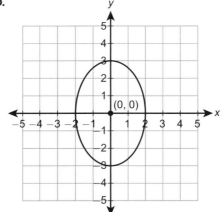

9. A. $(1, 0)$ **B.** 12 **C.** 8
D.

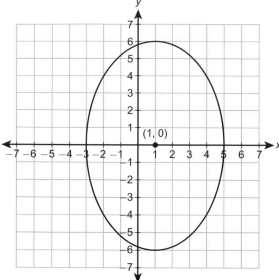

11. A. $(3, 6)$ **B.** 10 **C.** 4
D.

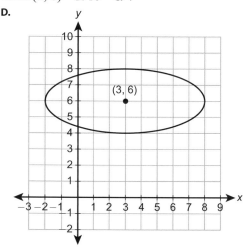

13. A. $(6, -3)$ **B.** 30 **C.** 26
D.

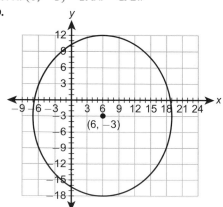

15. A. $(1, 8)$ **B.** 14 **C.** 8
D.

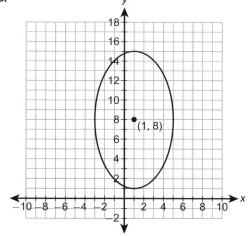

17. A. $(-1, 6)$ **B.** 24 **C.** $6\sqrt{6}$
D.

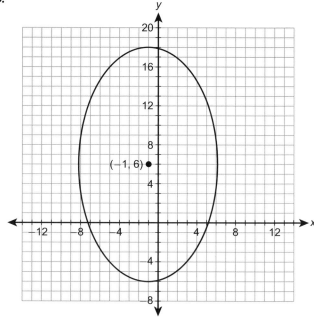

19. $(10, 8)$ and $(-2, 8)$ **21.** $\left(-2, 2\sqrt{3} - 8\right)$ and
$\left(-2, -\left(8 + 2\sqrt{3}\right)\right)$ **23.** $\left(2, 3 + \sqrt{6}\right)$ and $\left(2, 3 - \sqrt{6}\right)$
25. $\dfrac{\sqrt{19}}{10}$ **27.** $\dfrac{\sqrt{5}}{3}$

29. A.

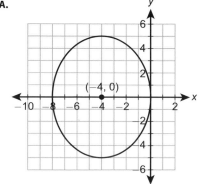

B. $(-4, -3)$ and $(-4, 3)$ **31. A.** Semimajor axis: 162 feet; semiminor axis: 98 feet   **B.** $32\sqrt{65}$ feet

C. $\dfrac{x^2}{26{,}244} + \dfrac{y^2}{9604} = 1$ **33.** $\dfrac{x^2}{225{,}000{,}000} + \dfrac{y^2}{144{,}000{,}000} = 1$

Pages 629–631

1. $\dfrac{x^2}{25} - \dfrac{y^2}{36} = 1$ **3.** $\dfrac{(y+4)^2}{36} - \dfrac{(x-5)^2}{49} = 1$

5. $\dfrac{(y-2)^2}{4} - \dfrac{(x+6)^2}{25} = 1$ **7. A.** $(0, 0)$ **B.** 20 **C.** 10

D. $y = \dfrac{1}{2}x,\ y = -\dfrac{1}{2}x$

E.

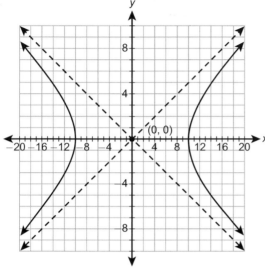

9. A. $(0, 0)$ **B.** 18 **C.** 8 **D.** $y = \dfrac{9}{4}x,\ y = -\dfrac{9}{4}x$

E.

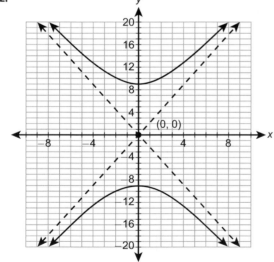

11. A. $(2, 0)$ **B.** 6 **C.** 4 **D.** $y = \dfrac{2}{3}x - \dfrac{4}{3},\ y = -\dfrac{2}{3}x + \dfrac{4}{3}$

E.

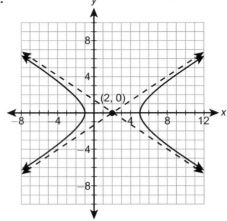

13. A. $(12, 10)$ **B.** 12 **C.** 14 **D.** $y = \dfrac{7}{6}x - 4,\ y = -\dfrac{7}{6}x + 24$

E.

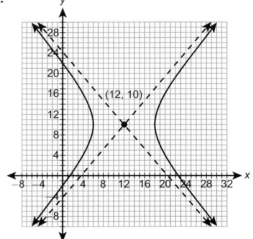

15. A. $(-10, 2)$ **B.** 18 **C.** 6 **D.** $y = -3x - 28,\ y = 3x + 32$

E.

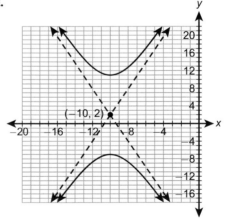

17. A. $(-9, -5)$ **B.** 14 **C.** $2\sqrt{85}$
D. $y = -1.3171x - 16.8539,\ y = 1.3171x + 6.8537$

E.

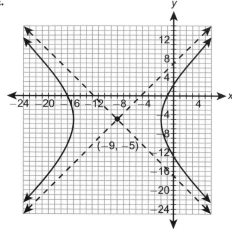

19. $(1, 10)$ and $(1, -10)$ **21.** $\left(-\left(8 + \sqrt{13}\right), -4\right)$ and
$\left(8 + \sqrt{13}, -4\right)$ **23.** $\dfrac{5}{3}$ **25.** $\dfrac{\sqrt{29}}{2}$ **27.** $(-4, 0)$ and $(4, 0)$
29. $\dfrac{x^2}{4.86 \times 10^{10}} - \dfrac{y^2}{2.27 \times 10^{11}} = 1$ **31. A.** Transverse: 60;
Conjugate: 100 **B.** $(0, 4)$ **C.** $\left(0, 4 + 10\sqrt{34}\right)$ and
$\left(0, 4 - 10\sqrt{34}\right)$
D. $\pm\dfrac{3}{5}$

Pages 636–637

1. $x - 1 = (y + 4)^2$ **3.** $y - 2 = \dfrac{1}{4}(x - 7)^2$

5. $y + 4 = \dfrac{1}{5}(x + 1)^2$ **7. A.** $(0, 0)$
B.

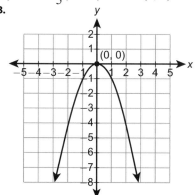

9. A. $(-1.4, 7)$ **B.**

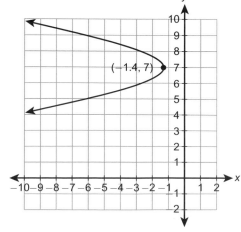

11. A. $(36, 25)$
B.

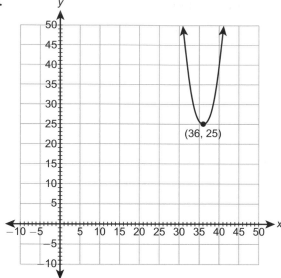

13. A. $(0, 1)$ **B.**

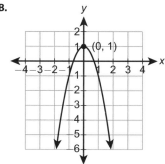

15. A. $(-4, -16)$
B.

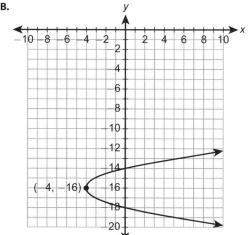

17. A. $\dfrac{1}{12}$ **B.** $\left(-1, \dfrac{13}{12}\right)$ **C.** $y = \dfrac{11}{12}$

19. A. $\dfrac{5}{4}$ **B.** $\left(9, \dfrac{5}{4}\right)$ **C.** $y = -\dfrac{5}{4}$ **21. A.** 1.25 **B.** $(2, -18.75)$

C. $y = -21.25$ **23. A.** $\dfrac{1}{20}$ **B.** $\left(-\dfrac{139}{20}, 1\right)$ **C.** $x = -\dfrac{141}{20}$

25. $(3, -1.5)$ **27.** $y - 4 = -(x - 3)^2$ **29.** $y - \dfrac{1}{2} = \dfrac{1}{6}(x + 1)^2$

Page 643

1. Ellipse   **3.** Circle   **5.** Ellipse

7. A. $\dfrac{(x - 4)^2}{10} - \dfrac{(y + 2)^2}{5} = 1$

B.

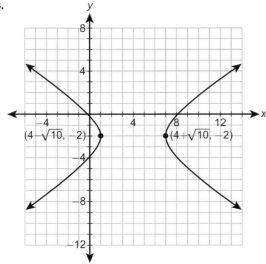

9. A. $\dfrac{(x + 1)^2}{36} - \dfrac{(y + 3)^2}{9} = 1$

B.

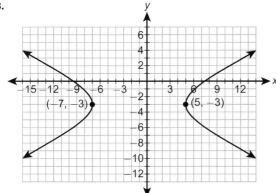

11. A. $\dfrac{x^2}{2} - y^2 = 1$ **B.**

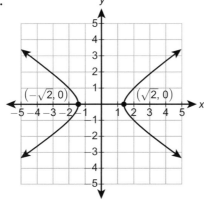

13. A. $y - 2 = 3(x - 4)^2$ **B.**

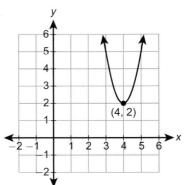

15. A. $y - 4 = (x - 1)^2$ **B.**

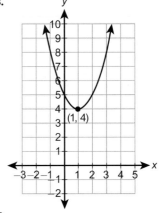

17. A. $\dfrac{(x + 2)^2}{15} + \dfrac{(y + 9)^2}{75} = 1$

B.

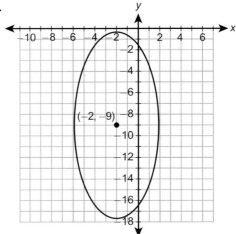

19. A. $(x - 4)^2 + (y - 3)^2 = 25$

B.

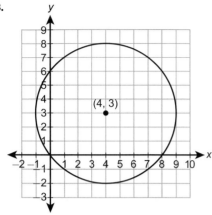

23.

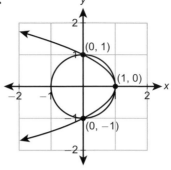

21. A. $(x - 3)^2 + (y - 8)^2 = 20$

B.

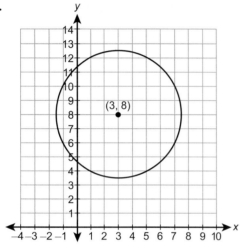

Illustrations Credits

Cover: All Illustrations © K12 Inc. unless otherwise noted Smoke against white background. © Dreamstime

Unit 1: © 2007/Anne Kitzman/BigStockPhoto

Unit 2: © 2008/Olga Utlyakova/BigStockPhoto

Unit 3: © Colorvision/age fotostock

Unit 4: © Jeff Smith/Getty Images

Unit 5: © Mark Evans/iStock

Unit 6: © Lynn Goldsmith/Corbis

Unit 7: © Paul Thomas/K12 Inc.

Unit 8: © age fotostock/SuperStock

Unit 9: © 2008/Christodoulos Fourouklas/BigStockPhoto

Unit 10: © David M. Phillips/Photo Researchers, Inc.

Unit 11: © Roger Du Buisson/Corbis

Unit 12: © 2006/David Rehner/BigStockPhoto

Unit 13: © Nicholas Rjabow/Dreamstime

Unit 14: © Kim Kulish/Corbis

Unit 15: © Roger Ressmeyer/Corbis

Index

finding the domain and range of a, 90, 123, 227, 233

finding the equation from the graph, 103, 229–230

floor, 114

graphing, 91, 194–195, 226–227, 229, 233–239, 259, 260–263, 289–294, 324, 343–344, 392

identifying, 89

integer functions, 114–117

inverses, 125–129

odd, 198

operations, 120–124

parent, 100, 366

piecewise, 106–113

power, 194–201, 226

properties of quadratic functions, 295–299

quadratic function applications, 315–319

reciprocal power functions, 226–232

representing as graphs, 96–97

square root function graph family, 260

step, 114–119

successive differences of power functions, 199

transform the graph of the parent function, 369

translating absolute value functions, 102

using function notation, 96

using function notation and evaluating a function, 287

using the graph of a function to find the equation for the function, 369, 393

using vertical line test, 90–91

writing a power function when given a point, 198

writing an absolute value function as a piecewise function, 107

G

Gauss, Carl Friedrich, 427

Geometric formulas, 41–43

Geometric probability, 490–495

Geometric sequences, 411–419

Geometric series, 426, 431–436

Graphing. *see also* Number lines

absolute value functions, 100

an ellipse, 619

an inequality on a number line, 133

a circle, 612

a compound inequality in one variable, 142

creating a graph, 515–517

a cube root function, 259, 262–263

describing the end behavior of a polynomial function, 196–197

exponential functions, 366–371

geometric sequences, 411–412, 415

a hyperbola, 627–628

a linear equation, 51, 53, 58–59

logarithmic functions, 389–392

ordered pairs, 500

a parabola, 634

the partial sums of an arithmetic or geometric series, 424, 434

a piecewise function, 107–108

a polynomial function, 343–344

power functions, 195, 324

putting conics into, form, 638–643

a quadratic equation to solve an inequality in one variable, 309

quadratic functions in factored form, 292

quadratic functions in standard form, 290

radical functions, 259–265

rational functions, 233–239

solving systems by, 73–74

a square root function, 259–262

using a table of values to graph an exponential function, 366–371

using a table to graph quadratic functions, 289

using the remainder theorem to graph a polynomial, 334

Greatest common factor (GCF), 180, 184, 188, 208, *see also* Factoring

Greatest common monomial factoring, 180, 184, 187, 188, 191

Greatest integer function, 114–115

Guess and check strategy, 180–183, *see also* Check your work

H

Half-life, 374

Half-planes, 147–149

Higher roots. *see* Fractional exponents and higher roots

Histogram, 517, 524–526

Horizontal asymptote. *see* Asymptotes

Horizontal lines, 53

Horizontal translation, 101–102, 103

Hyperbolas, 227, 606, 624–629, 638, 641

I

Identity, 33, 588–593

Identity matrix, 588

Identity Property of Addition, 19, 31

Identity Property of Multiplication, 19, 33

Image points, 576–578

Imaginary axis, 271–272

Imaginary numbers, 266–274

closure, 267–268

operations with, 266–268

performing operations with, 267

rationalizing denominators with, 268

Independent events. *see* Probability

Independent variable. *see* Variables

Index, 249–252, 424

Inequalities, 132, *see also* Comparing

conjunction and, 140–141

disjunction and, 141

graphing, 133, 140, 143, 148, 149, 309

linear programming, 159–165

nonstrict inequalities, 133

notation, 135–136

in one variable, 135–139

quadratic, 306–311

solving, 140–146, 153–155

strict inequalities, 133

systems of linear, 153–158

in two variables, 147–152

writing, 134, 142, 149–150, 156

Infinity, 134–135, 137, 226, 343–344, 429

Input values, 86

Integers, 7–8, 21, 34, 252

Intercepts, 52, 68, 343, *see also* x-intercept; y-intercept

Interest, simple, 43

Interpolation, 546

Intersecting lines, 606

Intersection, 9

Interval notation, 135–137, 140–142

Inverse matrix, 589

Inverse operations, 326, 389, *see also* Functions; Reciprocals

Inverse Property of Addition, 19, 31

Inverse Property of Multiplication, 19

Inverses, 589–592, 595–596

Irrational numbers, 7, 8

Irrational roots. *see* Roots

Iterative rules, 406–407, 410–411, 414–415, 425–426, 432–433

L

Law of large numbers, 492–493

Leaf, 501

Least common denominator (LCD), 204, 211–212, 216–218, 220–221

Least integer function, 115–116

Left-multiplying, 572, 595

Like denominators. *see* Denominators

Like terms

adding and subtracting polynomials, 174

computing partial sums, 443–446

of cubes in factoring patterns, 180, 181

evaluating a, given in sigma notation, 498

factoring and checking the, and difference of cube patterns, 186

factoring completely, 188

finding the average of two numbers, 499

finding the sum of the first n terms of an arithmetic series, 427–428

graphing the partial, of a geometric series, 434

graphing the partial, of an arithmetic series, 429

of two squares, 181

Summary points, 546

Summation notation, 424

Symmetric Property of Equality, 31

Symmetry, 286, 603–604, *see also* Axis of symmetry

Synthetic division, 329–335, 337–338, 340, 342–343, 349, 351–352

System of equations, 73, 556, 585–586, 595–596

Systematic sampling, 511, 512

Systems of linear inequalities, 153–154

T

Tables, 524–526

Tables of values, 86, 403

Technology, 43, 380, 381, 383–385, 391, 395–396, 419–421, 442–447, 536, 590–592, 596

Terms, 22, 171, 405, *see also* Like terms

Test point, 148

Transformations, 32, 40, 101, 115, 392, 575, 578–579

Transitive Property of Equality, 31

Translation, 101–103, 555, 579

Transverse axis, 624–627

Tree diagram, 453, 469, 474, *see also* Set notation

Trinomials, 173, 180–184, 209, 221, 292, 302

U

Unbounded intervals, 135–137

Undefined slope, 55

Uniform distribution, 525

Union, 9

Univariate data, 515–523

Unlike denominators. *see* Denominators

Upper limit, 424, 498

V

Variability, 506–510

Variable expressions, 27

Variable matrix, 594

Variables

identifying independent and dependent, in real-world situations, 98

independent, 68

isolating, 31, 57, 62

simplifying radical expressions containing, 253

simplifying and graphing linear equations in one variable, 53

solving an inequality in one variable with a restricted domain, 137–139

solving and graphing a compound inequality in one variable, 142

solving equations with variables on both sides, 32

solving literal equations and formulas, 40

substituting, 27, 41

Variance, 507–508

Vectors and matrices, 554–598, *see also* Matrices and vectors

Venn diagrams, 9, 10

Vertex form, 296–297

Vertex (vertices), 616

absolute value functions, 100–103

finding a quadratic function from a vertex and a point, 313

properties of hyperbolas, 625

properties of quadratic function graphs, 290

translating absolute value functions, 101

Vertical asymptote, 227–229, 234–237, *see also* Asymptotes

Vertical line test, 90–91, 126–127

W

Weighted average, 503

Whole numbers, 7, 8, 34

X

x-axis, 48

reflecting and rotating points and figures, 578

transform the graph of the parent function, 369

using coordinate rules to transform points, 555

using symmetry to find coordinates of a point, 603–604

x-coordinate, 48

x-intercept, 52, *see also* Intercepts

graphing a linear equation in standard form, 58

graphing a polynomial function by using roots, 344

graphing quadratic functions in factored form, 292

using a graph to describe solutions of a quadratic equation, 300

using intercepts to graph a linear equation, 52

x-value, 88–90, 97, 126, 226

Y

y-axis, 48

reflecting and rotating points and figures, 578

using coordinate rules to transform points, 555

using symmetry to find coordinates of a point, 603–604

y-coordinate, 48

y-intercept, 52, *see also* Intercepts

exponential functions, 366

finding a linear equation, given the slope and the, 61

graphing a quadratic function in standard form, 290

graphing linear equations, 58

using intercepts to graph a linear equation, 52

y-value, 89–90, 126, 148

Z

Z-scores, 532

Zero Exponent Property, 158, 358

Zero Product Property, 190–191, 221–222, 256–257, 323

Zero Property of Multiplication, 333

Zero slope, 55

Zero(s), 15, 36, 37

determining multiplicity of a root, 347

determining the number of zeros of a quadratic function, 290–291

factoring a polynomial over the set of complex numbers, 347

graphing rational functions, 236, 237

of a polynomial function, 290

using a graph to describe solutions of a quadratic equation, 300

using the factor theorem, 337–338